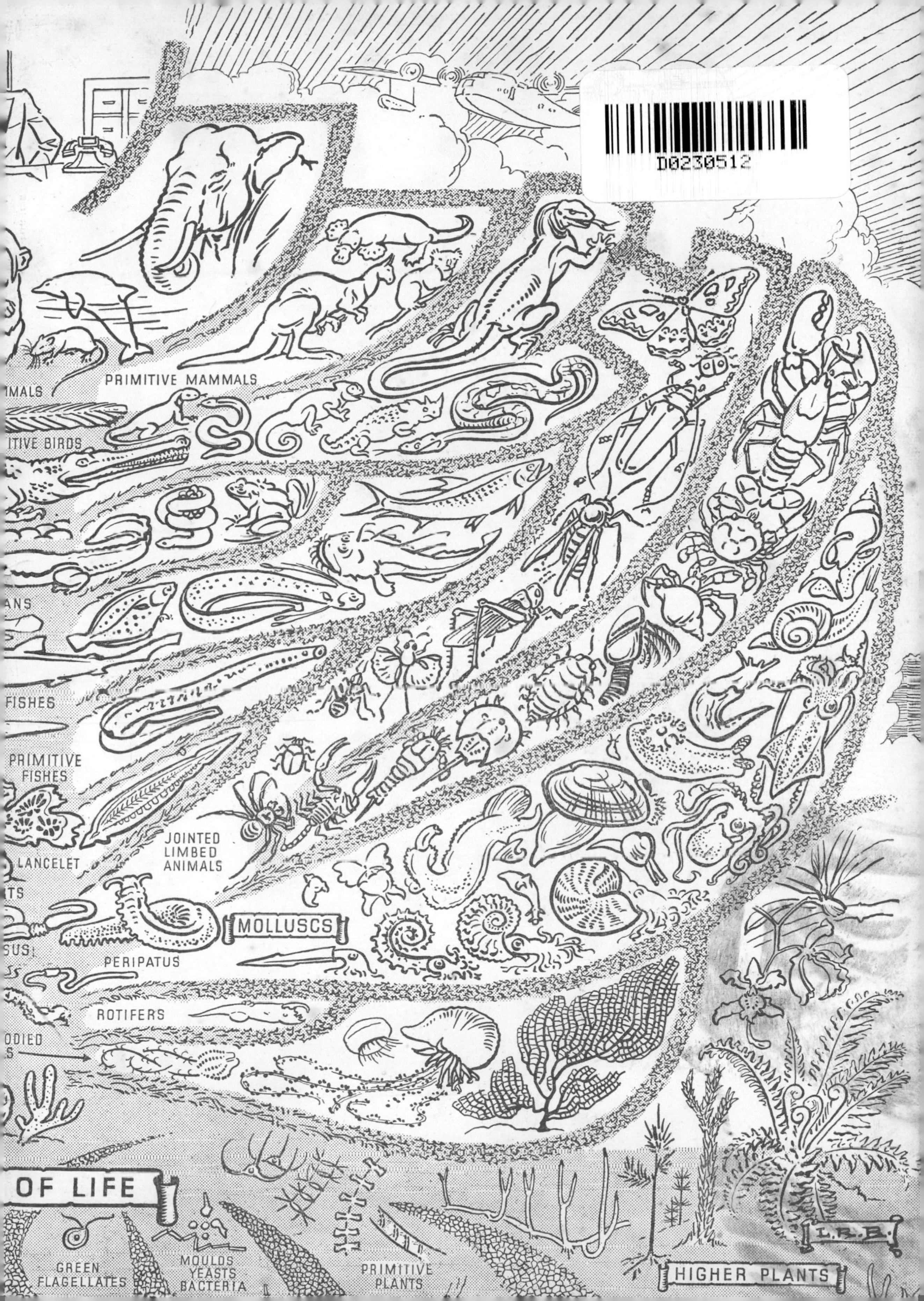
PRIMITIVE MAMMALS
MALS
ITIVE BIRDS
ANS
FISHES
PRIMITIVE
FISHES
LANCELET
JOINTED
LIMBED
ANIMALS
TS
MOLLUSCS
SUS
PERIPATUS
ROTIFERS
ODIED
S
OF LIFE
GREEN
FLAGELLATES
MOULDS
YEASTS
BACTERIA
PRIMITIVE
PLANTS
L.R.B.
HIGHER PLANTS

THE MIRACLE OF LIFE

MONDIALE

STUDYING THE MIRACLE OF LIFE

Peering through his microscope the biologist patiently scans every form of matter that he thinks may reveal the secret of Life. If he finds it, there will still remain the question—How did it begin?

THE MIRACLE OF LIFE

General Editor
HAROLD WHEELER
HON. D.LITT., F.R.HIST.S.

LONDON
ODHAMS PRESS LIMITED
LONG ACRE, W.C.2

Made and Printed in Great Britain by
Odhams (Watford) Ltd., Watford, Herts.

CONTENTS

PAGE

INTRODUCTION, *by Harold Wheeler, Hon. D.Litt., F.R.Hist.S.* 7
THE DAWN OF LIFE, *by L. R. Brightwell, F.Z.S.* 9
WHAT EVOLUTION MEANS, *by L. R. Brightwell, F.Z.S.* 13
LIFE THAT HAS VANISHED, *by L. R. Brightwell, F.Z.S.* 29
EVOLUTION AS THE CLOCK TICKS, *by L. R. Brightwell, F.Z.S.* 65
THE ANIMAL KINGDOM, *by L. R. Brightwell, F.Z.S.* 91–236
Camouflage and Colour in the Wild 127
Animal Courtship 137
How Animals Make a Home 151
Bringing Up a Family 161
Duration of Life 167
Many Modes of Travel 173
Feeding and Sleep 185
Animal Society 199
Animals in Relation to Man 217
THE PLANT KINGDOM, *by Alison Wilson, M.Sc., Ph.D.(Lond.), F.L.S.* . 237–298
The Reproduction of Flowering Plants 251
Plant Anatomy 265
Plant Breeding in Infinite Variety 281
Plants and Man 295
MAN'S FAMILY TREE, *by E. N. Fallaize, B.A.* 299
RACES OF MANKIND, *by E. N. Fallaize, B.A.* 317
THE HUMAN MACHINE AT WORK, *by U. Philipp, Ph.D. and Susan Mercer* 331–406
Digestion and Excretion 339
Circulation and Respiration 345
Reproduction 351
The Nervous System 355
Sense and Speech Organs 360
What the Ductless Glands Do 367
Man and His Environment 371
The Problem of Heredity 377
The Betterment of Humanity 386
The Conquest of Ill-Health 393
PSYCHOLOGY THROUGH THE AGES, *by H. C. Dent, B.A.* 407–456
Beliefs of the Behaviourists 425
Freud and Psycho-Analysis 431
The Nature of Intelligence 449
DISCOVERERS OF LIFE'S SECRETS, *By George Greer* 457
INDEX 477

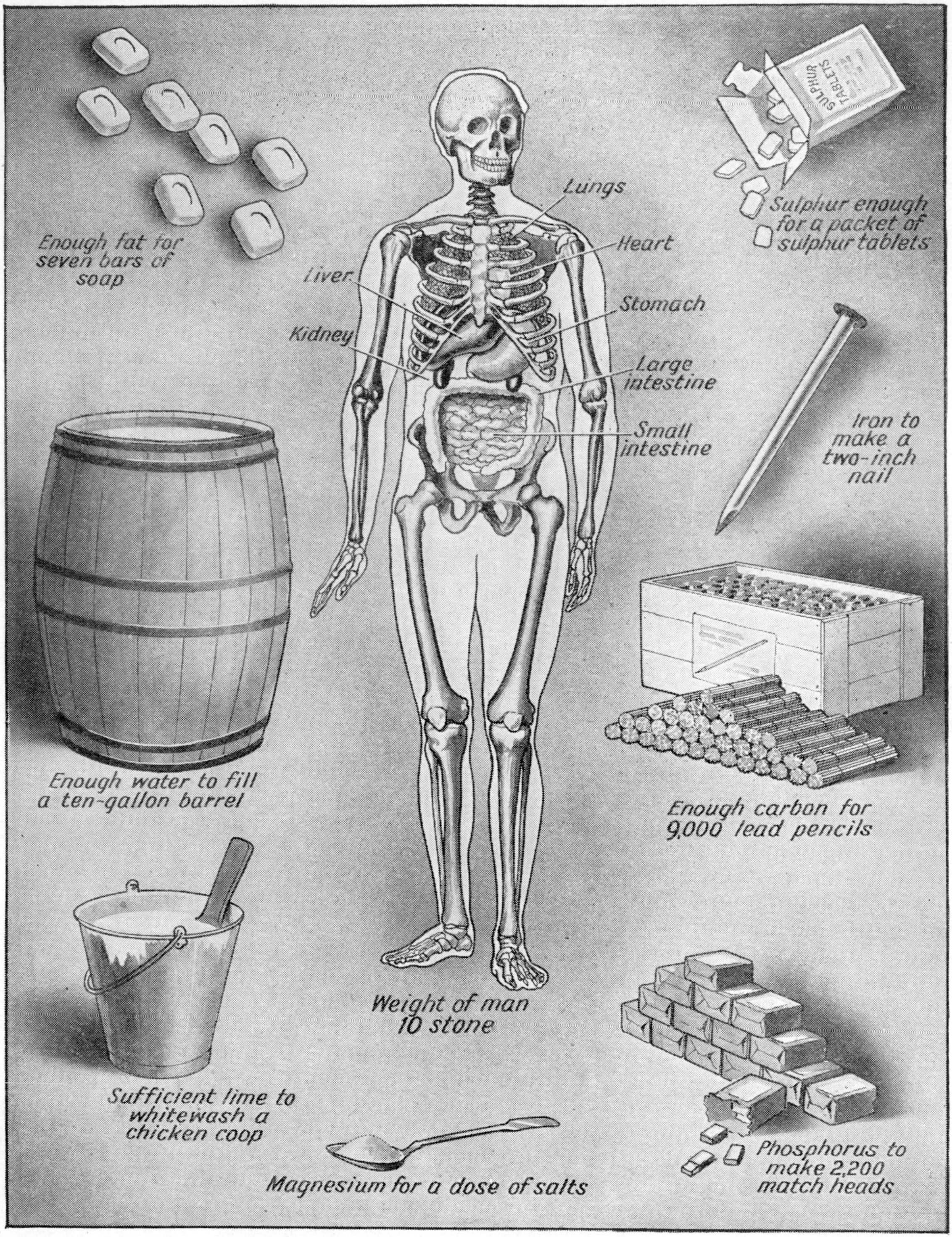

WHAT A MAN IS MADE OF

The chemical contents of a man weighing ten stone. It will be noticed that water, which consists of hydrogen and oxygen, is the chief constituent, namely about fifty-nine per cent by weight. The total cost of the various ingredients would not be more than a few shillings.

INTRODUCTION

THIS work deals with the most vital of all subjects in a frank and honest way. It is exact but not exacting. If the following pages cannot say what life is, and can only suggest what it means, they reveal the myriad ways in which it functions. They therefore fulfil an exceedingly important and practical purpose.

The story told is entirely worthy of the word " miracle," with its suggestion of an impossibility made possible, as it were, though the original Latin term from which it is partly derived means nothing more than " something wonderful," which every phase of life most certainly is. As to the dictionary definition of life, it cannot be said that it helps us very much. It is dull and colourless. " That state of an animal and a plant in which it is capable of performing its natural functions " is scarcely more enlightening than telling an ignorant person that a ship is a ship. Perhaps we shall not be far wrong if we regard life as the supreme expression of energy, and man the highest example of it.

We know much about the marvellous and intricate mechanism which enables the reader to peruse and understand these words and the writer to pen them, but of the vital spark, as the Greeks called it, which initiated and carries on the process we are entirely ignorant. That remains the riddle it has always been. If Dawn Man were capable of sustained thought, which is doubtful, the enigma must have puzzled him, as in all probability it will vex the mind of the world's last thinker as his body stiffens with the rigors of the final Ice Age.

This has not prevented searchers after truth from peering into Nature's secrets and discovering a very great deal. Rather has it been an incentive to effort. The failure to find out what life is has urged the Paul Prys of science to seek out and explain its manifestations. Thwarted in one direction, they have triumphed in many another, with the result that biology—the science of life—has taken its stand with the giants of knowledge. Painfully trudging along the thorny path of trial and error, it has turned stumbling-blocks into stepping-stones. Already it has made the crooked straight and the rough places plain in many directions, and the process gathers momentum as it proceeds.

Of the practical value of biology there can be no dispute. It is helping man to understand not only himself but also the other animals, plants and lowly creatures that share the secret and relentless urge of being. Each is linked in the endless chain of life. Single-celled amœba emerging from primeval slime, and many-celled man crossing the once inaccessible Poles in a device of his own fashioning that rivals the birds, come within the wide sweep of its comprehensive orbit. Miracle we call it. There should be a more emphatic word for so mighty a drama.

It is a tremendous theme, replete with what would appear to be plots and counterplots. By the simple and apparently effortless device of splitting into halves, an amœba can multiply itself under favourable conditions to sixty-eight thousand five hundred million in a day and a half. The speck of life does not, in fact, increase at the rate stated, for it resembles man in that it has enemies. It is precisely in this problem of capture or be captured that biology is most valuable.

The philosopher has a limitless horizon, and it may well be that all things work together for good, but for immediate purposes the whole creation groans by reason of persistent warfare, waged both within and without the body. " Life is a fight " is one of the oldest of proverbs. The sage who discerned it spoke truth.

Often enough it has been a very one-sided fight. Man's implements of warfare have destroyed no more than the mosquito carriers of malaria and yellow fever. The discovery of the culprits is comparatively recent. The anopheles mosquito may have brought about the fall of Ancient Rome. In more recent history it caused the failure of De Lesseps in his ambitious attempt to dig the Panama Canal. Thousands of men perished in the great unfinished ditch, and £50,000,000 sterling was irretrievably lost. At the time the death-roll was attributed to climate, which has been blamed too often for offences it has never committed. Before the task of reconstruction was begun by other hands and another nation, the real enemy had been discovered, with the result that the United States succeeded where France had failed.

The plague which raged in London in 1665, regarded as a visitation of God for man's wickedness, was in all probability caused by the fleas of rats. London is no longer subject to such a scourge because of improved sanitary conditions, greater personal cleanliness and precautions taken by the authorities. Knowledge provides both weapons and armour; is at once attack and defence. Even now the destruction wrought by rodents is staggering. Locusts are not deadly to man, but they remain as serious a menace as in the far off days of the ten plagues of Egypt. Recently they ate their way through eighty thousand acres of wheat, millet and maize in one country alone, and not a year passes without their becoming front page news in some part of the world.

Ignorance and misplaced enthusiasm have wrought untold harm. The prickly-pear, introduced into Australia as a novelty, spread so rapidly that it invaded territory like a victorious army. A few pairs of rabbits were taken to the island-continent in 1860 and became a menace of alarming proportions. First ferrets were used for the purpose of reducing the numbers, but it was found that they also killed sheep. Then foxes were tried, but they mated with the native dingoes, producing a race which also attacked sheep. The sourge is now being fought with a virus. What consolation there may be in the fact that rabbits are eatable by man does not obtain with the prickly-pear, though Luther Burbank succeeded in producing an edible variety. Fortunately it was discovered that certain insects appreciated the objectionable vegetation, with the result that millions of acres have been reclaimed.

This biological control, as it is called, is not always possible, and what is good in theory is not necessarily so in practice. The cure may be worse than the disease, but it does not need a vivid imagination to picture the immense amount of human suffering that was endured before man came out of his mental cave and determined to confront what he had hitherto regarded as an inevitable destiny. Faith and folly are near relations, as are fact and fancy.

Ignorance is not bliss. It is mere foolishness if the means of knowledge are available. The expert no longer keeps his dearly bought secrets to himself, and at long last scientific jargon is regarded as a crime. In this book much that has puzzled is explained in the simple way that is the supreme test of learning. There is plain speaking, but that truth always demands.

HAROLD WHEELER.

BYRD ANTARCTIC EXPEDITION II

BIRD LIFE IN THE GRIM ANTARCTIC

Life even penetrates the ice-capped wastes of Antarctica, though there are no land mammals. Among the few species of birds on the frozen southern continent are petrels and Emperor penguins, shown above.

THE DAWN OF LIFE

With the possible exception of the Poles, life is found on every portion of the earth's surface, and even for some short distance penetrating its crust. There is life, animal or vegetable, miles up the mountain side, and on the ocean bed miles below the surface. There is active life in the burning desert, and latent life, wanting only warmth to activate it, within a block of ice. Life in every conceivable form—the hermit and the herd, the giant and the pigmy—is on every hand.

Temperature is the dominant factor controlling life. Within the hot equatorial belt life swarms and multiplies in prodigal profusion; it decreases steadily, both in variety and in individual forms of expression, as we travel north or south.

Not that one needs to fly from Pole to Pole to appreciate the amazing richness of life. We can see its most startling extremes within the narrow confines of the village street. Here comes a shire horse back from work. He stands at the shoulder as high as an average man. One can almost feel the vibration made by his ton or more of bone and muscle as he leisurely plods along the road. He stops, and plunges a hoof into a nearby pond. By doing so he disturbs a whole world of swarming life.

In the Natural History Museum of New York stands a glass case one cubic yard in size. There is always a crowd surrounding this case, and well there may be. No imaginative writer or painter, past or present, has ever envisaged anything like this exhibit, though many may have borrowed from it. It seems to combine the thrills of the liveliest jungle film with the eccentricities of the most outlandish dreams of Mars.

Here are trees and shrubs worthy of the coal forests, festooned with creepers of nightmare design. Within and around all these extravagances is seen a medley of living forms that make the plants seem ordinary by comparison. That the whole display is wonderfully presented in coloured glass—representing years of patient labour and research on the part of many men—adds still further to its dreamlike quality. It is this, coupled with the knowledge that the exhibit is a simple statement of fact and no mere invention, which doubtless holds the attention, and excites the admiration of the motley gathering of human beings. For this exhibit represents one cubic centimetre of ordinary pond water !

Every day of the year our great libraries gather to themselves scores of volumes, pamphlets and other publications dealing with the visual world around us. But while every hour sees some former mystery explained, there still remains one outstanding question yet unanswered, though not of necessity unanswerable. How did it all begin? When we have traced life back through the records of the rocks, until we have come to its lowest denominator, a populace of minutest organisms neither plant nor animal, what then?

MYSTERIOUS BACTERIUM-EATERS

Life as we know it may one day emerge from the laboratory. The actual driving power which we call life is not essentially different from that operating the most obvious physical and chemical happenings of inorganic matter. Life differs from such only in its power to reproduce itself, and to reproduce itself over an infinitely wide range of conditions. It is not bound within the narrow limits which are set to the building of a crystal or a mountain.

One of the latest theories regarding the origin of life relates to the action of bacteriophages or bacterium-eaters. A bacterium-eater is an organism about one ten-thousandth of a millimetre across. The fact that such a speck of life, or almost life, is too small to be seen by the most powerful microscope throws no doubt upon its actual existence.

NO LIFE WITHOUT SUNLIGHT

If some of the fluid from an outgrowth, such as a blister caused by foot and mouth disease, be sieved of all matters visible to the microscope, and the resultant fluid injected into healthy tissue, trouble follows. Something living, even though immeasurable, must be in the fluid, and that something has been named a bacteriophage. Such an inconceivably small entity can only thrive when living upon live bacteria. Then it multiplies exceedingly.

Scientists are still at variance as to precisely what a bacteriophage is. It cannot be called alive until confronted with a bacterium, yet it is not strictly dead. Possibly some such organisms, under the action of sunlight, which

CHARLES A. HAMILTON

THE MIGHTY AND THE MINUTE

The extremes of existence can be appreciated within the confines of a village street, as when a horse weighing perhaps a ton plunges a hoof into a pond and disturbs a whole world of swarming life.

MONDIALE

AT THE BOTTOM OF THE SEA MILLIONS OF YEARS AGO

Some of the common but varied types of life which flourished at the bottom of the sea during what is known as the Devonian Age. Reconstructed from fossils that were once living organisms.

ultimately alone makes any form of terrestrial activity possible, may supply the answer to an as yet unanswered question.

Napoleon thought that life itself was brought about by the action of sunlight on mud. Prof. J. B. S. Haldane has suggested that an ultra-violet radiation in the earth's early history might have led to the synthesis or combination of organic compounds of high molecular weight which might be an important step in the generation of life.

" The ether pulsates with life," writes Sir Oliver Lodge, " but we cannot perceive it. Life is revealed to us when it enters organs that for one reason or another are sufficiently receptive. The material body in which life is displayed to us may take many forms. Life is so eager to proclaim itself that it may just as easily assert itself in a flower struggling for existence on a refuse heap as in the person of genius."

GREAT MINDS DIFFER

" Though inorganic phenomena do not do so," asserted Lord Kelvin, " yet the phenomena of such living things as a sprig of moss, a microbe, a living animal—looked at and considered as matters of scientific investigation—compel us to conclude that there is scientific reason for believing in the existence of a creative and directive power."

On the other hand Sir E. Ray Lankester held that we cannot know " or even can hope to know or conceive of the possibility of knowing," whence the mechanism of nature " has come, why it is there, whither it is going, and what there may or may not be beyond and beside it which our senses are incapable of appreciating. These things are not ' explained ' by science, and never can be."

WHAT KEEPS LIFE GOING ?

The fascinating speculations of scientists such as those cited above deserve attention and study. As Dr. Julian Huxley has said, " To be impatient with the biochemists because they are not producing artificial microbes is to reveal no small ignorance of the problems involved. . . We rightly praise the skill of the chemists who build up dyes and drugs to order, but to build up living matters, substances as complicated as their highest achievements in synthesis would have to be used as the basic bricks. In any attempt at making living matter, we begin about where the modern organic chemist leaves off, and we begin more than a thousand million years of evolution behind contemporary living cells."

In attempting to deal with some of these primary matters in reasonable order, there occurs another question, the answering of which has involved a vast outlay in ink and

ELLIOTT AND FRY, LTD.

APOSTLE OF VITALISM
Henri Bergson, author of "Creative Evolution," and a winner of the Nobel Prize for literature.

considerable confusion of thought. Accepting the fact of life having started, what keeps it going? Above all, what keeps it going in the manner which it apparently does, on a gradually ascending gradient? Having established itself as a world populace of bacteria, why did it not stay there?

We shall see in due course how the simplest forms of life gave rise to ever more complex forms. The manner in which such marvels transpire can at least be studied in detail, and set forth in clear and systematic fashion. But neither evolution, nor the simple explanations offered by many creeds, savage or civilized, will satisfy all; the world holds too great a diversity of men and of thought.

BERGSON'S "VITAL URGE"

In 1907 there appeared a very remarkable book entitled *Creative Evolution.* The author was Professor Henri Bergson, a winner of the Nobel prize for literature and a distinguished member of the French Academy. *Creative Evolution* was an exquisitely poetic word-picture of the march of progress, beginning in the darkness of a new-born world, and ending with the emergence and struggles of mankind. It crystallized the author's philosophy of life, which is that duration, change and movement are the only realities, that life is identical with time and change, and that we appreciate both, not with our eyes, ears, and possibly brains, but by intuition, whatever that, in this connection, may imply.

The author summed up *Creative Evolution* and its philosophy in the phrase *élan vital.* The vital urge or impetus explains everything—why potato plants do not produce pineapples, why a lion eats meat, why Jones becomes a bank clerk instead of a tight-rope walker. It is like being asked why a dog runs, and replying, quite well-meaningly: "Because it must."

THE ACID TEST OF SCIENCE

This same idea of a mysterious force making living things behave in their various ways, each according to its kind, has occurred to more than one philosopher. Mr. George Bernard Shaw showed it to us as "the Life Force" in the preface to his *Man and Superman,* published in 1903, and both the Life Force and the *elan vital* were interpreted over a century ago by Schopenhauer in his *World Will and as Idea* and *The Will in Nature.*

Such conceptions of life do not appeal to the scientist. He is concerned with facts alone.

SPENCER ARNOLD

INVESTIGATOR OF NATURE
Baron Kelvin (1824-1907) *believed in the existence of a creative and directive power.*

CHARLES R. KNIGHT (MONDIALE)

FORMER DENIZEN OF THE WILD

The mastodon, one of the many animals which have disappeared from the face of the earth. Mass slaughter, superior enemies and climatic changes have brought about the extermination of many species.

WHAT EVOLUTION MEANS

THE scientist, and perhaps most laymen, see the world as a place of trial and error, in which some learn and profit by their learning, while others fail and are forgotten. The lower animals are urged on by necessity; civilized man works deliberately towards a goal.

The conception of evolution as first publicly pronounced and widely disseminated through the writings of Charles Darwin is now part and parcel of every scientific worker's general belief, though few scientists are at complete accord with Darwin upon all the points he raised, nor in all probability will they ever be.

The average man accepts the idea of evolution much as he accepts the sunrise, and with considerably less understanding. Some of the old tags and catch phrases so freely used during the great Darwinian controversy still pass currency. To a large but probably decreasing number of people, the name of Charles Darwin stands for " the man who invented (or discovered) evolution," or " the man who said we came from monkeys."

That Darwin did neither detracts nothing from the popularity of these scraps of misinformation. What Darwin, at cost of so much labour and research, did have to say on evolution is still as vague in many minds as what Mr. Gladstone said in 1879, or at any other date.

Darwin was not by any means the first individual to appreciate that immense, unbroken series of natural phenomena which is summed up in the word evolution. He merely used the term as a convenient one to cover a general trend of events responsible for the forms and behaviour of plants and animals as we find them today, and believe them to have been in the past.

Centuries before the Christian era there were men who conceived the world around them, not as a haphazard dumping of ready-made plants and animals on the earth's surface, fixed and unchangeable according to their several patterns, but as part of an unrolling—a passing point upon an ever-unwinding curve. This is the true import of the Latin word *evolvere* (to unroll), from which is derived the term " evolution."

Some inkling of this can be traced in the writings of the Roman poet Lucretius, who lived about 98–55 B.C. The same thoughts, differently expressed, are apparent in the much earlier teachings of Empedocles (about 490–430 B.C.), Grecian physician and philosopher.

That astoundingly versatile genius Leonardo da Vinci demonstrated during the fifteenth century to the Florentine Court that fossils were

HAMILTON COLLECTION

ARTIST AND SCIENTIST

Leonardo da Vinci (1452–1519), *who showed that fossils were the remains of prehistoric animals.*

undoubtedly the remains of animals that had lived long ago, and which were, when alive, quite different from any creatures then in existence. The matter seems to have aroused no more than passing interest. But as the study of animals and plants, past and present, slowly increased, many minds conceived a quite different view of the world around them from that approved by the orthodox.

CHARACTERS ACQUIRED BY HEREDITY

Nearly three centuries after Leonardo da Vinci, Lamarck, the famous French zoologist, and Darwin's best known precursor, propounded the theory that the characters acquired by heredity were continually passed on, yet tended to change with changes in the individual's mode of life. Thus, the whale had apparently parted with its hind legs, much as the spider monkey had parted with its thumbs, from disuse. Every succeeding whale, though sprung originally from terrestrial stock, used what hind legs it had less and less, so these gradually atrophied or shrank; until whales were born with no hind legs at all. The law apparently held good even for accidental characters; a cat or a man, chancing to be born with six toes, would be likely to beget progeny some or all of which might present the same superfluity.

Very soon after Lamarck's time, the Abbé Johann Gregor Mendel elaborated this principle by years of experiment, chiefly with plants, and established those broad generalities of heredity summed up in Mendel's law, or Mendelism. These are now regarded as bed rock by all similar experimenters, including the eugenists, who advocate the scientific breeding of mankind.

LAMARCK STARTLES THE WORLD

Lamarck startled the thinking and still more the unthinking world, by suggesting that if characters acquired by use or disuse of certain parts were gradually handed on for long enough, there appeared another kind of plant or animal, a creature with specific characters marking it out from all others. This was the first blow to the school of thought which believed in a ready-made creation.

Contemporary with Lamarck was the Comte de Buffon, who turned the Jardin des Plantes, in Paris, from a wild beast show and den of necromantic herbalists, into the centre of

HAMILTON COLLECTION

NATURALIST AND WRITER

The Comte de Buffon (1707–1788), *who reorganized the Jardin des Plantes, Paris, as a zoo.*

RISCHGITZ COLLECTION

STUDENT OF HEREDITY

Gregor Mendel (1822–1884), *whose broad generalities on heredity are known as Mendel's law.*

scientific research and learning it is today. But the success of the reorganized Paris Zoo at the time depended largely upon the favours of Court and Church, rather than on the not too affluent scientists, and Buffon was shrewd enough to keep his views on evolution to himself.

Throughout the history of almost all human activities and beliefs it will be found that a host of workers may be engaged in the same field, often unaware even of each other's existence, and so continue for decades or centuries until one mind crystallizes the work of all, or at least supplies some vital factor hitherto missing, thus bringing about another and eventually universally accepted order of things.

POPULATION AND FOOD

During Lamarck's time an English clergyman, the Rev. Robert Malthus, was much engaged on a subject that is still causing anxiety to economists—that of population. According to him, the increase of the population was far in excess of the increase of available food supplies. In 1798 Malthus caused a sensation with his *Essay on the Principle of Population as it Affects the Future Improvements of Society*, in which he reviewed the whole question of man in relation to food, and urged late marriage or abstinence as the only way to avert impending disaster. He talked of " the struggle for subsistence," which was apparently as pressing in leisurely 1798 as in the present hectic age.

This essay, repeatedly revised in subsequent editions, was widely read during the first half of the nineteenth century, and amongst thousands of others by two young men, Charles Darwin and Alfred Russel Wallace. Both had travelled widely as professional naturalists and acquired at first hand a vast amount of knowledge of the world of nature. Both felt that the Lamarckian idea of new characters being handed on by heredity supplied only a half-answer to the question of how the world comes to be peopled with such a multiplicity of ever-changing forms of life; both found in Malthus's mention of " the struggle for subsistence " the other half.

GO ON OR GO UNDER

Animals and plants, they argued, could not be just turned out like living machines by their parents, in very slowly changing forms, much as one gradually improves some machine-made instrument. They must be also moulded by circumstances, which always compel a plant or

RISCHGITZ COLLECTION

INFLUENCER OF DARWIN

The Rev. T. R. Malthus (1766–1834), *author of a famous book on man in relation to food.*

animal either to make the best of its environment or go under.

A living organism that survives conditions proving too much for many of its contemporaries will naturally tend to find an outlet for its reproductive instincts in seeking a mate of like virility. Thus parentage, urged by forces from without, hands on unconsciously its gifts to the succeeding generation, and so—very slowly it is true—new kinds of plants and animals come to pass.

HAMILTON COLLECTION

FAMOUS FRENCH ANATOMIST

Baron de Cuvier (1769–1832), *a vigorous opponent of the evolutionary theory of Lamarck.*

This, in essence, is the meaning of the evolutionary theory as applied to living organisms. It is subject to much criticism and modification, but the broad facts of what is popularly and loosely termed Darwinism remain unshaken.

THE SURVIVAL OF THE FITTEST

Darwin, who had a true scientist's horror of half-formed and unproven theories, kept this conception of life's unrolling to himself for many years. Eventually he incorporated the idea in an essay of thirty-odd pages, which two years later (1844) became two hundred and thirty pages, so rapidly had his knowledge and convictions grown. Fourteen years after this, Wallace, then in Malaya, sent to Darwin for criticism an essay he had written *On the Tendency of Varieties to depart indefinitely from the Original Type.*

The genesis of this essay is most interesting. For three years Wallace had puzzled over " the question of *how* changes of species could have been brought about." While down with fever in the Moluccas he was brooding on the ideas in Malthus's *Essay on Population* when all of a sudden there " flashed upon me the *idea* of the survival of the fittest." Ill as he was he thought out this new theory, wrote it down, revised his manuscript, and sent it off to Darwin—all within three days.

Darwin saw at once in Wallace's paper his own views only slightly differently expressed, and his generous nature was all in favour of according full honours for the realization of the truths contained therein to Wallace. It was only as the result of the utmost urging, almost coercion by eminent friends, that he gave to the world in 1859 his monumental work *On the Origin of Species by Means of Natural Selection, or the Preservation of Favoured Races in the Struggle for Life.*

" THIS MONKEY DAMNIFICATION "

The work was a best-seller from the first. Its publication gave rise to a controversy waged with a bitterness hardly credible today. To churchmen Darwin's case for evolution seemed a direct attack upon the Christian faith; many scientists could not bring themselves to believe that man was of the same ancestry as the lower animals, while the ordinary educated layman felt there was something degrading in " this monkey damnification," as Thomas Carlyle called it.

It was concerning the origin of man that the battle—to be renewed again with fresh vigour on the publication in 1871 of Darwin's *Descent of Man and Selection in Relation to Sex*—was waged most fiercely. The scientist, the layman and even the divine found, on the whole, little objection to the notion that a hornless breed of sheep might in time develop horns, or even that a semi-starfish, provided enough time were allowed, might eventually give rise to such complex and very different looking creatures as an ostrich and an elephant. Such theories were, indeed, already generally accepted.

But when it was suggested that man was of the same stock as the lower animals, was bone

SINGLE-CELLED WATER PLANTS THAT HAVE LIVED DOWN THE AGES

Diatoms are tiny water plants or algæ with a single cell enclosed by two valves of silica. Some of the species, which number well over fifteen thousand, are identical with fossil representatives of the family.

of their bone and flesh of their flesh, and produced by the same gradual processes, the first shock of surprise gave way to indignation, and indignation to something approaching hysteria.

It was felt by all save the more pronounced "godless" scientists, that even if the other creatures were not the results of miraculous and cataclysmic creation, man certainly was. He stood alone, and to associate him with even a pedigree race-horse, far less a chimpanzee, was a direct insult to religion. Did not the Bible specifically declare, in the first chapter of Genesis, that "God created man in His own image"?

RELIGION v. SCIENCE

The Church took its stand on the Bible; Darwin along with an ever-increasing number of scientists (and, be it added, some theologians) took his upon the mass of evidence that he and others had collected to support his theory of evolution. Thus was originated the great and unhappy, but entirely artificial conflict between religion and science.

Thomas Henry Huxley, "Darwin's bulldog" as he called himself, was one of the foremost to rush into the fray. The meeting of the British Association at Oxford in 1860 found the rival armies drawn up in formidable array, and a battle royal was waged in the halls of that ancient seat of learning.

BITTER CONFLICT

When the Rt. Rev. the Lord Bishop of Oxford (Dr. Samuel Wilberforce) sarcastically asked Huxley if he was related on his grandfather's or his grandmother's side to an ape, Huxley replied that he would not be ashamed to have a monkey for his ancestor, but that he would be ashamed to be connected with a man who used his gifts to obscure truth. Some time later Huxley wrote to a friend, "In justice to the bishop, I am bound to say that he bore no malice, but was always courtesy itself when we occasionally met in after years."

This is a restrained specimen of the exchanges with which public meetings, private converse, and the Press were full. The Ape versus Angels controversy, as some called it, was given an added flavour by the return from Africa of Paul du Chaillu the French explorer, who in 1856 discovered the gorilla, the largest

ELLIOTT AND FRY, LTD.

POPULARIZER OF DARWINISM
Sir Edwin Ray Lankester (1847–1929). *He did much to popularize Darwin's theories.*

of the man-like apes. His highly-coloured stories of gorillas in the Gabun, though partly substantiated by actual specimens, were largely disbelieved and led to many stormy scenes. Once at the Anthropological Society he climbed over the benches and spat in the learned chairman's eye.

In reading accounts of that period one cannot fail to notice how many leaders of thought, even scientists, kept their science and their religion in watertight compartments. Some, like Charles Kingsley and Frank Buckland, great pioneers in popularising natural history, whilst admiring Darwin recoiled from the idea of evolution being applied to man, the one with hysterical, the other with half-humorous repugnance.

Professor Henry Drummond, a famous nineteenth-century Scottish evangelical writer, was typical of this mental outlook. Many years after the publication of Darwin's *Descent of Man* he replied with his *Ascent of Man* in which, combining his twin roles of scientist and evangelist, he sought to dispose of the former work, substituting for Darwinism the theory that wild animals, by their care and consideration for each other, powerfully influenced "the survival of the fittest." Drummond's book proved, if it can be said to have proved anything, that the author kept his considerable knowledge of natural history in one tightly locked pigeon-hole, and his religious convictions in another. Under no circumstances were the contents of the pigeon-holes allowed to intermingle.

THE GORILLA SERMON

This was the attitude of most of the reading public for years, and echoes of those stormy days are still to be heard, though at lengthening intervals. Comparatively recently one of the best informed and most vigorously intellectual divines allowed some reference to the evolutionary process to creep into a sermon. A furious but short-lived outburst of almost Victorian intensity was the result, and even now a section of the Press refers from time to time to what it joyously named "the Gorilla Sermon."

More serious and still more grotesque was the sensation caused a few years ago in a little town in Tennessee, U.S.A. A too-progressive young schoolmaster rashly told his wondering class something of evolution. When his astonished pupils took home with them each his own version of "what teacher said," the ensuing hurricane eclipsed that which had once raged in Great Britain. The town in Tennessee put the rash young pedagogue on trial, whilst the more progressive section of the United States looked on agog, and hilariously nicknamed the unfortunate but eminently respectable township "Monkeyville."

When we remember the furore caused by such mechanical innovations as the railway and the first motor car, it is perhaps not surprising that we should be so reluctant to hazard the more serious adventures of the world of thought.

Though it does not appear to any great extent in either of his most famous evolutionary works, the *Origin of Species* and the *Descent of Man*, Darwin's study of living forms was bound

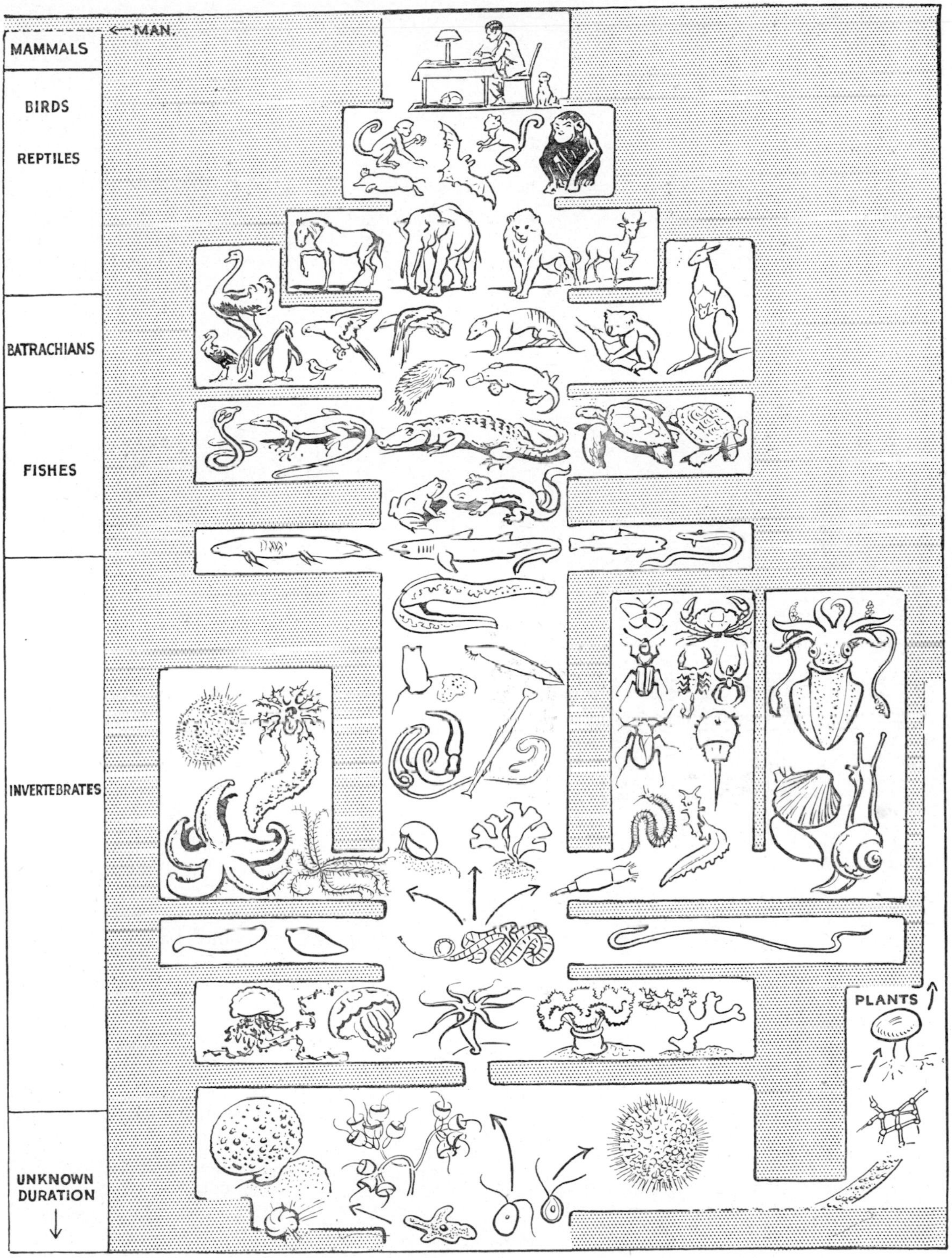

EVOLUTIONARY TREE OF LIFE

The approximate sequence of the main animal groups from amœba to man. Arrows denote the main directions taken by the various branches of the stem. The scale at left shows relative periods during which the groups arrived at fullest development, beginning with a time of unknown duration.

up with an equally detailed study of the innumerable creatures which are known to us now only as fossil remains.

Every modern zoologist and biologist now recognizes that an intelligent understanding of life as it is can only be possible if pursued in conjunction with a close survey of the life that was. The unborn puppy lives within its dam, as does the unhatched chick within the egg shell, through phases that clearly point to its original development from very different forms.

RISCHGITZ COLLECTION

ALFRED RUSSEL WALLACE

He thought out the idea of the survival of the fittest independently of Darwin.

In studying fossils one can trace back animal and plant existence through simpler and ever simpler forms, until in the oldest rock-formations we find ourselves back at the beginning—almost. We can, for the time being at least, go no farther. We are faced by the problem discussed in the previous chapter.

The earliest human records—drawings on the walls of caves—can be roughly dated as being some thirty or forty thousand years old. Written records are matters almost of yesterday. But what are commonly referred to as " the volumes of the Rocks " go back at least six hundred million years, and the information they contain, smudged and fragmentary as it is, points to a procession of plants and animals that, as regards sheer numbers of species, reduce existing species to a mere handful.

Our knowledge of the past grows daily, but in Great Britain it is garnered almost exclusively for the refreshment of the specialist. Little effort is made to popularize it, and the geological galleries of museums are usually a retreat for lovers or a haven for the drowsy.

England can show some amusing examples of how not to educate in geological matters. During the last two hundred years various charlatans have exhibited collections of bones strung together to form wonder beasts, and amassed fortunes in exhibiting them to a trustful public. Dinosaur and mammoth bones have been shown as evidence of men thirty feet high, and few have questioned their alleged origin.

BASED ON INSUFFICIENT KNOWLEDGE

In the early days of the Crystal Palace there was a passing fashion for prehistoric animals, and Waterhouse Hawkins, an architect who had long made the study of extinct monsters his hobby, originated a daring experiment. He erected a series of life-size effigies which still occupy a portion of the Palace grounds which was beyond the reach of the fire of 1936. The animals impressed everybody except the scientists.

Based on insufficient data, most of them are triumphs of absurdity. Richard Owen pointed out that the iguanodon, for example, had three and not five toes as in Hawkins's restoration, to which Hawkins replied that as they were toes and not corns they could not be removed, and there they are to this day. So enthusiastic was the sculptor that he took the moulds of his enormous creations, many of which were bigger than elephants, to America, with a view to setting them up in a public park. At the last minute the authorities broke up his moulds, not in view of their inaccuracy, but because they were " contrary to the accepted story of creation."

MODELLED AS IN LIFE

Forty years after the Crystal Palace adventure, Pallenberg, a famous German animal-sculptor, undertook to make a similar group for Carl Hagenbeck's animal park near Hamburg. Whole skeletons were now available, whereas Waterhouse Hawkins had but a handful of bones; indeed, had he been content to resurrect only such animals as he really knew, his entire effort might have been as successful as his giant sloth, Irish elk and extinct tapirs. Pallenberg, having made miniature models of the creatures he proposed to show life size, took them on a

European and American tour, showed them to all the leading authorities on the remote past, and solicited their severest criticism. The result was the unique collection that is now at Stellingen.

The United States has also seriously undertaken to interest people in the world that was. Some museums, following New York's lead, have gone one better than Germany and show the extinct monsters not merely in self-coloured stone but clothed with hair or scales according to their kind. In New York every skeleton has a miniature model of the beast " as in life " beside it.

REBUILDING THE PAST

The artist has also been called in. One sees in a series of gigantic frescoes the mammoth herds tramping through Siberian snowdrifts, ground sloths as big as oxen on the sunny plains of the South American pampas, and scores of similar peeps into the past. They delight and instruct the man in the street, just as they satisfy the critical scientist. These models and pictures are statements of fact, not mere spectacles to invite a momentary thrill. How are they achieved?

Rebuilding the past is one of the world's most expensive educational luxuries. When sufficiently generous sponsors have been found, a fossil hunting expedition sets out into the wild, perhaps for years. As in a trip to the barren tablelands in South Africa known as the Karoo, work may be possible only for a few months in every twelve. During the season of work the terrific heat, besides incapacitating many on the staff, exploded half the petrol supply and the scientists were faced with a premature return to civilization or death from starvation.

CHARLES DARWIN
His epoch-making work " The Origin of Species " was first published in November, 1859.

THOMAS HENRY HUXLEY
A stalwart believer in the theory of evolution, he called himself " Darwin's bulldog."

AIDED BY DYNAMITE

With its train of lorries and personnel, which may include hundreds of native porters besides expert naturalists, artists, plaster-workers, carpenters and camera men, a bone-collecting expedition suggests a belligerent army rather than a peace-time adventure. The collecting ground reached, there follow weeks of strenuous excavation with shovel, pick and dynamite. Often the bones of some giant beast, when finally unearthed, are so friable as to need swathing in plaster bandages. Small bones, bedded in a matrix of rock, may necessitate taking tons of solid earth to the museum, there to be sorted over months later. Assuming that all goes well, the work of a year or more may result in a

HAMILTON COLLECTION

CHARLES KINGSLEY

Although an admirer of Darwin, he recoiled from evolution as applied to the human species.

hundred-feet-long extinct lizard reaching New York packed in dozens of crates. Now the work of recalling the past may be said to start.

Each bone has to be cleaned and arranged, usually on the floor of a large hall or warehouse, in its proper position. The bones are drilled, wired together, and presently the dinosaur is hauled on to its feet by cranes, and its hips and shoulders supported by massive steel scaffoldings.

DRESSING A SKELETON

All being passed as life-like, there follows the clothing of the bones with " flesh." Usually a miniature model—one inch to the foot—of the skeleton is made, and a carcass of the nearest related reptile serving as a guide, trial muscles are made from wax or strips of brown paper and placed in their approximate positions. Each tiny knob and groove upon a bone has its significance. Dressing a skeleton may take a year or more. Finally the matter of scales, spines and so on has to be considered, and at last the monster stands complete.

Parallel to all this labour, other experts reconstruct from fossil fragments the plant life that must have been contemporary with the giant reptile, palæographers decide upon the nature of the ground the creature last trod, the approximate surroundings, and even the prevalent climatic conditions. Then, as in the vision of Ezekiel, do " the dry bones live," and the prehistoric past is resurrected.

The swiftest way in which any species can be exterminated is by mass slaughter. This has resulted within historic times in a still-growing list of creatures we can never hope to see alive again. Whole races of human beings have disappeared in like manner. Climatic changes have similarly obliterated not only hundreds of species of animals but whole races of them.

WHY SPECIES DIE OUT

Apart from the large numbers of creatures that at once succumb to climatic changes, there must arise the difficulty of a food supply which such changes automatically bring about. The customary food grows scarcer, and such as there is must be sought farther afield. Difficulties which few or none of the animals involved can cope with are encountered—changes of country, unforeseen and superior enemies.

SPENCER ARNOLD

SIR RICHARD OWEN

In his day one of the greatest authorities on extinct mammals, and a famous anatomist.

MONDIALE

DENIZEN OF THE DEEP ONCE TERROR OF THE SEAS

Restoring the fossil remains of an ichthyosaurus, an extinct reptile which lived in the sea. A full grown member of the species sometimes attained a length of forty feet. Work such as this may take many months.

In course of many years, scores of centuries perhaps, for the climatic change may be gradual, a few survivors have trekked far north or south, changed from cold to heat, arid land or swampy, or vice versa. Hairy creatures become less hairy, or pile on thicker coats. Other changes are in progress at the same time, until the original stock of beasts forced on the great hunger trek has died out altogether. The courageous few have kept on, begotten others after their kind; evolution is in progress.

TRAPPED BY TAR

There is evidence that extinction often came upon animals swifter than this. With no stone-arrow-hurling men to harm them, whole herds of animals have come to a sudden end and dragged down others with them into shadow-land. Many of their gigantic graveyards have come to light in recent years. One is the famous mastodon pit in Central Asia.

Here it is obvious that a race of strange elephants, with shovel-shaped lower jaws that hung close to the ground, browsed in peace, for many centuries no doubt, around the shores of an extensive lake bordered by a swamp. The shovel-tuskers, as they are called, apparently made deeper and deeper inroads on the swamp, digging up with their forked chins the lush vegetation that was their sole sustenance. Unknown to them, the lake was shrinking, and with it the swamp. There came a time at last, when, always reaching farther out for food, they foundered in the treacherous mud by scores, perhaps thousands, for naturally only the uppermost corpses, those of the last strugglers, have come to light.

Still more dramatic must have been the last scenes round the gruesome tar trap of La Brea, in California, U.S.A. La Brea is now one of America's chief sources of oil, and huge workings with offices and scores of dwellings, the outward and visible signs of human prosperity, surround the site of a prehistoric tragedy.

SANK TO THEIR DOOM

In this instance, thousands of animals came to their end, not as the result of food shortage but through drought. The now hard and safely worked asphalt beds were once fluid lava poured out from a volcano. In time the lava took on an appearance of solidity, and in the slight declivities of its oily surface precious water collected.

All kinds of animals must have shown a reckless daring to reach this, just as they do now at African water holes when the dry weather sets in. First to the tar pools came ponderous elephants, ground sloths scarcely less massive and much less intelligent, gigantic bison, deer, antelopes, horses, swine, hares, rabbits, moles, shrews and even bats. As the blundering elephants and sloths sank to their doom, the sabre-tooth tiger sprang upon their helpless bulks to snatch a meal, and the wolf followed to dispute the feast.

Then from the surrounding pines and cypresses came giant vultures to tear at wolf and sabre tooth, caught by the paws. All shared the same fate. The tar closed over their heads, until the scientist came to discover bare bones countless centuries later.

HAROLD BASTIN

FOUND FATHOMS DEEP

Vast areas of the ocean floor consist of the tiny but flinty skeletons of radiolarians.

The tar thus took to itself over thirty kinds of large mammals and scores of small species, thirty kinds of birds of prey and over forty other species. Seventeen elephants were found in an area fifteen feet by twenty-five feet, and thirty-five feet deep. The entire animal life of the surrounding country was represented in this cemetery, which comprised beasts unlike any now living and others found today in far distant areas. Noticeably scarce were remains of the crafty bear, possibly the most cautious animal of that era.

The giant lizards of the Age of Reptiles, far more witless than the least intelligent mammals, often died thus in mass formation, bogged beyond all hope of extrication. Sudden and local extermination may occur even in the sea. Thus in 1879 there was discovered in the Gulf of Mexico a peculiar species of tile fish which appeared to be abundant. Three years later ships reported large numbers of dead covering the sea surface for many miles in extent, the total death roll being estimated at approximately a billion.

The explanation offered was a prolonged chilling of the water through arctic currents driven inshore by north-easterly winds. The species was not seen again in any quantity until about thirty years ago. In 1894–95 the manatees of Sebastian River, Florida, were similarly all but wiped out by unlooked-for cold, while in the winter of 1920 New York lost almost its entire population of bluebirds, and Washington its fish crows.

TRUTH ABOUT FOSSILS

Thus it will be seen that cataclysmic happenings may all but remove a species at a blow. Volcanic eruptions pouring lava over land and poisonous gases into the sea, were more prevalent in the remote past than nowadays. But for the most part races and species have declined gradually, and sinking back into the earth from which they drew their sustenance have become converted, circumstances favouring, into the mineralized replicas of their former selves known as fossils.

The popular and incorrect definition of a fossil is " something that has been turned into stone." Silica, and certain combinations of lime or iron with sand particles do, in varying degree, mineralize various objects, but the scope for such fossilization is limited, and less common than one might suppose. Some things cannot be fossilized at all—the soft bodies of jelly-fish and anemones, snails, oysters and cuttle fishes, or the internal organs and muscles of vertebrates.

CASTS MADE BY MOTHER EARTH

Even bones cannot always be fossilized or preserved by time in any way. Mammal and still harder reptile bones preserve well, but not the air-filled bones of birds, or the partly ossified bones of fishes. When any creature dies on land where predaceous or carrion-feeding bone crackers abound, and the wind and rain and soil are brought to bear upon the carcass, the whole may be disintegrated before any kind of preservation can take place. It is matters such as these which make fossil collecting, and the

WHERE THOUSANDS OF BEASTS AND BIRDS PERISHED

The last scenes round the gruesome tar trap of La Brea, in California. The entire animal life of the surrounding country was represented in this cemetery when it was discovered countless centuries afterwards.

piecing together of the past, at once so fascinating and so tantalizing.

A large percentage of fossil plants, feathers, fish scales and other objects are no more than impressions or casts, made in much the same manner as the casts of a sculptor working with clay and plaster. Mineral matter closes in upon the object and preserves its shape, though the object itself entirely disappears.

MAMMOTHS IN ICE

Under favourable conditions a " modern " animal may die and in time its bones become fossilized, whilst the bones of an extinct creature like the great auk and dodo, or even a mammoth, remain relatively fresh. Mammoths have been found so well preserved in ice that the flesh has proved to be eatable. The so-called fossil ivory in London's dock warehouses is little different in constitution from that of living elephants.

An animal is most likely to be fossilized if it dies in a quicksand, or some quiet lake or estuary. Then as the skin and muscles disintegrate, mineral matter gradually supplants every portion of the bony structure until, in the course of ages, every bone and even ossified tendons are fossilized in the fullest sense of the term.

The shells of molluscs and other creatures may themselves be welded together to form solid rock masses, like the oyster rocks at Tillywhim Caves in Dorset. The chalk cliffs of Great Britain are largely composed of minute shells of exquisite design, the foraminifera. Vast areas of the ocean floor consist, to a depth of many feet, of the so-called globigerina ooze, the tightly packed flinty skeletons of the infinitely small and very simple creatures known as radiolarians. The depositing of lime on solid objects by the famous hot springs of Auvergne, France, is not fossilization but incrustation.

TREASURES REVEALED BY THE SEA

Probably only a small proportion of the plants and animals which eventually go the way of all flesh is immortalized by fossilization, and of the millions that are thus preserved a smaller number still are unearthed by man. Only when

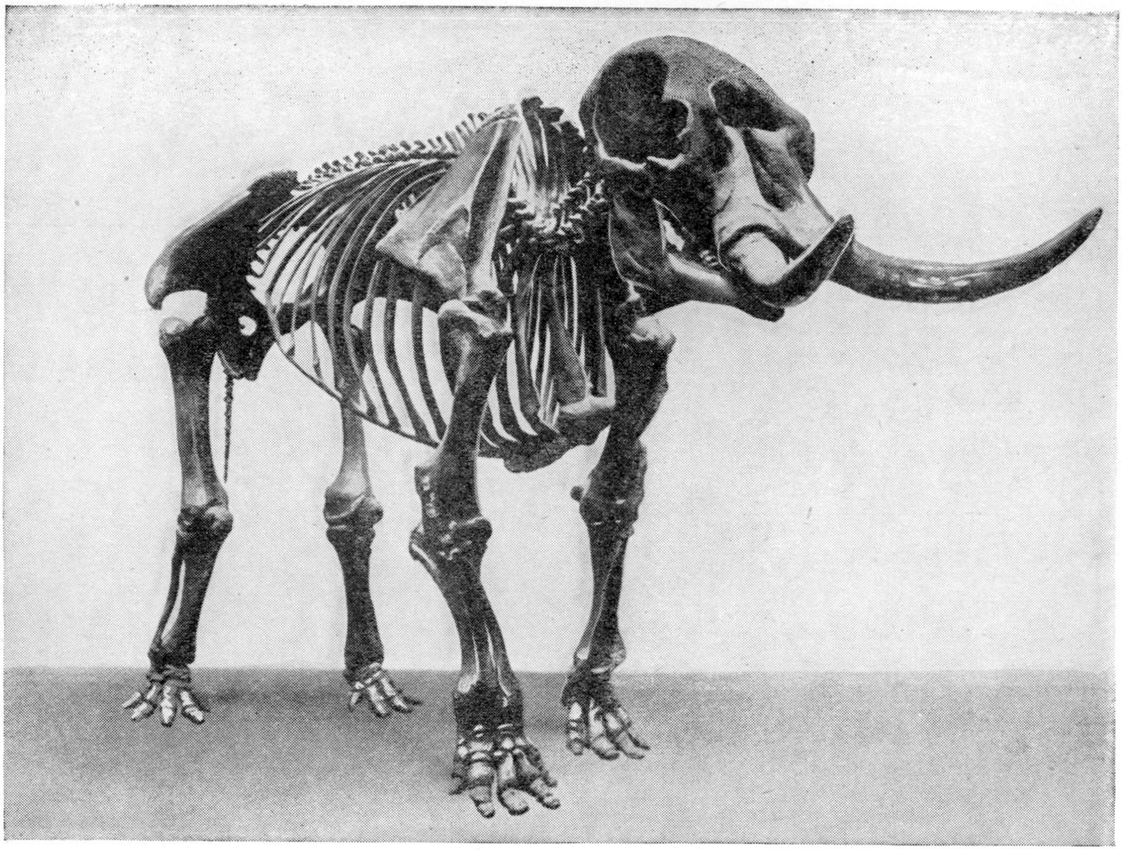

FRAMEWORK THAT SUPPORTED A BULKY BODY

The giant skeleton of a mammoth. Specimens of this animal have been found so well preserved in ice that the flesh has proved to be eatable. The so-called fossil ivory differs little from the tusks of living elephants.

the fossil beds lie relatively near the earth's surface, or are hurled up from below, or tilted up on edge can their treasures come within our grasp. Sometimes the sea or ice pares away a hillside till a cliff is formed, and then again we glimpse a graveyard of the remote past.

PREHISTORIC MARCH OF PROGRESS

Even when thus thrust under our notice, the getting of fossils is often a tedious, even dangerous and costly process. But despite difficulties, and often scantiness of material, modern geologists and palæontologists may be congratulated on the pictures they have given us of a former world. In the ensuing chapter the panoramas of animal life are based on no vague guess-work. Fossils have furnished accurate records of thousands of different kinds of animals and the plants they lived amongst, and afforded clues as to how the creatures walked and sat, swam, flew and fed. Even the actions of wind and rain are sometimes set down for us in the truly marvellous records of the rocks.

In arranging the long series of animal forms, one succeeding the other as revealed by rocks, it has been found necessary to divide the series into epochs, a term derived from a Greek word meaning " to check." The prehistoric march of progress is therefore marked off in epochs such as the Eocene or " dawn age," the Miocene or " less recent age," and so on. Each is calculated to cover a certain length of time in the earth's history, according to the age of the rock layers each epoch covers.

ROCKS ARE " RADIUM DATED "

The ages of the various rock formations can be ascertained with reasonable accuracy. This was only made possible by the discovery of radium in 1898 by Madame Marie Curie. The rocks are literally " radium dated." The first inscriptions of life upon their surfaces are traced back to between two and three thousand million years ago, and Nature is writing still.

THE MAMMOTH AS IT APPEARED IN LIFE

In 1937 it was reported that the frozen carcass of a mammoth had been discovered in Wrangel Island, off the Siberian coast. The animal once flourished in Great Britain, where remains have been found.

The marvels of mechanism and scientific discovery which the last few decades have seen are largely responsible for the progress now being made in recapturing the past. Prior to this fossils were mysteries to all save the learned.

STRANGE IDEAS OF THE LEARNED

It was once customary to believe that all kinds of animals could be spontaneously generated in mud or slime, so that their occurrence as dead remains in rocks was natural enough. They were merely creatures that had not succeeded in struggling to the surface, and succumbing, petrified. Theophrastus (about 372–287 B.C.), the Greek philosopher, observed of fossil fishes that they "either developed from fresh spawn left behind in the earth, or gone astray from rivers or the sea in cavities of the earth, where they had become petrified." Even Aristotle (384–322 B.C.), the father of ancient natural history, looked upon fossils as mere curiosities.

The revival of learning in the sixteenth century gave a new meaning to the fossilia, the " things dug up." Leonardo da Vinci's pioneer work in this regard was confirmed a century later by Nicholas Steno, Professor in the University of Padua, but for long after this the deluge of the Pentateuch was accepted as the cause of death wherever fossils were discovered.

The real nature of fossils was fully appreciated in 1778, when De Luc coined the word " geology," the science of the earth. From thence onwards a host of workers entered the field, and in 1834 H. D. de Blainville and Fischer von Waldheim presented the world with palæontology, now universally used to describe the science of ancient life—the reconstruction of the past.

SEA SERPENTS AND MONSTERS

To many people any review of the animal forms no longer extant seems like a nightmare, a piece of unreality. This, no doubt, coupled with that human craving for the marvellous and sensational which is present, in varying degree, in nearly all of us, is probably responsible for the still popular belief in a sea serpent. It explains the popularity of certain films and such grotesque affairs as the Loch Ness Monster and the Nandi bear. The latter is worth recalling because at long last the beast was run to earth.

Before the World War and immediately after it, there appeared in the Press at intervals accounts of a horrid monster in Kenya Colony. It was half-man, half-hyena, walked erect, and had a passion for strangling women and children.

TUSK OF A MAMMOTH

Nearly fourteen feet long, this wonderful specimen was brought to London from Siberia.

So persistent were these rumours that the British Museum at last circularized all game wardens and other responsible persons in Kenya and the surrounding country requesting concrete evidence. Doubts began to arise when a newspaper reproduced a copy of the bear's footprint, which showed six toes. Experts resolved this into the footprints of two separate hyenas, one print superimposed upon another. Before long concrete evidence arrived in the form of skins and skulls, but these never matched. Sometimes a large hyena's skull was associated with a leopard's skin, sometimes the reverse was forwarded as belonging to one and the same animal. That is presumably the last of the Nandi bear.

DISCOVERING UNKNOWN ANIMALS

As for the possibilities of yet discovering strange and even huge monsters new to science, they increase rather than otherwise with our ever-improving means of exploration. Animals hitherto unknown are added to the list of ascertained forms at the rate of a hundred or so a year, but seldom attract the attention of any but scientists owing to their small size. They do not get a "good Press."

On the other hand, news of the discovery of the remains of an animal with which the public is familiar is invariably recorded in the newspapers. For instance, the finding of the frozen carcass of a mammoth in Wrangel Island, off the coast of Siberia, in 1937, received considerable space. Hair several feet long covered the whole of the body, which was in perfect preservation.

It is well to recall that only in 1897 a party of scientists stumbled upon an amazing cavern in Patagonia, where it transpired that primitive man must have herded ground sloths as big as oxen, and killed them for his table as occasion demanded. Fresh skin and even piles of dung belonging to the giant sloths were found, with other equally surprising matters.

AGE OF MONSTERS NOT PAST

Just three years after this disclosure began a series of baffling rumours which ended in the discovery of the okapi. Later the bones of the largest land animal yet recorded, a seventeen-feet high rhinoceros, were recovered from the Gobi Desert.

The age of monsters is by no means past, and as regards the highest animals, the mammals may yet be far from having reached their peak.

VERNON EDWARDS (MONDIALE)

BIG IN BULK BUT SMALL IN BRAIN

Diplodocus, a vegetarian of the dinosaur order, inhabited the swamps of North America about one hundred million years ago. He was nearly ninety feet long, but his brain was small and very undeveloped.

LIFE THAT HAS VANISHED

In reviewing the pageant of past life on the earth, to start at the beginning is impossible. We cannot hope to know how long our planet whirled through space before it changed from a molten mass to a place capable of supporting any kind of life. The oldest rocks discovered have been subjected to such inconceivably great pressure from other and more recent layers piled above them that any traces of life they once contained are now irretrievably obliterated.

But at least we can guess with some assurance at the earlier forms of life. We are helped not only by the doubtful scraps of algæ and worm remains traceable in early rocks, but by our knowledge of embryology. It is an established fact that all life, animal or vegetable, starts as a single cell, or more usually a single cell resulting from the fusion of two cells, a female and a male.

It is not the least wonderful of scientific achievements in the last few hundred years, that until the latter part of the sixteenth century insects, worms and mollusca—lumped together as " creeping things "—represented the lowest forms of animal life known to man. Not till the microscope became a working possibility was the greater part of the world of living organisms revealed. As regards even a suspicion concerning cellular structures, the leading scientist was on a level with the illiterate.

A cell, or more properly a corpuscle, is not a blob of jelly, or protoplasm. Though usually of microscopic size, it is a highly complex mechanism containing a vital centre or nucleus, fluid, besides oil globules, worm-like, twisting objects, and other matters. It is an entity in itself, and as such is commonly represented by the amœbæ, abundant in both soil and water. An amœba can move in any direction, assimilate food, and multiply by just splitting in two. Cells, by a process not yet fully understood, can divide and sub-divide, yet cling together, and by absorbing nourishment of one kind or another, the whole mass increases in volume. Moreover certain cells in one of the aggregations do certain jobs—take food, or row the body here and there by tiny lashing hairs.

Quite early in the story of life some of these primitive entities made homes, exquisite in design and bewildering in variety, of silica or carbonate of lime. They rowed themselves about, feeding on minute plants as bizarre as themselves, and rioting for an hour or two—seldom more than a few days—begat their kind by subdivision, and then together with their homes, sank to the sea bed, there to form eventually rock.

One thing is fairly certain of this period in the world's story; there must at least have been light of some kind, for only so can plants exist, and upon plants all animal life turns. Below a certain depth no plants can grow, and so all life beyond that level is dependent for its

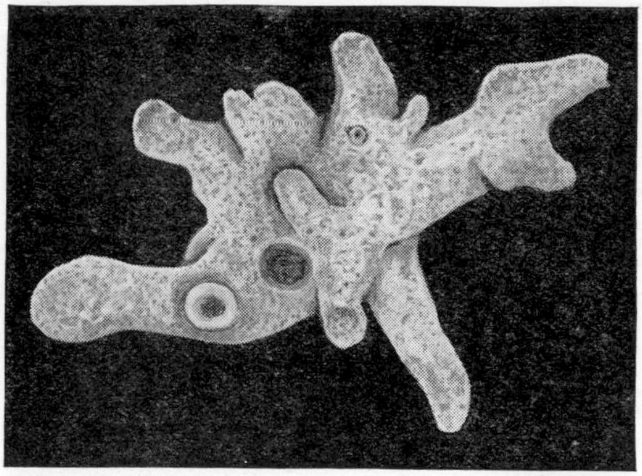

HAROLD BASTIN

ANIMAL THAT IS ALL MOUTH

About one hundredth part of an inch long, the amœba inhabits ponds. It is all mouth and is continually changing its shape.

sustenance upon a " food rain " from above—a constant downward flow of corpses.

Throughout the survey of animate nature one is impressed by the extraordinary speeding up of the evolutionary process as time went on. Today the wheels revolve at a bemusing pace. At a rough computation it is two hundred million years since anything that could be called a mammal first saw the light. Prior to this reptiles literally owned land, sea and air for one hundred and fifty million years. Quite ten times this period must have passed since the first vertebrates were in existence, and the vertebrates are, relatively speaking, a recent development. Measured by time, man and all his achievements have risen to what we find them today in one swing of the pendulum.

WITH OVER A THOUSAND CELLS

From what precise stock the more complex invertebrates sprang we cannot say. It may perhaps have been some comparatively involved organism such as the sun animalcula, a globular gathering of over a thousand cells. This beautiful creature, just visible to the naked eye, is a common inhabitant of most stagnant fresh waters. Whatever the original, from it must have sprung the great divergent groups the polyps and the sponges.

Here let us digress to point out that in the evolutionary series, animals are arranged in the order we know only for our convenience. They did in truth come into being in some such sequence, but not with the neat precision of a museum collection, or the contents of a natural history book. It is the failure to appreciate this that makes some people still ask " Why doesn't a starfish turn into a cuttle fish, since the cuttle fish is a step higher than a starfish?" One is reminded of the Victorian insistence that Darwin said we came from monkeys, which he most certainly did not.

The great main groups of animals and plants and their subsidiary groups have in all instances evolved by diverging from some main stock or common ancestry. Just as within the human epoch we have evolved certain generalized kinds of dogs from wolves, and then divided them by artificial selection and accelerated evolution into the chow and samoyed group, the pug and bulldog group, and so on.

SWIMMING SPECKS OF LIFE

So it happened that at some period long after the free-swimming animalcula were established there appeared two very different groups of animals, the sponges and the sea anemones, with such related forms as coral animals and jelly-fishes. Both groups began as free-swimming specks of life, but the sponges soon settled down, and whilst often enlarging to the dimensions of

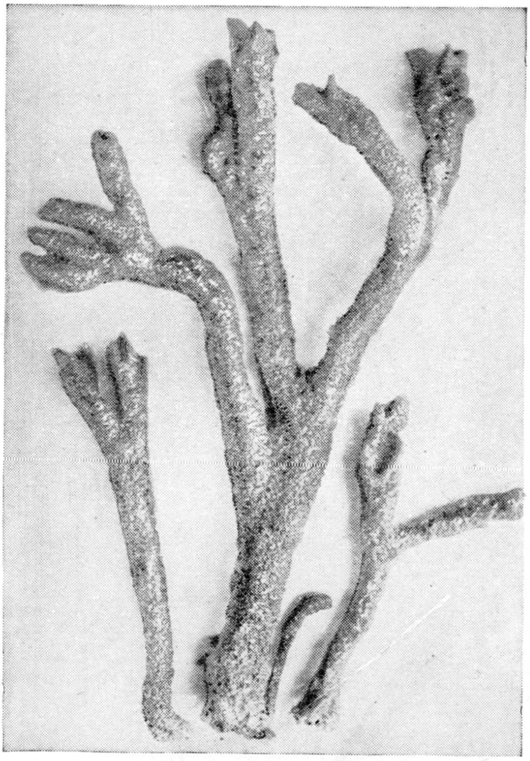

HAROLD BASTIN

FRESHWATER SPONGE

One of the few green animals, it owes its colour to the microscopic partner—algæ, in its cells.

small trees, remained anchored to one spot, and subsisted by sweeping food haphazard into their interiors by means of minute lashing hairs. Waste was cast forth by the same hairs, though through separate channels.

The anemones or polyps and their kind often anchored for life, and remained naked, or by enveloping themselves in carbonate of lime, raised huge reefs and islets, so fast did they increase. But many, like the jelly-fishes, remained mobile throughout life, and all had definite stomachs, which they filled at the dictates of hunger by means of their sting-bearing tentacles.

ANIMALS WITHOUT HEADS

The early sponges, with their flinty (to us horny) skeletons of interwoven hooks and anchors, and the corals with their stony homes, have handed down admirable records of themselves through hundreds of millions of years. There are even fossil prints of the fragile jelly-fishes. But some of the early polyps were unlike any polyps known today. They were in some degree related to the delicate sea firs cast up on every beach, but free-floating and curiously flattened, and in the fossil state at least so suggestive of mystic inscriptions that they have been named graptolites.

MONDIALE

FLOWERS OF THE SEA

Sea-anemones are often beautifully coloured. Their mouths are encircled with stinging tentacles which catch food for them.

BRITISH MUSEUM (NATURAL HISTORY)

BEAUTY IN SKELETONS

Corals are the skeletons of certain members of the group of organisms known as coelentera, *or "stinging animals."*

For millions and millions of years the seas, and probably the seas only, were populous. They housed a medley of animals not one of which could be said to have a head or even that bilateral symmetry which distinguishes all the higher invertebrates and every vertebrate. None of these animals was provided with blood, and blood allows of expansion in three dimensions. Even so some of the early animals grew to a considerable size.

FORESTS OF FLOWER-ANIMALS

It will be found generally that a given group enjoys several peaks in the onward march, unless, as sometimes occurs, it retrogresses, like the sea squirts. There were very big starfishes and sea urchins in the oceans of old, and the wonderful sea lilies, or stalked starfishes, today restricted to a few deeps, abounded everywhere. Few now exceed a few feet in height, but once the ocean floor must have borne writhing forests of these strange flower-animals, rearing fifteen or more feet aloft, and clutching with their fern-frond-like arms at everything which passed.

When dead, or at rest, some of the great stone lilies, coiling their jointed stems round their arms, looked like enormous snail or nautilus shells. There were also other relatives of the familiar starfish wholly unlike anything we know today.

On the southern shores of England is a beautiful little ten-armed starfish, the rosy feather, which begins life as a stalked sea lily, but later breaks free and leads a buccaneering life, untrammelled in any way.

These starfishes and starfish-like creatures are believed to have been derived from creatures having some features in common with flukes and tapeworm-like animals. Had evolution stopped here, the sea lilies and their allies might have been masters of all they felt, for none could truly

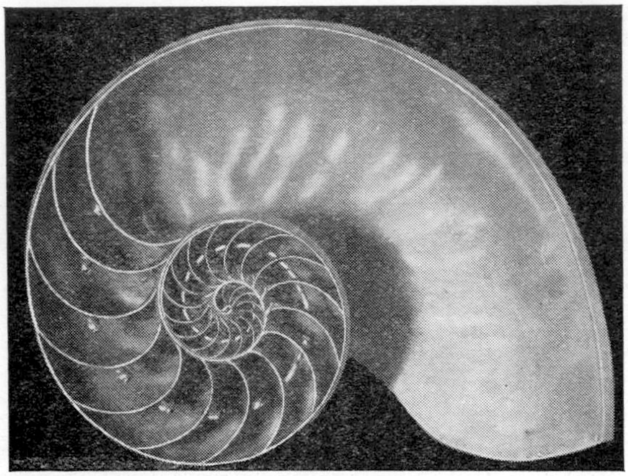

MONDIALE

HOME OF PEARLY NAUTILUS

In such exquisite shells (shown here in section) dwell the "living fossils," last representatives of an ancient race.

see, but parallel to them there was progressing a very different set of animals. These were the two-sided segmented creatures, with a blood system and far more complex organizations generally, and still other forms, two-sided but unsegmented. The one presently expressed itself in the now extinct trilobites, the other in various kinds of molluscs.

DOMINATED THE OCEAN FLOOR

Discrete and mostly unadventurous, the molluscs still abound, and many have changed little since their kind appeared millions of years before the first vertebrates. Amongst the soft-bodied shell-bearing molluscs of the past, now only seen as the dead shells crowding some cliff face laid bare by erosion, the ammonites once housed octopus-like creatures with scores of small sucker-tipped arms.

The nearest living representatives of these creatures, which sometimes had shells several feet in diameter, are the nautiluses, confined now to a few tropic seas. Once the ammonites dominated the ocean floor, and it is surmised that at that time and for long afterwards, until the close of the Age of Reptiles perhaps, the earth's temperature generally was more or less tropical.

The molluscs we know eventually conquered the land, but first to climb free of the water may have been certain jointed-shelled creatures that superseded the trilobites. In general appearance these primitive crustaceans blended the still surviving king crab with the familiar woodlouse, and like the ammonites they swarmed by countless myriads, and no doubt provided many a meal for the aggressive molluscs on the ocean floor. But the lumbering, retiring trilobites of five hundred million years ago were ill-equipped for a world that almost daily added to its implements of rapid progression—and be it added—of destruction.

GREAT SEA SCORPIONS

The trilobites gave place to a race of highly mobile, streamlined creatures, suggesting in their make-up both the lobster and the little brine shrimp so much used now as a food for aquarium fish. The great sea scorpions, as they are called, sometimes measured nine feet in length, and must in their day have been all but invincible. We say "all but" advisedly,

RAY PALMER, F.E.S.

ANIMAL WITHOUT BRAINS

The starfish has no brains but around its mouth is a nerve-ring by which its movements are co-ordinated.

SHELLS WOUND AS TIGHT AS WATCH SPRINGS

Beautiful shells that once housed ammonites, extinct representatives of the class of cephalopods, *among whom are numbered the pearly nautilus, the octopuses and the squids. The* cephalopods *form an important item in the diet of the toothed whales.*

for they too disappeared, but it is possible they left descendants of a still more progressive kind.

Of slightly later date are some semi-scorpion animals that it is believed adventured sometimes ashore, reverting like some modern land crabs to the water for a refreshing lubrication of their breathing apparatus, not yet fully accommodated to inhaling air.

Whilst the jointed creatures were thus pushing onwards, the starfishes and their allies, dependent on the lime-charged sea water for the reinforcement of their shelly coats, remained submerged, and there they are unto this day, exclusively marine throughout the world.

THE SHARP SPUR OF NECESSITY

Amongst the many unanswered, or only partly answered questions regarding these remote times, is the conquest of land by the molluscs. The most active, well-armed and intelligent of them all, the octopods and cuttle fish, remained, like the more lowly starfishes, in the sea. Only the snails adventured out of salt water, and today they abound both in fresh waters and ashore between the temperate belts.

As with every other group of animals, both above and below them, the ammonites, the octopus-like molluscs of olden times, adventured in all kinds of directions, experimenting under the sharp spur of necessity. At first they trailed long conical shells behind them, a cumbrous performance exposing them to many enemies. Then the shells were loosely coiled, and finally wound up as tight and flat as watch springs. But too slow adaptation to altered requirements can be fatal in the wild, as elsewhere, and the survivors of the ammonite today can be counted by tens where once there were tens of millions.

The vertebrates, or animals with backbones, appearing relatively late, still found the dimly lit, vapour-shrouded seas of tropic or sub-tropic heat. Britain's chalk hills, formed beneath the early seas, show beds of long-spined thorny oysters such as now live on the Great Barrier Reef. All the signs point to almost equatorial conditions, and the riot of invertebrate life such conditions—given moisture—invariably invoke.

A possible foreshadowing of the vertebrate animals is seen today in the little glassy creatures called lancelets, found burrowing in gravel far out in deep water off the southern shores of England. If these flourished in prehistoric times, as they may have done, the absence of any fossil remains will be easily understood. To find anything that might be called a vertebrate of the remote past, we must search rock layers that once rested anything from eighteen to twenty-five miles beneath the earth's crust. Beneath that tremendous pressure surviving remnants of animal forms are scanty enough.

KING OF THE HERRINGS

Traces of cartilaginous backbone are thought to represent some kind of chimæra, or king of the herrings, a primitive fish still surviving in deep waters of the North Atlantic and as far south as the Cape of Good Hope. In ancient rock formations of Russia small teeth attributed to some kind of lamprey have been found, and in England traces of fish-like animals, seldom over two inches long, are believed to belong to the same primitive order.

Higher up in the rock layers we meet fish in abundance, creatures totally unlike any fish known today, but still clearly recognizable, however superficially unlike. As an example of how we are indebted to people of every walk in life for our knowledge of the past, it may be mentioned that these early fishes were first brought to light by a Forfarshire quarryman, Hugh Miller (1802–56). He it was who helped to unearth the giant sea scorpions, which his fellow quarrymen called seraphims, regarding their great paddle legs as suggestive of the conventional angel's wings so frequently shown in stained glass windows.

DR. GRAF ZEDTIVITZ (MONDIALE)

ROMAN SNAIL

A greater concentration of nerve-centres is in snails and cuttle fishes than in other backboneless animals.

These first fishes must have been contemporary with the great sea scorpions, and although so much smaller, contrived to survive them. Perhaps the war of brains versus bulk was already under way. We cannot tell if the sea scorpions—which much suggest the larval stages of some modern crabs—themselves passed through a complex metamorphosis, but they almost certainly produced eggs. No doubt the first fishes sought these out and swallowed them, besides accounting for many a baby sea scorpion, particularly when enfeebled by its struggles to cast its old shell. Throughout the tale of Life we are constantly witnessing the triumph of David over Goliath.

In the semi-darkness of the sub-tropical Silurian seas, the first fishes must have passed in great shoals, gleaming like burnished metal amongst the ever increasing seaweed forests. None of these first fishes had true jaws, and so were seemingly at a disadvantage beside the great sea scorpions with legs converted into very efficient machines for seizing and mincing food. The jaws of all true fishes are modifications of one of the gristly rings supporting the gills, and the copper-plated Silurian fishes had only round suctorial orifices for mouths. When no better fare offered they probably dredged the silt for anything it might contain, gulping up a mouthful and spitting it forth much as a goldfish goes gleaning on the aquarium floor.

WITH BOX-SHAPED BODIES

The early fishes had box-shaped bodies, with the tail hinged, not continuous as in all living fishes save the little trunk and coffer fishes of tropic seas. They had but one pair of fins heavily cased in armour, and more like the flippers of a turtle or legs of a crab than fins as generally understood. Altogether they looked very like the crustaceans they alternately eluded and pursued.

Most fishes have a high percentage of oil in their compositions, and the pioneer fishes must have been similarly supplied, for the grease they contained not only helped to preserve their own bodies when dead from the decaying influences of moisture, but also helped to consolidate the strata of the English Old Red Sandstone in which their remains abound. They helped to bind the sand and mud which covered them just as a plaster cast gains durability by being boiled in oil.

FISHES WEDGED TOGETHER

Even in the temperate and moist climate of Great Britain, an occasional drought spells disaster to freshwater fishes by drying up their fluid habitats, or small marine fish may be stranded in shallow tidal pools and literally cooked before the sea can recover them. Each year in Illinois, U.S.A., game wardens rescue quantities of bass that would otherwise be lost in this manner, and a dry spell in Texas often sees thousands of armoured gar-pike ranging from a foot to seven feet in length, wedged shoulder to shoulder in small pools, which represent all that remains for the time being of a spacious river.

Disasters of this kind perhaps account for the huge numbers of primitive fishes found

EVOLUTIONARY CHAPTERS IN THE CONQUEST OF THE LAND

Reading from top left and across the page: A primitive fish. The development of paired limbs. The fish, with air bladder converted into lungs, shuffles ashore. An early batrachian laying eggs in water but living partly on land. The fins have become hands and feet, fingered and toed. An early reptile laying hard-shelled eggs on land. A reptile of the mammal type. A mammal-reptile, forerunner of carnivorous mammals. A "dawn mammal," precursor of horses, etc. Opossum, a mammal with feet converted into hands.

wedged together in the sandstone. This may well have been the case, for the close of the reign of the primitive fishes saw, and was perhaps hastened by, a slow but steady changing and reduction of the waterways. There were great sub-aqueous upheavals that presently altered the entire face of the earth, remodelling the fishes' world. The land was rising.

Another factor doubtless made for the reduction of the armoured shoals. These first fishes, like the crustaceans and monster millipedes, now tentatively exploring the newly-risen land, had all their hard parts on the outside. But some among them underwent a change. The carbonate of lime that turned their skins to inflexible plates and bucklers, gradually spread to other parts of them.

GRISTLE BECOMES BONE

By slow degrees their gristly spinal columns and other parts hardened into bone capable of supporting ever more powerful muscles, to which the unyielding armour must soon become an irksome encumbrance. It split up into an increasing number of plates and bosses, giving ever increasing capacities for movement. Primitive sharks appeared, and later scaled fishes. These latter, the dominant fishes of today, are regarded as descendants of the early sharks.

WHEN SCIENCE GUESSES

The old saying of "Every dog has his day" occurs to one continuously in tracing the rise and fall of succeeding animal forms in the panorama of life. As the primitive armoured fishes may have hastened the sunset of the sea scorpions, so they themselves could have been no match for the monster fish, like dinichthys (terrible fish), that later came upon the scene, or the numerous strange sharks, some rivalling the largest known today, and amply armoured with bony tubercles and long spines.

The story of the fishes is the most difficult of all the vertebrate chapters in the tale of life to piece together, and the half of it is not yet told. Hugh Miller's brown-paper model of one of the strange Red Sandstone fishes is a very accurate presentment, despite its homely workmanship, but of many other fish we can only guess their shapes and affinities from tantalizing enigmatic fragments.

Today it is realized that an appreciation of present forms of life is only possible when living and extinct beasts are studied side by side; one helps the other. Fifty years ago, all kinds

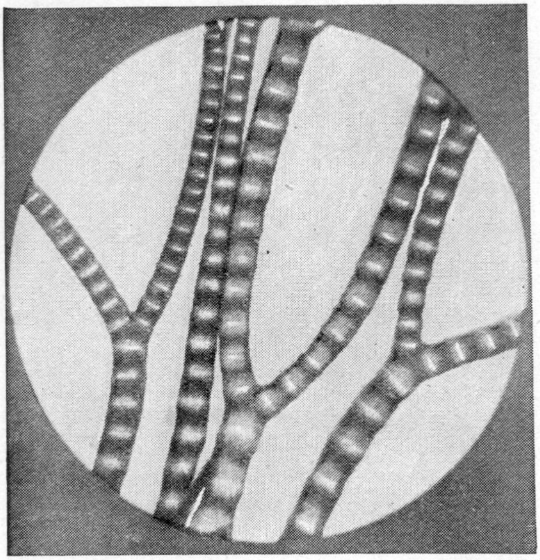

HAROLD BASTIN

FORERUNNERS OF MOSSES

Like the fungi, with which these plants are classed, the algæ show no distinct divisions between root, stem and leaf.

of scattered teeth and spines were attributed to scores of different kinds of fishes, but now many of these teeth are regarded as having belonged to the same species. The reason for this is the discovery of the little tropical Port Jackson shark.

The jaws of this shark show several quite different kinds of teeth, which pass in a regular sequence from sharp-cutting tools to rounded grindstones suitable for crushing crabs and cockles. The Port Jackson shark is a "living fossil," as we say, though scarcely more so than the weird little elfin or goblin shark. This extraordinary fish was regarded as a fossil until as late as 1898, when it was discovered, very much alive, in the Sea of Japan.

Thus, from a world of semi-darkness wherein the waters alone were populous, and that with the minutest forms of life only, the seas and rivers gradually showed an ever increasing variety of creatures, great and small. A great deal more than half of the world's history from the dawn of life must have been spent in bringing into being its swelling legions of fishes, molluscs, crustacea and the rest, and a slowly increasing growth of vegetation.

ADVENTUROUS ALGÆ

Most people at some time or another have stood beside some desolate moorland pond or fern-bordered lake and been impressed by the utter silence, although the waters might be known to teem with fish, and every foot of surrounding soil has its animal citizens. So must the world have been for fully two thousand million years after life first stirred beneath the growing light. No sound broke the awful stillness save the wind's wild music amid crags and canyons, and the noise of water as it lapped the desolate shores.

The land was more bereft of life than any desert known today, nor was animal existence possible until some few adventurous algæ, ever adapting themselves to a state just a little less dependent on the waters, gradually invaded the shore. At first these unearthly looking plants, the crude forerunners of our mosses and horse tails, no doubt merely skirted tidal ways, and gradually land-locked pools. Then, bit by bit, they marched inland. With them came some hardy semi-crustaceous creatures whose hard shells, protecting their moisture-laden gills from the sun's rays, aided them to leave the water for longer and longer intervals.

ARRIVAL OF THE INSECTS

This was but a step to the abandonment of gills for a respiratory system of tubes, and thus the first insects came to pass. These pioneers were all members of the more primitive families. First there were creatures like the spring tails, still found on the sea shore, or the little silver fishes that forage on larder floors for crumbs, or seek to invade the flour bin.

Later appeared primitive cockroaches, and others of their kind, insects which betray their lowly origin by producing families very much like themselves direct from the egg, instead of passing through the complex metamorphosis of the creeping grub and dormant chrysalis.

As the vegetation spread and steadily reared higher above the steamy earth, a new sound—the chirpings of the first grasshoppers as they scraped their spiny legs upon their horny wing cases—was heard. It was instrumental and not vocal music, but momentous for all that. It heralded the conquest of the land.

Perhaps the grasshoppers were not allowed to rejoice in their brave new world for long. The earth had already known several alternations of excessive cold and heat, but genial conditions must have marked the advent of the insects, and all life responded to the opportunities offered. The time possibly marked the greatest warm spell that the world has ever seen. Vegetation soon made amazing strides, covering vast acreages, and assuming gargantuan forms.

FISHES TAKE A TRIP ASHORE

The insects no doubt rejoiced in it, but as with every other kind of animal, competitors were on their heels, to dispute their earthly paradise, and in large measure wrest it from them. When some chance gust of wind swept a grasshopper—past its zenith perhaps—on to the surface of the receding waters, an enterprising fish rose to it, as does the trout to the angler's fly. But such chance casualties were but a hint of massacres to follow. The fishes followed the insects ashore.

Dr. Julian Huxley has likened the first footprints recorded in the rocks to the finding of Friday's footstep by the marooned Crusoe, and no simile could be happier. But for the factor of drought, which forced some scale-clad, bony fishes to breathe the air and take a trip ashore or perish, the world of men would never have come to pass. All the triumphs and disasters of the human race date from the days that made the water untenable for certain fishes.

LIFE IN THE COAL FORESTS

There are still living quite a number of fishes tolerably at home out of water. The lung fishes of Australia, Africa, and South America can, thanks to their swim bladders which serve in some measure as lungs, survive droughts that would kill any other fish. The eel makes nightly journeys overland, the eastern climbing perch can travel hundreds of yards over rough roads or even ascend trees, and the little mud skipper habitually goes hunting after flies along the mud flats, or scuffles nimbly up and down the mangrove roots, high above water mark.

How some fishes not only lived to produce others with swim bladders converted into lungs and paired fins modified to form short legs and arms, with stumpy-toed and fingered hands and feet, is told elsewhere in this book. Accepting the mechanical adaptations that made some fish independent of the water, let us see what followed.

Forced ashore by drought, just as the drying of a pond turns the American aquatic axolotl into a terrestrial salamander, the fish became

GRASSHOPPERS ON WHEAT

Grasshoppers are a menace in Australia. They periodically descend in countless swarms on wheat-fields, destroying many acres.

newts and dragged themselves about the reeking mud and tangled vegetation of the coal forests. The coal that brightens our hearth may in its day have borne the slimy weight of some gigantic eft greater than the salamanders five feet in length that still live in the mountain streams of Japan.

Our picture, based upon all the known vegetation and animals common to the period, gives a general idea or summary of one of those vast forests that once covered every portion of the earth where coal is found, and probably many more places that await discovery. For anything from ten to twenty million years a forest such as that depicted represented life at its highest.

In an atmosphere and half darkness similar to that of the present-day rain forests on the equator, the vegetation of the coal forests rose out of steaming mud for a hundred feet and more. The next time you come upon a clump of horse tails growing by some stagnant pool, try to picture yourself a pigmy one inch high. That would be more or less the sensations of a modern man suddenly transported back to the days when our coal mines, so indispensable to comfort and industry, were in the making.

MOSSES BIG AS TREES

Immense horse tails, tree ferns, and mosses exaggerated to the size of trees rose on every hand. Plants often discharged huge seed vessels. Vegetation vast and rank shut out the light, save where it percolated through the grotesque tracery overhead, and sent down spot lights on the heaving life below.

The coal forests, humming with insects often of a size unknown today, had for its rulers a race of super newts and salamanders. Perhaps these great batrachians were silent as their living representatives. Possibly the insects alone lent a splash of colour in the pervading gloom, for no blossoms we know today relieved the interminable greens and greys of stems and foliage.

Of the shapes that crawled upon the mud and writhed about the waterlogged tree ferns and oak-sized mosses we have copious evidence in fossils, and even in fossil footprints. There were tiny slippery-skinned creatures very like the newts and sirens of the present time. They doubtless preyed upon the countless insects until they themselves were victimized.

Whereas our two living species of giant salamanders, each no more than four or five feet long, are the longest amphibians known today, the coal forests sheltered monsters that could have disposed of such at a gulp. There were creatures like the so-called mastodon lizard measuring ten feet long with a waist line of a yard and a half, crocodile shaped creatures scarcely less bulky, and pick-axe headed newts with gapes that spread from one tip of the axe head to the other, twenty-four inches or even more.

Like the fish, these monsters seemed impregnable in their forest fastnesses, but again climatic changes worked their undoing, and, sweeping into the limbo of forgotten things the great majority, forced a remnant to explore new lands and found a hardier race. The fishes met their Waterloo through drought. The crisis that came upon the heyday of the monster newts was ice.

ICE INVADES THE SWAMPS

Ice which had twice swept the hardier and more adaptable animals from the northern hemisphere, now converged on the steaming swamps from north and south. Swamps were drained and dried, great mountain ranges appeared, and everywhere animal and plant life, terrestrial or submerged, was forced into new ways if its existence was to continue. Though no fossil tadpoles have as yet come to light, the great newts must have passed through a gill-bearing stage, born of a gelatinous egg, and to such modes of reproduction cold and drought alike are unfavourable. The great tree ferns and mosses wilted before the coming cold, and

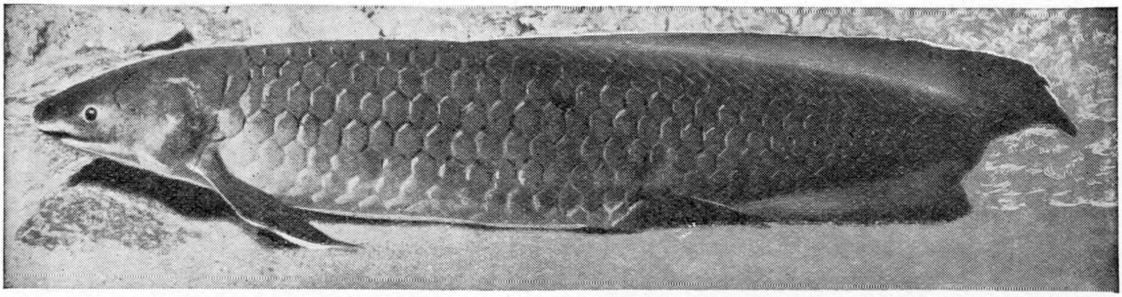

LINK BETWEEN FISHES AND AMPHIBIANS

Known scientifically as dipnoi *: popularly as mud- or lung-fishes, these differ from other fishes in possessing lungs, almost three-chambered hearts, and multi-cellular skin-glands. They survive severe droughts. The amphibians left them behind in the evolutionary race.*

WHERE NOW STANDS NEWCASTLE-UPON-TYNE

Forms of life such as these flourished in England for from ten to twenty million years where coal is now being mined. Giant newts and salamanders wallowed in mud amidst the eternal gloom cast by mammoth ferns.

with them went the crocodile newts and salamanders. Frogs and toads formed no part of the coal forest fauna; they are relatively beasts of yesterday, so far as we can tell.

The land, as always, suffering more than the sea under climatic changes, responded to the new conditions in a variety of ways. The next long chapter in the earth's story is called the Jurassic Epoch, since it was during this period that the Jura Mountains came into being. It saw the end of the giant mosses and their kind, and heralded the Age of Flowering Plants.

BETTER WAY OF REPRODUCTION

Plants opened up a new world to the surviving insects, a world of nectar and pollen, of wood and leaves for building homes, and a host of other possibilities. Up to this time all the insects had been of relatively crude, rough-hewn design. Cockroaches and grasshoppers must keep going from the start. Any prolonged food shortage spells their end.

The more modern species of insects of the Jurassic period not only evolved new ways of feeding, sucking up blood or honey as opposed to just chewing, but they found a better way of reproduction. There was evolved the grub, feeding with gusto whilst food abounded, then facing ensuing food shortage from cold or drought with equanimity, wrapped in the tough shroud that we call a chrysalis.

REPTILES RULE THE WORLD

The most noteworthy of all changes perfected at this time concerns some descendants of certain of the salamander clan. These animals had developed tougher skins, able to resist heat, and not needing constant lubrication with water. They had more effective lungs, and above all they produced their young, not from submerged gelatinous capsules, but from hard or at least elastic-shelled eggs strengthened with lime and deposited in mud or snug burrows dug by themselves, secure from foes above the water line.

When the monster newts saw their world vanishing before Nature's gigantic drainage operations, the layers of hard eggs, with some of their worst competitors removed, came into their own. The pioneer reptiles took the stage, and their descendants held it, almost undisputed,

MARTIN JOHNSON (WIDE WORLD)

FISH WITHOUT LEGS THAT CLIMBS TREES

Though without legs this fish is able to travel on land and climb trees. Fins and scales are its means of propulsion. It leaves the water at regular intervals because it would die if it did not do so.

for between one hundred and two hundred million years.

Of all the great epochs or chapters in the book of life, the so-called Age of Reptiles has been, with the exception of the human period, the only one to enjoy what may be termed popularity. There is much excuse for this because for most of us the Age is associated with the word "dinosaur," meaning terrible lizard, a term first used about 1824, when the first dinosaur to be recognized as such was discovered near Oxford. Dickens refers to the megalosaurus in the opening chapter of *Bleak House.*

WHAT RADIATIVE ADAPTATION MEANS

Although the dinosaurs did undoubtedly bestride the world like veritable colossi for a long period, they did not make the Age of Reptiles. For millions of years after its opening there were no dinosaurs at all. The first reptiles were relatively small creatures, and like the earlier members of all groups of animal life showed a remarkable uniformity, a pronounced sameness of design. Their further development presents a striking example of what is known as radiative adaptation.

One may picture a family of "quins." For some years they not only look alike but behave alike, playing with woolly monkeys and rag books, and so graduating through meccano sets and toy soldiers to cricket. But once launched upon the world, and such bents as they have shown are developed, each goes his way. One becomes a clerk, another an artist, another joins the navy, and so on. On rather different lines something of this kind happens with animals. Wanderers by nature, the members of an ancestral stock spread out like the sticks of a fan, and each taking a different road, makes the best of what it meets with—or perishes.

CLUMSY AND SLOW-FOOTED

The early reptiles, contemporary with the great amphibians, were not unlike in general shape and size. Some scaled six to ten feet long; many were much smaller. But as time went on they began to develop peculiarities which clearly marked the various families and species. The teeth tended to be of the stock reptilian pattern—not set in deep sockets, but leaning up against a sort of shelf and held in position by the gums—and very uniform in type, as in most living reptiles. They seem to have been clumsy of form and slow footed.

There were others, appearing late in the series, with teeth graded into molars or grinding teeth, chisel teeth, and sharp fangs or dog teeth. Indeed, their skulls, excepting that the lower jaw was hooked on to the skull in typical reptilian style, bore a striking resemblance to the skulls of certain of the more primitive mammals.

Yet others of these strange early reptiles did queer things with their teeth. Some lost all of them bar the dog teeth, which grew into huge tusks, and others dropped even these and fell back on horny beaks for cutting food in the manner of tortoises. The strangest of all must have been aquatic, for their backs had huge sail fins some three feet or more high, and with yard-arm extensions to the supporting spines.

BEAST-TOOTHED REPTILES

As with the super-newts these reptiles, particularly the more active beast-toothed ones, seemed for a time to command all they surveyed, but they too largely succumbed to climatic changes. The survivors, however, gave the first impetus to a second and extraordinary outburst of development and enterprise, colonizing all the warmer parts of the earth. The climate, save at the extreme poles, seems to have been uniformly tropical or sub-tropical. The later and most prosperous phases of the Age of Reptiles saw the establishment of the rich and varied vegetation we know today, and this was no doubt largely responsible for the amazing opulence of the group.

It was during this second and greatest push of the reptiles that the lizards such as we know today, and the tortoises and turtles came into being. The curious primitive or anomalous reptiles, as they are called, persisted side by side with the more spectacular forms, but made no great show until considerably later.

VERNON EDWARDS (MONDIALE)

PRIMITIVE REPTILE OF AMERICA
Dimetrodon gigas *lived in North America two hundred million years ago. It was about the size of a St. Bernard dog.*

VERNON EDWARDS (MONDIALE)

HELMET-CHEEKED LIZARD
A helmet of bone covered the skull and cheeks of Pariasaurus baini. *A vegetarian, it lived on land.*

Besides the dog-like teeth of some, there were noticeable other peculiarities, such as very mammalian shoulder blades. One of these animals suggested a hyena almost as much as a lizard. Although we cannot know for certain, this or some similar forms may have been anticipating the transition from cold to warm bloodedness, and an exchange of scales for hair.

COMING OF THE DINOSAURS

But for a long time to come, the world was to see a series of extravagant developments and lavish experiments in numerous directions. The relatively lately-risen land masses were very different from what they are now. From North America stretched a palmy way through Greenland and Northern Europe to Asia. A great gap between North and South America led into a sort of inland sea that continued into the Mediterranean, and so, via a sort of canal, now the Indian Ocean, to Australia. South America, Africa and India were one.

Here, until a subsidence rearranged the main portions of dry land, roamed an extraordinary medley of forms, gaining in size and complexity as time went on. Over five thousand kinds of dinosaur have been listed. They are broadly divided into four groups, beast-footed, bird-footed, lizard-footed and armoured dinosaurs.

Availing themselves of the lush herbage, some turned from an insect or mixed diet to an exclusively vegetarian one. They must have scarcely stopped eating to support their vast bulks. For all this they were proportionately light for their size. The accepted plan of such monsters was an elephantine body with a long neck, an absurdly little and almost brainless head, and a serpentine tail. So small was the cranial capacity that an appreciable interval must have passed for one of these giants to realize that someone had trodden on its tail.

The skeleton of a seventy-four feet long whale

VERNON EDWARDS (MONDIALE)

BIRD-FOOTED REPTILE

This four-toed, plant-eating dinosaurian reptile climbed the trees of the Isle of Wight one hundred million years ago.

weighs nearly eighteen thousand pounds, but the bones of a dinosaur the same length weigh only about ten thousand pounds, so that browsing off a tree top forty-five feet above ground would be accomplished by the beast just hoisting itself up on its hind legs. The largest dinosaur known, one lately found in Africa, stood nearly twenty feet high at the shoulder, and could normally carry its head thirty-five feet above ground level.

Monsters built on this generous plan, and all closely alike save in minor details, have been traced in North America, Greenland, India, Africa, Mongolia and Australia—even where London stands. Some eminent authorities believe that these mountainous lizards largely browsed off bankside herbage whilst keeping their bodies submerged. If such safety-firs precautions were the rule, there was admittedly good reason for them.

GIGANTIC FLESH-EATERS

Parallel with these lizards, and other huge kangaroo-shaped herbivores like the iguanodon, there grew up a race of gigantic flesh-eaters. They must have been truly terrible lizards. Whilst the carnivorous dinosaurs were often no bigger than blackbirds, the largest stood fourteen feet high when raised upon their hind legs, which were proportionately much larger and stouter than those of the heftiest kangaroo.

These brutes when in action walked erect, with the tail clear of the ground (we know this by their fossil footprints), and must also have been able to make tigerish leaps. The fore-limbs were disproportionately small but bore claws like those of a lion, and the huge jaws bristled with two-edged teeth four or five inches long.

It invariably happens that an aggressor sooner or later compels the aggressed to pursue one of two lines of conduct—flight or defence. Some of the largest dinosaurs, unable to seek refuge in the water, or evolve, like some others, on ostrich-like lines, began to pile up the most massive armour.

HEAVY ARMOUR AND LIGHT BRAIN

In North America, which was at this time unusually rich in dinosaurs, there occurred the great bird-footed lizards known as stegosaurians, or spine-armoured lizards. Some of these creatures had the hips or entire back roofed with bony plates, and big horn-covered spikes of bone surmounting the shoulders and ranged along the sides like the blades on Roman chariot wheels.

The mightiest stegosaur had two rows of triangular spines ranged along its back, and several pairs of spines on the tip of its tail. The beast measured about twenty-four feet over all, stood seven feet at the hips, and its tallest spines were two feet or more from base to apex. But what it boasted in armour it lacked in sagacity. The brain weighed only two and a half ounces.

As though to counter this there was a sort of secondary nerve centre, or huge swelling of

CHARLES P. KNIGHT; VERNON EDWARDS (MONDIALE)

DINOSAURS OR "TERRIBLE REPTILES"

Upper: Trachodon Mirabilis, *a duck-billed monster of the Cretaceous period. It was a vegetarian and a hopper. Lower:* Centrosaurus apertus, *which lived eighty million years ago in North America. It was more ferocious in appearance than in reality.*

the spinal cord in the pelvis. This auxiliary nerve centre weighed ten times more than the brain proper, and possibly controlled the hind legs and wagged the flail-like tail. Small wonder that when Professor Marsh made this monster known for the first time the American Press hailed it as the lizard with two brains.

There was another group of armoured dinosaurs, also chiefly American, that, whilst showing rows of spines on back and tail, concentrated chiefly on the defence of the head and shoulders, protecting the latter by a huge

VERNON EDWARDS (MONDIALE)

STEGOSAURUS STENOPS

Armoured with scales, bony plates and spikes. This dinosaur lived on plants and laid eggs. When full grown it was about twenty-five feet long.

frill of bone sprouting from the hinder part of the skull. In the largest kinds the head bore a huge horn, two feet long or more, over each eye, and an equally impressive weapon on the nose. It has been suggested, with reason, that the armour of this beast became in time so heavy as to defeat its own object, and becoming too cumbrous to move with ease, led to the extinction of the group.

For many years it was debated whether the animals laid eggs or bore their young alive. Many scientists were in favour of the latter suggestion, but in digging out the smaller forerunners of the group in Mongolia, about a dozen potato-shaped objects, each nearly a foot long, came to light. One such showed a break in the outer crust, and within, petrified like the adult skeletons, was revealed an infant dinosaur—so some at least laid eggs.

The dinosaurs, whilst dominating dry land and river margins, were not the only reptiles of the period. Just as the insects, evolved from aquatic creatures, returned to aquatic life in such forms as alder and dragon flies and water beetles, so some of the reptiles became entirely aquatic, and fed presumably on fish. Foremost of these were the huge fish lizards or ichthyosaurs, superficially combining the crocodile and porpoise in the form of head and body and paddle-shaped flippers. Some grew in their adult stage to over thirty feet long.

NECK AS LONG AS BODY

These swift-moving monsters, which took the place of whales, must have had amazing sight. The eyes were provided with bony diaphragms, as seen in birds, and the converging plates, adjustable to command a wide range of vision, might measure fully a foot across. Crocodilian as to their exteriors, these terrors were very fish-like within. Fossil castings of their excreta have been found, and these, naturally taking the shape of the intestine, show a spiral formation similar to that observed in living sharks.

A little later to appear than the first fish lizards were the curious monsters known as plesiosaurs, or near lizards as the Greek name implies. They were as large as the ichthyosaurs and very similarly shaped save for the head and neck. The small lizard-like head was mounted on a neck quite as long as the body, and accounted for about a third or even more of the total length. Despite its snaky appearance this neck must have been curiously inflexible.

RELATIVES OF THE MONITORS

Possibly the fish lizards bore their young alive, as do some sharks, for their relatives the near lizards have been found with their fossilized infants caged within the body-wall of the parent. Great hawk-headed turtles, twelve feet across the flippers, shared the seas with these terrifying monsters, but one imagines all must have quailed before the mosasaurs.

These lizards were distant relatives of the existing monitors, but had the feet converted into paddles, and a tail that constituted more than half a possible total length of forty-two feet. The mosasaur must have possessed an

VERNON EDWARDS (MONDIALE)

FORMER DENIZEN OF ENGLISH WATERS

Ichthyosaurus, a marine reptile, was about thirty-five feet long. It had a long snout, with sharp teeth, short neck, two fins and four swimming-paddles. It visited the shores of the British Islands about one hundred and fifty million years ago.

unusual swallowing capacity. The lower jaw was hinged about the middle at either side, so that when an unusually large mouthful was contemplated, the whole contraption simply bowed outwards like the lower jaw of a pelican, and so the seemingly impossible meal became an actuality. Thousands of these creatures have been unearthed, ample testimony to their one-time abundance.

The biggest sea-going reptile we know today is the Estuarine crocodile of Eastern waters. It grows to twenty feet or more. The early crocodilians of the Age of Reptiles were not so unlike those now living, but probably more adapted to a life in open water. Some had curiously hooked lower jaws, and in many ways suggested the slender snouted fish-eating gavials of India and Malaya. Some must have fed on cuttle fish, for stones—swallowed perhaps to aid digestion—have been found in their interiors, dyed black with sepia shot out by the squids when being swallowed. Many of these marine crocodiles have been dredged from the Thames estuary and other parts of England, clear indications of the tropic climate of the Reptile Age.

All living crocodiles have the closable nostrils placed at the extreme tip of the snout, but a number of the early forms, like the great fish lizards, had their noses set immediately in front of the eyes or even on top of the head, as in modern whales.

The tortoises also were well established by this time. Whereas the few giants now left are scattered over distant island groups and seldom scale more than six hundred pounds, during the Age of Reptiles there were monsters twelve feet over the curve of the carapace or shell, and weighing more than two thousand pounds. One of these was found in 1923 in the Siwalik Hills of India. Some had horned heads.

The tortoise and turtle represented the last word in armament. Scattered plates or bands of bone coalesced and cemented to the ribs and spine till an ovoid box was the result. Complete enough as a covering to limbs and head, it greatly hampered movement, and the land tortoises without exception are tardy to a degree. Yet they persisted where many more mobile monsters met with extinction.

WIDE WORLD

LAST WORD IN ARMOUR

The turtle carried armour-plating to an extreme, and though it thereby became extremely slow it managed to survive.

While the giant reptiles were piling up armaments and eventually crippling themselves in so doing, others developed on quite other lines. Fishes may already have essayed tentative attempts at the conquest of the air : the reptiles made it an accomplished fact.

The flying dragons, or more correctly pterodactyls (wing-fingered reptiles), attained flight upon lines being successfully followed by some other and less well-known animals. They anticipated bird structure in the shape of the head and its being set on the neck at right angles, in their dense but light bones, and keeled breast bones. But the actual organs of flight were unique, for the skinny wing membrane stretched from thigh to ankle, up the creature's sides, and finally found attachment on the enormously exaggerated little fingers.

The rest of either hand was free, and no doubt the animals scuffled and scrambled about rocks and trees in a very squirrel-like manner when not soaring above the waters and diving for fish, on which they are believed to have chiefly fed. There were pterodactyls with short tails, and some with long ones. Teeth might bristle in the jaws like thorns on a briar, or be altogether wanting.

AMERICA'S FLYING DRAGONS

Very perfect impressions of the wings have been found in the lithographic stone quarries of Bavaria. The race seems to have been world wide, to have steadily increased in numbers and average size as time went on, and to have reached a grand climax which coincided with that of the dinosaurs. Some flying dragons from America show a wing-span of twenty-five feet, more than twice that of the largest condor, and had extraordinary pick-axe shaped heads, the hinder portion perhaps counterpoising the horn covered beak, or as some suggest supporting special muscles wherewith to operate the enormous wings.

The above will serve to give some idea of the more devious forms of life that populated the earth for so long more than one hundred million years ago. The great herbivorous mammals, big cursorial birds and slayers of every grade as we know them today were caricatured by cold-blooded scaly-skinned reptiles. They seemed destined to own the earth for all time, but as they rose to their zenith the processes of sunset were at work.

COMING OF THE LIZARD BIRD

The land masses were becoming more defined, but from the north, as happened several times again in the earth's history, the cold was steadily encroaching on the dinosaurian paradise. In response to this, perhaps, certain small and unobtrusive reptiles were fortifying themselves against the things to come.

From the lithographic stone of Bavaria there were retrieved in 1861 two very remarkable little skeletons showing the lizard bird or bird lizard, now known as archeopteryx, or " ancient winged " animal. This creature, represented it

LIZARDS OF TODAY AS GROTESQUE AS THOSE OF REMOTE AGES

Reading from top: Bearded Australian, frilled and fin-tailed lizards. Although most of the two thousand five hundred known species have a ferocious appearance, only the Gila monster of Mexico is poisonous. The processes of evolution may be strikingly observed today in the Dalmatian Islands, where two species of lizard are rapidly separating into numerous varieties.

is thought by two distinct species, is described in the chapter entitled " Evolution as the Clock Ticks."

So unlike any bird we know today, it was all the same a bird in very fact, happy in that one feature the reptiles lacked to save them from impending disaster. The lizard bird had feathers. Relatively speaking, cold would have

VERNON EDWARDS (MONDIALE)

REPTILE THAT FLEW

Pteranodon Occidentalis *had a wing-span of eighteen feet. His beak was toothless and his legs were weak.*

no terrors for it, and once having achieved this, it had comparatively little more to learn. It could command the air at altitudes impossible to pterodactyls, and no doubt place its eggs well out of reach of most reptilian competitors. This, it will be realised, was an extremely important consideration from the point of view of survival.

That reptiles did not leap at a bound from crawling things to the aerial magnificence of archeopteryx will be obvious. There must be many other half-way types bridging the gulf between reptile proper and reptile bird awaiting discovery or lost for ever. Scales split into feathers gradually, and there must have been much ineffectual leaping and amateurish gliding ere flight was fully under command.

Birds attained " perfection " much sooner than did most other groups. Once feathers and flight were theirs avian education was complete, and in essentials modern birds have altered little from their forbears millions of years ago. One does not think of the early birds being any very serious menace to the great reptiles. Perhaps some served as tick gatherers to the lumbering vegetarians, like the ox peckers and cattle egrets of today.

DYING MONSTERS

But there were other reptiles changing upon another plan, and in them most scientists see one primary reason for the dramatic closure of the Age of Reptiles. These beast lizards, as they may be called, though small, had, unlike the birds, met cold by growing hair instead of feathers, but like them possessed warm blood, if many degrees colder than that of the average bird. These first beasts, little egg-laying burrowers, were in all probability great egg stealers. It is almost universally accepted that there ensued an epoch of egg rolling and egg smashing. Monsters-to-be were routed out and devoured ere they could chip the shell, and this coupled with the encroaching cold, closed the Age of Reptiles for ever. Suddenly, as the drawing of a blind or the turning of a switch, the dinosaurs and pterodactyls, the plesiosaurs and other sea raiders came to an end—utterly.

UPSTART NEW-COMERS

There is nothing to parallel their finish in all the earth's long story, so sudden and irrevocable, so universal in its sweeping effacement. The little egg smashers, valiant in their warm furs and high living, went on to spread to all points of the habitable landscape, to colonize and meet all objects as they occurred, and so open the third and last chapter in the Pageant of the Past.

Different though the upstart new-comers were from the giants they had ousted, history, as with all the foregoing groups, in some way repeated itself. Once again there was to be observed that curious uniformity, a sameness amongst the ever-increasing mammals. One could not at haphazard say this is an insectivore, that a carnivore, this a vegetarian, or again, that that beast was obviously fitted to catch and devour fish.

The cataclysmal upheavings of earth which drained the dinosaurs' rich semi-aqueous pastures and piled the dying monsters one upon

EXTINCT BIRDS COMPARED TO AN OSTRICH

The existing ostrich is marked X. 1. *Archeopteryx, the ancestral bird.* 2. *Diatryma with a primitive horse in its beak.* 3. *Great cariama.* 4. *Dodo: a modern species lived in Mauritius until the latter half of the* 17*th century.* 5. *Solitaire.* 6. *Inva.* 7. *Odontopteryx.* 8. *Gannet.* 9. *Wingless diver.*

another, as we find their fossilized remains today, must have taken toll of many mammals, but the mass won through. It is likely that a few of the lighter bird-like dinosaurs still lingered long after the bulk of the giants had vanished. The ostrich and the crocodile today represent, in various anatomical features, the nearest approach we have to dinosaurs, and some of the light cursorial types were very ostrich-like in general appearance.

They could run after the early mammals, which they caught in the open, and almost from the first the warm-blooded hairy beasts must have faced many difficulties. For about ninety million years after the close of the Age of Reptiles the mammals showed as very generalized types, some living in the remaining swamps, others the cooler and dried areas marking the uprising temperate regions, which were still warmer than would be considered normal now.

The end of this transitionary period saw the beginning of what is called the Dawn Age.

WIDE WORLD

HAS DINOSAUR FEATURES

With the possible exception of the ostrich, the crocodile is the nearest approach to the dinosaurs alive today.

The mammals began to find their feet, and a wonderful tale is told by the wealth of fossils belonging to that time. Many crude birds with tooth-filled jaws, one in particular being a huge flightless diver, followed archeopteryx, and in turn gave way to birds of modern types. But the greatest changes were seen amongst the mammals. They largely tended to have five toes on each foot, and in these plantigrade creatures, chiefly of fox size and probably barred or spotted, we see the first precursors of the beasts we know.

Already competition had set in with a vengeance. Slayers appeared, and those animals that clung to a vegetarian diet met the usual alternatives to extinction—armour, concealment or flight. Some of the little fox-like beasts rapidly developed as runners, the heralds of the horse. There were tapirs no bigger than pigs, flesh-eaters of a fox-bear-hyena type, big weasel-bears, bear dogs, monkeys, lemurs, small hornless horsey rhinoceroses, and the strange monsters called dinoceroses, beasts with terrible horns. They were elephantine in build, about the size of cows, and the head fairly bristled with horns, knobs and tusks. For many millions of years the brain cases of most mammals were vastly smaller than those of modern beasts, but life was now a war of wits for all that.

CAMELS NO BIGGER THAN HOGS

Very grotesque armour marked some species, but they continued to hold the stage for a short time only. Antelopes had horns on their heads and noses, and grew long tusks like living musk deer and water deer. There were hogs as big as ponies, and weird humpless camels no bigger than the hogs.

The bone beds of the time cast some interesting side-lights on the lives of the creatures. The camels went in big herds, trekking from grazing ground to grazing ground, from water-hole to water-hole. They halted at night, and in times of drought, dawn found them on the move—but leaving a mass of dead and dying behind.

In North America the tale of earth at this time is particularly lucid. Life just swarmed everywhere. On the plains were burrowers, particularly marmot-like beasts with two horns above the eyes, and the swamps were haunted by the weird titan beasts rather like rhinoceroses. These were hornless at first, but later some developed huge paired horns, and one a single horn two feet high with a flattened mushroom top.

CHANGES ON THE MAP

Sea still separated North and South America, but the bridge between North America and Europe had submerged, so had the land between North America and Greenland. North America seems to have been the headquarters of the titan beasts, as also of the terrible horns, but Asia also adventured in this direction.

There was a marked and steady increase of size in all the main mammalian groups, and Asia presently produced the vastest animal of all—the baluchitherium, found only a few years ago in Baluchistan. This was the hornless rhinoceros standing seventeen foot at the shoulder, and able to browse off trees twenty-four feet from the ground. Its brain was negligible.

Once again a back-to-the-water movement showed itself. A pig-like creature, destined to found the race of elephants, haunted the

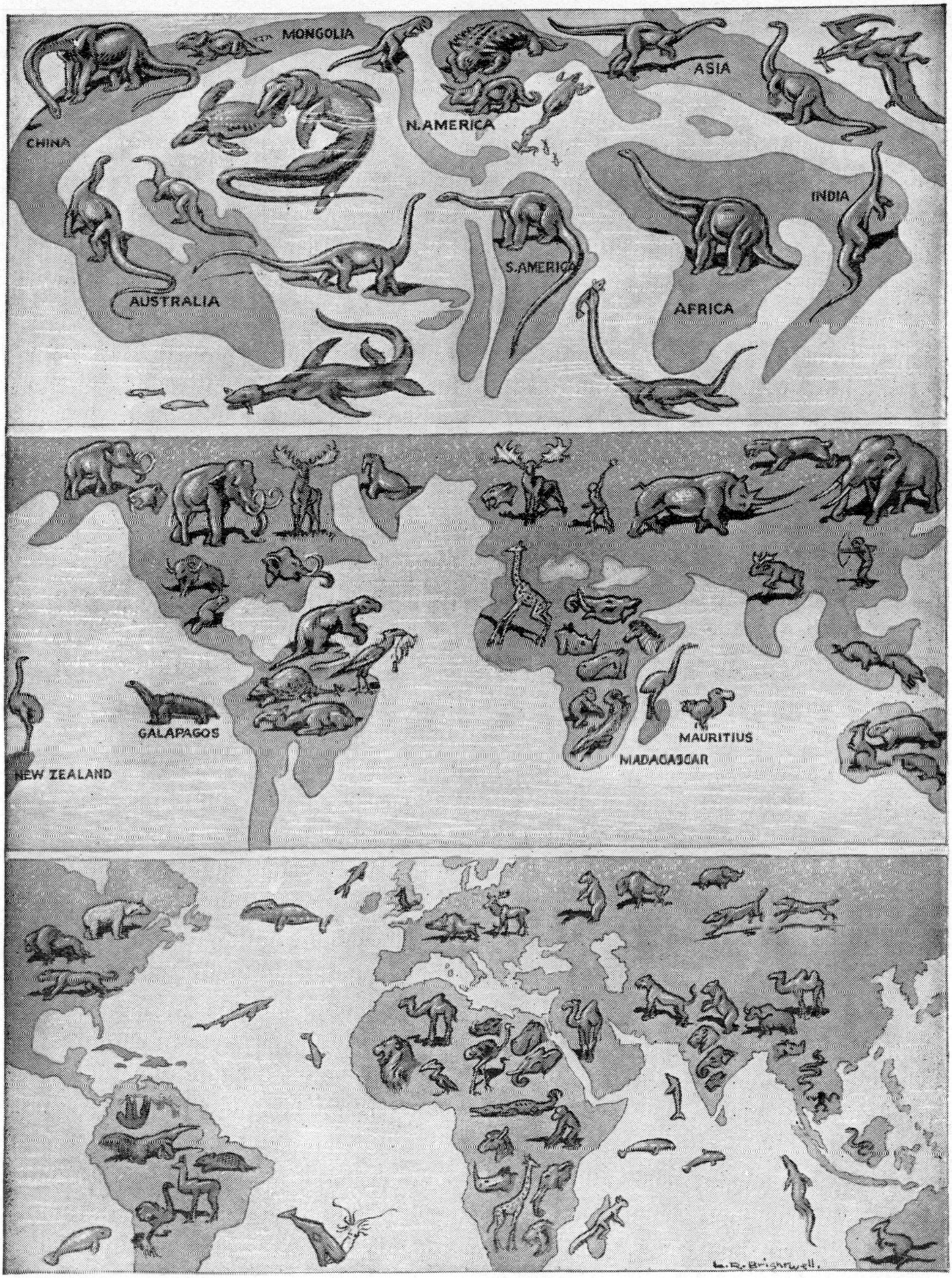

DISTRIBUTION OF CHIEF LAND MASSES AND CHARACTERISTIC ANIMALS

At the top of the page the main portions of the world are mapped as in all probability they appeared some ninety million years ago, in the centre as they were one million years ago, at the bottom as they are now.

CHARACTERISTIC MAMMALS OF NORTH AMERICA

1. *Dawn animals* (*one hundred million years ago*). 2. *Giant pigs, titan beast, rhinoceroses and camels* (*fifty million years ago*). 3. *Clawed grazing animals, antelopes and elephants* (*twenty million years ago*). 4. *Camels, horse and manatee* (*five million years ago*). 5. *One million years ago. Heavy lines = five feet.*

CHARACTERISTIC MAMMALS OF SOUTH AMERICA

1. *Primitive "generalized" mammals, marsupials, armadillos and sloths (one hundred million years ago).*
2 3 *and* 4. *Marsupials, toxodonts and primitive hogs of fifty, twenty and five million years ago respectively.*
5. *Giant sloth, armadillos and browsing animals that lived one million years ago until almost historic times.*

CHARACTERISTIC MAMMALS OF ASIA

1. *Dawn animals that shared Asia and North America* (*one hundred million years ago*). 2. *Baluchitherium, largest of known land animals, on extreme right (fifty million years ago).* 3, 4 *and* 5. *Coming of the elephants, giraffes, etc., and primitive man* (*twenty, five and one million years ago respectively*).

CHARACTERISTIC MAMMALS OF EUROPE

1. *Primitive mammals. On right a once cosmopolitan whale (one hundred million years ago).* 2 and 3. *Archaic mammals and some living kinds—ant bear and pangolin, now confined to Africa and Asia (fifty and twenty million years ago respectively).* 4. *Various tropic mammals (five million years ago).* 5. *Mammals of the Ice Age.*

CHARACTERISTIC MAMMALS OF AFRICA

1. *Dawn mammals. Extreme left, the ancestral elephant (one hundred million years ago).* 2. *Steps in elephant progress, primitive flesh-eaters and the two-horned monster of the Fayum, Egypt (fifty million years ago).* 3 *and* 4. *Typical animals, some still living (twenty and five million years ago respectively).* 5. *Living mammals and (left) extinct giant lemur of Madagascar.*

ANCIENT AND MODERN TYPES OF AUSTRALIAN ANIMALS

Above: marsupials living on the great island continent about one million years ago. Below: modern types of animals. The aboriginal in the top left-hand corner indicates relative size of the creatures.

margins of many waterways, but certain elephantine beasts and some carnivores of unknown origin were taking to water as a possible source of fresh food supplies and a refuge from terrestrial foes. The aquatic carnivores were the first whales, some eight or twelve feet long, with ferociously toothed jaws. The elephantine water animals were probably the forerunners of the now vanishing manatees and dungongs with primitive, "smooth" brains.

CLOSE OF THE DAWN AGE

The close of the Dawn Age saw the bridge joining east and west again upthrust. Strange flocks and herds passed over it, back and forth from Old World to New. The titan beasts, bigger than modern rhinoceroses, were in their heyday. The rhinoceroses of that time showed quaint digressions. Some were light and horsey, some "dachshunded"—to coin a word—so stumpy were their legs. The elephantine group was now recognizable. Using the snout for browsing, and the tusks for digging, these features increased with grotesque results.

Big cats were developing huge upper canine teeth, and the five- and four-toed fox-horses ran from them. Placing continually more weight on the central toes, the outer ones wasted and receded up the leg. The horses of the future were taking shape. Wild dogs, of all patterns, were more abundant now than at any time in the world's history. The various rodent types, squirrels, hares and mice, were in evidence, and beavers were steadily increasing in size.

ELEPHANTS MARCH INTO AFRICA

South America seems to have been curiously left out of all this activity. A few armadillos were its only characteristic inhabitants. Elephants, of stocky size, with short trunks and long chins, marched into Africa; after them came apes and monkeys migrating from the north.

Towards the zenith of this great epoch, the Oligocene or "small new period," following the Dawn Age, South America began to develop a strange fauna which remained with her for æons after. It started with the big club-tailed armadillos, clumsy bear-shaped

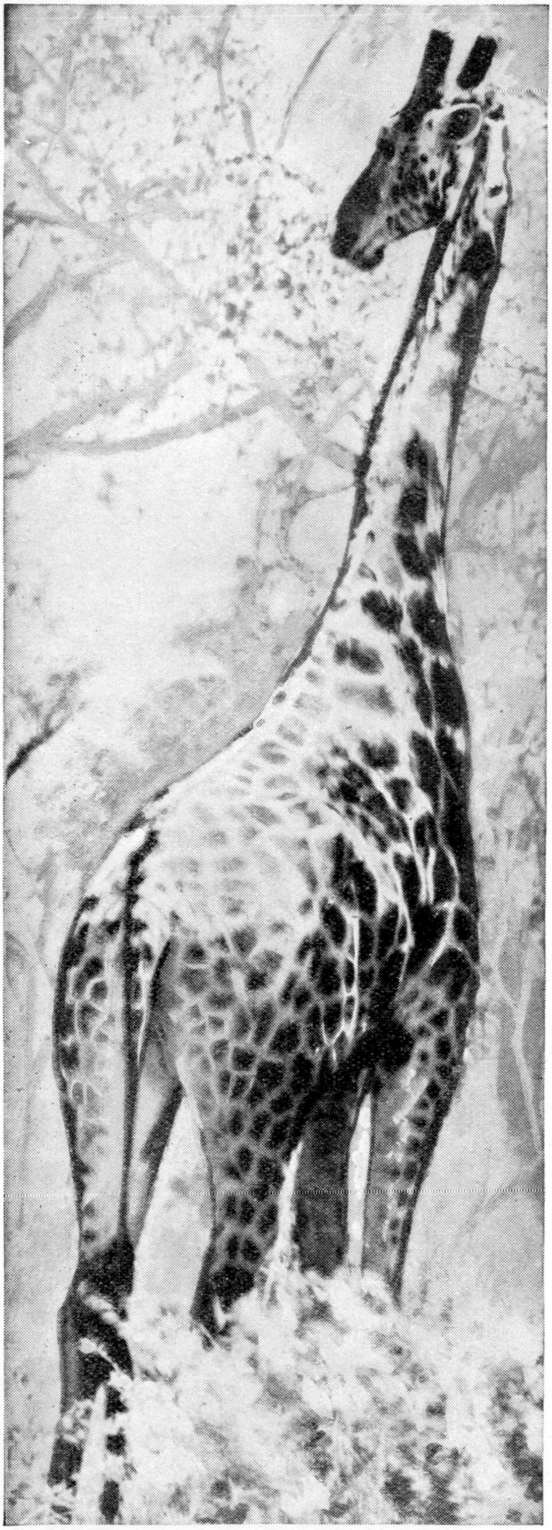

ONCE CALLED CAMEL-LEOPARD

At a tolerably recent period the giraffes appear to have become isolated in Africa.

marsupials as big as cart horses, giraffe camels, gazelle camels, possible forerunners of the modern llamas.

In the north were the lumpish hippopotamus-like animals called amblypods, and diatryma, a terrible-looking bird quite incapable of flight, but evidently a killer, and equal to walking off with one of the little three-toed horses, now grown to the size of sheep. The pigs of Europe and North America were as big as rhinoceroses by this time, and in Africa were monsters without their parallel today even in that last refuge of the great game animals.

MONSTER OF THE FAYUM

The first of these was something between a rhinoceros and an elephant but trunkless, and with a pair of horns a yard high on its nose. They were hollow and so could be brought into action with effect against the hyena bears that may have plagued this beast in its swampy fastnesses, where now lies the Fayum desert.

The other beast, from Central Africa, was an elephant of a kind. It is known as the terrible beast and had a pair of enormous semi-circular tusks hanging from its chin only. Like many other queer experiments on Nature's part, it seems to have developed on lines that militated against success, for it died out after a comparatively short lease of life.

BUILT ON CAMEL-LIKE LINES

About the same period a bizarre essay on camel-like lines wandered in North America. This beast, known as moropus, looked like a huge, awkward cart horse with the head of a Shetland pony. Its glory lay in its feet. There were three toes only on each foot, and the inner toe of each forefoot had a claw such as no mammal living possesses. The teeth of this witless monster point to a plant menu, so the claws must have been for digging rather than aggression, and incidentally must have given the moropus a most extraordinary gait. Throughout this time the horses tended to run more and more on their middle toes only, and the elephants' faces grew longer and longer.

Great Britain, by serving at intervals as a gangway between east and west, acquired an extraordinary fauna. Forms characteristic of both the Old and the New World figure in the soils and rock stratas of the British Isles, pointing to the flow of animal traffic through the geologic ages.

FIELD MUSEUM (MONDIALE)

MEMBERS OF THE TITANOTHERE FAMILY

Titanotheres, now extinct, once roamed the plains of North America and Asia. The earliest known specimens were not much larger than sheep, but some of their descendants had a greater bulk than the present-day rhinoceros.

Many geologists regard Asia as one of the great cradles of the mammalian race. Unfortunately the extraordinary variety of its fauna in times past is difficult to study : expeditions are costly, and the rigours of the climate sufficient to deter all save the most enthusiastic. We have already seen that Asia was the home of the largest land mammal, the shovel-tusked mastodons, and the battering ram titanotheres. In the remote past it also harboured huge giraffe-like animals; one named sivatherium, the beast of Siva, after the Indian goddess of destruction, had a head covered with horns of various sizes. Another giraffe-like monster suggested a giant okapi.

GIRAFFES ISOLATED IN AFRICA

At a tolerably recent period the giraffes seem to have become isolated in Africa; the giraffes proper amid the acacias of the plains, and the okapi in the heart of the Ituri forest. There, we are told, thin pencils of light piercing the gloom shine only on its hocks, so that its pattern of stripes, so conspicuous in a zoo, there blend perfectly with the background of dense vegetation. Unlike the true giraffe, the okapi feeds upon fruit as well as leaves.

We are fast approaching relatively recent times. The Pliocene period dates from not much more than six million years ago, and it found the mainland masses disposed much as they are now. It lasted five million or so years.

Africa had a fauna not unlike that of today. Australia had a strange collection of huge pouched animals, somewhat like those once common in South America. There were wombats as big as bears, phalangers—" pouched cats " as large as or larger than lions—big kangaroos and other strange animals.

SOUTH AMERICA'S MENAGERIE

South America presented a unique menagerie. Strange tapir-pig animals, once common, were less numerous, but extremely abundant was a variety of camel with a long slender half trunk with which it must have plucked leaves as a giraffe gathers them with its tongue. Most striking of all was its collection of sloths and armadillos. Some of the former were like those that came to a tragic end in the tar traps of California, but much bigger.

The megatherium, or big beast, was as massive as an elephant, with a gigantic lower jaw and pendulous snout. This and other great sloths could not, of course, have climbed like the little modern sloths. They must have squatted on their massive haunches and tails as on a tripod, and dragged down tree branches with their enormous arms.

With these were armadillos, big as the biggest tortoises and, like them, enclosed in a single box-like shell. The ordinary banded armadillos also lived at or about this time, and some had two pairs of long, sharp-pointed horns on their heads. But the giants were quite unique. Even the tail was enclosed in heavy armour, and in some species the tail was tipped with a veritable bush of great spines, strongly reminiscent of the clubs used by medieval knights.

MONSTER BIRD OF PATAGONIA

At this time the birds developed proportions surpassing any that we know today. In Patagonia stalked a huge flightless monster suggestive of a cariama, but with a disproportionately big head nearly a yard long, whilst the whole fowl stood eight feet or more in height. A fox would only have made an unsatisfactory mouthful for it. There were big flightless pigeons like the dodo and the solitaire, and flightless sea birds like the Galapagos cormorant and the great auk of Iceland.

Most conspicuous were the ostrich-like birds isolated for the most part upon islands where, unmenaced by competitors of any kind, they developed to a huge size. The modern ostrich is a big bird if it stands eight feet in height, but it would seem a mere chicken compared to some of its extinct relatives. They were characteristic of the southern hemisphere.

One species, believed to have lived in New Zealand at the time of Captain Cook's visit (1777), was known as the moa, and named by Professor Richard Owen in 1839 as *Dinornis struthioides*—the terrible bird like an ostrich. It was, we may suppose, exterminated by the Maoris. The largest species, for there were many, probably stood fully ten feet in height, whilst the smallest kinds scaled no more than three feet. Giant birds of this kind, as well as emus, flourished in Australia, but all of them were dwarfed by certain huge and completely wingless birds living in Madagascar.

Like the dodos, great auks and many other birds, these feathered giants seem to have owed their large size and inability to fly to the seeming security of island life. The inventors of scientific names fairly exhausted their list of superlatives in attempting to give the great cursorial birds fitting titles. Great, high, terrible, titan, thunder and elephant-footed—all these terms figure in the list.

FEATHERED GIANT

The largest of all Madagascar's big birds was the giant aepyornis. Its eggs are still found buried in the salt mud surrounding lakes and river mouths, and even occasionally floating out at sea, having been washed clear of their burial places and made buoyant by the oil within.

Such an egg may measure over a foot in length, and have the capacity of six ostrich eggs, one hundred and forty-eight hen's eggs or thirty thousand humming bird's eggs. One can only wonder what the future might have held for these birds, and all other islanders, had they been left to enjoy their seeming security indefinitely. But an island only gives security so long as no foes can gain access to it. The seas that saved the moas, dodos and all

MONDIALE

CLASSED WITH THE EXTINCT MOAS

The ostrich, the largest living bird, is classed by scientists with the extinct moas. The huge eggs of the giant aepyornis had the capacity of six ostrich eggs, shown above.

BONY FRAMEWORK OF A MAMMOTH OF THE DEEP

The whales are the largest living animals and show a higher development than any other aquatic mammal. Representatives of the sulphur-bottom species attain a length of eighty-seven feet. Whales survived because they learned to like the cold, within limits. Here workers are putting together a whale's skeleton.

other helpless monsters from many predaceous mammals, were no safeguard against the most predaceous of all—man—and so soon as he conceived the canoe, an island refuge proved but a fool's paradise.

SABRE-TOOTHED CATS

The last of the geologic periods—the "newest" as its scientific appellation Pleistocene implies—saw the highest peak of mammalian development. Giants were not only abundant everywhere, but the same kinds of giants enjoyed an enormous range.

Some of the big sloths of South America pushed northwards as far as California, nearly a dozen kinds of wild horse inhabited the New World (there were others in Europe and Asia), elephants, camels, deer, antelope and flesh-eaters of all kinds were equally common.

Almost all the main mammalian groups show a steady increase of stature with the passage of time. In the Pleistocene epoch all the carnivorous families could show members just a little larger than is customary now. The slayers without parallel were the latest representatives of the sabre-toothed cats, which began as creatures not much bigger than a modern lynx.

The biggest of all now had upper tusks nearly a foot long. They were two-edged instead of rounded, and some authorities think the beast usually hooked itself on to its victims by means of these grapnels and drank blood, licking it up from between its front teeth like the present-day vampire bat. Whether the beast died from over-specialization, sudden climatic changes, or man's agency we shall never know; it has passed unlamented.

KILLED BY COLD

The whole of the last great prehistoric chapter in earth's story was, as already mentioned, punctuated by alternate invasions of ice from the north and inter-glacial periods of relative prosperity. The cold spells, and there were apparently four of them, on each occasion swept away whole races of giants. Surviving animals, revelling in the return of warmth and vegetation, prospered like nations between wars, and launched out upon a hundred prospects of expansion and development—until the next set-back.

Cold, though still unfavourable to the great majority, was by its constant imminence a less devastating happening than the cold which ended one hundred and twenty-odd million years of reptile exuberance. The tropics still nurtured giant reptiles—hundred-foot monitor lizards, and even a sixty-foot poisonous snake with fangs as big as a tiger's claws.

LARGEST OF THE DEER

The elk is found in the subarctic forests of both hemispheres. The extinct giant elk was of a different species.

But there were many of the mammals which had learnt to like the cold, within limits. They could at least live on the edge of it, and since cold affects water less quickly than it does land, plenty of aquatic mammals, the whales and enormous sea cows—relatives of the elephants—habitually wandered northwards, finding abundant and satisfying food there.

Terrestrial mammals, living on the edge of the ice, found moss to eat beneath the winter's snow, and enjoyed a short but riotous banquet of high living during the brief Arctic summer. The fur bearers were in evidence, elk and musk oxen, wild sheep and beavers as big as bears, and on the heels of all these the usual harassing hordes of carnivorous animals.

Two races of elephants were now at their highest development, the stately mammoths—represented today by the Asiatic elephant—and the short-legged mastodons, so named from the nipple-shaped protuberances on their grinding teeth. Both these races, instead of fleeing like many other beasts before the ice, hovered on its outskirts, and both developed dense coats of coarse reddish hair. The mastodons seldom stood more than nine feet high, but the imperial mammoth reached about fourteen feet—a yard more than the famous Jumbo—and had tusks fifteen feet in length and extravagantly curled.

MYTH OF THE MAMMOTH

An animal like this was found embedded in the frozen mud of a river in Russia, and steps were taken to saw it out piecemeal and transport it to civilization, but the bank gave way and all was lost. Another found in 1799, in the River Lena, was thawed out of its tomb, the tusks sold and the abandoned carcass left to feed dogs and wolves, which it did for a year or more. Here, luckily, the bones and part of the shaggy hide were saved for science.

"Mammoth" is now one of our most convenient synonyms for huge, and many people quite excusably hold that some such idea originated the word. Its actual derivation is the Siberian *mamantu*, meaning a ground dweller. The Russian peasant, finding the dead bodies always embedded in frozen or thawing mud, seriously believed the greatest of all elephants to be a kind of mole, burrowing in soil and perishing when by accident it tunnelled up into the daylight.

HIPPOPOTAMI IN YORKSHIRE

The hippopotamus, essentially a feeder on lush vegetation, needed in enormous quantities, never penetrated farther north than that part of Europe where today the Yorkshire moors are spread. The rhinoceros, like the elephant a browsing beast well able to subsist on grass and leaves, also pushed northwards, and likewise met the cold with a pelt almost worthy of a Yorkshire terrier.

Some modern rhinoceroses, like those of Java, show a very appreciable covering of hair. The woolly rhinoceros had two enormous horns like those of the living white rhinoceros. But though so formidable it had a restricted range, and by all the signs kept clear of regions favoured by an even larger rhinoceros bearing one huge horn in the middle of its forehead. This monster was probably also a shaggy animal, but less hardy than the true woolly rhinoceros, and so, refusing to go so far north, kept the smaller animal more or less penned.

IMPASSABLE BARRIERS OF TODAY

It will be realized by now that a million or a few million years pass like so many minutes on the great clock of geologic time. In all earth's wonderful history, there is nothing more arresting than this comparatively swift conversion of the mammals, originally sprung from undoubted tropical ancestry, to conditions that repeatedly decimated the terrestrial animals of remote times. Seas, deserts and mountain ranges now raise impassable barriers between the animals of the great land masses, and as we find each characteristic fauna today so it is likely to remain until widespread sinking or uprising of the land once more effects a redistribution.

Within the Arctic Circle conditions are relatively uniform, and the creatures that finally found sanctuary within it show corresponding uniformity. The polar bear, the beaver, wolverine, elk and many more mammals of the frozen north are identical in both hemispheres. Each recurring winter sees a repetition of the mass migrations which each glacial period invoked, but on a smaller scale, and with the inherited knowledge that spring will permit a return to more northerly regions to which the animals have grown accustomed.

HOW BIRD MIGRATION BEGAN

The annual " miracle " of bird migration no doubt had its first incentives in the recurrent cold periods of the Pleistocene epoch, and what were then perhaps the adventures of a few species driven to desperation, have now become habitual to an increased number of species. Africa, and particularly its great plains, present the nearest living picture we can hope to see of what must have been the world's general conditions, so far as its land fauna was concerned, during the earlier interglacial periods.

This chapter set out to sketch the broad movements of mammalian life during kaleidoscopic changes of alternating heat, cold, aridity and drought. For millions of years the mammals dominated the habitable globe, and they are the most progressive animals alive today, whether on land or sea. Once a mammal attains a certain size it has little to fear from fish, reptile or bird. This is true, though admittedly a broad generality. Only an elephant perhaps can afford to ignore a poisonous snake, and no mammal is safe from such fish as the swarming carib of the Amazon, but these are exceptions which according to the proverb are supposed to prove the rule.

In the war of wits into which the Age of Mammals early resolved itself, one of the least armed of all presently took control. It is

MONDIALE

DISAPPEARING VEGETARIAN

During the Miocene and Pliocene periods rhinoceroses roamed both hemispheres, but now live only in Africa and Asia.

estimated—and the roughest estimate only is possible—that approximately one hundred million years separate the first primitive mammals from the first simian stock, and that at least ten million years passed ere that stock yielded anything resembling a human being.

Man's records in the rocks are far less satisfactory than those of the horse, elephant or camel. The remains of even our more recent forerunners are disappointingly scanty. In rocks dating from shortly before the million or so years we call the Pleistocene period, are remains of man-like apes similar to those living in Africa and Asia, but coming from Europe. Monkey remains are known from strata at least twenty million years earlier.

The lemurs—representing a stage lower than the true monkeys—go back earlier still. Today all the lemurs are quartered, with few exceptions, in Madagascar, where a species fully man-size lived until a few centuries ago. Lemurs, like the little tarsius of Borneo, however, enjoyed a very wide range, and many authorities believe that the human race came into being from tarsius stock.

WIDE WORLD

WHITE BEAR OF THE ARCTIC

The polar bear's feet are fitted with bristles so that it may walk with safety on the ice.

Man is unfortunately one of the rarest fossil animals, and this perhaps may be his own fault. The funeral pyre was a very early institution of our species, which may account for the bones of early man being much less abundant than the mural decorations and innumerable implements he left behind him. But though the concrete facts of our origin, reliably set forth, are immeasurably outnumbered by theories and surmises, it does not follow that they never will be known. The last few decades have seen great advances in this direction, and a mass of evidence has been collected since the remains of an " ape-man " were discovered at Trenil, in Java, in 1892.

If Asia, that gave birth to so many mammals, was also the cradle of our race, then the inmates of that vast nursery migrated westwards and, like all other mammalian stock, progressed by radiative adaptation. The more intelligent probably killed off the lesser, and the strong annihilated the weak : a simple policy which may have inspired human conduct for many centuries.

It is not pleasant to regard battle, murder and sudden death as characteristic traits of human mentality in the early history of the race. Some authorities hold that primitive man was not pugnacious towards members of his own species. But it must be remembered that in the far-off days with which we are dealing, morality as we understand it must have been in the earliest stage of development. Idealism had yet to make its twilight gleam on the mind. Early man, like an invading army, was doubtless governed by his stomach.

MAN'S EARLY HISTORY

Here the end of our journey brings us to ground obviously offering much scope for gibes from the cynical but not from the thoughtful. Amid a babel of prophecies, the ordinary man goes his way, not greatly concerned whether humanity is destined for an international Utopia, or universal chaos. At least " it can't happen in my time " he consoles himself. Perhaps the present chapter in the history of the human race may close as hinted in a wise and sober paragraph by Dr. Frederic A. Lucas, Director of the American Museum of Natural History :

" There is good reason to believe that we of the northern hemisphere may be living in the midst of an interglacial epoch, and if this be so, that even now slowly but relentlessly the hosts of the ice king are being marshalled to dispossess man of his fair heritage in the north.

JOURNEY'S END

" Gradually is being assembled the army that will sweep man before it even as it did the mammoth and mastodon in past ages : advancing a few feet this year, retreating a foot or two next season, but never losing all the ground it has gained, the great ice sheet is slowly shaping out of mist and snow the vast fighting machine that will drive man from the populous cities of the north. And who shall say that one hundred thousand years from now, when the great earth pendulum has swung the other way, some race of supermen, working northwards as the climate changes, may not be investigating . . . and reconstructing the habits of the poor, unintelligent inhabitants of what was once New York." The name of the city is immaterial. The above might apply to any centre of civilization.

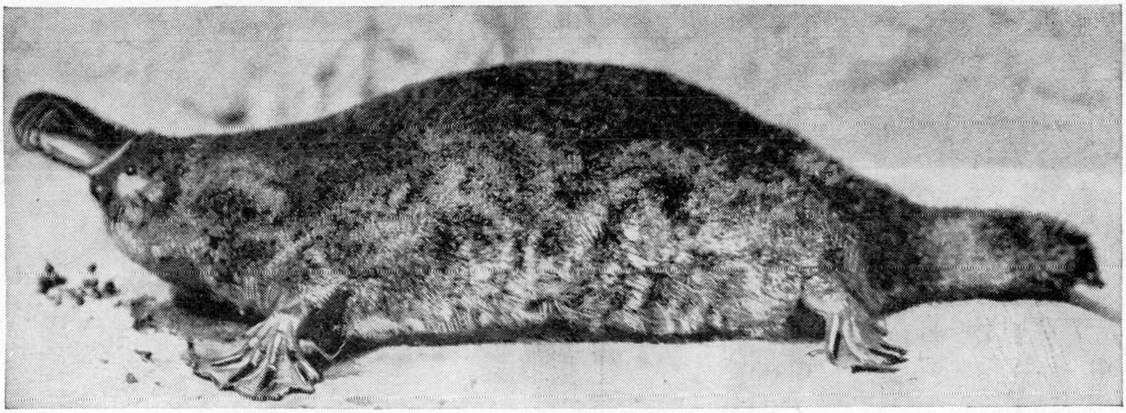

MOST PRIMITIVE AQUATIC MAMMAL

The Australian duckmole, or duck-billed platypus, is one of the most curious animals alive. It lays eggs like a reptile, suckles its young mammal-wise, burrows like a rodent and has a duck's bill and webbed feet.

EVOLUTION AS THE CLOCK TICKS

One may safely say that the broad principles of evolution as already touched upon are very generally accepted. No educated person today regards plants and animals as having simply "happened." It is realized that they are all part of a vast upward and forward movement, incidents in a world programme of continuous change, covering hundreds of millions of years.

It is the failure to accept or realize the immense periods of time marking the steps in evolution that largely militates against its general appreciation. The average man or woman simply cannot be brought to "think in millions." This is not surprising when we reflect that the momentous happenings of a single human life are compressed within the compass of some three score years or less.

How animal forms may change can be the better visualized if we confine ourselves to those creatures which man has taken under his charge during the last fifty centuries or so. Nothing that man touches remains unchanged for long. His restless energies, no matter on what they may be concentrated, make automatically for speeding-up. Often the impetus he gives to things astonishes himself. Take, for example, the animal with which man has been chiefly concerned—man.

The modern European, Chinaman and North American Indian present sufficiently obvious differences in their make-up, but these and all other races of mankind have enough in common to justify their being scientifically included in a single species, *Homo sapiens*. Occidental and Oriental alike have a perfectly upright carriage, straight legs and a convex cranium. These features alone mark them off in strong contrast to the Neanderthal man of a million years ago.

The being whose remains were discovered in the valley of Neanderthal, Rhenish Prussia, to which place he is believed to have migrated from Syria, was unquestionably a man. He made tools and weapons, hunted, and roasted his food over a fire. But anatomically he presented features seen in none of the men who followed. He inclined to be below the medium modern height, had broad round shoulders and crooked legs. His nose was "squashed," his cheek bones were prominent and his chin receded. Above all, his cranium was flattened, far more so than that of the most primitive living bushman. By present standards he would certainly pass for human, but only just.

Mr. H. G. Wells has painted some rather startling pictures of the human race as it may be half a million or a few million years from now. In *The Time Machine* he portrayed the human race as having evolved upon two such divergent lines that the world knew only a subterranean breed of sub-human toilers, and a scarcely more attractive, though visually charming, decadent aristocracy. Other peeps into the future have shown us a human race freed from most bodily ills, through having dispensed with much of its internal economy—appendices and other matters—and living largely on concentrated essences " enjoyed " via the medium of a hypodermic syringe.

Another view has shown a race in which the growing tendency to specialize has been carried to extremes, giving us a world of giant soldiers, four-handed sailors, chemists with huge noses, road workers with arms like those of a gorilla, messengers and jockeys little larger than dwarfs, and so on, till the mind reels. None of these glimpses of our future has yet been realized. Yet the fact remains that man has undergone some visible changes within the last few centuries.

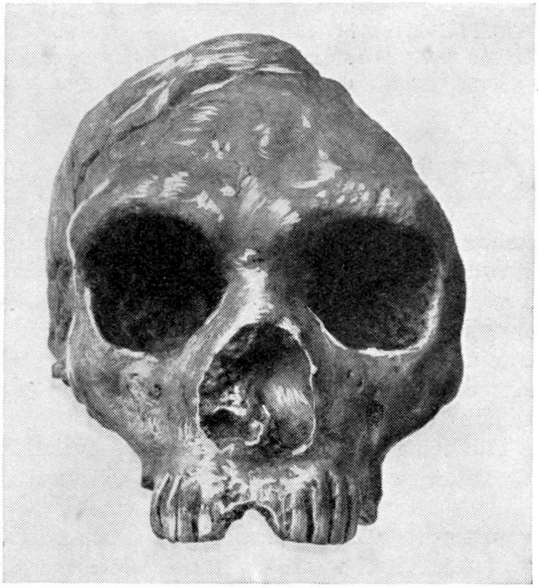

BRITISH MUSEUM (NATURAL HISTORY)

ONLY JUST HUMAN

A skull of this type was first found in the Neanderthal Valley, Prussia. Its owner made weapons and roasted food. No living race is so primitive.

Man is bigger than he was. The average individual finds it difficult to squeeze into some of the earlier suits of armour. The man of tomorrow will be even bigger. Thanks to the recent care given to problems of nutrition and physical education, the present generation of children shows a marked increase in size and weight over those of the last.

" The average boy of fourteen," reported the School Medical Officer for Sheffield in 1937, " shows an increase over his forerunners of three and a quarter inches in height and nineteen and a half pounds in weight. Girls of fourteen show, on an average, an increase of two and a half inches and fourteen and a quarter pounds." This is consistent with the general trend of evolution. Almost every branch of the animal kingdom has had its hey-day, has risen to a summit, and developed to its fullest capacity.

It would be hazardous to say that man has necessarily become more intelligent during the last few hundred years. The world still awaits another Shakespeare. But the brain case tends perhaps to increase; there would be some difficulty in finding a " fit " amongst early helmets.

OUR DEGENERATE LITTLE TOES

Our quite unnatural clothing and varied artificial diet are working other changes in our make-up. There is an increased tendency to bodily hairlessness and amongst males, at least, to baldheadedness. Dental ailments are increasing, and there is a tendency for our back teeth to be crowded out; future man may have less than the accepted complement of thirty-two teeth. Footwear is making its imprint on our toes. The little toe is fast lapsing into a state of degeneracy, and a few million years—much less perhaps—may see man a four-toed animal.

Yet man with all his clamouring for variety is a conservative animal. He persists moreover in directing his own affairs, and anything like scientific breeding of human beings on lines laid down by accepted authorities is still, fortunately or otherwise, a long way off. Where domestic animals are concerned, we see evolution being speeded-up at an astonishing pace. The strange fruits of modern " artificial selection " are instances of evolution—within the literal meaning of the word.

DOGS OF RECENT BREED

In no creature is this more apparent than the dog, perhaps the most malleable of all mammals. Some of our accepted breeds are of great antiquity, but many are of quite recent growth. Prior to the founding of the Kennel Club in 1873, dog owners generally were content with a few " serviceable " breeds, for guard or hunting purposes. When the first dog show was held at Newcastle in 1856, only about a dozen breeds were recognized. Today nearly a hundred separate breeds are "benched" at all important shows.

This semi-scientific cult of the dog has rung incredible changes on the canine form as generally accepted. The fancy has fixed on

VARIETIES OF DOMESTIC FOWL

Artificial selection in the breeding of poultry has produced some extraordinary results. Certain features have been developed to fantastic extremes, as can be seen in the tail of the Yokohama fowl and the leg-feathers of the Cochin-China.

certain features in a breed, and often developed them in the face of all accepted standards of art and even humanity. The Kerry Blue, Griffon, Yorkshire terrier and others can scarcely see through their lavish suits of hair; the show-bench greyhound is useless in the field, the bulldog can scarcely breathe and its disproportioned head renders its birth almost a death warrant to its dam. Of late years there has been a certain revolt against the production of monsters, and there is an increasing tendency to award prizes for general intelligence.

CHANGES IN CATTLE

Domestic cattle have also undergone surprising changes in a short time. When the famous Smithfield Club, the world's oldest cattle-breeding society, was founded in 1798, a prize ox weighing some four hundredweight would stand over five feet six inches at the shoulder, and would be a mountain of fat. Four years were required to attain this standard of "perfection." Now a champion steer will still weigh four hundredweight, but be only two years old, stand not much more than four feet high, and be a compact mass of nutritive beef, in other words flesh from head to tail.

The world of the poultry and pigeon fancier runs the canine cosmos close in extravagant and unreasoning excess. As regards pigeons, man the creator has produced the fantail, unable to walk properly; the tumbler, incapable of straight flight; the tottering pouter, nun and jacobin; and the dragoons and trumpeters, birds whose bills bear a mass of tumorous fungus flesh outweighing the head itself. Other breeds again have such heavily feathered legs that specially constructed cages must be provided for their accommodation.

ALWAYS STARING UPWARD

Poultry has similarly been at times "improved" with little regard for utility or the birds' comfort. The limit in grotesqueness is reached by the Japanese game fowl, or Yokohama. The tail coverts of a prize cock may measure between twenty and thirty feet in length. Such a bird lives its life perched at the top of a cylindrical cage, and is exercised daily on a perfectly clean floor, with a train bearer in attendance.

A creature, it may be noticed, suffers in exact proportion to its responsiveness to the evolutionist's dictates. One final example may be quoted—the goldfish. For many centuries past China, land of its origin, has been " ringing the changes " with wonderful results. Thus we have the veil tail, floating in a gossamer cloud of its own fins, some of which are duplicated. The tumbler suffers from spinal curvature and rolls head over heels in the course of its progress. The telescope-eyed fish suggests a piscine snail, and the star-gazer stares from birth to death at the surface above. The egg-fish has been shorn of most of its fins, and the lion-read suggests permanent mumps.

WIDE WORLD

VEIL-TAILED GOLDFISH

Ingenious breeders have been experimenting on the goldfish for many hundreds of years in China, their original home.

Many of these abortions are the direct results of deliberately perpetuating deformities caused in the first place by breeding under the worst possible conditions. A staggering example of oriental ingenuity is seen in the Japanese waltzing mouse. By breeding in the first place from mice suffering from cerebral disease there has come to pass a strain which now punctuates all its doings by plunging at a moment's notice into a frenzied dance. In the midst of play, feeding, or even sleep the urge to waltz may come upon the animal, and it revolves nose to tail with fast accumulating speed, until it literally becomes an animated wheel.

For reasons not yet fully understood, animals vary much in their responsiveness to " accelerated evolution." The slim race-horse and the massive shire or percheron, whilst sufficiently unlike the ancestral type, still living in Mongolia, are recognizable as creatures evolved from some common stock. The same could scarcely be said of the greyhound and the pug. In like manner the guinea pig, rabbit and—to instance a domestic bird—the turkey have not greatly altered, in essentials, from their wild ancestors.

CONSERVATISM OF THE CAT

A yet more striking case of conservatism is presented by the domestic cat. Hundreds of distinct breeds may be listed by the " fancy," but under their skins they are all much alike. Apart from the tail-less Manx, domestic cats, despite centuries of " improvement," chiefly differ only in the quality and colour of their fur.

Artificial selection, it may be further noted, must be the subject of ceaseless care and supervision, or Nature, asserting herself, will, so to speak, reclaim her own. The processes will be reversed, and the creature throw back to its original form.

This was once amusingly demonstrated. Many years ago a delegation from Madagascar was touring Europe, and amongst the many marvels brought to its notice was the goldfish. So delighted was the delegation that it took back to Madagascar a large consignment of the wonder fish, and gave them the run of home waters.

ANIMALS THAT REVERT TO TYPE

The result was disappointing. Within a depressingly short time the goldfish, finding little fighting spirit amongst existing native fish, ate them up and became lords of all they surveyed. Moreover, the tendency of artificially selected animals to " throw back " to the ancestral type asserted itself. Slowly they slipped back to the drab livery of the wild carp, from which their race had originally sprung, and the goldfish that were to have enlivened all Madagascar were soon nothing but a memory. An importation of additional goldfish, unless on a grand scale, would probably not have checked " reversion " in the long run.

Up and down the world, on the great land masses and innumerable obscure islands, we meet with pigs, dogs, cats and other animals that have similarly slipped back to a wild or

WIDE WORLD

FANTASTIC TELESCOPE-EYED FISH OF CHINA

A striking example of the goldfish breeders' efforts at speeding up evolution. Another type, appropriately called the star-gazer, stares from birth to death at the surface or the sky above.

semi-wild form. This is ever the way of a domesticated animal unless man deliberately and unceasingly directs it along the special lines he desires.

One of the chief stumbling blocks which still hinders the general appreciation of evolution is the apparent disconnection between the main groups of the animal kingdom. Up to about thirty years ago the public was continually crying for " missing links." The discovery of the Java ape-man and other semi-human creatures seems to have somewhat relieved the general anxiety. It is still, however, far from widely realized that every animal is a link in the chain of life, and that between almost all the main groups of living things are to be found creatures that serve to join one to the other, by merging the characters of both.

MAN'S SPINELESS LINKS

Take for example, what most will feel to be a much-needed link, one between backboned creatures like ourselves, dogs, birds, reptiles, fish and so on, and spineless creatures such as lobsters, oysters, worms, and the insect hosts. There are plenty of links between these two so widely contrasted groups; they are to be found all over the world. All round the coasts of Great Britain are to be seen the curious soft-bodied creatures known as sea squirts. They hang, like gelatinous bladders, from caves and harbour piles and encircle shells and seeds.

Readers who have visited the famous cave in the Roches Douvres at Jersey, will appreciate Victor Hugo's description of the place when he said in *Toilers of the Sea*, that " the walls were splashed with crimson stains, as if giants had been fighting there." In some restaurants in the same island what look like large and very unattractive potatoes are sold as " violets of the rocks." Both these and the crimson stains in the Roches Douvres are sea squirts, creatures apparently as far removed from ourselves as one could well imagine.

INTERNAL ORGANS THAT DISAPPEAR

When it emerges from the egg the sea squirt is a minute but well formed, extremely lively tadpole, and save for its small size and that it has but one eye, might reasonably be expected to develop along lines approved by the frog. It has in particular a well defined central nerve cord, just like that of a vertebrate. Yet after a few hours, or at most days, of active independent life, it undergoes an extraordinary transformation. The suckers on its head, features it shares with the frog tadpole, it attaches firmly to a rock or other anchorage, and so stays poised, tail upwards. Then one by one its internal organs literally " fade out," though the creature itself increases steadily in bulk.

By the time the creature is fully grown—and some sea squirts reach a foot or so in length—it is little more than a stomach into which food is swept by minute but ceaselessly lashing hairs. Edible particles are carried in through one simple aperture, and waste matter is washed out through another. Indeed the creature lives much as do the oyster and pond mussel, and like the former is anchored for life without the slightest capacity for further directing its destiny.

HAROLD BASTIN

ANCHORED FOR LIFE

Within a few days of birth the sea squirt changes from a tiny tadpole into a large formless mass.

In the Channel Islands, and on many tropic beaches, the fisherman when digging for bait often finds a strange worm-like animal which unfortunately has no more homely name than *Balanoglossus.* It varies from a few inches to several yards in length, according to species, often advertises its presence by a powerful odour of iodoform, and like the earthworm feeds by simply passing a non-stop stream of mud throughout its entire length, retaining only minute edible matter in transit.

Like the sea squirt this weird animal is an important link, for its nerve cord not only shows close resemblance to that of the vertebrates, especially in the unborn stages of development, but its eggs hatch out into larvæ very like those of sea urchins. Many naturalists mistook them for such until, by keeping the minute creatures alive, they found to their astonishment that they turned into something very different from the familiar " sea egg."

The shrimp trawl sometimes brings on deck a transparent animal about two inches long, looking rather like a laurel leaf made of glass. This is the lancelet, which scientists called " the sheet anchor of the evolutionist " before it was recognized that everything living is similarly a sheet anchor.

HAIRS AS FOOD GATHERERS

The lancelet at first develops on lines very like those of many worms, but it ends up not unlike those crude " almost-fish " the lampreys. It has the first beginnings of a spinal column, but made of gelatinous stuff, as in the lampreys, and it has no true mouth with jaws and teeth such as only vertebrates possess. Instead food is swept into its inside by lashing hairs surrounding a small opening.

Here then are three distinct groups of beasts linking man and the familiar vertebrates with the " soft-bodied creatures." No doubt many more such links have existed on the earth, but for obvious reasons there is no tracing them as fossil remains.

Let us glance at one or two more " links " in the chain of life which have been a source of much puzzlement and heated controversy amongst naturalists in the past.

ONCE OWNED THE SEVEN SEAS

In the deep firths of Scotland, and on the fishing grounds north of the Shetlands, the trawl often brings up hundreds of what most people would describe as " some sort of shellfish." But whereas a " two-piece " shellfish, like an oyster or mussel, anchors itself by one shell, or a bunch of threads pushed out from between its two shells, the lampshells, as these spurious shellfish are called, anchor themselves by means of a cord threaded through a hole in one shell only.

Some naturalists argued that these creatures were molluscs, like the snail and oyster, others that they were akin to the seaweed-like moss-animals one can pick up on every beach. Today they are usually placed in a special group, midway between the spiny-skinned sea urchins and the shelled animals or molluscs that have

MONDIALE

ONLY LIVING WILD HORSE

The Mongolian wild horse, otherwise known as Prejvalsky's horse after the man who introduced it to science in 1879, *was once thought to represent the ancestor of all domesticated breeds, but this now appears unlikely.*

now largely usurped their place in the scheme of things. But once the lampshells owned the seven seas, when the oyster and its kin were only in the making.

Most people think they know a worm from a centipede, or a lobster, or a butterfly's caterpillar; but confronted with the animal known as *Peripatus,* they might reasonably be afflicted with doubt. That indeed was the attitude of zoologists for many years after its first discovery. *Peripatus* is a soft-bodied creature common in many hot countries. It is a few inches long, has a beautiful velvety sheen, and with its many pairs of legs ambles along sedately like a caterpillar. When annoyed it shoots out long white threads of a milky appearance and extremely sticky nature.

REGARDED AS A GRUB

For a long time this strange animal was just a " grub," until about sixty years ago a member of the famous *Challenger* expedition made a study of it. Both its internal economy and mode of reproduction proved that it was a link between the higher worms and that legion of jointed animals represented by the pill bug, lobster and butterfly.

A particularly interesting link connecting the great extinct sea scorpions with more recent animals is the so-called king crab, or horseshoe crab, common in shallow tropic waters on both sides of the Atlantic. It has been likened to a small boy crawling beneath a zinc bath and trailing a broomstick behind him.

GROTESQUE " LIVING FOSSIL "

Although this grotesque " living fossil " may measure a foot across, and twice as long, it has scarcely an eggcupful of meat in it. Even when it is young and its shell relatively soft, only the largest skates and rays appeared until recently to have any use for it. Now comes news that an enterprising syndicate has found a way to make something of the king crabs in Delaware Bay and has there almost exterminated them by turning them into pig food and fertilizer. Nevertheless this species of crab seems destined to remind the world for long to come of that remote past when life moved only in the shallows of the great waters.

The links enumerated, though vital in explaining the intimate associations between groups of animals at first sight very dissimilar, are admittedly of little immediate importance to man. Therein lies part of the explanation of their survival. They have as yet been of no economic value, but neither have they offered any resistance to man's progress, and so have been left to go their ways in peace. Further, most of these links are creatures of small size,

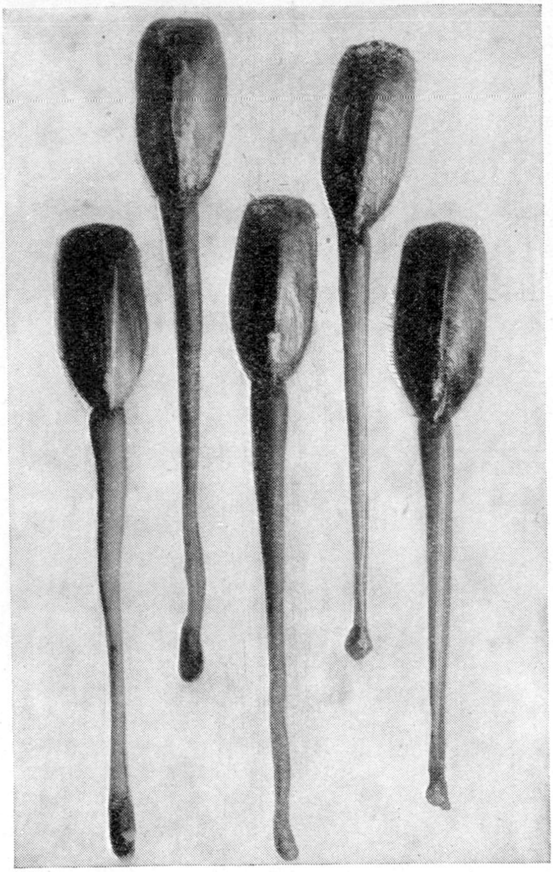

JAMES HORNELL (MONDIALE)

CONSERVATIVE ORGANISMS

Lampshells have existed in the same form for hundreds of millions of years. The cord by which they anchor is threaded through one shell only.

and unobtrusive, furtive habits, for which reasons they escape the notice of the foes to which so many other creatures succumb. They hide beneath stones, burrow in mud, plunge down into the abyss, and otherwise evade the attentions of a curious and ever-hungry world.

EVIDENCE FROM THE UNBORN

Every living animal is a link between the next-of-kin immediately above and below it. This is often more clearly evidenced in the living but unborn or unhatched embryo than in the fully developed creature. Within the parent or the egg-shell it hints not merely at its great-grandparenthood but its remote ancestry, and when we examine a number of embryos of widely different species we find that they have much in common, pointing to an origin from some generalized stock.

FAMILY LIKENESS

Broadly speaking, that toilsome road from crude beginnings to perfect man, dog or sparrow, is traversed again within the ovary. Von Baer, one of the great embryologists of a century ago, confessed that having preserved a number of embryos, but omitting to label them, he was later quite unable to say which were those of mammals, birds, reptiles, or fishes, so great was the general family likeness. This family likeness holds good throughout the animal kingdom. The "unborn lives," that is, the embryonic existences, of all vertebrates can be traced back to a gilled stage, proving clearly that the air-breathing creatures dominating

DORIEN LEIGH

LAST REPRESENTATIVE OF AN ANCIENT RACE

The fantastic king, or horseshoe, crab, whose ancestors flourished before birds flew, is not a crab at all. It is more nearly akin to the scorpions. It has thirteen pairs of limbs and unique book-like breathing organs.

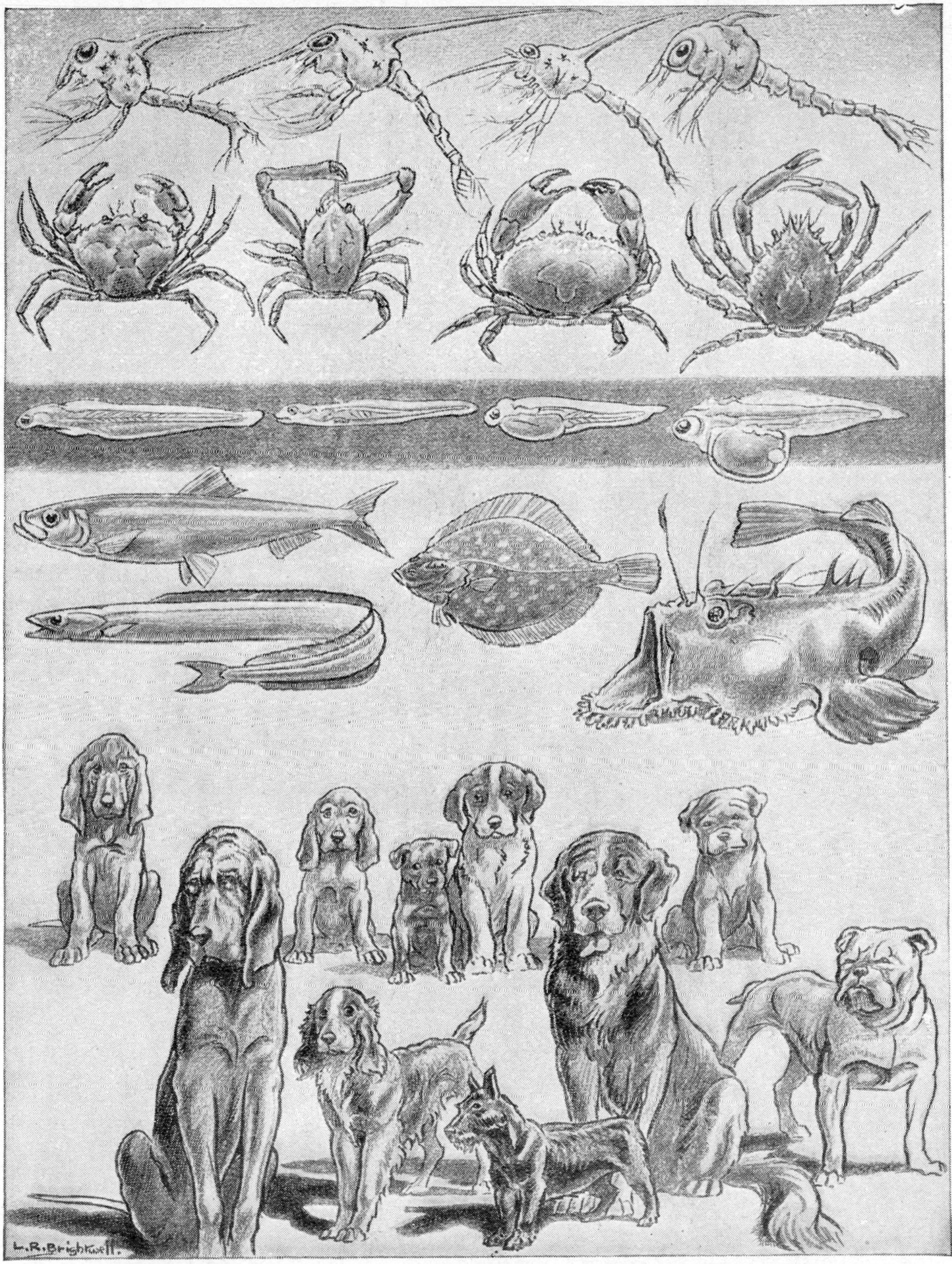

SIMILARITY SHOWN BY YOUNG OF DIFFERENT MEMBERS OF THE SAME GROUP
This close similarity indicates their common ancestry. The bulldog pup, for instance, has a fairly large nose at birth. Top rows: Shore crab, marked crab, edible crab, spider crab. Middle rows: Herring, sand eel, plaice, angler fish. Bottom rows: Bloodhound, cocker spaniel, Scottie, St. Bernard, bulldog.

the world today had their beginnings in aquatic forms.

Even when at last the human infant sees the light, it still bears sufficient traces of its more recent ancestry. Mr. Jones has more in common with the so-called "monkey man" when born than he has in later life. How truly a baby animal is its own great-great ancestor is apparent in many familiar beasts around us.

BABIES AND THEIR ANCESTORS

All dogs, with the exception of extreme forms such as the bulldog, show a remarkable degree of resemblance when first born; the still blind greyhound, dane, poodle, and Scottie pups give little hint as to the widely divergent roads that they will shortly take. Even the bulldog has a relatively generous allowance of nose at birth, proving a canine ancestry, however deftly art may later force him to suggest a toad.

Baby animals are of absorbing interest in the hints they give of ancestors of which the only portraits are colourless fossil remains. To take but one instance, zoologists insist that the lion, now a creature of the open plains, was once a forest dweller, and has taken to its present mode of life by stark necessity rather than choice. No cat voluntarily stalks abroad for all to view beneath the midday sun.

FROM FOREST TO PLAIN

The lion of remote times probably lurked in deep forests, as the leopard still does, and was similarly coloured. So also may have been the vegetable feeders on which it preyed. But with the fear of death ever behind them, these latter sought safety in the open—and the lion followed. Spots were of little use in the new environment, and so gradually they gave place to that self-coloration typical of the lion today. The lion still wears his spots, however, whilst in the nursery. All lion cubs are spotted, and some zoo-grown specimens have been scarcely distinguishable from leopard cubs, which retain their spots throughout life.

Scientific artists such as Livingstone Bull, Charles Knight, Horsfall and others who specialize in reconstructing creatures of the past, usually represent the now extinct giant

WIDE WORLD

ZEBRA PREY OF THE KING OF BEASTS

The lion now prowls about open plains but his ancestors were denizens of the forest, like the present-day leopard. This we know from the fact that lion cubs are spotted, a coloration suitable for forest dwellings.

MONDIALE

FALLOW DEER DISCARDS ITS SPOTS IN WINTER

Most deer have spots at birth but lose them when they are mature. The fallow deer wears its spots during all the summers of its life, discarding them only in the winter when they are no longer valuable.

hogs and many deer, etc., as striped or spotted. The view is justifiable, since most wild pigs, tapirs, and deer come into the world wearing jazz-patterned nursery suits which, like those of the lion, disappear with maturity. There are exceptions. The Indian axis deer and the fallow deer, both largely woodland dwellers, keep their spotted coats, and so "fade into the landscape," as did the leopard in the *Just-So Stories*.

GENEALOGY OF ANIMALS

There are ingenious and painstaking individuals who undertake to build up an imposing ancestral tree for the least distinguished commoner. The genealogy of animals goes back to remote times and is highly involved. The records of the rocks, of embryology, and many other factors must be considered. Tracing a mammal's immediate ancestors is relatively a matter of yesterday; tracking down the common origin of mammals and birds is a harder task. That both owe their being to a reptilian stock is now well established, and an immense amount of cumulative evidence is provided to support this belief. Not a hundredth part of this evidence can here be cited, but one or two of the more interesting items may be given.

BIRD'S KINSHIP WITH THE REPTILE

The bird's kinship with the reptile is largely established by the study of skeletons, and particularly that portion of the bird's bony framework termed the "parson's nose." The end bone of this shows clearly in adults, and still more so in embryos, that it is really five bones welded together—a reptilian tail telescoped, so to speak. The "knuckle" of modern birds suggests little of a reptile hand in its adult form, but in the embryo there is often a close similarity, and the chick of the Brazilian hoatzin can actually scramble about tree branches on all fours, using very serviceable clawed fingers on its wing "knuckles" to augment beak and feet.

Many fossil birds possess typical reptilian teeth. The reptilian origin of birds is fairly clinched by the half-way bird archeopteryx, only two skeletons of which are known. This creature, which lived some one hundred and fifty million years ago, blended bird and reptile in a remarkable way, for it had a jointed tail like a lizard, teeth—which no living birds possess—wing-fingers and indisputable feathers.

" ONLY JUST " MAMMALS

In like manner the mammals' claim to reptilian ancestors can be established, and the more convincingly perhaps since two mammalian counterparts of archeopteryx are still to be found living in Australia. The duck-mole and the porcupine ant eater are " only just " mammals. They have hair, warm—or fairly warm—blood, and suckle their young. But they also have very reptilian skeletons, very reptilian—or bird-like—brains, and in common with birds and the majority of reptiles they lay eggs.

Fishes can similarly be traced to a common ancestry, although the checking up of each successive stage in a fish's past offers special difficulties. One cannot follow a fish at will in the water as one can a bird or beast on land, and the comparatively flimsy nature of most fish has resulted in their fossil remains being disappointingly scanty and seldom complete. Yet enough is known to be certain that early fish evolved from much more primitive creatures, like crustaceans perhaps, that they had no true mouths but only suctorial discs similar to the lampreys, and that they had only gristly skeletons that developed into bone much later in the history of the group.

Fish, like dogs, poultry and other creatures, have a marked sameness about them when very young. Unless such an infant fish can be reared to something like maturity in an aquarium, often a hard task, it is impossible to identify on sight the parentage of a " toddler " picked up in the trawl or tow net.

Strange as it may seem, the baby stages of the numerous fish that live in the seas which surround Great Britain and Ireland are tolerably well known, but those of the fresh-water fish of the British Isles either await discovery or, save for a few species, are at best debatable. Tracing these early stages constitutes an important part of the work done at the Fresh Water Research Station on Lake Windermere, the first institution of its kind in England.

One often hears the remark that animals are perfectly fitted to their environment, in short that all animals find themselves in the best of all possible worlds for their purposes.

This is a lazy way of explaining things, and is also untrue. Animals, like ourselves, find themselves where they happen to be by reason of a variety of causes, and either make the best of things or go under. Environment plays an enormous part in the evolution of creatures of every kind.

WHEN CONTINENTS JOINED

A glance at the three maps on p. 51 will show how greatly the contours of the world's land masses have changed in ninety million years—quite recently as the earth's history goes. The more heavily outlined land masses are the more fertile ones, and it will be obvious that the period has seen not only great changes in the amount of land above watermark, but drastic alterations in climate.

It was whilst America and Europe, Asia and Australasia were linked up by land bridges, that the roving herds and flocks gravitated to

H. STOKES (MONDIALE)

ONE OF THE SILUROIDS

The bodies of catfish are never ordinarily scaled, being either armoured with bony plates or else naked. They represent a great advance on the early fish whose skeletons even were not of bone, but of a gristly material.

AMONG THE OLDEST DOMESTIC ANIMALS

The dromedary, or Arabian camel, is not known in the wild state, unlike the Bactrian (two-humped) species, which is found wild in Eastern Turkestan. Even after many centuries of domestication the dromedary remains savage and stupid.

what time has proved were to be their final homes—or at least their homes to date, for the world still changes. Thus each of the great land masses has its characteristic animals.

THE FIGHT FOR LIFE

There came a time when Nature pulled up the drawbridge, so to speak, and there was no returning whence they came. But many of these creatures might do extremely well in another country, provided it offered a not too different climate, sufficient of the right food, and no new enemies with which the transplanted beasts might be unable to cope. How well some animals may do when transplanted we now know to our cost. The camel has proved most useful in Australia, but the rabbit has become a curse, and dogs and pigs introduced by man are in many places destroying native animals.

Let us leave human agency in determining an animal's environment out of the question for the moment, since it is dealt with at some length in another section. On the great continents competition in the fight for life was keen, and so the animals launched out in a variety of directions, each kind giving rise to numerous varieties or species, each adapting itself to whatever territory it annexed. One striking example of how a given "strain" developed to its utmost capacity may be cited in the marsupials or pouch-bearing animals.

These creatures rank amongst the most primitive of mammals, next to the reptile-like duckbill and echidna. When mammals were first coming into their own, the pouch-bearers must have been in their hey-day, and spread over much of the warmer parts of the earth. Now an animal that must spend its infancy in a pouch is at a great disadvantage compared with creatures that are nursed outside their parents. As this latter type of animal became dominant, the remaining marsupials went under. Their small brains could not cope with those of the quick-witted milk drinkers who were nursed in nests and caves, and early taught to work for their own livings.

MAROONED IN AUSTRALIA

Very soon, that is to say in the course of a few million years, some of the pouch-bearers were making a last stand upon the mainland—in America. Others, seeking refuge far eastward, were isolated from their more intelligent competitors by the encroaching sea, and found themselves marooned on what we now call

BRITISH MUSEUM (NATURAL HISTORY)

RELATED TO DUCK-BILL PLATYPUS

The echidna, or spiny ant eater, is, like its famous cousin, a burrowing, egg-laying mammal, but does not swim. Its home is Australasia.

Australia. The American marsupials, unable to hold their own against the growing tribes of bears, racoons and monkeys, dwindled till we find them today represented by a few small species, leading a hole-and-corner existence; the tree-dwelling opossums owe their continued existence to their small size and nimbleness in escaping foes.

RIOT OF EVOLUTION

In Australia the small-brained pouch-bearers had things all their own way and, feeble folk though they were, embarked on a riot of evolution. In the course of ages they evolved on so many different lines that they mimicked practically all the better known mammalian types of the Asiatic mainland.

Kangaroos took the place of the big grass-eating camels, deer and oxen; little kangaroo-rats imitated the dainty antelopes. Other species, such as wombats, developed on the lines of terrestrial bears, and the more arboreal bears were portrayed in the tree-climbing koala, the "teddy bear" of our nurseries. There were imitation wolves and leopards, mice and rats, monkeys and ant eaters, but they all had pouches, and pouches they have to this day.

POUCHED BEARS AND LIONS

There were for many thousands of years pouched bears and pouched lions, but for reasons which still remain unknown they fell in the race, and today the herbivorous kangaroos are the largest pouch-bearers alive—living only so long as we let them.

The so-called "bears" and "lions" of Australia—to give them their popular titles—often exceeded the largest kangaroos in sheer body bulk, though not in span of limb. Their demise—unless through human agency—is a mystery. Probably they fell, as did the sabre-toothed tiger in England, to the crude weapons but nimble wits of early man.

What happens on most islands applies also to the watery world. Large isolated bodies of water, lakes and inland seas have their own peculiar fauna. The inhabitants of the open sea are more generalized. Many are cosmopolitan, or if restricted to certain areas, differ little from local species some thousands of miles distant, provided conditions of life are similar. Thus many of the crabs found off the coast of England are almost identical with allied species in Japan. Similarly the denizens of the ocean abysses show a remarkable uniformity in design.

There is an extraordinary parallel to the pouch-bearers of Australia in the sand-hoppers

LARGEST LIVING POUCH-BEARER

The kangaroo, largest living marsupial, or pouch-bearer, is a magnificent jumper. He lives in Australia, continent of marsupials.

WIDE WORLD

THE ORIGINAL TEDDY-BEAR

The koala is found in the south-eastern parts of Australia, where it is popularly known as the native bear or the native sloth. A marsupial, it belongs to the same family as the wombats. It is about two feet long and lives on a vegetarian diet, mainly consisting of the leaf-tips of the eucalyptus or gum tree.

HAROLD BASTIN

SAND-HOPPERS OR BEACH FLEAS

Members of the amphipod order, they are found in every part of the world. In Lake Baikal they have launched out in widely-divergent directions.

of Lake Baikal in Siberia, the deepest isolated body of fresh water in the world. The sand-hopper, or beach flea, that gets into English luncheon baskets and swarms beneath the drift weed left by the tide is much the same kind of creature the world over, save in the Siberian lake. There it has launched out in scores of widely-divergent directions, and rings every change on sea life, from the glassy, free-swimming jelly-fish, to the lumbering crabs and lobsters far below.

SEX THE DRIVING FORCE

In another section of this book it has been shown how all living forms are the result of cellular multiplication, the piling of cell upon cell, and the gradual modification of those cells into groups, each performing some special action—feeding, warning off enemies, reproduction and so on.

It is quite possible for certain plants and animals to multiply without the aid of another individual. But such production is like that of a convict condemned to perform the same mechanical tasks year in year out—it leads nowhere. The bulk of living forms depend for their multiplicity upon sex.

Sex is the driving force, the internal combustion engine of the world. Mr. Aldous Huxley in his *Brave New World* paints an interesting picture of synthetic humans, creatures grown in test tubes according to patterns laid down by the State. One can only wonder how long such a State would continue. It is only the constant pursuit, the adventure brought about by sex that gives variety, change, without which there can be no real progress. The idea of synthetic humanity is not original. It is borrowed from the insects, and if put into practice would probably end in the insects' mechanical and unreasoning kind of life.

REPRODUCTION WITHOUT SEX

In a very large number of the lower animals reproduction is quite independent of sex. If one takes a little flat worm, such as crawls in abundance about the weeds of any pond, and cuts it in half, the worm suffers no inconvenience or pain. In a short time the head half grows a new tail, and the tail half a new head. Cut the worm down the central line, and each half soon makes up its missing portion, and life goes forward as before. Cut anywhere without detaching a piece, and the exposed surfaces by cellular multiplication begin to

HAROLD BASTIN

COMMON EARTHWORM

The earthworm will survive considerable mutilation. Thus either the head or the tail will grow again if severed cleanly.

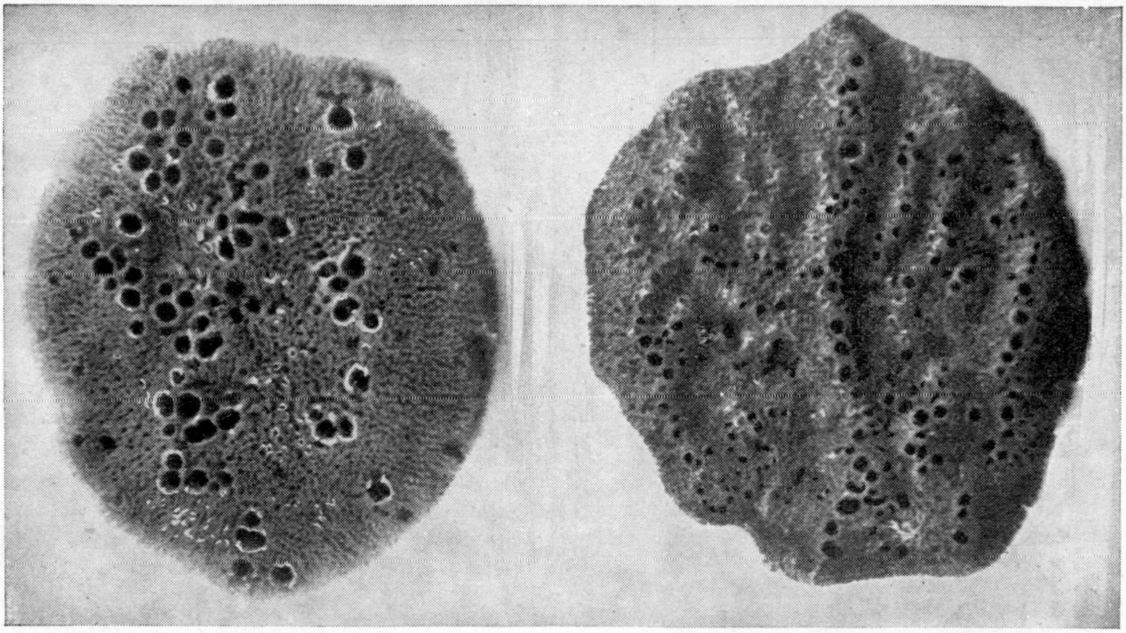

DR. C. M. YONGE (MONDIALE)

SPONGE IN LIFE AND IN DEATH

On the right is a live sponge; on the left one that has been killed and cleaned. This animal is unique in that bits cut from it and planted out will grow without difficulty.

sprout new individuals, so that a very strange monster with several heads and tails presents itself.

Some of the more primitive worms multiply by literally bisecting themselves. There comes a time when the worm appears to be trying to walk two ways at once. It breaks in the centre, and each half becomes a complete worm adventuring on its own.

The same sort of thing can be seen happening in certain sea anemones, or in the only fresh-water anemone found in Great Britain—the hydra. This little creature, hated by fish breeders and aquarists for the toll it takes of young fry, simply cannot be destroyed by mutilation. Perhaps the mythical monster after which it is named was first conceived by some imaginative man of ancient Greece who observed how many simple animals renewed themselves when apparently destroyed.

MULTIPLICATION BY MUTILATION

An instance of this multiplication by mutilation occurred on oyster beds some years before the World War. The starfish is the bane of the oyster farmer, for it eats his precious shell-fish on the grand scale. When therefore the oyster dredge came up, as it often did, crammed with starfish, the disgusted fishermen simply tore the animals in halves, and flung the pieces overboard. But the starfish came back. It came back twice over, for each half renewed itself, and the oysters paid the price of the farmer's ignorance. Today starfish are taken ashore and used as a fertilizer.

Of late years it has been found possible to fertilize artificially—i.e., fertilize at second hand—salmon eggs, cods' eggs, and even dogs and horses, but so far the only creature which commerce has made to increase by mutilation is the bath sponge. You can plant out clippings of the sponge—which is undoubtedly an animal—and they will flourish like clippings of rose, geranium and many other plants.

CANNOT GROW LOST ORGANS

The power to regenerate lost parts seems to decrease as we ascend in the scale of life. One of the marvels of our age is plastic surgery. It can turn an old person into the likeness of a young one—for a short time—help a criminal to escape justice by altering his features, or convert a man whom the instruments of war have made hideous into the fair semblance of a normal human being. But though our various tissues have wonderful powers of renewal, we cannot grow again lost organs. A severed finger is gone for ever.

This holds true of all mammals and birds, and to a large extent of reptiles. A lizard can certainly grow a new tail, but the " join " always shows. Injury which just stops short at complete severance of the tail results in a forked tail, a grotesque attachment of more hindrance than help to its owner. But in the amphibians, half-way between reptiles and fishes, whole limbs can be renewed, though here again injury without severance may lead to a five-limbed animal, a clumsy, handicapped monstrosity. Fish renew damaged fins in like manner. This plasticity of vertebrate flesh was often turned to unpleasant account by old-time showmen, as when the Zouaves produced their " rhinoceros rats " by grafting a piece of a rat's tail on to its rightful owner's nose.

Regeneration is seen at its best amongst invertebrates, even in such complex ones as

W. S. BERRIDGE (MONDIALE)

TO ATTRACT A MATE

The male fiddler crab develops one brightly-coloured claw half as big as itself. This grows again if severed.

the crab. If a crab loses its claws or legs, the stumps are cast off at special joints, and the animal goes about crippled until the time comes to change its shell. Then it presently reappears with a new set of limbs, though the regenerated ones are not normal until several changes of shell have taken place.

REGENERATION IN THE EGG

This curious habit has been turned to account on the coast of Portugal, where there abounds a kind of fiddler crab, the male of which grows one claw half as big as himself. The fisherman simply collects this claw for market, and the crab obligingly grows another, though of slightly inferior quality.

In some of the lower vertebrates, such as the frog, regeneration can take place even in the egg. It is possible by nearly or very gradually completely severing a frog's egg to produce either " Siamese twins " or two complete individuals.

Sex appears quite a long way down the animal scale, and becomes more and more insistent and essential as we ascend.

A great deal of attention has been paid of late years to sex proportions—or ratios—in all creatures, more particularly man and domestic animals. Darwin ascertained that the greyhound showed a greater disproportion of the sexes than any other animal, one hundred and ten males being born to every hundred females. Roughly, however, in vertebrates at least, the proportions tend to be almost equal. How far this is controllable only the future can show.

The offspring of the long-suffering frog have here, as elsewhere, suggested possibilities. Thus if a clump of frog spawn is hatched at a high temperature, or in acidulated water, more males than females result, and enforced retention of the eggs by the female produces an almost femaleless family. On the other hand frog spawn which is victimized by drought lets loose a swarm of female frogs on the world.

CASES OF SEX REVERSAL

Quite recently one or two very extraordinary cases of sex reversal (aided by surgical operation) in human beings have been made public. One can only wonder how such people fared in medieval times. In 1474, the councillors of Basle—who once tried a sow for murder—accused a cock of witchcraft, and had the wretched bird burnt in the market-place by the public executioner. The cock had laid an egg. Centuries later Professor F. A. A. Crew reported a buff-orpington hen which, after being a good layer and a good mother, wound up her career by growing spurs, crowing, and becoming an equally efficient father. Post-mortem revealed disease of the reproductive organs.

Low down in the scale of life sex reversal can be the normal, and vital to the continuance of the race. The Mexican swordtail fish is a popular pet of the home aquarist. There is often a marked outnumbering of males by females. As though to make up for this, a female after delivering her third family may become a male, the anal fin becoming modified to form a pairing organ. Many molluscs habitually change sex, a familiar case being that of the oyster. As an adolescent it is a male, then it changes to female, and for the rest of its life lives alternately each succeeding year as male or female.

HAROLD BASTIN

NATURE AS THE SUPREME ARTIST

One of the gorgonias or sea-fans, beautiful corals which often grow to a width of three feet. In the course of one summer a sea-fan's offspring will develop to their full size and found new sprays of coral.

Usually, though not invariably, an animal's rate of increase is proportionate inversely to its complexity of mechanism. Many of the animalcula are only creatures of a day. A sponge clipping may swell to big proportions, and let loose a flood of eggs upon the waters within a few months. A plastic coral, such as a sea-fan, can lay its eggs, which will develop into jelly-fishes, and each jelly-fish settle down and found a new spray of coral between spring and autumn.

PUZZLES AND PARADOXES

A large number of insects pass through all the gamut of egg, crawling grub, dormant chrysalis, and pregnant parent in a few weeks. But as we ascend the scale there is a noticeable slowing down in the reproductive process, a slowing down often in direct proportion to the animal's size. The machine stays longer in the workshop.

The more the naturalist studies animals and their development, the greater becomes his caution in laying down hard and fast rules. Puzzles and paradoxes arise at every turn to confound the new-born theory. Thus amongst fishes, the more primitive types, such as sharks and rays, apparently produce more " perfect " babies than do most highly-constituted types. Often the infant is delivered in an almost impregnable egg case, or it may be born alive. The infant sawfish—a blend of shark and ray—swims into the world with saw complete, the teeth wrapped in a tough covering to prevent injury to the parent's body wall when it makes its exit.

AT THE MERCY OF ALL

Most bony fish spend some time at the mercy of all and sundry before they themselves can become a menace. They enter life burdened with a yolk sac, and until this is absorbed have neither eyes nor appetites for live food. The baby troughs of a trout hatchery present a grotesque sight when full of fry, each infant fish skating about the tank floor on a big ball of yolk, like a man trying to crawl on all fours with a cushion lashed to his chest.

Reptiles can almost without exception make a living at somebody else's expense immediately after being hatched. Not so the birds. Many, like the sparrow and robin, are helpless for weeks after hatching. In contrast the chicks of the ostrich are up and doing as soon as their baby clothes are dried. But this is partly a special adaptation to their exposed mode of life and a natural outcome of having rested longer within the egg. A sparrow can raise three or even four broods in a year, an ostrich only one.

Amongst the hairy milk-fed animals called mammals the advantages of leisurely manufacture are even more obvious. In the vast majority of mammals the unborn young one derives nutriment from its mother via the placenta, or after-birth, a spongy disc heavily charged with blood vessels. Thanks to this, the infant, however helpless it may appear, comes into the world in a very high state of development, and given favourable conditions soon asserts itself, in innumerable ways, as a creature far ahead of the average reptile or bird.

WIDE WORLD

MOTHER AND CHILD

Unlike most mammals, marsupials have no true after-birth, so the young come into the world in a very helpless condition. It is only an inch long.

KANGAROO BABY AN INCH LONG

At a casual glance the marsupial, as represented say by the kangaroo, may seem quite " up to " the dog or ox. But if we could see a baby kangaroo born we should soon realize its inferiority to a dog. The nature of the phenomenon was a matter of the vaguest speculation until a naturalist at the Sydney Zoo actually saw a baby kangaroo make its début. It was known that marsupials have no true after-birth, but not until the birth of a kangaroo was witnessed did scientists appreciate how undeveloped are these primitive mammals on their first appearance. The infant kangaroo, even in the big five-foot-tall " old man boomer " species, is at first only an inch long. In some kinds it is smaller. It is quite blind, naked, and with short hind legs.

INSIDE THE POUCH

The nature of the birth is as follows. The mother sits with her tail stretched out between her forelegs, and on to the tail rolls baby. Usually the maternal brain is of such poor quality that no effort is made to help the infant. One of two things may happen. It may fall off the tail and feebly creep away in the wrong direction, to be picked up by the first rat or crow. On the other hand it may be lucky, and, clinging to its mother's abdomen, painfully struggle on knees and elbows up through a forest of hair until it literally stumbles on the pouch. Once inside, it attaches itself to a nipple. The tip of the nipple swells like a bulb inside the baby's mouth, and there the infant stays attached, so far as we know, for months perhaps, until strong enough to venture into the open.

Still lower than the marsupials are those strange creatures the duckmole and the various porcupine ant eaters of Australasia. These are mammals, since they have mammæ, or teats, connected with milk glands, albeit the teats are

MARCUSWELL MAXWELL (MONDIALE)

SIZE AS A FACTOR OF BIRTH

The embryo elephant spends no less than twenty-two months within the parent, whereas a litter of lions or leopards can be produced in three or four months. The corresponding period for man is nine months.

of very crude design. The porcupine ant eaters lay leathery-shelled eggs, and then nurse the young kangaroo-fashion in a pouch. The duckmole also lays eggs, and when the young emerge feeds them not by means of true teats but by exuding milk over a considerable portion of its abdomen, which is porous and oozes the fluid food in an irregular and one would imagine rather wasteful manner. Mammalian babies such as these are scarcely on an equality with the calf that can stagger to its feet five minutes after birth.

MAMMALS IN THE MAKING

Size would seem to be a factor in determining the length of time a mammal spends in the making, though it will probably be long before we have anything like complete information regarding the various periods of gestation. We do not know precisely what period intervenes between the kangaroo's conception and introduction into the pouch; the gestation periods of the echidnas, armadillos, and ant eaters are equally enigmatic. Neither do we know very much of the pre-natal whale.

Of the more familiar beasts the elephant heads the list by spending twenty-two months within the parent, which is seven months more than the giraffe, whilst ranging from eleven to thirteen months are the zebra, camel, llama, rhinoceros and sea lion. The dog, like the wolf, is " in pup " only about nine weeks. Possibly a cold climate slows down gestation, for the polar bear is not far behind the sea lion, with eight or nine months, whereas five months suffice for the more sheltered brown bear to produce its annual twins.

QUICK AND SLOW BREEDERS

The big cats are, for their size, quick breeders, twelve to sixteen weeks producing a litter of leopards, tigers or lions, which is only seven weeks longer than the domestic cat. Most of the monkeys and the big bats need six months, the majority of the man-like apes, as ourselves, are about nine months in the making, and so is the little red river hog.

Pigs are nearly related to the elephant, but the farmyard sow with her twice-yearly litters of a dozen piglets is no doubt a triumph—or victim—of that speeding-up which has overtaken most of our domestic animals. Wild pigs usually produce only three or four young at a time.

Most of the rodents are notoriously rapid

breeders. The porcupine, one of the largest, needs three and a half months to produce a family, a very elephant amongst the gnawing mammals. Compare it with the common rat. Many authorities have estimated its productivity, and though their figures vary, all are sufficiently horrifying.

A rat is sexually mature long before it is fully grown, and can reproduce its kind when only four months old. A pair can produce in twelve months six litters averaging eight rats each. Calculate England's annual rat output starting with a capital of at least ten million couples. The annual additions to the population of mice must be equally impressive. Fortunately disease and other influences prevent these animals from annexing the country.

FROM SEA TO LAND

The sea lion's gestation period is about three months longer than man's. It comes ashore to give birth.

Animals, apart from limitations imposed upon them by size, also regulate their families largely according to the available food supply. An interesting example of this is offered by the common herring. A herring just under a foot long produces about forty-seven thousand eggs, as opposed to the six-foot-long ling which, as the most prolific of all animals, launches one hundred and sixty million young upon the world. It would be logical to expect the lings to far outnumber the herrings in the sea, yet the reverse is the case.

MULTITUDES STARVE TO DEATH

Both herring and ling are highly predacious fishes, and to live must from the first find prey smaller than themselves. For the herring this is an easy matter. The upper layers of the sea, to which the herring fry make their way, swarm with minute crustacea, and so the young fish prosper from the first. The ling, which inhabits lower levels, can find no such abundance of food, and long before game comes in sight, the bulk of the one hundred and sixty million have starved to death, or themselves provided meals for larger fishes, or jelly-fishes. So far as dominating the seas by force of numbers is concerned, neither herring nor ling is in the long run better off than the little shore blenny which carefully guards its few hundred eggs.

OYSTERS BY THE MILLION

Another example of how the output of animals is levelled up may be cited. The marine oyster ejects from one million to two million fry; four times as many as the equally abundant fresh water zebra mussel. The oyster spends most of its life cemented to a rock or shell. The zebra mussel spends the major part of its existence anchored by silken threads to a lock gate or water main. Both shellfish, however, commence life as free-swimming fry or larvæ. Why are not valuable oysters four times as abundant as the worthless zebra mussel?

The oyster fry, swimming hither and thither aimlessly by means of innumerable minute, restlessly lashing hairs, soon fall victims to all kinds of other animals. The mussel fry act with some circumspection. Each sinks to the river bed and waves aloft a single strand of silk. This attaches itself to the first passing fish. Eventually the baby mussel itself is thrown against one side of the fish and attaches itself by means of two sharp teeth, one on either valve of its shell.

Its presence causes the fish's skin to grow over it, and here the little mussel abides for some time, safely ensconced in a tough cyst. It may stay thus for three months, at the end of which time the cyst bursts, and the young mussel, now much changed in form, sinks to the river bed and becomes anchored for life. Its vulnerable stage has been passed in relative security.

Often a family cancels itself out in the course of nature long before outside forces offer it violence. The big spongy masses of egg capsules laid by the whelk litter every beach after a storm. Some hundreds of capsules may go to each of these round honey-coloured balls, and in each capsule is about one hundred eggs. As soon as the first eggs hatch, the fry set to work on their unhatched cradle companions, so that at last a mere thimbleful issue, to be gobbled up by the nearest fish.

WIDE WORLD

CALLED THE CAMEL OF SOUTH AMERICA

The llama is a domesticated member of the guanaco family. It has been used as a beast of burden for many centuries in South America. Its period of gestation is about the same as the sea lion's.

CANNIBALISM IN THE NEST

This self-massacre of the innocents is not confined to invertebrates. A parallel is offered by that highly constituted, intelligent bird of prey, the buzzard. Its eggs, like those of most birds of prey, are incubated as they are laid, one at a time, the first to hatch augmenting the mother's warmth to incubate its little unhatched brothers and sisters. It is a pretty picture of family co-operation.

But mother must often wander far afield for mice and young birds to feed her first-born. This, in bad weather amid mountain crags, may mean a long fast for the baby buzzard, and it sometimes breaks it by eating the next below. Thus it happens that families of three are common with buzzards living on the sheltered lowlands, but in Spartan climes are comparatively infrequent. Similar cannibalism can be seen in any village pond during the tadpole season.

The actual size to which any given kind of animal may attain is largely a matter of mechanics. The make-up, as much as food and environment, says "thus far and no farther." The principle can be demonstrated with a metal cylinder poised on four legs. If the legs are too slender they collapse. In a lifeless dummy the legs can, of course, be any girth, but this will not apply in a living mechanism.

BRAIN WEIGHS SEVENTEEN POUNDS

It is generally believed that the unwieldy proportions of some animals in the past did actually work their downfall. The elephant marks the limit to which legs may attain in thickness, and therefore weight of body. The lumbering amblypods, great hippopotamus-like

HAROLD BASTIN

GREAT HOUSE-BUILDER

The giant clam remains anchored in one spot all its life, devoting its energies to building a colossal home.

brutes that lived about sixty million years ago, piloted tons of body about with a brain of only a few ounces in command. Even the five-ton elephant with his seventeen-pound brain gets into difficulties at times but is seldom hopelessly bogged, as the amblypods must frequently have been.

Lungs, a bony skeleton and a tough skin are amongst the essentials to generous growth in an animal, which is why all the largest creatures are mammals. Numerous factors have kept down the other groups. Insects breathe through small and complex tubes, and the largest insects have never exceeded a wing span of above two feet. The crustacea once reached in the giant sea-scorpions a length of nine feet, but here the constant necessity of casting the shell exhausted energy and so a size limit was reached.

Shelled molluscs must use an immense amount of energy in constantly adding to their cumbrous residences with successive layers of carbonate of lime. The biggest sea-snail has a shell two feet long, about half the length and not a tenth the weight of a giant clam's residence, but the giant clam remains anchored

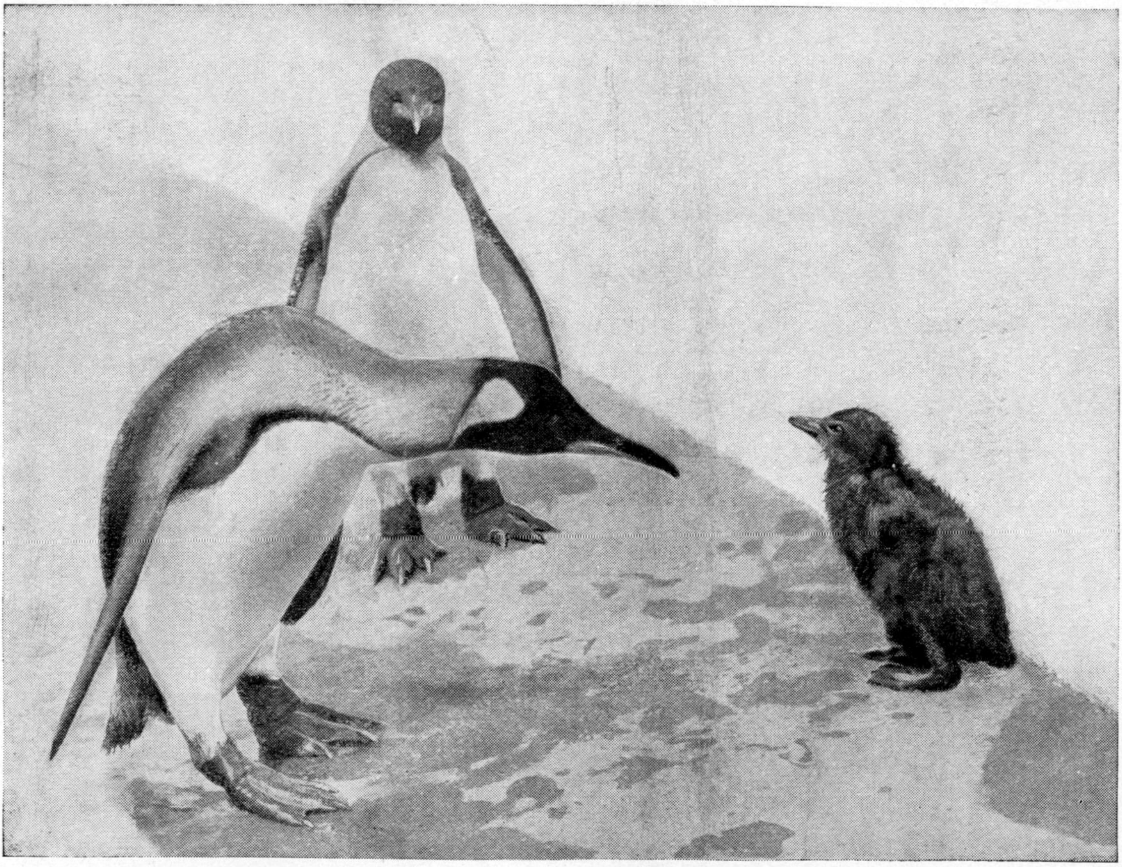

WINGS OF SERVICE ONLY WHEN UNDER WATER

No wonder the two king penguins on the left are so critical of the chick, since the latter is of a different species, being the offspring of a black-footed penguin. It will soon lose its fluffy coat.

HOW THE KEELED BREASTBONE IS ESSENTIAL TO FLIGHT

An end-on view of the breastbone of 1. *Man.* 2. *Ostrich.* 3. *Eagle.* 4. *Penguin.* 5. *Bat.* 6. *Pterodactyl.* 7. *Swift.* 8. *Humming bird.* 9. *Dodo. A man would require a breastbone projecting four feet to support the wing muscles necessary to raise his eleven stone.*

to the sea bed for life, and so has more energy for house building.

With very few exceptions land mammals have proved winners in the race for size. They are beaten only by a few aquatic vertebrates.

GIANTS OF THE SEA

In the water weight is relatively of no account, and so a few groups of mammals, which it is believed changed from a terrestrial life to one afloat, left the landlubbers far behind, though at the expense of their legs.

Not even the much-sung dinosaurus, or baluchitherium, the seventeen-foot high extinct rhinoceros, could have outweighed the living sulphur-bottom whale that sometimes measures just one hundred feet from nose to tail flukes. Its nearest competitors are the forty-foot whale-shark and the giant squids of the Atlantic deeps, monster molluscs with a body length of only ten feet or so, the rest of them being just snaky tentacles.

Where the conquest of the air is concerned still greater limitations are imposed upon the size attainable. The ostrich, weighing perhaps 200 pounds, has no more power of flight than a man. The biggest flying bird is the condor with a weight of only forty pounds. Some of the giant flying reptiles had a wing span of twenty-five feet, more than twice that of a condor, and it is now being questioned whether they enjoyed anything like the condor's powers of sustained aviation.

IF MAN HAD WINGS

For a man to be able to fly it has been estimated that he would need a breast bone reaching to his knees and projecting four feet in front of him, in order to support the wing muscles necessary to raise his eleven stone. The heaviest bird for its size is the penguin. The king penguin, though standing at most only three feet high with neck outstretched, weighs from forty to sixty pounds. Its wings can only be put to practical use when it is deep under water, where its heavy bones give it stability and its vast jacket of fat buoyancy. The penguin's action under water corresponds exactly to the flight of other birds in the air.

Looking back over the vistas of the geologic ages we see that every one of the great animal groups—as also the vegetable groups—has risen to a zenith and then declined. Just as primitive plants—mosses and ferns—once attained to the dignity of trees, so with the animals. Coral builders, starfishes and sea-urchins, insects, molluscs, fish—each has for a time dominated the world's stage. It is true that all these groups can still show giants of a kind. There are six-foot long sea anemones, starfishes a yard across, crabs covering eighteen square feet of ground, and squids as big as skiffs, but like other giants these are exceptions; they are no longer the standard of their class.

With the mammals, now the dominant form of animal life, a fair size is the standard rather than the isolated exception. It may be objected that large numbers of the great mammals have fallen by the way. Where are the giant elk of Ireland, the sabre-tooth tiger and the great cave bear, creatures that probably shared the world with man less than a million years ago? The answer is that they have died out because their brains refused to march with the times.

The moment the mammals appeared, growth became a matter not only of mechanics but of intelligence. To grow, an animal had also to be a colonist. When climates changed and food supplies dwindled, the dinosaurs collapsed but the mammals pushed on. When existing food supplies gave out, they roved in all directions looking for more, eating what they could *en route* until they found a land of plenty.

Modern man is not only a member of the highest class of mammals, the primates, he is the biggest animal in that class. He lacks the musculature of some man-like apes, but he tends to a greater average height than any of them. The gorilla can certainly throw a bigger chest and tip the beam occasionally at more than three times the weight of an average man, but will it always do so? We may be a long way from presenting a race of supermen, but we have some hopes of doing so : the gorilla none.

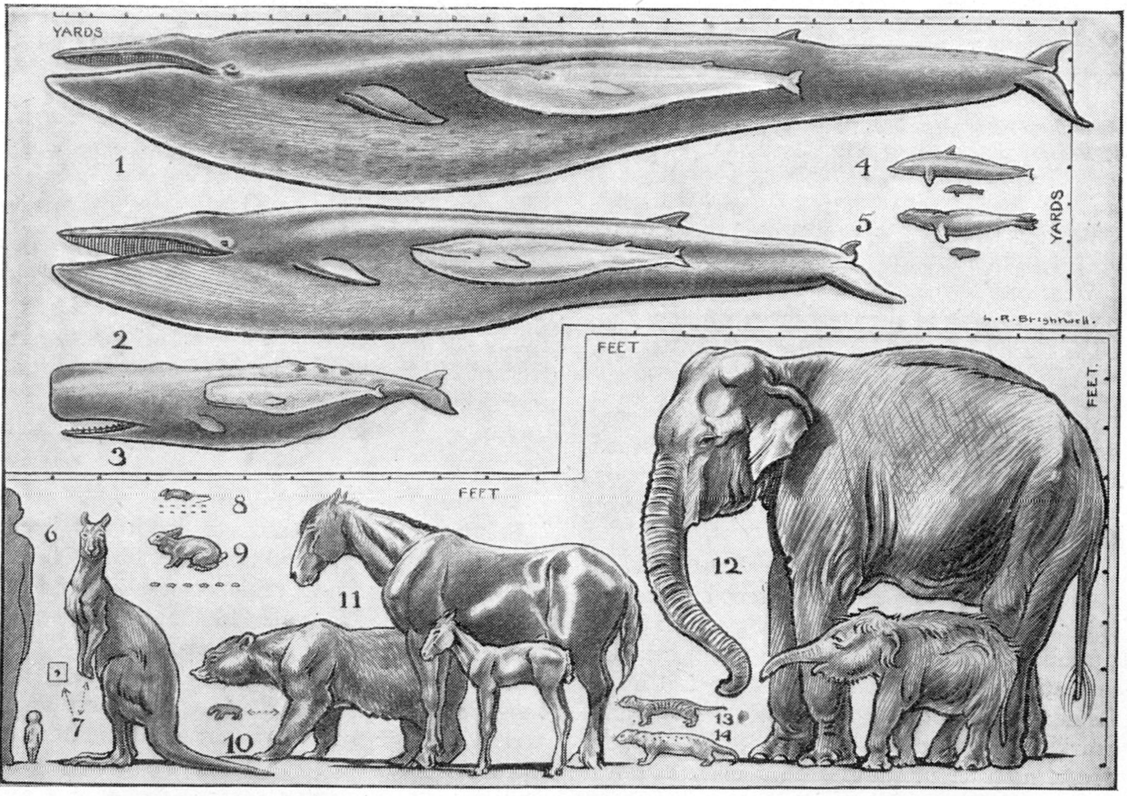

SIZES OF SOME OF THE MAMMALS AT BIRTH AND AS ADULTS
1. *Blue or sulphur bottom whale.* 2. *Fin whale.* 3. *Sperm whale.* 4. *Porpoise.* 5. *Elephant seal.* 6. *Man.* 7. *Giant kangaroo.* 8. *Brown rat.* 9. *Rabbit.* 10. *Brown bear.* 11. *Horse.* 12. *Elephant.* 13. *Tiger.* 14. *Lion.* *Length and height are indicated.*

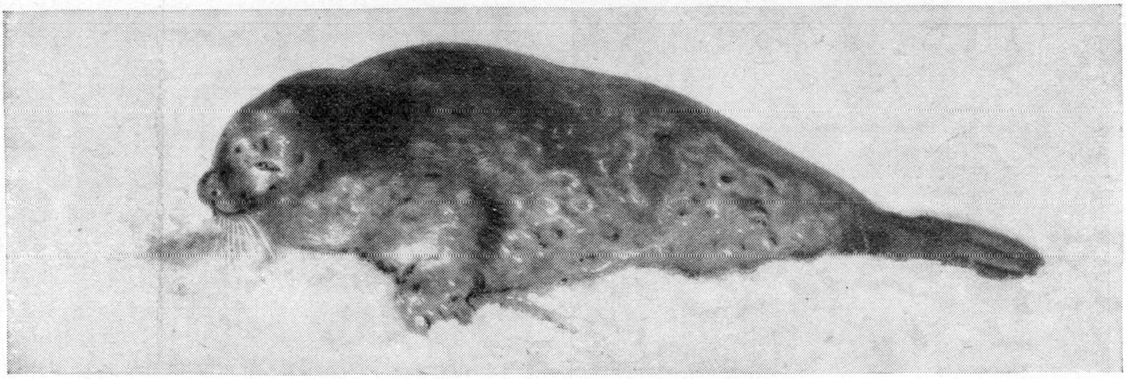

WIDE WORLD

LIVES ON LAND AND IN THE SEA

The seal represents a mammalian mode of life half-way between that of the whales, which remain always in water, and those mammals that never enter it. Its feet are the main organs of aquatic propulsion.

THE ANIMAL KINGDOM

WHAT is an animal? The question sounds simple enough, but one has only to overhear a group of ordinary people discussing a sea anemone to realize that the general conceptions of what constitutes an animal are far from clear. The dictionary does not entirely satisfy the average man's uncertainty. It tells us that the word is derived from the Latin, *anima*, breath; and that it means " a living creature possessing power of voluntary motion, as distinguished from, and contrasted with plant, on one hand, and from man, human being, on the other."

Modern scientists sum up the matter more lucidly when they state that an animal is a living organism dependent for its maintenance upon organic matter. Plants, it is true, depend very largely upon organic matter, and sometimes, as in the case of the pitcher plant and sundew, even upon living organisms. But they can also convert the air and sunlight directly to their needs in a way which no animal yet discovered can do.

Ever since the days of Ancient Greece, man has been persistent in his endeavour to " arrange " the world about him, to demonstrate the order which exists in apparent chaos. By the untiring labour of many generations of biologists, the plants and animals of the earth have been ranged in groups according to their affinities, and to each species a name has been given. The medium which science has adopted for its nomenclature is a strange blending of Greek and Latin which appears to the non-scientific mind both cumbrous and difficult, but the use of the classical languages is a necessity if the same nomenclature is to be used and understood by scientists all over the world. A multiplication of nomenclatures would spell the direst confusion.

There are today over half a million recognized different kinds of animals in existence, and the list is being added to at the rate of over a hundred a year. Many have no popular names in any language, while such as have, frequently possess so many as to be a source of confusion even in the countries of their origin. In Great Britain alone the common stickleback is known by over a score of local appellations, and other countries in which it occurs have been equally generous. It is not surprising therefore that science has decreed the fish shall be recognized throughout the scientific world by one official cognomen, *Gasterosteus aculeatus*. The first title is known as the generic name—it tells us to what particular *genus* or group the fish belongs, whilst the second or specific name is that of the species or family. This marks the stickleback off from all other kinds of similar fishes included in the same group.

The whole system of scientific classification is based upon a complex process of working from the general to the particular, a gathering of all creatures into certain broad, main groups, and then dividing and sub-dividing upon a basis of increasingly minute distinction. It may be likened to the military arrangement of

MINUTE BUT MANY-CELLED
A rotifer, or wheel animalcule, feeding from a sea-moss spike. Minute in size, it is yet many-celled.

a fighting force into armies, an army into corps, divisions, battalions, companies, platoons and sections.

It will greatly facilitate our review of animal activities if the main groups of animals are clearly recognized. All living animals are divided into nine great armies, called variously sub-kingdoms or *phyla*—both terms signifying for ordinary purposes main groups.

Until fifty years ago naturalists were at great variance of opinion as to the true positions of many animals belonging to the more primitive *phyla*, and even today one has only to hear general conversation to appreciate how vague are popular conceptions regarding the placing of such familiar forms as the jelly-fish, spider, and even the sea-lion. In any circus audience you are fairly certain to overhear a controversy as to whether the sea-lion is an animal (mammal), a fish, or a blend of both.

FIRST ANIMALS

In the lowest rank of the Legion of the Animals are placed those primitive creatures called the *Protozoa*—or first animals, and more popularly *Animalcula*. They swarm in the waters, both fresh and salt, and some even invade the soil. All are minute, and the simplest forms are little blobs of protoplasm with a central nucleus. A typical example, the amœba, teems both in soil and water, assuming all manner of shapes as it forces its way through whatever medium it happens to be in, and assimilating edible matter by literally " surrounding " it.

More complex forms build elaborate houses out of mineral substances suspended in water, which later go to form deep deposits on the sea floor, and eventually under compression, beds of solid rock. Others again are termed flagellates or whip bearers, since each has a minute hair-like attachment by which it literally whips itself through the water.

" HAIR WHIPS " OF THE SPONGES

In the next group, the sponges (*Porifera*), we see this device of the whip amplified. It often takes the form of dense manes of violently agitated hairs, which form very efficient organs of propulsion. The familiar sponges have their interiors filled with " hair whips," forcing water, and with it minute food particles, through the entire organism.

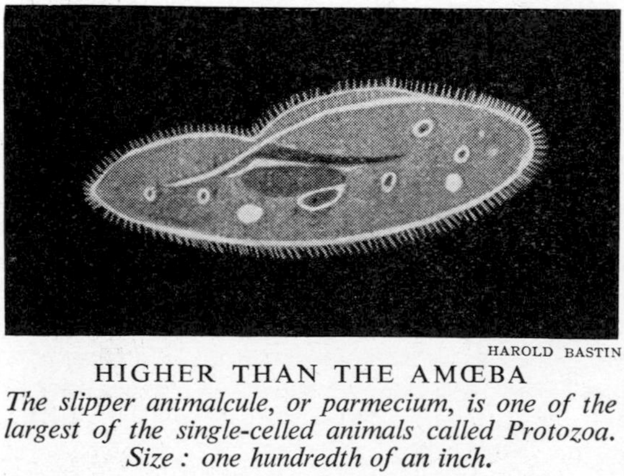

HAROLD BASTIN

HIGHER THAN THE AMŒBA
The slipper animalcule, or parmecium, is one of the largest of the single-celled animals called Protozoa. Size : one hundredth of an inch.

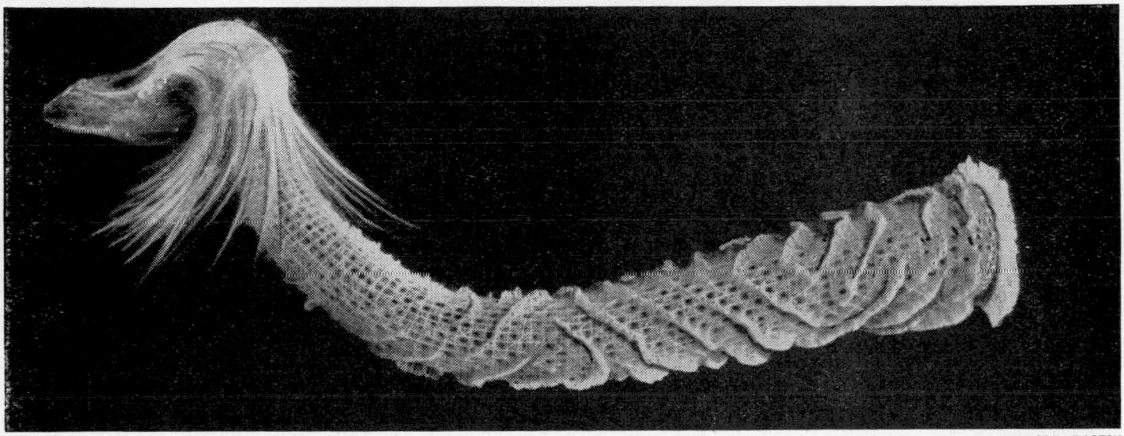

HAROLD BASTIN

VENUS'S FLOWER-BASKET

The flinty sponge Euplectella, one of the most beautiful of marine animals, lives in the mud on the floor of the sea, where the enormous pressure of water forces it to assume an extremely diffuse and ethereal form.

The second section, *Coelenterata*, or hollow-bodied animals, includes the corals and jelly-fish. Here we see the first beginnings of a stomach, for the entire animal is little more than a bag, into which food is passed by special organs — the feeders or "petals" of the anemones; the "streamers" of the jelly-fish.

The vast army of the worms (*Vermes*) brings us to another group presenting an infinite variety of forms, built on a cylindrical plan, and more complex than the foregoing in that there are separate orifices for the assimilation of food and the ejectment of waste matter.

MOSS ANIMALS MIMIC CORALS

The moss animals (*Annelids*), typified by the sea-mat common on the beaches of the east coast of England, stand midway between the worms and the next legion, that of the spiny-skinned animals (*Echinoderms*), the starfishes, sea-urchins, etc. Although many of the moss animals mimic corals in their adult stages, their larval or immature forms are often easily mistaken for those of some worms. The precise relationships of these abundant animals are still matter for controversy, and the group is here placed in the general scheme only for the time being.

SKIN FORTIFIED WITH LIMY MATTER

Sea-urchins, starfishes and sea-cucumbers, though very unlike at first glance, have many points in common. All are built upon a pentagonal plan, and the skin is fortified with calcareous matter gathered from the surrounding water. Since only enough of this limy housing material is available in salt water, all the species are marine. They have a most complex system of internal canals, which force water through innumerable hollow "tube

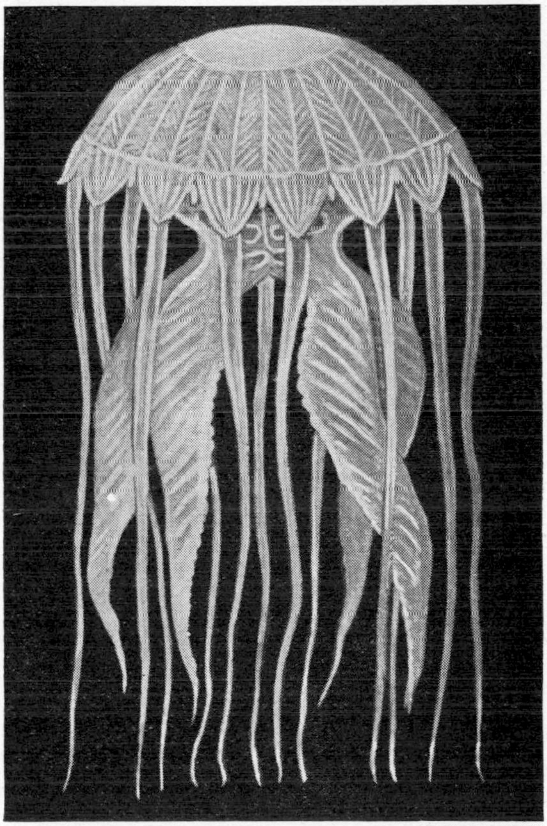

HAROLD BASTIN

ANIMATED FOOD-BAG

The jelly-fish is a member of the Cœlenterata phylum, in which we see the beginnings of a stomach.

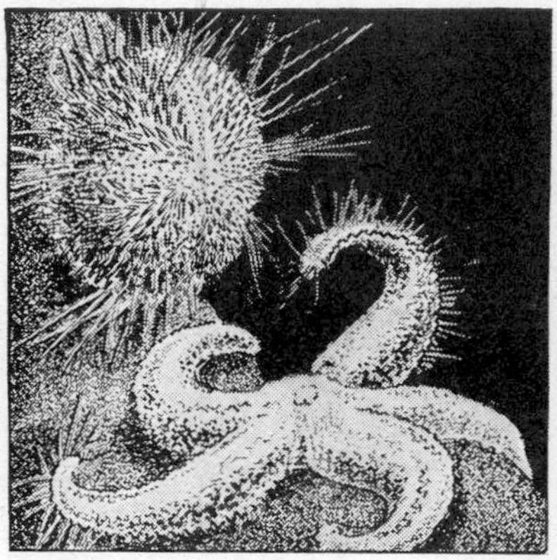

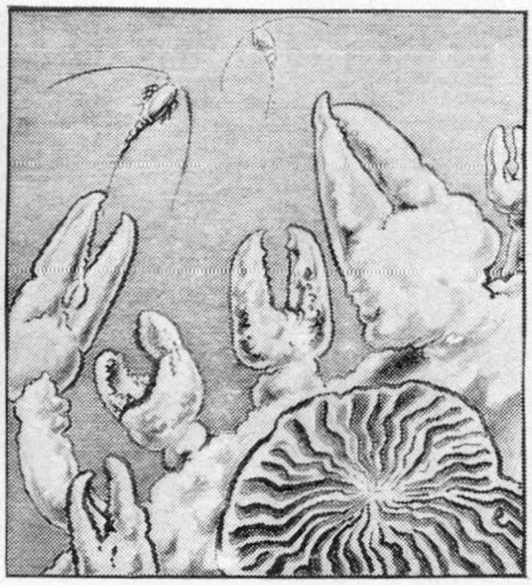

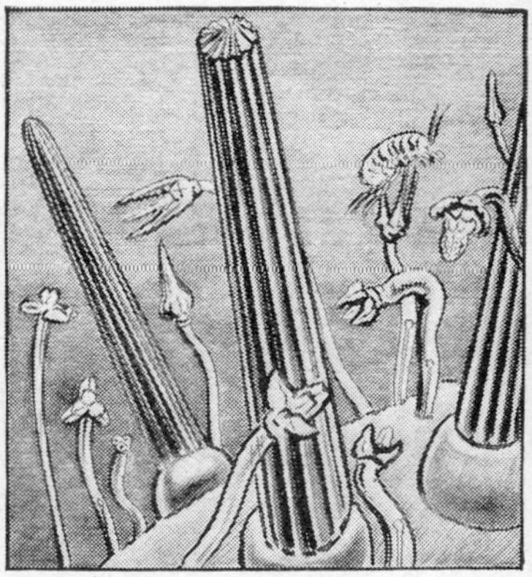

COVERED WITH STRANGE APPENDAGES

Sea-urchin and starfish. Upper surface of the latter and also of the former, showing spines, sheers, pincers and grapnels invisible to the naked eye but useful for feeding, cleaning and protection.

feet," enabling the animal to progress over rocks and other difficult objects.

A sea-urchin is literally a starfish "sewn up," that is with all the arms bent over till they touch, and cemented together at the edges. This is shown in the illustration, and also how the spiney-skinned animals in addition to their "water legs" are covered with strange appendages—spines, sheers, pincers and grapnels, invisible to our naked eyes but perpetually busy feeding, cleaning or protecting their owners.

The curious link group termed lampshells, or *Brachiopods*, mentioned in a previous section, stands midway between the great army of the starfishes and the *Mollusca*. The *Mollusca* include such familiar forms as the oyster, mussel, whelk, snail, octopus and cuttle fishes.

The *phylum* of the jointed animals probably forms the greatest of all the several main groups, both numerically and as regards variety of species. It includes the crustaceans —water-fleas, barnacles, crabs, crayfish, lobsters—spiders, scorpions, mites, centipedes and insects. The last are recognizable from all the others in that when they arrive at the adult or perfect state they have three pairs of walking legs.

All members of the group are segmented, that is to say the body is divided into rings, each bearing a pair of appendages. Some of these may be reserved for walking purposes,

HAROLD BASTIN

SEA URCHINS: STARFISHES SEWN-UP

Members of the spiny-skinned Echinoderm group. They are all marine, have their skins fortified with limy material, and are built on a pentagonal plan. They climb over rocks by means of "tube-feet" through which water is forced.

JAMES HORNELL (MONDIALE)

OCTOPUS LYING IN WAIT FOR PREY

Of the Mollusca group, its cousins include cuttlefish, snails and mussels. The circular orifice (shown about an inch below the eye) is the termination of a tube through which water is expelled with great force, driving the creature along back first.

others modified to form wings, feeling organs or a number of complicated mouth parts. Terrestrial forms breathe by a system of tubes through which air is pumped; aquatic species respire by means of gills or air tubes.

"THE BRIDGE-THAT-WALKS"

Lastly we come to the great army of creatures having a central nerve chord. The *phylum Chordata* or *Vertebrata* embraces certain obscure "links" such as the sea squirt, and more importantly the fishes, amphibians—animals such as frogs and newts, that spend part of their lives in the water and part on land—reptiles, birds and the hair-covered, milk-fed creatures termed mammals.

It is this last group which naturally enlists our chief interests and sympathies. We have more fellow feeling with its various members than with the invertebrates, or backboneless animals, however great their scientific interest. The outstanding feature of the vertebrate is its vertebral column or backbone. On this has been founded the long series of adventures in land colonization which has culminated in man.

All vertebrates, however unlike in shape and habits, are built upon the same general plan, which, like the main theme one hears in a musical composition, can be seen running through the entire series. The study of this main theme and its variations forms that most fascinating of the sciences, comparative anatomy, and it can at least be glanced at without involving any cumbrous technicalities.

The vertebral column or backbone has been very aptly called by Professor W. K. Gregory, of Columbia University, "the bridge-that-walks." It is a suspension bridge built on the same essential principles employed to span the Forth.

BEGINNINGS OF THE BRIDGE

The animal bridge had its beginnings in the primitive fishes that first developed paired fins. Some living fishes offer hints as to how the bridge was first brought ashore. We see the common angler fish—the "rock salmon" of commerce—and the common gurnard crawling or shuffling over the aquarium floor by means of their breast fins. Some tropic fish like the mud skipper and climbing perch can even shuffle out of the water and on to dry land, or even struggle up vertical surfaces.

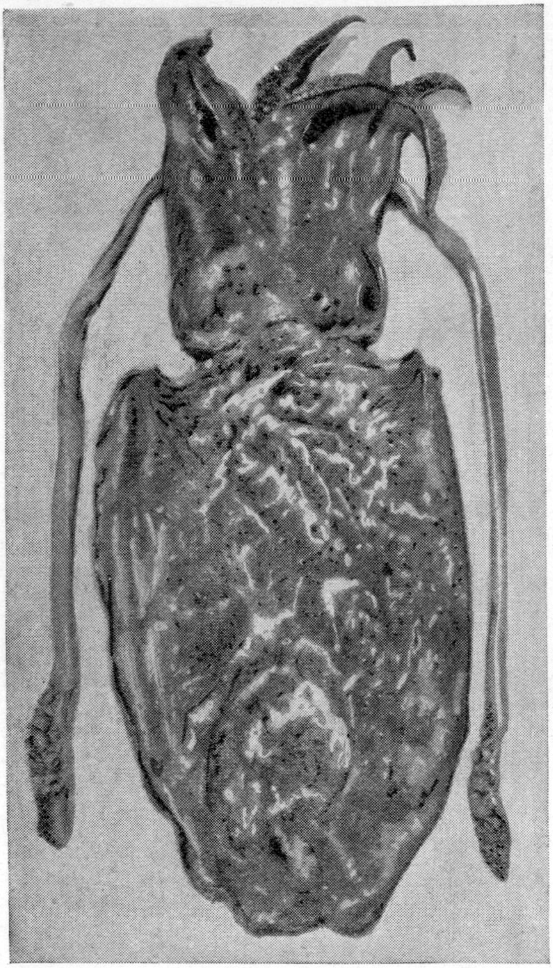

HAROLD BASTIN

DEVIL-FISH

The common cuttlefish is one of the cephalopods, regarded as the most advanced invertebrate animals. They have well-ordered brains.

A number of fish thus survive long periods out of water, thanks to such devices as accessory breathing organs derived from specially modified swim bladders. Such first lungs made further progress in the early amphibians, the fish-reptile creatures that swarmed in the primeval forests now represented by our coal measures. These creatures, often of enormous size, are known to have made excursions ashore, but like our modern newts and frogs could never be independent of the water for long. Amphibians have soft spongy skins, and partly breathe through them.

This porous quality of the skin has always been a heavy handicap to amphibians in colonizing the land. Any excursion far from water involves the danger of literally drying up. In March, when the toads are searching for a pond wherein to deposit their eggs, one can often find some that have fallen by the way. Here the sun has caught them and mummified them where they died.

PERFECTING OF THE LUNG

For breathing apparatus to work on dry land it must be kept moist. Unless our lungs enjoy a certain amount of humidity respiration is impossible. The precise stages by which certain amphibians developed hard heat-resisting skins, and lungs sufficiently capacious to sustain them for periods without other aid, are not entirely known, but once this transpired the conquest of the land was assured. The perfecting of the lung and the toughening of the skin literally set the vertebrate upon its feet.

PIONEERS OF MILLIONS OF YEARS AGO

To the casual observer a newt and a short-legged lizard are much alike, but gently prod each of them, and the difference is demonstrated in striking fashion. The newt practically rows itself over the ground; its human-looking hands and well-formed limbs are little better than oars. The lizard raises its belly clear of the ground, and in a moment leaves the newt far behind. The bridge at last walks.

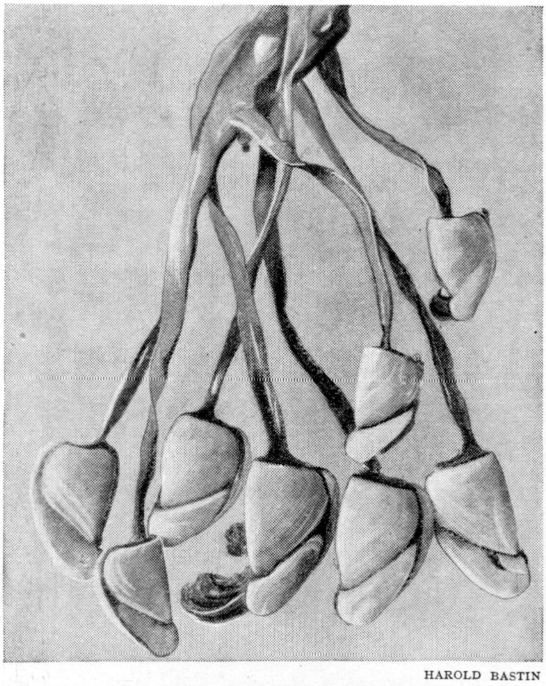

HAROLD BASTIN

OF THE CRAB FAMILY

Barnacles belong to the phylum of jointed animals. The ancients thought that geese were bred from these organisms.

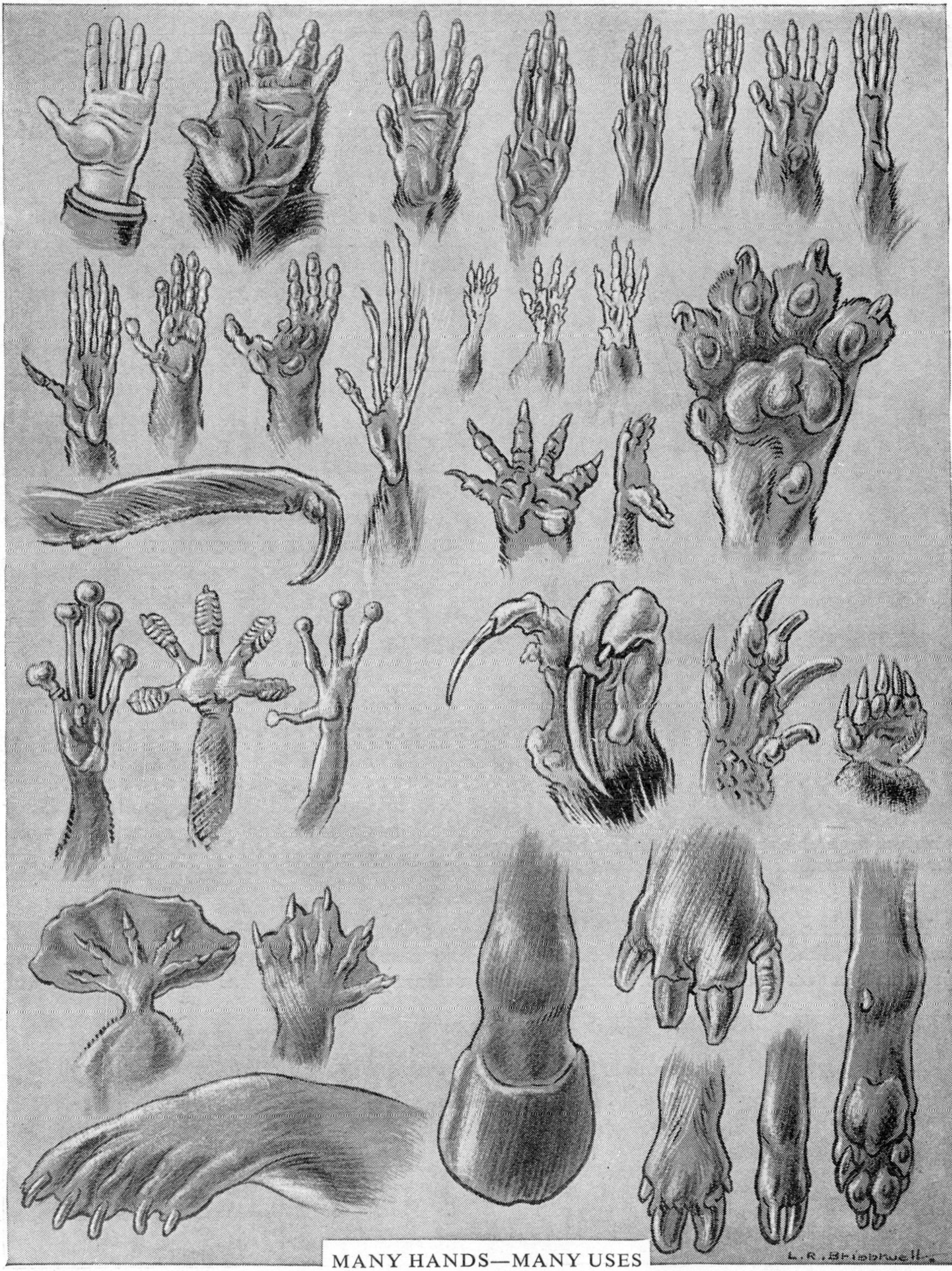

MANY HANDS—MANY USES

Holding hands: Man, gorilla, chimpanzee, orang-utan, gibbon, rhesus monkey, baboon, spider monkey, woolly monkey, lemur, patto, aye aye, shrew, rat, squirrel, sloth, kangaroo, chameleon, leopard. Sucker-pad hands: Tarsius lemur gecko lizard, tree frog. Digging hands: Ant eater, armadillo, mole. Swimming hands: Duckbill, otter, seal. Running and walking hands: Horse, tapir pig, deer, hyena.

WIDE WORLD

BURGER'S CRAYFISH

Crayfishes are among the most highly developed of the crustaceans. This species is found along the South African coast.

When this was first achieved, about two hundred million years ago, the bold pioneers presented a certain sameness. Those early terrestrial reptiles rather suggested a child's crude attempts at portraying a quadruped. The pioneer walking bridge had a shortish tail hung at one end, a rather shapeless head at the other, and was itself slung between two pairs of extremely undistinguished "generalized" lcgs.

FINGERS AND TOES

But life ashore offered enormous possibilities for exploration, it invited the adventurers to not merely waddle but to walk, run, dig, climb and fly. Astonishing variations were soon played upon the simple theme of the jointed limb, with its terminal digits—fingers and toes—which are really only modifications of the fin-rays seen in fish.

Every conceivable kind of limb was in course of time hung at either end of the bridge, according to its owner's needs. At a first glance there is admittedly very little in common between the forearm of a man, frog, deer, bear or sloth, the wing of the bat or bird, and the flipper of the whale. But reduce these all to the common denominator of dry bones, and their essential oneness or homology is at once apparent.

VANISHED THUMBS

The first exponents of the walking bridge had five fingers and five toes. These were useful enough for just paddling over the ground, but their scope was very limited. In course of time some animals found five toes too many. They made swift, sustained progression impossible, and so some were eliminated, as in the horse, deer, and pig.

Where the hind limbs only were used for progress, the fore limbs remained normal, as in the case of the kangaroo, which retains an ordinary hand, but has dispensed with one

BURROWERS

These animals are all unrelated, but they are, nevertheless, all built along the same general lines, because they all burrow in the same way. Basset hound (once used for badger-hunting), mole, cockchafer grub, mole cricket, burrowing prawn.

TEETH USED AS TOOLS

Differing vastly in many respects, for their other habits are very dissimilar, these animals yet have teeth of the same type, since they use them in the same way. Elephant, walrus, beaver, Chinese water deer.

hind toe altogether and is well on its way to converting two of the remaining toes into one.

Some animals, still keeping their bridge in a horizontal plane, took it aloft, and hauled it about, upside down, amongst the tree-tops. Here again wonderful modifications took place in the bridge's supporting columns. The orang-utan turned four of its fingers into hooks, causing the fifth or thumb to dwindle from disuse. In some monkeys and other arboreal quadrupeds it vanished altogether. The sloths have wiped out two, or even three fingers and toes, much as the horse and deer have pushed some of their digits into the background, not by climbing but by persistently hammering hard earth.

HANDS AND FEET FOR DIGGING

When the hands and feet were used as digging instruments, again there was at once loss and gain amongst the digits. This is suggested in the series of " digging " tools pictured. It will be noticed that whereas the hands are in some cases altered past recognition as hands, the feet, being mainly used only as spades to fling aside the earth excavated by the fore limbs, have undergone comparatively slight divergence from the original theme.

One of the most fascinating features of comparative anatomy or animal make-up is the manner in which totally different animals, by leading similar ways of life, have developed the same parts of the body in the same fashion. Unlike in all other respects, they still have these features in common.

WALKING ON THE CEILING

No one could mistake the little monkey-like tarsier of Borneo for the tree frogs of the same region. But if only the hands and feet of these creatures were shown some confusion might be excusable. Tarsier and frog spend their days clinging for life to slippery bamboo stems, and like the gecko lizards that see the world by walking on the ceiling, have developed adhesive sucker discs whereby to conquer a " skating " surface. In the matter of flight, we shall find the same principle holding good, i.e., the hand made to do the same work in similar ways by totally dissimilar animals.

The living bridge had its origin in the water and was dragged ashore. Some animals dragged it back into the water. It is now generally believed that the whales, and also the sea-cows and manatees, the largest aquatic mammals, are the descendants of land animals which, either in pursuit of food or to escape from foes ashore, put the clock back, so to speak, and reverted to the source of their origin, the great waters.

In these two very different groups of mammals the hand once more became a fin, but only superficially as regards its construction. Strip off the skin and fat, and below we find the familiar fingers—fingers that could no longer retain their grip on land. Another parallel line of development seen in whales and sea-cows is the loss of the hind limbs. When existent at all they remain only as vestiges.

DWINDLED BY DISUSE

The seal and sea-lion present a " half-way " state of reversion. They have reached the same goal, a life spent partly ashore and partly afloat, but by different roads. The seal has made its feet the chief organs of propulsion. Placing them sole to sole, it waggles them, as does the seaman his oar over the boat's stern, and so progresses in a lateral plane, like a fish. The sea-lion swims with its fore limbs, steers with its hind, and is altogether a more handy beast.

The seal's arms and hands have dwindled by disuse almost to the point of impotence. It uses them ashore to scramble over rocks, but is at almost as great a disadvantage as a too fat man trying to perform a similar feat with his hands and feet manacled.

One animal alone successfully tilted its bridge on end. In the course of a million or more years man achieved this, partly as a result of special modifications of his pelvis, but chiefly by developing the lumbar curve or small of the back, thus enabling him to poise the centre of the body over the centre of support.

NECK AND TAIL AS BALANCERS

The apparent uprightness of such bipeds as birds, or semi-bipeds like kangaroos, merely mimics the human pose. The bird's long neck and the kangaroo's tail both serve as balancers, and the same applies to those nightmare creatures of the past, the bipedal dinosaurs.

The average bird has a much longer neck than meets the eye, as all who have plucked a chicken will have realized. Without this the bird would tumble backwards, and the kangaroo, shorn of its tail, would similarly pitch forward on to its nose.

We will now examine in more detail some external features common to vertebrates.

" Tail " is one of our many loosely used words. We speak of the lobster's tail and the

FOX

ONE OF THE CRAWLERS

The gurnard, like the angler fish, crawls along the bottom of the sea by means of breast-fins. Some tropical species, like the climbing perch and the mud skipper, can crawl on dry land and even up vertical surfaces.

CRANE PACIFIC EXPEDITION (WIDE WORLD)

BIRDS, REPTILES AND A MAMMAL

Seen on a lava ledge in Narborough Island, Galapagos Archipelago, five hundred miles west of Ecuador, in the Pacific, four cormorants, two gulls, five marine iguanas and a sea-lion. The cormorants' wings are too weak for flight.

tail-end of a wasp, but the tail is truly a vertebrate phenomenon. It is a piece of the vertebral column or bridge "left over," and originally helped to propel the adventurers on land ashore. The few terminal bones of the human spine, spoken of as the *os coccyx*, are a legacy from our remote ancestors the fishes. As one authority has aptly put it, "with our tails we swam to supremacy."

MANY USES OF THE TAIL

The tail was primarily an organ of propulsion. It is still largely the driving force of the twenty thousand species of fishes living today, although some have learnt to employ it as more than a simple organ of locomotion. The thresher shark uses it to round-up schools of fish, the conger-eel and sea-horse use it as a grapnel or anchor, the mud skipper and anabas employ it to heave themselves along when making a shore excursion. But most aquatic creatures, whether fishes, crocodiles or otters use their tails to force the water aside with a wagging motion, i.e., in a horizontal plane.

In all such animals the tail is compressed to form a blade with two edges, one above and one below, the former sometimes augmented by a crest. When the tail is compressed to form a horizontal blade, it is moved up and down and not from side to side, driving its owner forwards with a rocking motion.

This sort of tail is much less abundant than the wagging kind, but we can see it working with wonderful efficiency in the whales and manatees, and to a lesser degree in the beaver. The beaver also uses its tail with a lateral and slightly screwing motion to serve the purpose of a rudder. Unique amongst tails, it can also function as an alarm gun by dealing the water surface a sounding smack when danger threatens.

When the tail was finally carried upon dry land a host of other jobs awaited it. The first pioneers, the lizards, swung it just as they had done in the water, and if an enemy stood in its way, so much the worse for the enemy. A big monitor lizard or a crocodile can knock a man off his feet with a single swing of the tail, and the African ant-bear when cornered can put its tail to a like purpose. In some extinct beasts, like the stegosaur and the giant armadillos that once ranged the pampas, the tail bore enormous spines that must have spelt destruction to anything in their path.

TAIL AS SHOOTING STOOL

In wild Nature the tail very frequently literally wagged the dog. Having rowed its owner ashore, it gave greater freedom to his fore limbs by helping him to raise them both together from the ground. When developed on sufficiently generous lines, the tail makes a good shooting stool. Many lizards past and present so use it, and it has served in this capacity for the extinct giant ground sloths and countless generations of kangaroos. In the latter it is powerful enough to take the animal's entire weight.

When two male kangaroos fight they heave themselves aloft upon their tails and meet heel to heel, each fencing with one free foot for the chance to lay bare his opponent's interior. The woolly monkey uses his tail as a stool in a different manner. Curling the tip into a circle, he plants this firmly on the ground, and then, making the rest of his tail rigid, leans back upon it in a luxurious fashion.

With the great majority of quadrupeds the tail serves largely as a fly whisk, and subconsciously it is an eloquent index to the owner's emotions of the moment. The "language" of a dog's tail needs no elaboration, neither does the cat's nor the cow's tail call for comment. When the tail is generously haired it may, as in the case of the squirrel and the ant eater, make a handy coverlet at bed-time, and the scaly ant eaters or pangolins use their tails as door stoppers, blocking the entrances to their burrows against unwanted callers.

Yet another rôle played by the tail is that of a tribal badge, or follow-my-leader sign. This is usually its last use, the only employment that can be found for a tail too short or immobile to do more active work. The rabbit's "bob" is an example that will occur to all. More decorative amplifications of the idea are seen in the short dark tails of many deer and antelope, neat little appendages set in strikingly marked or coloured frames of horseshoe design.

When a vertebrate took to life in the trees, the overflow from its walking bridge entered on another phase of usefulness. The strictly arboreal vertebrate animals without tails can be almost counted on the fingers of one hand. The sloths are tailless, and so also is the Australian teddy bear or koala, but both are forced to cling tenaciously to any support

WIDE WORLD

TREE CLIMBING UPSIDE DOWN

The two-toed sloth, a native of tropical Central America, always climbs upside down. His movements are slow compared with those of most monkeys, because, unlike them, he has no tail to act as a balancer.

MEANS OF LOCOMOTION IN THE WATER

Left: two-oar swimmers, using paddles; boatman bug, swimming crab, frog, sea-hare, cormorant, sea-lion, penguin. Right: one-oar swimmers, using their tails as propellers; dolphin, seal, crocodile, fish, otter (swims dog-fashion, aided by tail).

offering, and both move in slow motion. So too does the orang-utan. It is dangerous to hurry a Blondin act without a balancing pole.

LIFE ON THE TREE TOPS

A balancing pole is indeed a tail's first function in tree-top life, and is essential to rapid movement. The only nimble arboreal mammal that dispenses with one is the gibbon, but it makes up the deficiency by spreading its abnormally long arms horizontally. All arboreal squirrels, monkeys and lizards have long tails, and in a review of these we meet every degree of development between the tail that is a balancing pole only and the tail that is much more—a fifth hand.

Only two lines of reptiles, the chameleons and the snakes, have developed hand-like tails, but amongst mammals the grapnel tail manifests itself in such diverse forms as those of the various South American monkeys and honey bear, the Himalayan catbear or binturong, the tamandua and little ant eaters, various porcupines, and a regiment of opossums.

The honey bear or kinkajou uses its tail with even more effect than the various monkeys who vie with it in raiding birds' nests and wild hives. The honey bear, dangling head downwards from a branch when committing one of its raids, stages a quick get-away from the irate owner by simply climbing its own tail, and so fading literally into the night. One monkey, the woolly monkey of Brazil, converts its tail into a hammock by hitching the tip over one branch, its toes over another, and then, leaning back against its caudal appendage, swings at ease a hundred feet above the ground.

GLANDS TO LUBRICATE PLUMAGE

The tail in most birds is no more than a support for feathers and the oil glands which serve to lubricate the plumage against the incursions of damp. To such uses has the lengthy appendage brought into the world by archeopteryx, the first bird, been converted. In many aquatic birds, such as ducks, divers and guillemots, the tail is a serviceable rudder, and in a few diverse species it even functions as a stool.

This is seen well in some penguins, who make a tripod of heels and tail, but more remarkable is its similar employment by the woodpeckers. These birds live, as do—in working hours—steeple-jacks, namely up a pole. The steeple-jack retains his stance in this perilous position by means of a strap round his waist and a pair of climbing irons. The woodpecker has the climbing irons—its toes—but no strap. To compensate for this deficiency it plants its wedge-shaped parson's nose firmly against the tree trunk, and with claws dug well in, leans back upon it, as confidently as does the earth-bound penguin or kangaroo.

An almost exact parallel to this is seen in the little arboreal scaly ant eater. Mounting a slippery palm trunk, it clasps it firmly with its hind limbs, and then leans back upon its long prickly tail with a tenacity that makes its dislodgment extremely difficult.

FIRST BACKBONED LAND ANIMALS

The body machine attached to the vertebral column was led into a variety of adventures once it had made its way to land. But before all its latent powers could be developed, certain vital changes were needed in its outer covering, which stood between it and the vagaries of climate.

The first vertebrate land animals were reptiles. Like their ancestors the fishes, most of them were probably covered with scales, and like the fishes were cold blooded. That is to say, their bodily temperature was similar to that of the air or water around them. A rise of atmospheric temperature worked a corresponding excess of energy in the body machine; a fall in temperature caused its mechanism to slow down.

The truth of this can be readily appreciated by any one who keeps as pets, frogs, lizards, or the familiar goldfish. A fall in temperature renders all these creatures dull and sluggish, and finally comatose. A rise in temperature just as noticeably stimulates them to healthy appetite, and as a corollary, exuberant energy.

FEATHERS AND HAIR

When, towards the close of the Age of Reptiles, a period probably covering several hundreds of millions of years, the first mammals appeared, there is every reason to suppose they wore hair. The first birds wore feathers of a kind; feathers or hair are essential to maintaining a body temperature independent of climatic influences.

How a rise in the body temperature first came about is not exactly known, but it must have been manifested in those small pioneer beasts and birds who weathered the sudden fall in temperature heralding the Ice Age which swept into oblivion most of the giant reptiles and myriads of smaller species. The once almost universally genial climate which bathed our earth gave place to a cold which slowly crept northwards and southwards from the poles; the few surviving giant reptiles were

DORIEN LEIGH

USES ITS TAIL AS A DOOR

The pangolin, or scaly ant eater, makes sure that its sleep will be undisturbed by blocking the entrance to its burrow with its bite-proof tail. Despite its reptilian scales, this West African is a true mammal.

herded within the equatorial belt, while a remnant of small and puny reptile forms lingered in temperate lands at the mercy of the growing band of furred and feathered new-comers.

BATHED IN NATURAL BRILLIANTINE

Hairs and feathers seldom leave satisfactory traces in the records of the rocks, so that their first beginnings still lie in the land of surmise. If, however, we picture scales becoming smaller and finer, splitting up perhaps from the edges inwards, we can at least form some conception of how feathers arose. Hairs are built upon a different basis, having roots with special glands surrounding them for their lubrication; they are bathed in a kind of natural brilliantine which keeps them supple. A bird's feathers are largely lubricated from twin oil reservoirs situated near the tail, and the bird has to ladle the oil on to the feathers with its beak.

We get a hint as to how hair or feathers may have arisen in certain fishes. There is in particular a South American catfish, the male of which carries quite an impressive beard round its lower jaw. The scales of that region are so split up that any one might be excused for regarding them, at first sight, as genuine hair.

Hair or feathers gave their wearers enormous advantages over the reptiles. Scales may keep out damp and resist coarse vegetation or the claws of enemies, but they offer scant resistance to cold. A mammal or bird " fluffs up " its fur or feathers automatically, and so creates a cold-resisting layer of air between itself and the outer temperature, much as does our cellular underclothing.

FOX

TRIBAL BADGE

Many antelopes and deer have their tails framed in a horseshoe of white, as a distinguishing mark.

WIDE WORLD

SECRET OF THE RABBIT'S "BOB"

The rabbit's tail is too short for service as a tool or a blanket, but it has value as a sign.

FEATHERS RESIST COLD

Human clothes may have become largely an expression of vanity, but with dwellers in cool temperate climes at least they are a necessity. We have lost the power to " fluff up " what little hair we have. When we experience " goose flesh " we are being reminded that nature is vainly endeavouring to raise our hair by tightening our skin, but there is scarcely any hair to raise.

The bird's feathers enable it to maintain a higher temperature than any mammal, and so survive greater cold. In this, feathers have played their part in the bird's mastery of the air, apart from their obvious conversion into propeller blades. Except for the spasmodic aerial adventures of bats and a few other small beasts, the mammals remain earthbound, but their hair still adapts itself to a vast number of varied requirements.

Hair generally responds very noticeably to

changes of temperature. Some animals, such as the sheep, if taken to cold countries grow a thin outer skin and long hair, but if transported to a hot country reverse these features. Very great cold is needed to lengthen the fur of some animals, which is why grey squirrels cannot be successfully farmed in England.

Interesting parallels to the sheep are the elephant and rhinoceros. Both these beasts once roamed the northern latitudes and grew dense coats of wool. Today they are confined to warm countries, have grown thick outer skins, and have scarcely any hair at all. For some years in succession pygmy hippopotami belonging to the Zoological Society of London have been given a holiday at Whipsnade, which stands hundreds of feet higher than Regent's Park. At the close of the holiday, in early autumn, when there is a bite in the air, these beasts return to London with such few hairs as they possess noticeably increased in length, though not in numbers.

Hair growth is not entirely a matter of climate. In some instances it is controlled by heredity. No amount of heat will shorten the hair of the Alaskan musk ox, and cold will not lengthen that of the almost naked water buffalo. In steamy Burma is a small tribe of otherwise normal human beings so grotesquely hairy that they suggest enormous sheep dogs walking erect.

Long hair may generally be looked for in the polar regions and the tree tops, for when trees are tall enough those who haunt their summits meet with bitter nights. This accounts for the apparent inconsistency of the dense coats worn by the Brazilian woolly monkey, and its mates of the jungle, the sloths.

WIDE WORLD

PROVIDED WITH A GRAPNEL TAIL

The marsupials known as opossums are found in many parts of America. Their diet includes fruit, birds and insects; and, because they live mainly in trees, most species are provided with long, naked, prehensile tails.

Complete hairlessness can be produced by artificial selection, instances being certain dogs and cats found in China and Mexico.

The part hair plays in camouflage, courtship and other matters will be glanced at later. Here we will consider the hair itself and its modifications. It is but a step from hair to spines, and in a porcupine or hedgehog, or a tenrec shrew, one can see every intermediate stage between the two extremes. The porcupine's quills stand erect with terrific effect quite automatically when the wearer's skin goes goosey in sudden alarm, but certain of these hairs can be put to other use besides discouraging foes. In the tail are certain large quills with hollow shafts and open ends which, when vibrated, give out a musical rattle, something like that of a rattlesnake. Opinion is divided on the origin of this device, but it may be intended as a warning.

NATURE PROVIDES A NAIL BRUSH

In South America abounds a guinea-pig-like rodent called the viscacha which excavates deep burrows in very adhesive earth. After a hard night's work the viscacha is in the condition of a navvy after some hours trenching in wet weather. But it soon makes itself spruce by means of its hind feet. One toe of each foot carries an arrangement of bristles exactly resembling a very stiff nail brush, a most effective cleansing implement.

Creatures like the porcupine and spiny tenrec have a certain amount of hair mixed up with their spines, but there are some few creatures in which the hair is almost completely confined to the underside. This seeming topsy-turvydom is accounted for by hair on the upper parts being rendered unnecessary owing to the extraordinary development of the skin. This is thrown into hard plates, as in the armadillo, or modified to form huge overlapping scales, a style of clothing which makes the scaly ant

CAPT. C. W. R. KNIGHT (MONDIALE)

TAIL AS A LEG

The woodpecker and the kangaroo have at least one feature in common; both use their heels and tails in the same way to form a tripod.

FOX

ALL PUFFED-UP

This Turkestan owl has been frightened and has gone "goose-flesh," with the result that its feathers are on end.

eaters or pangolins of Africa and Asia look far more like reptiles than mammals.

Nearly all beasts and many birds retain strong ridges of hair above the eyes, and numerous long hairs round the nose and lips. These are scientifically known as antennæ, more popularly as "whiskers," and serve as organs of feeling.

HAIR AS WEAPON

Strangest of all uses perhaps to which hair may be converted is the formation of a tool and a weapon by compression.

Nature has gathered together the hair upon the rhinoceros's nose to form the familiar "horn," a structure sometimes reaching a yard long, and equally serviceable for digging roots, guiding a refractory infant in the way it should go, or charging an enemy, which appears to be its primary avocation. True horn, it may be mentioned, such as tips our fingers and toes, surmounts the cow's head, forms the horse's hoof or encases the armadillo is simply an intensification of the skin, a corn become armour.

How hard a substance hairs may form if gathered in sufficient numbers and subjected to great pressure can be gathered from examining one of those " hair balls " which are sometimes found in the digestive systems of horses and cattle. These calculi may reach a foot in diameter, and can only be cut through with a sharp saw. They accumulate as the result of continually licking the coat.

WAR OF WITS

When the first birds and mammals brought into being body machines so much more complex than those of the reptiles, the latter far outnumbered the new-comers, and were often immeasurably their superiors in size and strength. Long before the encroaching cold came to the aid of bird and beast by wiping out the giants, the odds were on the smaller animals.

It has been suggested that they helped in the extinction of the dinosaurs by digging out and eating their eggs. This is more than likely, for the whole story of the mammals at least reads like the saga of a war of wits. They owe their present supremacy to a heightening of all the sensibilities, and with them, and as a natural corollary, of the intelligence.

The senses overlap, or merge together, and cannot very well be isolated; touch and hearing, taste and smell for instance are practically interchangeable. For example, if we pass a heap of burning refuse, we are not only very aware of the smell, but often of a noticeable " taste in the mouth." Similarly, when the Guards' band passes, the drums, that make conversation difficult, send a " thrill " up our coat sleeve or walking stick. The crash of a big gun feels like a slap in the face. Almost certainly one of the first senses to be acquired was that of touch. It must have been very active in those primitive scraps of life, the protozoa or animalcula, creatures quite devoid of sight or hearing.

FORFEITED FOR CIVILIZATION

In the course of his development man, and especially civilized man, has largely forfeited some of the senses which mean so much to the lower animals, but almost every part of his system is acutely sensitive to touch, and by it he acquires impressions of every kind. His senses of smell and taste are called chemical senses, but they are still to a certain degree senses of touch. Particular organs receive the impact of molecules, infinitely minute particles

DR. GRAF ZEDTWITZ (MONDIALE)

ALMOST BUT NOT ENTIRELY NAKED

The pigmy hippopotamus has a few hairs, relics of a distant past. Ordinarily these are not noticeable; but it has been observed that specimens kept at Whipsnade increased the length of their hairs with the approach of winter.

PLOUGHING WITH A WATER BUFFALO IN HAWAII

The amount of hair an animal wears nearly always depends on climatic conditions, and increased output often follows migration to colder climes. In some cases heredity is the dominant factor; water buffaloes, for instance, remain naked in the coldest climate.

of chemical substances, which come to us from the surrounding air, or our food and drink.

Man has no great cause for self-congratulation as regards his nose. He has adorned or mutilated it at the dictates of fashion, but has allowed to sink into insignificance the function for which it was primarily intended, that of smell. Tea tasters and chemists still make some effort to preserve and cultivate the faculty, but such persons are in the minority. The human nose is of small account beside the eye and ear.

SMELL AND TASTE

To appreciate how intimately smell and taste are associated, one has only to securely close the nose, shut the eyes and then attempt to distinguish between such similar substances as beef and mutton, plain cake and bread, or pear and parsnip. Both senses can function only when moisture is present, so that minute particles of matter may impress themselves on the mucous membranes of the nose, or the taste buds at the back of the tongue.

There is no doubt that these senses are present in the more primitive animals, insects, molluscs, and so on, but they vary much in degree, and often their seat is extremely problematic. A sense of smell seems sometimes to lie in an insect's antennæ or feelers, and also in the lobster's "horns." Taste in these creatures appears to be very crude; anything sweet or pungent will appeal to most insects, and putrefaction is apparently the lobster's ideal. A sea anemone will seize a pebble and even swallow it before finally rejecting it.

Even in vertebrates a sense of smell or taste is not confined to the nose and tongue. Some fish can taste by means of the finger-like barbels depending from the jaws; some can even smell through their breast fins.

EXPERIMENTS WITH FISHES

The appreciation of either flavours or odours may be deadened by drought or even extreme hunger. A bad cold puts our noses out of action, and very dry air also dulls its edge. Experiments with pollack at Plymouth Aquarium showed them to be hypersensitive

P. A. TAVERNER (MONDIALE)

AMERICAN PORCUPINE

Old-world porcupines have a certain amount of hair mixed up with their spines, but in American varieties hair sometimes completely covers the spines.

to odours when not particularly hungry, but when ravenous they showed complete approval of worms soaked in alcohol, paraffin and other non-appetizers. Isaac Walton records a cunning old angler who enjoyed wonderful success as the result of soaking his bait in oil distilled from ivy berries.

In the higher vertebrates, the reptiles, birds and mammals there is always present a tolerably well defined organ of smell, and by its size and position, as also by the so-called smelling bulbs of the brain, we can form a good idea of the creature's susceptibility to anything in the wind.

HOW SMELL IMPRESSIONS ARE RECEIVED

Lizards and crocodiles probably smell better than snakes, except for the remarkable egg-eating snake of South Africa. This reptile, with a head no larger than one's finger tip, can engulf a hen's egg, but it will rather starve than accept an egg ever so slightly stale. The sense of smell is at a low standard in birds, and finds its highest development in the kiwi, just as the parrot has the most delicately adjusted sense of taste, and the snipe and duck that of touch.

On the mammalian face the nose sits

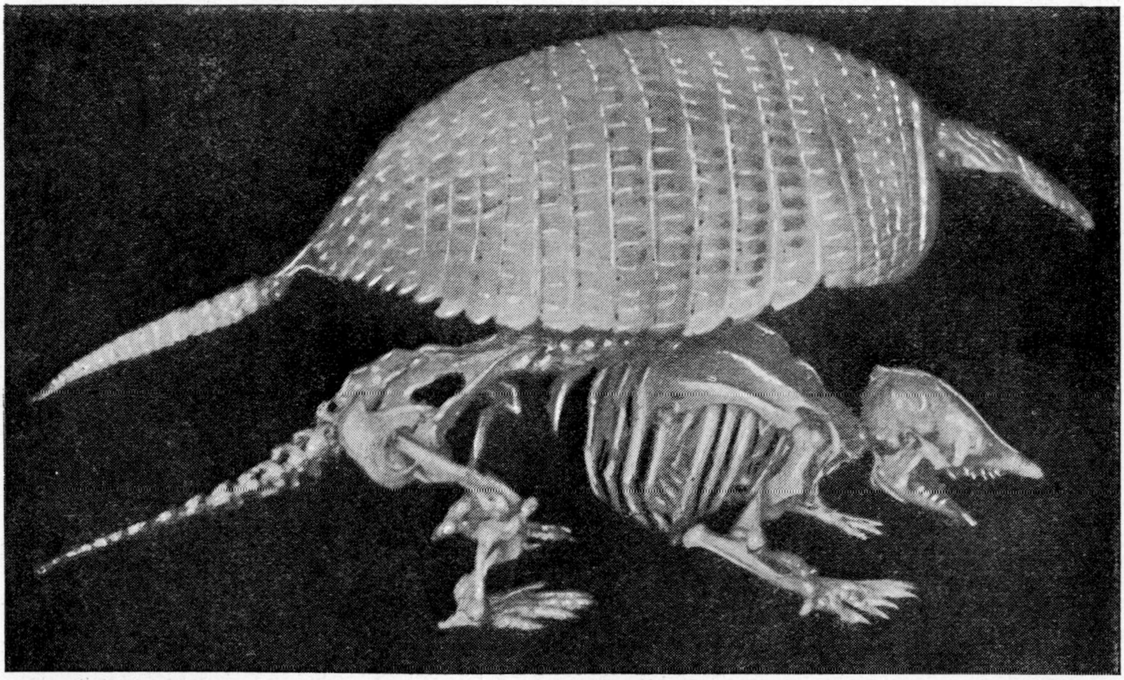

HAROLD BASTIN

CAN ROLL ITSELF INTO A BALL

Since his body is covered with hard plates, the armadillo can dispense with the fur coats so many other animals find necessary. It is the only creature capable of rolling itself into an unwindable ball. Here the carapace or outer covering has been removed to show the skeleton.

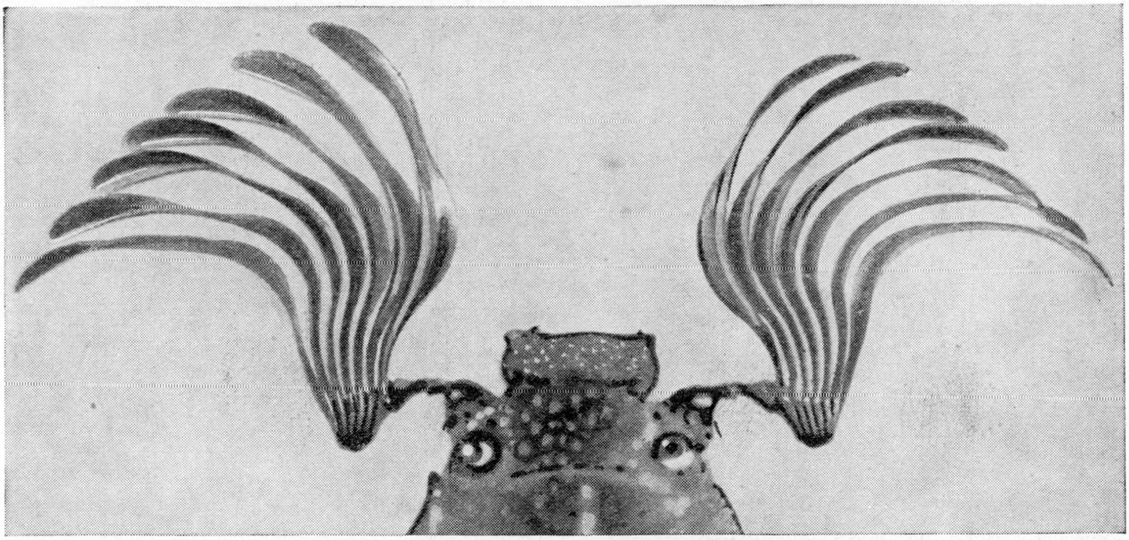

HAROLD BASTIN

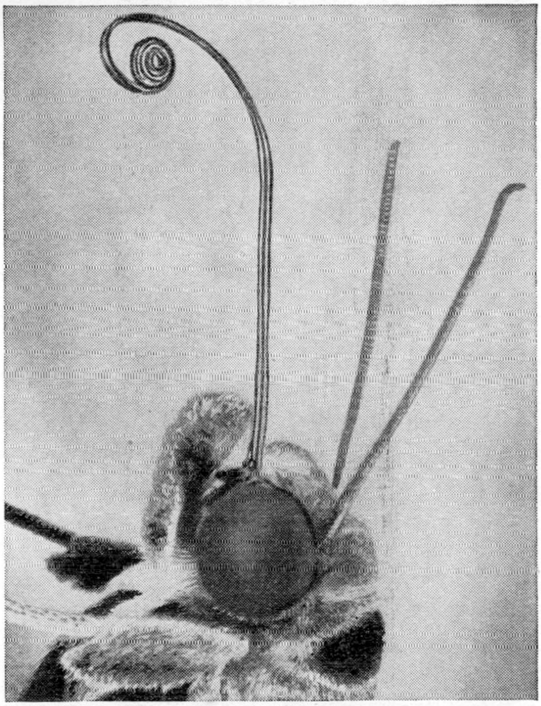

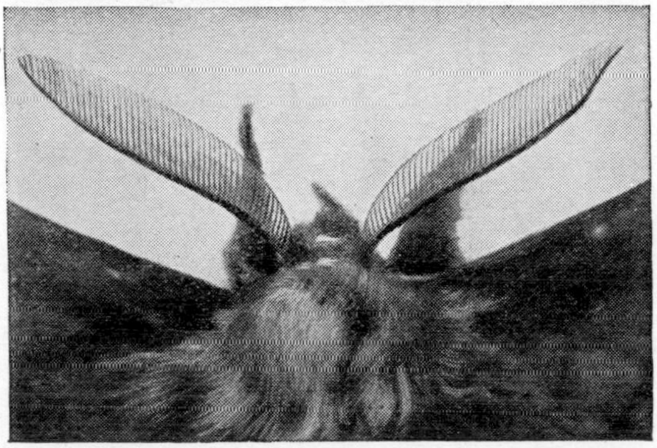

INSECTS' ORGANS OF SMELL
Top: antennæ of the may-bug or cockchafer. Middle: extended proboscis and antennæ of the oleander hawk-moth. Bottom: feathered antennæ of the male drinker moth. In its antennæ probably lies an insect's sense of smell.

enthroned. By its owner's standards it is often the crowning glory, at once a sense organ of rare receptivity, a tool and an adornment. In all mammalian noses there are two parallel chambers, each containing a cylindrical bone most delicately sculptured so that it suggests a sponge or intricate piece of filigree work. In the ox each of these bones is as big as a man's two fists. Over these spongy bones are spread the soft membranes upon which smell impressions are received and passed to the olfactory lobes of the brain—the odour office of the animal concerned.

SCENTED FOR MILES

Every hunter knows the importance of keeping to windward of his quarry, and many authentic tales are told of deer and arctic foxes scenting food or foes from a distance of several miles. Today the pig and dog are still employed to hunt truffles by scent. The dog's memory has been aptly likened to "a card index catalogue of smells."

The whale, though far from figuring at the lower end of the mammalian scale, makes the human nose seem by comparison a magnificent organ of smell. In a whale or porpoise the nostrils, placed on top of the head, are just convenient outlets for spent breath. As organs whereby to catch the odours in which the sea

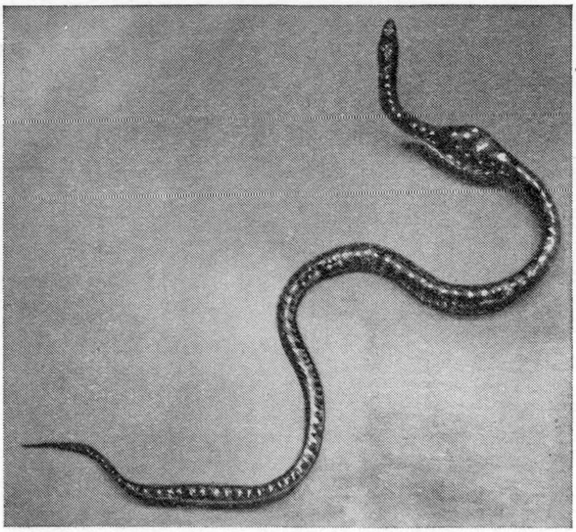

W. S. BERRIDGE, F.Z.S. (MONDIALE)

FASTIDIOUS REPTILE

The egg-eating snake has a sense of smell so acute that it would starve before touching stale eggs.

must abound, they have virtually ceased to exist.

Man is the only animal to augment the natural beauties of his nose by adding paint and powder or piercing it with rings and quills. His next of kin, the monkeys, appear to be the only mammals who value a nose from the decorative standpoint, and amongst the monkeys " nose wear " is nearly always an exclusively male prerogative. A notable instance is the male mandrill's scarlet muzzle, set off by fluted cheeks of vivid azure.

STRETCHING THE ELEPHANT'S NOSE

The male proboscis monkey of Borneo starts life with a snub nose, but ends with a pendulous nose that must surely be an embarrassment at meal times. Almost as grotesque is the snub-nosed monkey of Asia, with a retroussé nasal organ pointing to the sky. Also unique in their way are the glaring white noses common to some of the guenon or face-making monkeys of Central Africa. It has been suggested, if not actually proved, that these noses, gleaming like traffic lights in the eternal twilight of the rain forests, help members of a troupe to keep each other in sight, on the principle of the rabbit's white "bob" and the deer's horse-shoe-marked rump.

Every mammalian nose is beautifully attuned to its owner's requirements. In Kipling's famous *Just-So Story* you will remember " the elephant's child " has his " mere smear nose " pulled out to trunk size by a crocodile and a python, the one hauling at the tip, the other lashed to the elephant's hind legs and pulling in the opposite direction. The actual process of stretching the elephant's nose covered more than forty million years, and the most interesting feature of this wonderful adventure in facial adjustment is that the elephant was not alone in the endeavour. A host of other creatures were always striving in the same direction, but the elephant won the prize for the world's longest nose, and it appears as though he will retain it.

NOSE AS SAFETY DEVICE

Living pigs and tapirs are competitors in the great nose race, and the pigs in particular have made good progress. Once a crack is found in a macadam-paved yard, a wild pig will undertake to uproot the whole surface. This has happened in more than one zoo. The rhino's highly prehensile upper lip is a hint at the trunk's first beginnings; it almost exactly imitates what must have been the appearance of the upper lip in the mœritherium, the little hog-sized forerunner of the elephant.

In fossil beasts a study of the nasal bones permits experts to reconstruct accurately the nose that once covered them. Thus we know that in South America, a million or more years ago, something like trunks were developed by now vanished elephant monsters, big ungainly camels, and that strangest of all South American products, the giant sloth.

The modern moose of Canada and Alaska and the bizarre Saiga antelope are alone amongst living ruminants with trunk-like noses. No

SPENCER ARNOLD

NOT MERELY ORNAMENTAL

The kiwi's nose is the most efficient olfactory organ to be found among birds. It is also useful for grubbing out insects.

doubt these are of some help in grasping foliage, but it is believed the primary intention of the downward projected nostrils is to exclude driven sand and ice particles from the delicate nasal cavity. The sea elephant's inflatable trunk is purely for ornament.

One detects strivings in the direction of a trunk amongst the various little insectivorous mammals, and such a structure must be of very practical service to a beast who lives by nosing out the unwilling worm and pill bug from its earthen retreat. The common shrew has a very trunk-like nose, for ever restlessly questing for food and tasting the air, just like the trunk of an elephant. The nose of the South African elephant shrew does actually dangle far below the chin, in approved Jumbo fashion.

FOX

BANDED ANT EATER

This Australian marsupial uses his nose for digging into ant hills. The American great ant eater and the South African aardvark are very similar.

MORE HINDRANCE THAN HELP

The moles, nearly related to the shrews, also develop long noses, the usefulness of which is easily understandable. The nose of the North American star-nosed mole, however, is something of an enigma. It is surrounded by a ring of more than a score of finger-like expansions that suggest more hindrance than help in excavating operations. Perhaps they have something in common with the extraordinary nasal appendages seen in so many bats.

Great Britain's native species have very normal faces, but some tropic kinds suggest the ferocious masks of South Sea devil-dancers. The animal world offers no counterparts to these amazing fleshy appendages which often render the wearer's face unrecognizable as a face at all. Owing to the extreme difficulty of studying bat ways their use can only be surmised, and the most plausible suggestion is that they serve as crude aerials which pick up vibrations or give warning of coming events hidden to the senses of sight, smell and hearing.

WIDE WORLD

SEA ELEPHANT'S INFLATABLE TRUNK

The purpose of the inflatable trunk, or proboscis, of the sea elephant is entirely ornamental.

TONGUE NOT AN ORGAN OF TASTE

As already noticed, the tongue proper is not an organ of taste. Shut your eyes tightly, put out your tongue to its full extent, and get someone to drop a pinch of salt or pepper on the tip of it. Until you withdraw the tongue and bring the titbit in contact with your taste buds, it might be anything—dust or flour.

The tongue's job is to " handle " the food, to roll it into a bolus and then tip it backwards into the gullet. Next time sheep's head figures on your menu, look at the back of the tongue and you will see it is supported by a framework of quite large and solid bones, arranged somewhat in the form of a tuning-fork or a pair

MARKHAM (MONDIALE)

SHREW'S TRUNK-LIKE NOSE

The common shrew uses his nose as does the elephant his trunk. Both animals are ever searching for food.

of tongs. The prongs or handles are fitted on to the back of the skull, the whole embedded in powerful muscles that thrust the tongue in and out, like a piston.

TONGUE ANCHORED TO BREAST BONE

This arrangement is quite good enough for the general run of vertebrates, but there are some tongues which need to be thrust out so far that special kinds of roots are required to give them the right impetus. The ant eater's long worm-like tongue has roots anchored to its breast bone.

Woodpeckers and humming birds use the tongue either to extract insects from fissures in bark and wood or to pick them daintily from the depths of large tropic bell flowers. For such work the tongue needs to be pushed out with great force, and in both these kinds of birds the roots of the tongue actually curl up over the back of the head and are fixed at the base of the bill, just between the eyes.

SPINES AS A STRAINER

Most mammalian tongues are soft and fleshy, but in those of cats the surface is covered with spikes for rasping away scraps of meat, and in many fish, and such fish-eating birds as penguins, the whole tongue is one mass of long spines used for preventing the escape of a slippery and unwilling mouthful, once it is seized.

Another wonderful tongue is that of the flamingo. In this bird the tongue fills the whole of the capacious beak, and is fringed with soft spines. The flamingo fills its mouth with mud and water, and using the tongue as a strainer forces the unwanted material out at the sides of the mouth, leaving only such shrimps and pond snails as the mud may contain.

In the giraffe and sloth the tongue serves as a hand for grasping and tearing off bunches of leaves, and in one group of primates, the lemurs, it even acts as a toothpick. Lemurs have very fine and complex teeth, which easily

DR. PAUL WOLFF (MONDIALE)

LONG-TONGUED AND LONG-LEGGED FLAMINGOS

Fringed with soft spines and so long that it fills the capacious beak, the flamingo's tongue serves as a tool whereby to force unwanted material out of the sides of its mouth, leaving behind snails and the like.

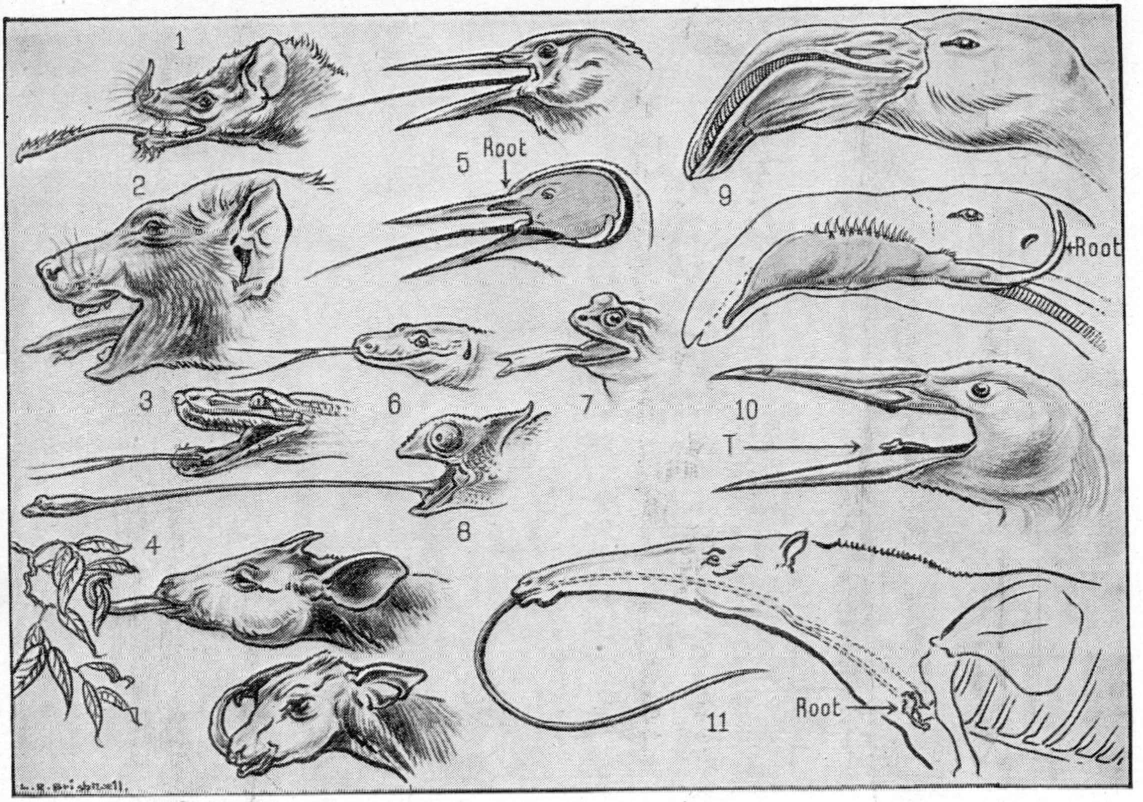

TONGUES FOR EVERY PURPOSE

1. *Tropical bat.* 2. *Double tongue of lemur.* 3. *Snake.* 4. *Okapi; used as leaf-picker and face-flannel.* 5. *Woodpecker.* 6. *Lizard.* 7. *Frog.* 8. *Chameleon.* 9. *Flamingo.* 10. *Gannet.* 11. *Ant eater; roots of tongue attached to breast bone.*

collect pips from the animal's fruit diet or become clogged with hairs as the result of much grooming. On the underside of the tongue is what virtually serves as another tongue, smaller and with the tip frayed out to form a rake or comb, which being thrust between the teeth dislodges oddments, and so saves the teeth from decay.

WATCH-SPRING TONGUES

Many invertebrates have tongue-like organs which are worked on totally different principles from those controlling the tongues of beasts, birds and reptiles. Moths and butterflies have long watch-spring tongues that can be shot out much as the " paper tongues " or " ladies' terrifiers " still popular on occasions of public rejoicing. Organs of impressive magnitude, they seem quite insignificant beside the wonderful ribbon tongues used by snails to rasp away vegetation or to eat out piecemeal some defenceless clam from the seeming security of its shell.

The tongue can easily be drawn out from a cooked limpet. It is a tough horny ribbon half as long again as the entire animal. A low-power microscope reveals it as being set with hundreds of teeth arranged in ranks and literally marching twelve abreast as the sea snail pushes its tongue over some weed-encrusted rock.

The common garden snail has one hundred and five teeth in each of its one hundred and thirty-five rows, making a total of fourteen thousand one hundred and seventy-five teeth.

OVER TWELVE THOUSAND TEETH

The common pond snail has over twelve thousand teeth. In squids and octopuses the " tongue-teeth " are in the form of a horny beak, exactly reproducing that of a parrot, but often much larger. They form a large part of ambergris, the valuable secretion found in the intestine of the sperm whale, which feeds on cuttlefish.

These examples by no means exhaust the possibilities of a tongue. Insect-eating creatures such as the chameleon and frog have adhesive tongues which literally act as fly papers. The chameleon's can be shot forth to a distance equalling its owner's length; the frog's worked with equal velocity reverses the normal arrangement of a tongue, for its roots are attached to the inner side of the lower lip, with the tip dangling down the amphibian's neck. When a fly is sighted the whole contraption completes a half circle, catches the insect, and then tosses it into the frog's interior.

Save in the chameleon, reptile tongues serve only one simple purpose, that of a probe. The forked tip goes in advance of the owner, exploring like the stick of a blind man.

SECRETS OF HEARING

" He that hath ears to hear, let him hear," cried the Teacher of old, but science has given a wide implication to the term hearing, and vast numbers of animals hear without any ears at all. The line of demarcation between sound and touch is a fine one. Sound, as we understand the term, is the reception of certain vibrations agitating the atmosphere, and hearing is therefore a kind of feeling.

Receptivity to sound varies enormously, and in the appreciation of sounds, as in the appreciation of smells, some animals—the dog for instance—leave us far behind. The minute and complex bones of the inner ear pick up vibrations impinging on the drum, such apparatus being a vertebrate monopoly. But it is far from universal. In whales this contrivance is reduced to two big shell-like bones; sometimes each is as large as a man's two fists.

SOUNDS MAN CANNOT HEAR

Carnivorous beasts have the hearing installation contained in two big inflated bulbs, and it seems likely that such animals may be sensitive to sounds entirely lost upon the keenest human ears.

Snakes have no hearing apparatus at all, and the tuneless efforts on gourd flute of the so-called charmer are just a little piece of professional bluff. The snake really " dances " by following the rhythmic swayings of its charmer's body. In most bony fishes there are placed within the cranium two flattened bones, popularly termed ear bones, but as much concerned in maintaining the creature's balance as in responding to vibrations. Injury to one of these makes the fish swim lop-sided,

W. S. BERRIDGE, F.Z.S. (MONDIALE)

BLOOD-SUCKING VAMPIRE-BAT

In nothing are certain members of the bat tribe so remarkable as in their nasal appendages. Zoologists are in doubt concerning the evolution and uses of these organs. They may serve as aerials for picking up vibrations.

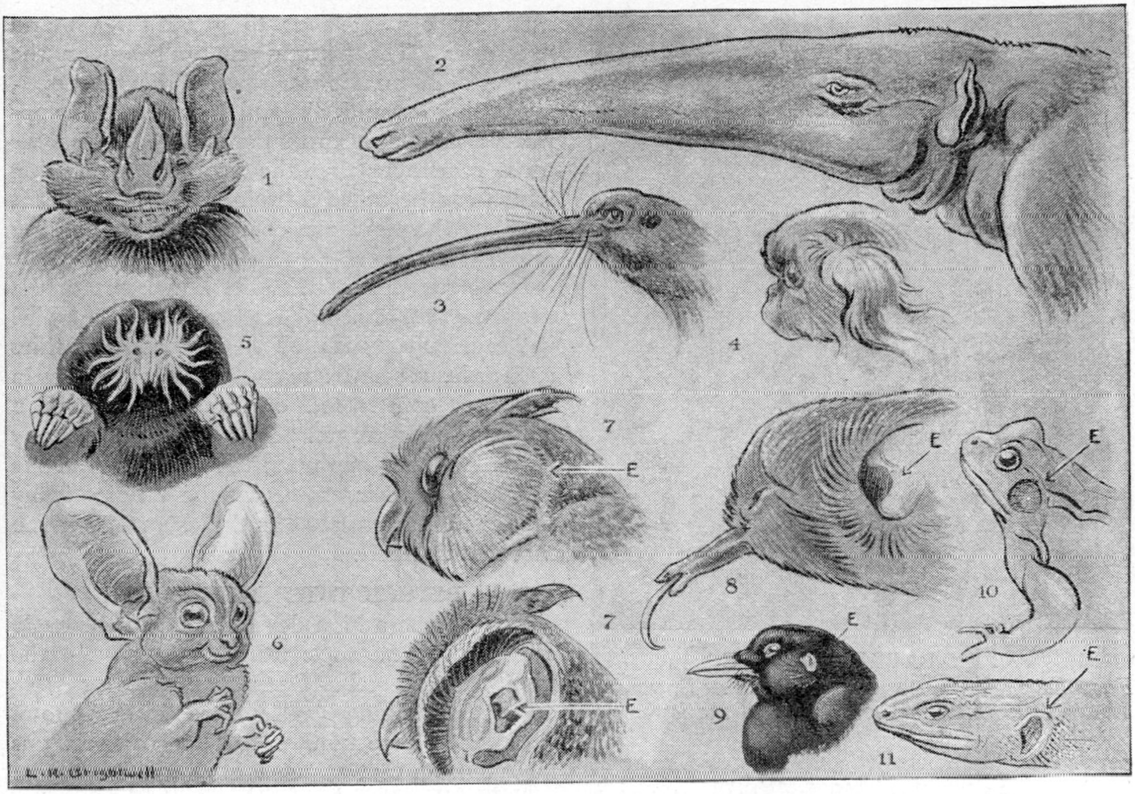

NOSES AND EARS IN RICH VARIETY

1. *Bat.* 2. *Great ant eater.* 3. *Kiwi.* 4. *Pekinese spaniel.* 5. *Star-nosed mole.* 6. *Galago.* 7. *Long-eared owl; feathers turned back to show ear.* 8. *Echidna; hair turned back to show ear.* 9. *Blackbird; showing ear.* 10. *Frog.* 11. *Lizard.*

and the reader may have noticed that some deaf persons have great trouble in maintaining their equilibrium on a bicycle.

The receptivity of fish to sound waves is still the subject of experiments. At the Plymouth Aquarium, for instance, a buzzer was installed in a food box within a tank, and various fishes soon learnt to rush to the spot as soon as the buzzer was set in motion. One young codling, however, having once grasped the significance of buzzer and box, took up permanent residence in the latter, presumably being determined to take no chances.

HEARING WITHOUT EARS

Hearing of a kind can be enjoyed without anything approximating to an ear as ordinarily understood. The osiphone was a device to give relief to the totally deaf, the apparatus being placed on the elbow, or even the back of the neck and so conveying vibrations to the afflicted person. During recent years Dr. Calman, of the British Museum, ascertained that lobsters possessed what he named auditory hairs on certain limbs, which connected with special nerves and so transmitted vibrations in the water to the animal's brain.

Hearing is most unevenly dispensed amongst the insects. It is most noticeable, and not unnaturally, in species that themselves produce sounds. Grasshoppers and crickets have auditory drums on their thighs or other limbs, and the mosquito—principally the male—hears through its antennæ.

OUTWITTING THE MOSQUITO

The male mosquito is always listening for the high-pitched buzzing of his lady-love, but he is also attracted by the notes of a violin, the human voice, or the whine of a dynamo. This last susceptibility was turned by a clever engineer to the mosquito's undoing. He rigged up an electrically charged apparatus the song of which so pleased mosquitoes that they hurled themselves upon it and were straightway killed.

In the illustration are shown some typical outer ears of mammals, their size and shape sufficiently indicative of the wearer's hearing

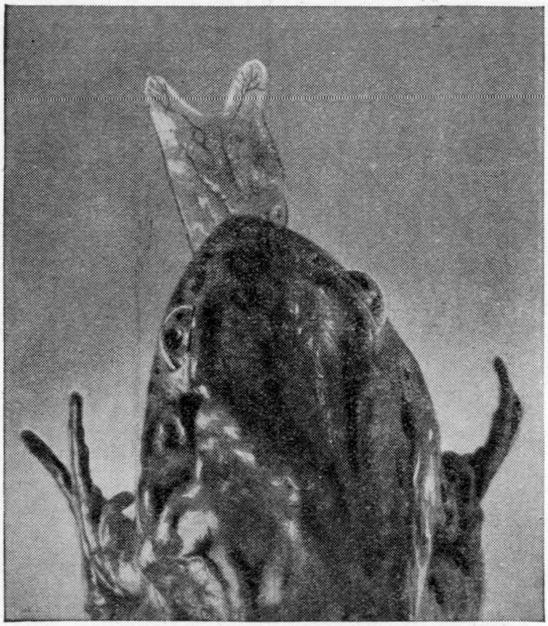

HAROLD BASTIN

FLY-PAPER TONGUE

Frogs have adhesive tongues which act as fly papers. The roots are attached to the side of the lower lip.

capacities. Amongst the birds' ears the owl's easily take pride of place, and it is interesting to note how bird-like is the ear of that reptile-bird-beast the porcupine ant eater or echidna. The " psychic " aspects of animal hearing will be noticed later.

Sight, so vital a sense to ourselves and most mammals, is here placed last because it was probably the last of the senses to attain perfection. Until we come to the jointed animals and the mollusca, true sight is practically non-existent amongst the invertebrates. Worms, for instance, although sensitive to light, have no kind of seeing apparatus, neither have the starfishes and their allies, the anemones and jelly-fish, nor the countless hosts of the animalcula. Insects, with their often large and compound eyes, turning hundreds of facets to the world, probably have far keener sight than the crustacea.

TWO ROWS OF EYES

A crab is conscious only of dim shapes impinging on its retina, and so always assumes a fighting pose on the principle of safety first when confronted with almost any object, harmful or otherwise. In molluscs the seeing eye varies greatly. Octopods and cuttlefish, for example, have enormous hard, crystalline lenses, and from early times these have been used for ornament or to garnish idols and mummies. The homely scallop bears on the fringes of its mantle two rows of gleaming eyes, presenting a wonderfully high state of development almost akin to mammalian eyes, but we must remember that the scallop has nothing which can be called a brain, and the images it receives therefore are comparable to nothing in our experience.

Not even the redoubtable Hawk-eye of the Mohicans could compete with the average bird in keenness of vision. Birds and some reptiles such as lizards have a marvellous range-finder in the eye, constructed on the principle of a camera's diaphragm. It is a series of bony plates, working one upon the other so that the aperture in their centre can be automatically increased or decreased as the exigencies of the moment demand.

PYTHON WITH A GLASS EYE

They reach a high development in the eagle and hawk, and their utmost capacity in the night hunting owls. Such eyes, however, were eclipsed by some gigantic lizards in the Age of Reptiles. These monsters had bony diaphragms measuring a foot or more in diameter.

In nocturnal mammals and some reptiles, the pupil, which lets in the light and with it the image to the retina, can be contracted to a slit when day demands a mitigating of the light. In this connection an amusing incident

WIDE WORLD

WEAPONS OF THE PORCUPINE FISH

This formidable looking fish puffs itself up when attacked, and like its namesake erects its spines.

occurred at a certain zoo when a large python, losing an eye by accident, was fitted with a glass substitute. As a result, night found the reptile with apparently normal eyes, but by day the living eye of course contracted its pupil, the false never budged, and so day and night conditions were reflected simultaneously.

The loss of pigmentation which causes albinos often extends to the eyes. The blood vessels, unprotected by colour from the light, give to the eye its peculiar red or pinkish appearance, such an eye being painfully sensitive to strong lights. A zoo monkey thus afflicted was continually shading its eyes with one hand until relief was found for it by fitting the beast with smoked spectacles.

Thus far we have glanced at a few of the more obvious externals in animal make-up, and the wonderful changes which Nature has rung upon the same organ in various creatures, according to their needs. We will now consider some more generalized uses to which almost any part of an animal may be put—the age-old matters of offence and defence.

WEAPONS IN NATURE'S ARMOURY

Almost any part of an animal may be converted into a weapon. Horns and hoofs, teeth and claws are among the more obvious weapons in Nature's armoury, and in tracing their development it is interesting to note that, just as in the story of human warfare, each succeeding instrument of death brought into being the means for its repulsion or evasion.

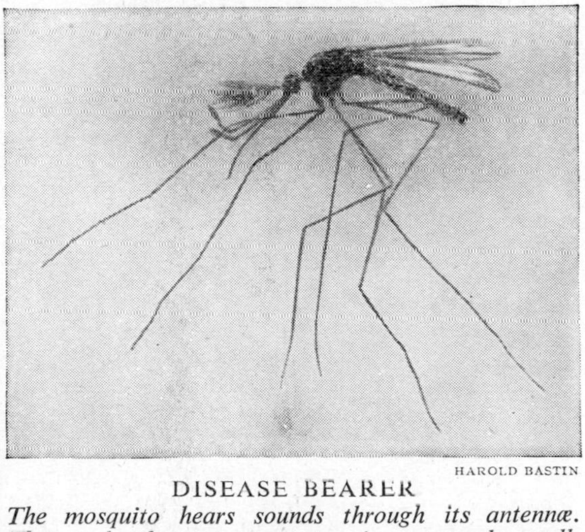

HAROLD BASTIN

DISEASE BEARER

The mosquito hears sounds through its antennæ. The male hearing apparatus is extremely well-developed.

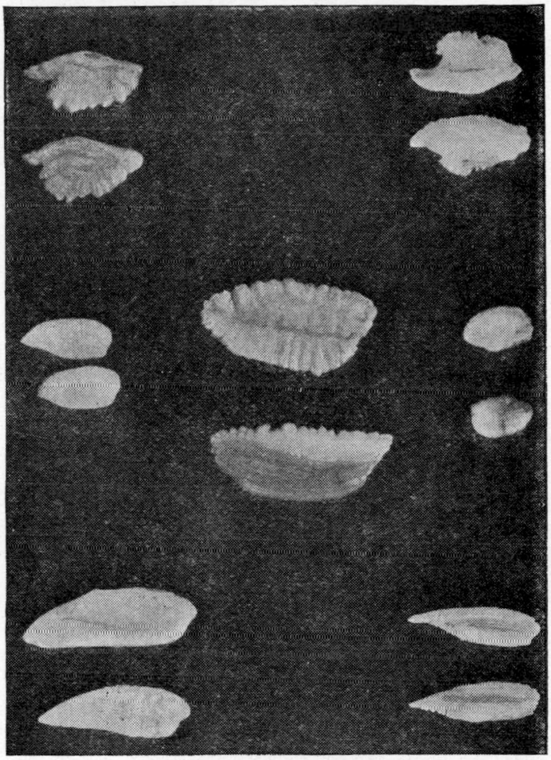

HAROLD BASTIN

EAR BONES OF FISH

Situated within the cranium, these bones are as valuable in maintaining balance as for hearing.

Knightly armour became at last so heavy as to defeat its own purpose, and in a study of the geologic past the moralist might find abundant material for a lecture on the futility of armaments. There is little doubt that the horns and shields of some of the dinosaurs became at last almost too cumbrous to navigate. Nature seems to have evolved one monstrous device after another and scrapped it, when at last it reached its peak. Vast horns and tusks fell, one after another, before more lightly armed animals whose feebler weapons held the field rather by their skill in usage than by their own weight.

DEER IN CONFLICT

Even today we see animal weapons turned against their possessors. The deer's antlers are exceedingly tough and springy, and when two bucks meet in conflict the horns easily become so interlocked that death by starvation or at the teeth and claws of wandering carnivores overtakes both champions.

Many of our most modern weapons were anticipated by Nature hundreds of millions of

DR. GRAF ZEDTWITZ (MONDIALE)

FATAL LURE OF THE BEAUTIFUL SEA ANEMONE

Though it shows no signs of knowing it, this fish is about to die. Within a few seconds the anemone's nettle-capsules will explode and harpoons will shoot out on long white threads to pierce the victim.

years before mankind appeared. The hollow-bodied sea anemones, jelly-fish, etc., sting, but their stings—crowding the delicate tentacles—have no analogy to the irritant hairs of nettles.

HOW JELLY-FISH STING

A high-power microscope reveals each sting as a barbed dart, with sharp flukes, folded close to a shaft to which is attached a neatly coiled line. Contact with a foe touches off the whole apparatus by means of a hair-trigger, and the barbed dart, suddenly expanded, plunges into living tissue. Shaft and line are dragged after it, and when hundreds of such darts find their way into a bather's blood stream, as when he collides with a big jelly-fish, it is small wonder he later suffers from irritant blisters. This fiendish little weapon largely parallels the gun and harpoon mounted on the prow of every whaler.

Some anemones fling out their darts in the form of long white threads, each charged with its little harpoons and coiled lines. Such threads will pour out at the sides of the common parasitic anemone always found on whelk shells tenanted by hermit crabs. Threads of another kind form the weapons of the big black sea cucumber, sometimes found in rock fissures at extreme low tide.

Disturb one of this kind and yards of long white threads shoot out from its hinder end, suggesting the streamers we use at jollifications. But the sea cucumber's streamers are elastic and adhesive, and a big lobster once involved amongst them is rendered impotent, bound claw, legs and tail past all possibility of movement. It takes an hour or more for the threads to rot, and by the time the lobster, if not suffocated, regains its freedom, the antagonist has leisurely crawled to safety.

BEETLES THAT USE GAS

The throwing of missiles is an art that does not reach its highest perfection amongst monkeys. There are certain soldier white ants or termites that squirt fluid at a foe, the said fluid hardening on contact with the air so that a luckless spider thus sprayed is literally petrified. A tiny lizard of the Californian deserts squirts blood from the corner of each eye, and several mammals beside the skunk can eject nauseating fluids.

HAROLD BASTIN

MARINE LODGING-HOUSE WITH MANY TENANTS

Numerous animals making use of the house left by a whelk. Inside is a hermit crab, and on the outer walls tenaciously cling two sea anemones (one large, one small) and numbers of barnacles and worm-tubes.

Explosives would appear to be the secret of one class of creatures only, a family of small and obscure beetles that have earned the title of bombardiers. Several species are native to Great Britain, and if disturbed, as by upturning a stone beneath which they may be hiding, amaze the obtruder with a volley of sharp pops followed by little puffs of acrid smoke. The beetle ejects a drop of volatile fluid which ignites on contact with the air, and a well-aimed discharge may lay a big cockroach on its back.

FISH WITH WATER GUN

One fish at least has evolved the water gun, but rather as a legitimate means of livelihood than as a weapon pure and simple. The little Malayan archer fish squirts a jet of water from its spout-shaped lips at any chance fly perching on water-side vegetation, and the insect, fairly struck, is quickly engulfed as it falls upon the surface of the water. Rarely does the archer fail to hit the target.

Poisons of all kinds are widely distributed throughout the animal world. Many of us have had first-hand experience of insect poisons such as those of the ant, which consists largely of formic acid, or of the mosquito, bee and wasp. In the last mentioned the poison is conveyed from two glands, one containing an alkaline, the other an acid fluid.

SPIDERS KILL BY POISON

All spiders kill their prey by means of poison injected through their hollow fangs, but only the venom of a few large tropical species affects human beings. In the mollusca, poison glands and fangs are confined to one family of sea snails, the gorgeous cones of tropic waters, and their venom may have serious, though never fatal consequences.

Amongst the vertebrates quite a number of fishes carry poison glands, notably various sharks, the notorious sting rays, the chimæras, the North American catfishes known as mad-toms, and the weever fish. Two kinds of weever fish are found in England, the great weever measuring over a foot and the lesser

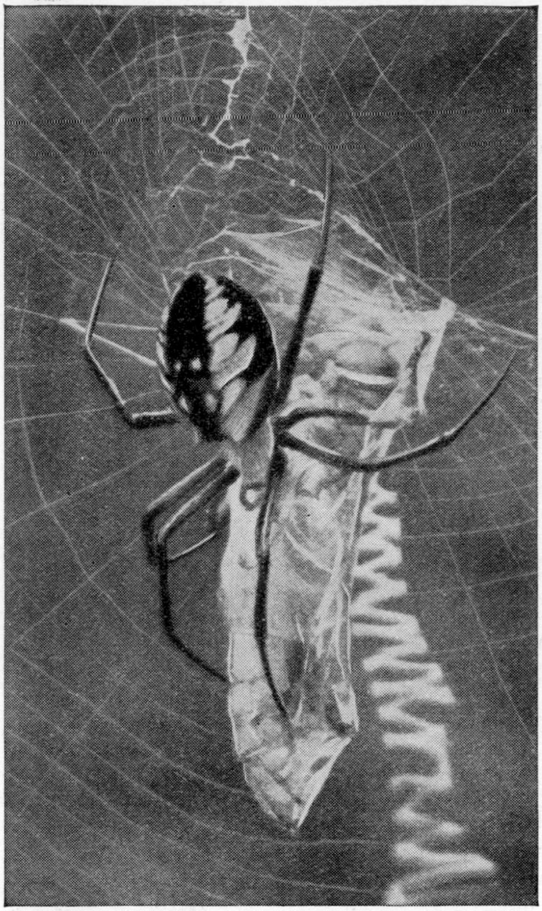

HAROLD BASTIN

EIGHT EYES AND EIGHT LEGS

Top: Golden spider trussing-up a grasshopper which ventured near its web. Bottom: House spider. Its eight eyes enable it to see in more than one direction at once. In the background are its eight legs. All spiders kill their prey by means of poison injected through their hollow fangs.

weever of only a few inches long. The latter abounds in sandy bays, and carries hollow spines on its gill covers and back fin which connect with poison glands. If a person bathing treads on one of these fish as it lies half buried in the sand a very painful wound results.

The dangerous qualities of these little fish must have been known long ago, for the name is derived from the Latin *vipera*, signifying a viper or a serpent. One sometimes sees the notice " 'Ware Weevers " displayed on pier heads; and in France, where the big weever is commonly eaten, a special law has been passed enforcing the removal of the spines before the fish is exposed for sale.

SNAKE TOLL OF HUMAN LIVES

Most of the amphibians, such as newts and toads, exude poisonous secretion in the warty protruberances covering their skins, and even today the newt and toad have bad names in some remote country districts. Normally one suffers no inconvenience from handling these otherwise harmless creatures, but experiment has shown that if their secretions enter a cut or the mouth very painful results follow, and the fluids when injected under the skins of small mammals even cause death. Anyone who has seen a dog confronted with a toad, will have guessed the latter has something about it which renders it a highly distasteful mouthful.

About one-third of the one thousand five hundred-odd species of snakes now living are poisonous in varying degree. The viper, found in Great Britain, inflicts no more than half a dozen " stings " on human beings perhaps in the course of a year, although its venom is more often than not fatal to dogs. In contrast to this, the kraits and cobras of India alone account for some twenty thousand human lives annually.

ONE VENOMOUS LIZARD

The poison is derived from specially modified salivary glands, forming two large almond-shaped bodies, one on either side of the head. In a few snakes, such as the night adders, they extend down the interior as far as the heart.

Always the poison is injected through hollow teeth in the upper jaw, usually by a lightning stroke or a chewing action. A few snakes actually squirt the venom from their fangs, a notorious example being that of the deadly South African spitting cobra or ring-hals. Its venom invariably causes blindness if it enters

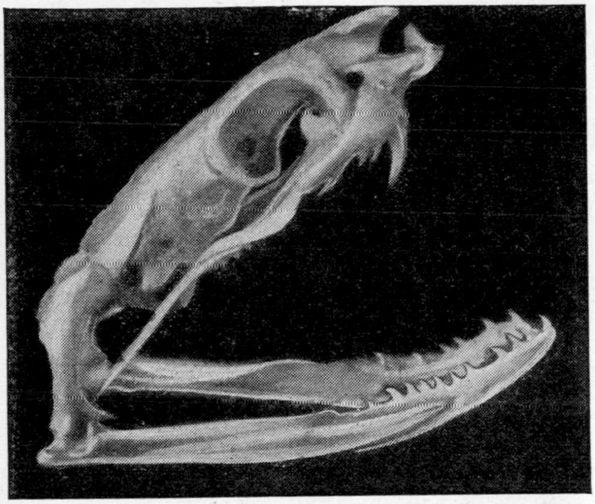

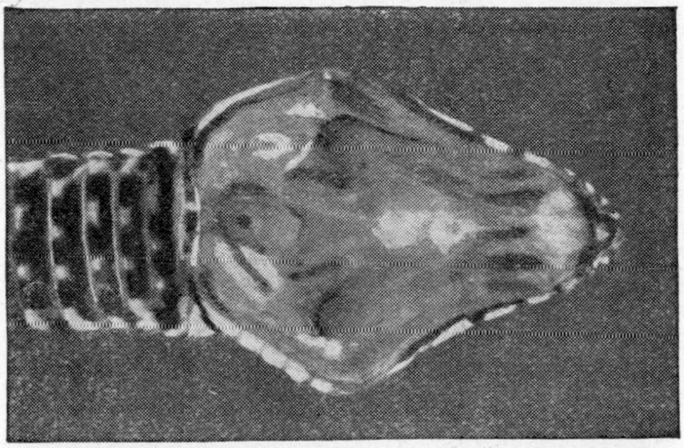

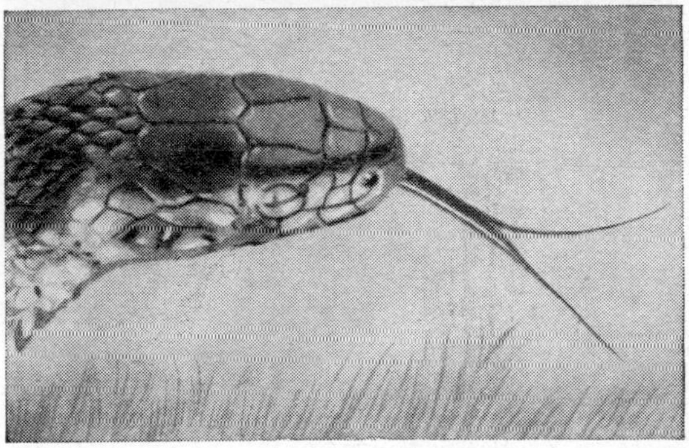

HAROLD BASTIN

REPTILIAN WEAPONS

Above: Skull of the hamadryad, showing poison fang. Top right: Adder's head. The mouth is open with the lower mandible pulled back to reveal position of poison glands. The adder is the only venomous snake in Great Britain. It is able to inject poison six times before its reserves are exhausted. Bottom right: Head of common grass-snake. It is non-poisonous.

the eyes, and should it penetrate a cut, death follows in an hour or two. Only one venomous lizard is known, the Gila monster or heloderm of Arizona. It possesses glands and fangs like those of a snake, but rarely if ever causes human fatalities.

Electricity played its part in the World War, and is a recognized instrument of death in the penal codes of several countries. In Nature its use as a weapon seems to be confined to fishes, having been evolved by several quite unrelated groups, each having batteries in an entirely different portion of the system. The outstanding electrical fishes are the electric eel, which is only eel-like in general shape, the electric catfish, and various skates and rays.

FISHES THAT GENERATE ELECTRICITY

The so-called eel of Brazilian waters has the tail muscles—which constitute four-fifths of the body—converted into powerful batteries, a six-foot eel being able to give a shock of several hundred volts. At New York Aquarium one of these fishes was used to light an aeroplane beacon, ring a bell, and even launch an aeroplane.

The catfish of Arabia has the entire body wall converted into an electric organ, the fish being invested with one big battery as with a garment. It uses this weapon, not like most electric fish to stun its prey but to shock other fishes into disgorging their meals, which it appropriates. Something like this is seen in the unattractive diet of the Squa gull, which forces other birds to disgorge by the cruder methods of mere bullying.

The electric rays, common in all warm seas, often visit English waters during a heat wave, and notify their presence to anyone treading on them as they lie buried in sand in a very dramatic manner. The French very aptly call this fish "M'sieur Touchez." A big electric or torpedo ray can give a shock of about thirty volts, the batteries being arranged in the form of hexagonal cylinders laid out vertically in two groups, one on either side of the body. When a fish, such as a grey mullet, swims unsuspectingly above a half-concealed torpedo, the latter rises, "shocks" the mullet by deliberately cannoning into it, and then engulfs the prize before it can recover.

MASSAGE BY TORPEDO RAY

In olden times the torpedo ray was made to furnish a crude form of vibro-massage, rheumatic sufferers being required to stand bare-footed on the fish as long as the medical adviser or their own powers of endurance dictated. At Brighton many years ago a wily old longshoreman happening to catch a big torpedo, exhibited it as a catch-penny device by inviting all and sundry to " guess its weight." Nobody held the fish long enough to form an opinion until a knowledgeable bystander picked up the fish by the tip of its tail, the only insulated portion.

The phrenologist has rushed in where science fears to tread. He has mapped out the brain into certain well defined areas, each of which he claims to be in charge of some particular attribute—courage, religious zeal, artistic capacity, and so on. To the scientific brain specialist the mass of nervous tissue controlling an animal organism is still largely an uncharted sea, full of mysterious currents and unplumbed depths.

No mechanism, natural or man-made, can even approach the brain in intricacy or subtlety. We will here attempt only to point out the varying capacity of the brain, and the work it can do. Many of the misunderstandings and heated controversies of our times are the result of misconceptions concerning animal mentality as opposed to human.

BIG AND LITTLE BRAINS

In the two great divisions of the animal world, the vertebrates and the invertebrates, the mammals on the one hand and the insects on the other, have outstripped all competitors. Although the insects immeasurably exceed all other invertebrates in their varied ways of life and organizations, which often seem to mimic our own, their mental capacities are exceedingly limited—by their size. The largest insect has an infinitely smaller brain than the tiniest fish. As a result the insect brain works within the narrowest limits; it is like a machine fashioned to do certain things, and those only.

When the unforeseen happens, or initiative is called for, one might as well expect the insect brain to rise to the occasion as one might expect a sausage machine to suddenly take on the task of a typewriter. Faced with a crisis the insect still blunders on in the same rut it followed when all was well.

If a wasp is cut in half, the forward portion continues to feed. If a cockroach be decapitated, the jaws still bite at any food within reach, and the headless body continues to go about its business, walking and even flying until, being unable to take in more fuel owing to the loss of its head, the mechanism finally runs down.

BRAIN CAPACITY

Initiative, adaptability to altered circumstances, manifests itself in even the lowest vertebrates, and increases proportionally with increase of brain capacity as we ascend the scale. In judging the brain capacity of mammals, one may easily form a false judgment if guided by external appearances only. Many an impressive " dome of thought " owes its seeming bulk, not to the brains within but to hollow bony structures giving the skull strength combined with tightness, or to huge masses of muscular tissue animating the jaws.

An X-ray view of the brains of familiar animals would come as a surprise to some. Man, for example, heads the list with a brain roughly one-sixtieth his own weight. He is easily the brainiest creature for his size the world has ever known. The chimpanzee, his next of kin, has a brain only one-third the human weight. The elephant, despite the portentously brainy appearance of its great head, has a brain less than one six-hundredth its body weight.

The domestic cat, though so much the lion's inferior in size, has a proportionately much

W. S. BERRIDGE, F.Z.S. (MONDIALE)

EEL THAT GIVES POWERFUL ELECTRIC SHOCKS

The electric eel, found in the swamps of Brazil and Guiana, is not an eel, but it certainly is electric, since it is capable of giving a shock that will stun a horse. Other " electric " species give lesser shocks.

BRAWN VERSUS BRAINS

A. *Elephant*. B. *Baluchitherium*. C. *Civilized man*. D. *Giraffe*. E. *Brontosaurus*. 1. *Man*. 2. *Chimpanzee*. 3. *Cat*. 4. *Dog*. 5. *Monkey*. 6. *Lemur*. 7. *Tarsier*. 8. *Horse*. 9. *Crocodile*. 10. *Man*. 11. *Chimpanzee*. 12. *Dog*. 13. *Ox*. 14. *Porpoise*. 15. *Echidna*. 16. *Duckbill*. 17. *Kangaroo*. 18. *Rabbit*. 19. *Marmoset*. 20. *Pigeon*. 21. *Elephant*. 22. *Salmon*. 23. *Frog*. 24. *Lizard*. 25. *Alligator*.

larger brain. The horse, in spite of being almost humanized by some of its admirers, cuts a poor figure in the gallery of brains beside the average dog.

Human brains show great uniformity of weight, though apparently so variable in quality. The guide book to the College of Surgeons Museum in London, describes a cast of the brain cavity of Dean Swift there displayed as " of mediocre size and common shape, quite unlike the products of the brain which the cast represents." It is also pointed out that " many more brains of men with specially developed faculties must be preserved for investigation before any definite statement can be made as to a relationship between any particular part of the brain and the manifestation of a particular faculty."

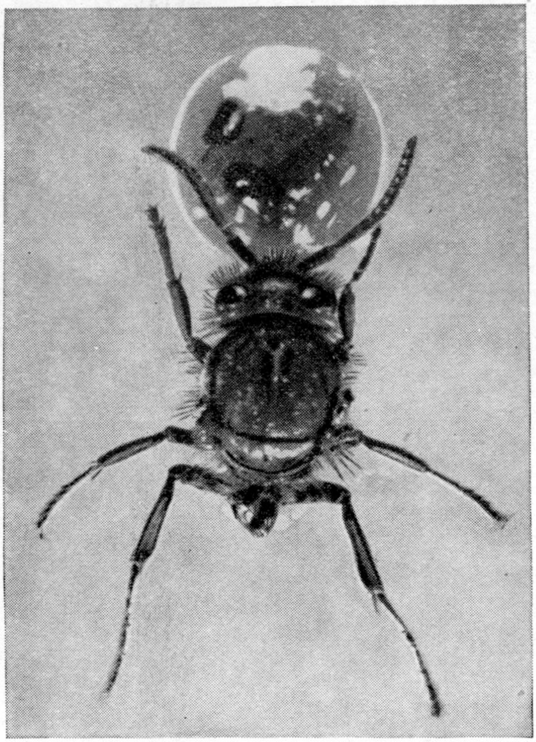

HAROLD BASTIN

DO INSECTS FEEL PAIN?
Capacity to feel pain depends on brain-power. This wasp having lost his posterior half, continues to eat.

There are solid grounds for believing that the general area of the brain offers a clue to mental capacity. The greater the number of creases or convolutions into which a brain is thrown, the larger the area it would cover supposing it could be spread out flat. There is a marked decrease in the brain's convolutions as we descend the vertebrate scale. We pass from man's complex brain by almost imperceptible degrees to a mere blobbiness, and one cannot fail to be struck by the curious uniformity of birds' brains, and their close similarity to those of some reptiles.

As in all other matters appertaining to Nature, we are here confronted with some seeming contradictions and paradoxes. Whales have brains rivalling that of man in complexity, and the brain of the common porpoise, a " pocket whale," is relatively heavier. The little squirrel monkey and the marmoset have slightly bigger brains for their size than has a man, but must be of inferior quality, judging by the owners' general deportment.

BRAIN AND PAIN

The brain animates and directs the body, and tells the animal when the body is in trouble by registering those signals from the nerves which we call pain. Pain is appreciable in direct proportion to the brain power.

Failure to appreciate this simple principle still gives rise to endless controversy concerning sport, the use of animals in medicine, and many other matters. There are still plenty of well-meaning persons who put guinea-pigs, goldfish and butterflies on a mental level with human beings. Where an animal, such as a rat, renders itself unpopular, sympathy is less apparent.

Equally muddled are many persons' conceptions of cruelty as evinced in the lower animals. A cat playing with a mouse, or a tiger toying with a wounded man, are placed almost on a level with sadistic Nero. Cruelty, the conscious and deliberate causation of pain, is a sole monopoly of adult, responsible humanity.

RAY PALMER (MONDIALE)

GREAT WATER SCORPION
The insect brain is like a machine fashioned to perform certain functions, and those only.

AMERICAN MUSEUM OF NATURAL HISTORY, NEW YORK

STRIPES AMID SUN-LIT GRASS

The tiger's coat of reddish fawn striped with black enables it to appear inconspicuous against the long grass of plains and swamps. The under parts of the body and the inner sides of the limbs are white.

CAMOUFLAGE AND COLOUR IN THE WILD

To human spectators colour goes far to make the pageant of life the never palling spectacle it is. But colour as such is not always so significant to the lower animals, colourful though they themselves often are. A very large number are, in varying degree, colour blind. They live in a photographic world. To such, however, pattern still has a meaning, which accounts for the often striking designs which many colour blind creatures present in their markings.

In this matter of colouring, the human anxiety to find a reason for everything is not always easily satisfied. Why, for example, should so many desert animals be sand-coloured? The obvious answer of course is concealment, but here we meet with a difficulty. Many desert animals that might well seek concealment are quite strikingly coloured, and others again are nocturnal, so that their camouflage seems wasted.

When we consider another class of creatures living in very uniform surroundings, namely the stygian blackness of the ocean deeps, the case is more understandable. Black and red, by absorbing so much light, both appear black in the darkness, and hence it is that many very diverse abyssal animals are either red or a uniform black. Very often indeed animal coloration makes for concealment.

Uniform coloration harmonizing with a similar background need not necessarily constitute a cloak of invisibility. Light from above casts a shadow not only on the ground but on the creature's underside, thus rendering it conspicuous enough. To counter this the back must be darker than the belly, so nullifying the effect of the light and the shadow it casts. This is a very general principle in the coloration of a large number of creatures, both vertebrate and invertebrate.

In the surface waters of the sea, and also to a lesser extent of lakes and rivers, there swarm the larval forms of all manner of animals—fish, crustacea, molluscs, worms and so on. Science, as already noted, calls this medley by the not unpoetic name of plankton—the wanderers. Now a high percentage of plankton is entirely colourless. Not only the "jellified" creatures, but larval fish with backbones, and the shell-encrusted crabs make a ghostly, dancing phantasmagoria, only discernible when a strong light—as from an electric torch—is cast upon a haul of them imprisoned in a collecting jar.

Later in life many of these creatures sink down through the water, to live out the rest of their time in the mid depths or on the sea floor. It is then that, gradually, pigmentation shows itself, first in scattered spots which, increasing slowly, merge and invest the creature's entire body. Those which elect to live always at the surface acquire prevailing tints of blue. Jelly-fishes, such as the Portuguese man-o'-war, are typical of this surface fauna.

MONDIALE

RAREST MAMMAL

The giant panda, representing the link between the bear and the raccoon, has an unusual colour-scheme.

SPENDING LIFE UPSIDE DOWN

Light is an essential to rich and varied colouring, and it is noticeable that shells tend to be most pigmented on the upper surface. But in the open sea there is a sea snail which reverses the normal snail behaviour. Instead of crawling on its belly foot with the spire of the shell pointing upwards, the violet snail floats throughout life with the mouth of the shell directed skywards. This portion is suffused a lovely violet, which fades to whitey blue towards the spire.

On Egyptian friezes a curious fish is often depicted swimming upside down. This is perfectly correct, and the fish in question is still common enough in Egypt. It is coloured differently from all normal fishes in that it is dark below and light above. The sloth, hanging head downwards in the tree-tops, presents a similar reversal and so does the badger. Here we are met by a difficulty. The badger habitually walks right side up.

This strange reversal is apparent in many allied animals, the ratels, skunks, pandas and coatis, animals well able to take care of themselves and sometimes armed with intimidating scent glands. It may therefore be a warning form of coloration, retained from their more formidably armed ancestors. One very strange instance of this abnormal shading is seen in a little crustacean, miscalled a louse, often seen clinging horizontally to small rock fishes. The upper side is always darker than the lower.

COLORATION FOR CONCEALMENT

Coloration for the purpose of concealment is apparent everywhere. The stoat, Arctic fox, mountain hare and ptarmigan put off their grey and russet with the close of summer, and gradually assume coats that blend with a world under snow. Very striking too are the heather mixture dresses of various heath and shore birds. Not only are the feathers so mottled as to blend perfectly with moorland and pebble ridge, but even the eggs are similarly tinted, so much so as often to defy detection by the keenest eyes.

There can be little doubt that birds have a very lively colour sense. In no way else can we explain such dresses as those of the peacock, the various cock pheasants and male birds of paradise. Where colour is wanting, the bird often finds means to lure a mate by song; it is seldom that we find both attractions in one and the same bird.

Colour again can have a warning significance. "Hands off" says the wasp's gaudy attire of black and gold. Yellow is a very prevalent warning colour. The skunk walks abroad clearly labelled an untouchable, and so also do the caterpillars of the cinaba moth, and to a lesser degree those of the swallowtail butterfly. The cinaba moth itself is conspicuous in its dark blue spotted a lurid pink, and as with its caterpillar, no bird will touch it twice.

Save for seasonal changes, the colouring of mammals and birds is constant, but amongst the lower vertebrates and invertebrates this is reversed, often in dramatic fashion. The little green tree frog can blend with its surroundings

WIDE WORLD

BADGER'S COAT IS DARKER BELOW

The badger is one of the animals, like the skunks and the pandas, which reverse the usual coloration-practice in having the under parts of their coats darker than the upper parts. This makes them conspicuous.

to a certain extent, and so can many lizards.

How the chameleon earned world fame as a quick-change artist must remain a matter for surprise. It is far surpassed by many other lizards, and all kinds of molluscs and insects. Exhaustive experiments conducted at the New York Zoo made the promoters wonder how the old tale of the chameleon exploding when placed on a tartan plaid could have arisen. Whether the creature was associated with bright green leaves, dead twigs, or white sand, the reaction was always the same, a dull yellow.

Very different are the responses shown by certain common flat fish such as the sole and dab. If made to swim from a sandy floor, where they are invisible, on to an area marked in geometric patterns of black and white, the fishes become one with their surroundings in a few minutes.

HYPNOTISM IN NATURE

Fear, hunger, rage or other emotion, produces just as startling changes in many other kinds of fish. In the John Dory a vivid streak appears down the centre of the fish's face when food appears, and it has been suggested that this holds the attention of a prawn until the dory can engulf it. Still more striking is the way in which some tree snakes have the tongue coloured uniformly with the head. When a bird or other prey is sighted the tongue is shot back and forth, producing an extraordinary face-making effect, which is believed to "hypnotize" the bird into immobility.

Colour plays a great part in camouflage, and is doubly effective when aided by form. The python in the jungle might well pass for a lichen-encrusted, sunlight-flecked tree branch. In this connection it may be mentioned that forest animals tend to present light spots on a dark ground, simulating the play of sunlight through leaves, whilst dark spots on a light ground are the rule with plains-dwelling animals, especially on pebble-strewn areas. Stripes blend well with sunlit grass; the tiger and zebra are obvious examples of this type of protective coloration.

RESEMBLING THE DESERT

Some desert lizards, like the Australian moloch and the Mexican toad, both clad in dense coats of sharp spines, are absolutely indistinguishable from the sun-baked sand sprinkled with dry thorn scrub or splinters of quartz and hornblende.

The shores of Great Britain provide some of Nature's most perfectly camouflaged animals. The word camouflage, be it noted, means literally a disguise, and is comparable with camouflet, signifying a puff of smoke in the face, in which connection its war-time application is sufficiently apparent. In summer the octopus visits England's shores, and no creature is more difficult to detect upon a weedy and rocky sea bed. It can dilate certain pigment cells and contract others so that an immense range of colour changes is at its command, rendering it adaptable to almost any environment.

Many fishes have exaggerated fins or special embellishments of skin which perfectly simulate weeds. In the common angler fish even the eyes are so marked as to counterfeit the starry sea squirt which encrusts weeds and stones. Some tropic sea horses are literally lost amongst their voluminous decorations. One sees the same principle at work on every hand. Sea slugs counterfeit the anemones on which they feed. Anemones mimic gravel beds and corallines; crabs, worms and shells pass themselves off as almost anything but what they are.

WIDE WORLD

HIGHLY-COLOURED BIRDS

Male peacocks cannot charm their mates by song, but they do so with bright colours and will fight for the possession of a desired hen.

In the spider crabs we meet an amazing degree of what may be designated artifice, amazing since they have no brains comparable to those of even the lowest vertebrates. These crabs have rugged shells covered with hooked bristles. The animals very deliberately take cuttings of sea weeds and corallines, chew the ends to give them better purchase, and then affix them amongst the hairs on carapace and limbs, where they take root, and in time entirely conceal the gardener.

This is not all. The crab shows minute discretion in making its fancy dress blend with its surroundings. If a crab dressed in red weeds be placed in a tank filled with green sea plants, the old dress is methodically removed and a green camouflage substituted. Instead of hooked hairs some of the spider crabs have a "pipe-clay" surface to the shell which gives an ideal anchorage to the sponges which these crustaceans use exclusively in their "make-up." When neither weeds nor sponges are available, pebbles may be laboriously piled upon the back.

DRESSING-UP BY CHANCE

When vertebrates dress up it is the result of chance rather than of premeditation. The sloth acquires a powdering of lichens; the mud turtle and limpet gather vegetable growths as the result of their sedentary lives. The only case of dressing up analogous to that of the spider crabs is seen in a family of tropical sea snails known as carrier shells. Like other molluscs these add to their shells by means of superimposed layers of limy secretion. But the carriers show originality in that they incorporate bits of the ground they live on with the cement, and shell collectors divide them into mineralogists and conchologists according to the nature of their disguise. In either case it blends perfectly with local scenery.

NATURE AND THE WORLD WAR

Self-contained camouflage resolves itself chiefly into breaking up the animal's outline with a dazzle pattern. Thayer, the animal artist, may be regarded as the originator of that complex system of camouflage which the World War brought into daily life. We painted ships much as the killer whale and sea unicorn are marked, and even took a hint from the spider crabs when we covered guns and ammunition dumps with netting sewn all over with scraps of green and brown rag.

The essence of a camouflage dress is to make its wearer look like something else. A very common form is plant imitation. The leaf butterfly of India even shows holes and mould spots on its wings, which in shape perfectly counterfeit leaves even to the stalk. The South American leaf fish has a stalk-shaped nose, and

spends much time drifting sideways or standing on its head, in which posture not one man in a hundred would suspect its true nature.

Stick insects perfectly suggest dead twigs in their every feature, and the leaf insect not only turns from green to brown in autumn, but lays eggs so like plant seeds as to deceive the expert botanist. The leaf insect's colouring, like that of the bright green bones of the garfish, is due, not as is normal in animals to pigment, but to chlorophyll, the prevalent colouring matter of plants. Some few insects like the tropic " orchid spiders " and mantids counterfeit flowers, less to evade enemies than to lure insects within reach.

DISGUISED AS HARMFUL

Natural selection has achieved one of the subtlest and most effective of all camouflages, the disguising of a harmless as a harmful species. Such a piece of bluff may be seen in the common hover fly, which many birds mistake at first glance for a wasp. As in most cases of this kind, the bluffer is less common than its model, otherwise the lesson of its warning colours would be wasted. The clear wing moths simulate bees and hornets, and the American viceroy butterfly, itself tasteful to birds, imitates the nauseous monarch butterfly inhabiting the same regions.

Most remarkable of all these devices possibly are the pantomime dresses of certain plant bugs. The thorax is prolonged fore and aft so that it spreads like a roof over the insect's head and abdomen, and this roof is made to resemble

HAROLD BASTIN

NATURAL WEAPONS

A wasp wears a bright yellow jacket as a warning to other animals that if attacked it can give a good account of itself in spite of its smallness. The wasp's sting is composed of three distinct parts; a sheath, and inside it, two barbed needles. Above; left, the sheath ; centre, one of the barbed needles ; and right, the tip of a medium-sized sewing-needle. Right; The whole stinging apparatus, showing poison-bag at top and weapons at bottom.

ZEBRA'S DEFENCE
The zebra's stripes render it very conspicuous in captivity, but not in its natural surroundings, for stripes blend well with grass in strong sunlight.

all manner of objects, so saving the tasty and defenceless little bug beneath from foes. In one species the roof suggests a thorn, another a plant bur, or the distasteful cocoon of a moth. The climax is reached in a species whose roof actually mimics the head and body of an ant.

FACE-MAKING BLUFFS

These plant bugs are tiny objects and might pass unnoticed disguised or otherwise, but the make-up of the South American lantern flies is so large and glaring as to rout a foe by shock tactics. They have immense hollow structures projecting from the front of the head. Some species are larger than mice and so impossible to ignore. All are sufficiently arresting, but one has the hollow structure or lantern painted in bright colours so as to suggest a fearsomely grinning and glaring reptile of uncertain species but unquestionable savagery. No bird or monkey coming upon this suddenly stops to investigate further. The face-making bluffs of puss and lobster moth caterpillars seem tame beside this insect's lantern, the precise import of which, save as an intimidating device, is unknown.

All these camouflages, in which a harmless animal mimics a harmful one, merely excite our interest, but one at least must be taken seriously.

DEADLY CORAL SNAKES

In the southern United States there are two, and in tropical South America twenty odd species of reptiles known as coral snakes. They almost invariably present red, yellow and black rings, arranged in varying order, and all the species are venomous, some fatally so. Wherever they occur there are also found harmless snakes so similarly marked as often to be mistaken for the deadly kinds.

In the harmful species the black rings are single and bordered with a pair of yellow rings, whilst in the innocuous kinds the yellow rings are single and bordered with a pair of black rings. Unfortunately the average person, even though aware of this, seldom remembers it at the right time, and the annual death rate due to coral snakes is considerable.

The most cunning camouflage may sometimes fail in its aim; discretion as to its use is half the game. Birds like the woodcock, and certain moths which mimic lichenous tree trunks, owe as much of their effective concealment to a wonderful capacity for keeping still as to their faithful imitation of surroundings. Movement on the animal's part would at once give the show away.

All tree bark imitators, like the various moths,

LIKE ONE OF THE GIANT DINOSAURS
Two male horned chameleons from Kenya. Most members of this sub-order of lizards lay eggs but the variety shown above produces its young alive. The chameleon's capacity for changing colour is often exaggerated.

W. S. BERRIDGE, F.Z.S. (MONDIALE)

WALKS AT THE BOTTOM OF THE SEA

The angler fish, or fishing frog, has more than one peculiarity. Out of its head grows a fishing "rod" whereby it attracts its prey ; and it lives at the very bottom of the sea, walking there by means of its fins.

lichen geckos and the cobego, a flying mammal, have wonderful powers of immobility. All the nightjars blend perfectly with moss-grown tree boles, and some, when alarmed, do not like the moths or lizards flatten themselves out, but sit bolt upright, in which pose they pass for stumps of branches or prominent knots.

In Central India is an expert race of thieves. Its members, if pursued in the open, run at high speed and then suddenly "freeze" as game stalkers say, into some grotesque attitude, remaining thus in statuesque immobility until the pursuer has passed. The fugitive's naked, black and well oiled body passes muster as one of the twisted, fire-blackened tree stumps dotting the plain.

In like manner the little tent-peg squirrels of America and other animals elude pursuit by

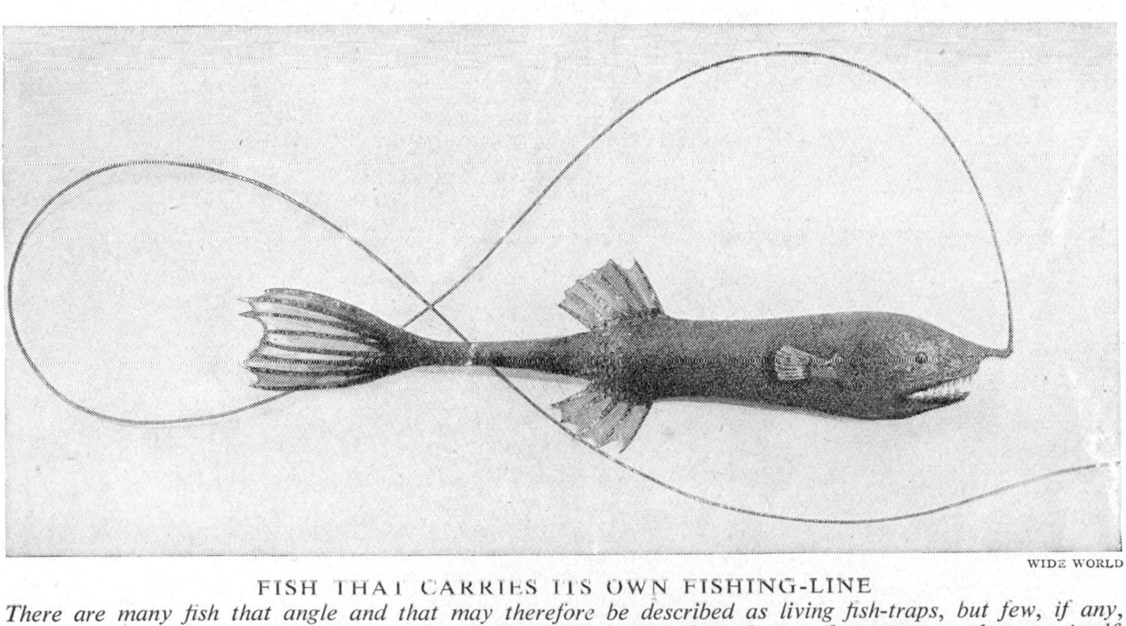

WIDE WORLD

FISH THAT CARRIES ITS OWN FISHING-LINE

There are many fish that angle and that may therefore be described as living fish-traps, but few, if any, are so well provided with tackle as Gigantactis macronema, *whose line is four times as long as itself.*

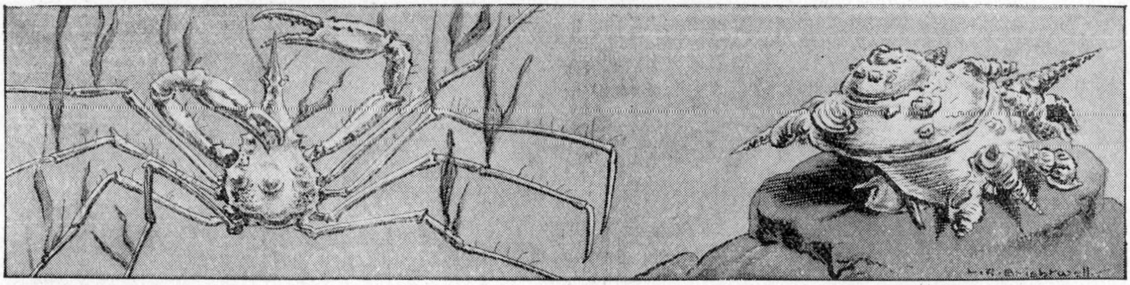

ANIMALS THAT HIDE BY DRESSING-UP

Left: A spider-crab "robing" itself in seaweeds. Right: A tropical "carrier-shell" sea-snail dressed in the dead shells of other molluscs. Spider-crabs sometimes shelter within the tentacles of sea-anemones.

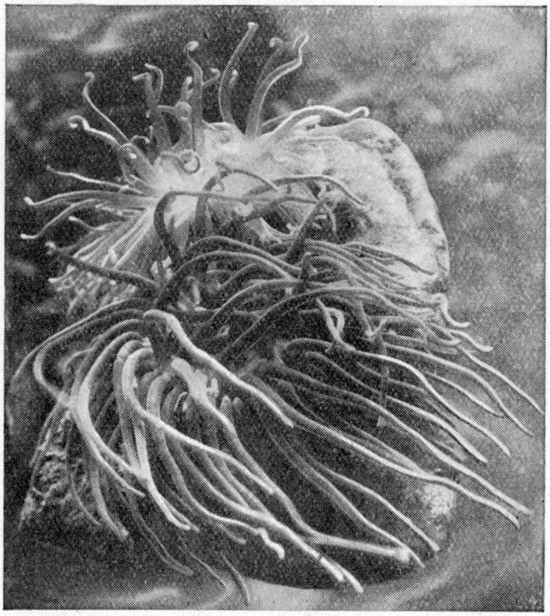

WIDE WORLD

INNOCENT-LOOKING POISONER

The sea-anemone waves its poisonous but harmless-looking tentacles as it waits for its prey. Sea-anemones are akin to the corals, but do not form skeletons or produce colonies. Forty species are to be found in the waters surrounding Great Britain.

suddenly ceasing to run when the enemy is almost upon them. One of the greatest exponents of this art is the grotesque frilled lizard of Australia. Rising on its hind legs it runs at incredible speed and suddenly stops. The pursuer having run well past it, it at once heads the opposite way and makes good its escape.

SAVED BY FEIGNING DEATH

A form of camouflage is that in which an animal may imitate itself. The Indian sand boa and a few other snakes have the extremities so alike that it is not easy to say at a glance which end goes first. Sometimes the tail can be raised in a manner highly suggestive of a head about to strike, in which case the real head has a still better chance to obtain an early start in the eventuality of pursuit.

Feigning death is the animal's last line of defence. A tropic grasshopper thus saves itself from foes when passing through an intermediate stage between its larval form—when it mimics an ant—and its perfect state, when it resembles a growing leaf.

The past master in this art of immobility is the American hog-nosed snake, which not merely remains quiet, but goes limp, offering no

FISHES THAT IMITATE PLANTS

Certain fishes find it convenient to camouflage themselves by posing as plants. Left: Two slender pile fish. Centre: A tropical sea-horse. Right: A fish whose stripes enable it to blend with the weeds.

more objection to being handled than a piece of string.

Raymond Ditmars, the deservedly famous American student of reptiles, once thought to impress his native porters on an expedition with his occult powers. Taking up a lively hog-nosed snake, he apparently "killed" it with a few mesmeric passes, the snake of course automatically simulating death. Then, placing it on the ground, he made some more passes, when the snake, according to custom, having made sure it was no longer in danger, cautiously came to, and made off.

PLOT THAT REBOUNDED

The effect of this was unfortunate. The porters were not only impressed by their employer's psychic powers, but aghast at them, and yelling with terror, decamped into the gathering dusk, leaving the scientist alone with his baggage in a desolate and lawless region.

In our sophisticated way we may be inclined to laugh at such an incident, forgetting that for long our forefathers believed in the most fantastic of travellers' tales. The mantids, for instance, were fortune-tellers. The appearance of one of these insects was invariably held to foretell famine or death, possibly both. As to the praying mantis, "so divine a creature" was this esteemed that if a child asked the way to a place where supplications are made to the gods, the insect "will stretch out her feet and show him the right way, and seldom or never miss. Walking softly, she retains her modesty and shows forth a kind of mature gravity."

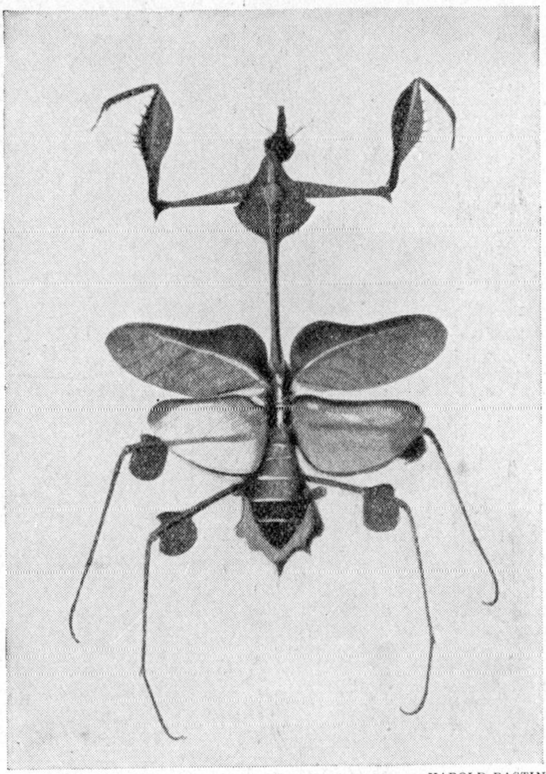

HAROLD BASTIN

POSES AS A FLOWER

Gongylus gongyloides, *an Indian member of the mantidae family, is coloured to resemble a flower.*

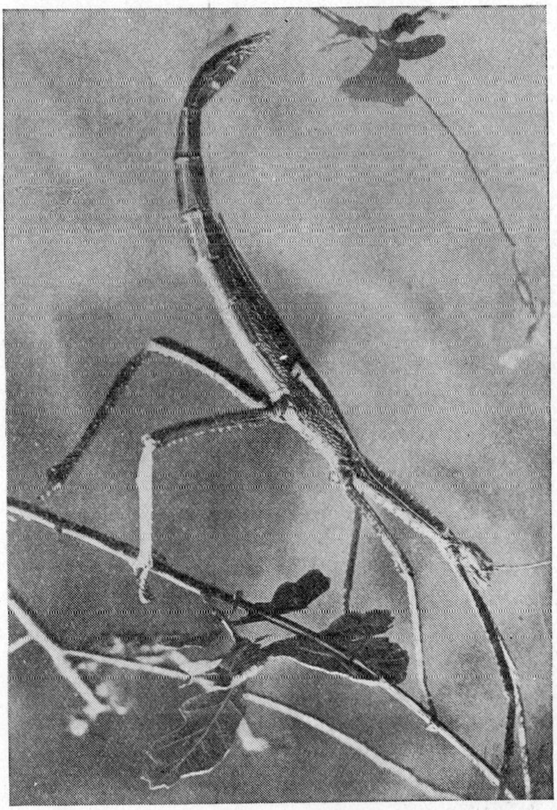

WIDE WORLD

STICK INSECT

This insect, one of the phasmidae, is so long and thin that it looks like the branch on which it rests.

DEATH-WATCH SUPERSTITION

Another superstition is in connection with the noise made by the death-watch. When heard it is held to portend bereavement, hence the name. Science, cold and calculating, reassures us. The listener is far more likely to lose money than a friend. The knocking is caused by the male beetle tapping its head on wood as a signal to his lady-love. The destruction caused by death-watch grubs burrowing in timber is incalculable. The insects did grievous harm to the roof of Westminster Hall.

FOX

WHY THE LION HAS A MANE

Charles Darwin suggested that the lion's mane, like that of the baboon, serves as a shield to protect the wearer when fighting to the death with another of his kind for a mate. A device with a similar purpose is the goat's beard, which on occasion is a tuft of considerable length. Many extremely quarrelsome animals, however, are without face-trimmings of any kind.

COURTSHIP AS CONDUCTED BY THE ARTHROPODS
1. *The male fiddler crab and* (2) *a spider dance before their prospective partners.* 3. *The scorpion's parade; the male holds the female's claws and then proceeds to walk backwards a considerable distance.*

ANIMAL COURTSHIP

In his play *You Never Can Tell*, Mr. Bernard Shaw makes two bright young people declaim in duet :

" In spring, and also in summer, autumn and winter, a young man's fancy lightly turns," etc.

Therein, neatly stated, lies one of the great fundamental differences between the courtship of man (and the man-like apes), and the courtship of almost every other kind of animal. With very few exceptions the beasts, birds and other creatures seek their mates at given seasons, but the higher primates are less chained by time.

Courtship in the lower animals is also more subject to a certain machine-made uniformity. Any fifty stags or crickets taken at random will go about their wooing with slight deviation from racial tradition, but even in our own conservative and custom-bound nation, courtship may ring millions of changes between the crudest horseplay and badinage on the one hand, and on the other the sonnets of a William Shakespeare.

Regarded simply as a spectacle animal courtship is of absorbing interest, and at times seems to offer curious parallels to that of human beings, although, as we shall see, such parallels are often more apparent than real. The urge on the part of the male to court, as distinguished from merely advertising his existence to the opposite sex, though becoming more and more obvious as we ascend the animal scale, is very unevenly distributed, and some creatures we might expect to court show no inclinations in this direction.

Courtship, where it exists, is nearly always conducted by the male, and polygamy is probably more frequent than monogamy. Polyandry—the selection of many males by one female—is, as amongst human beings, of less frequent occurrence, though it undoubtedly occurs in some fishes and insects.

Perhaps the beginnings of courtship show themselves in certain marine bristle worms. The males at a certain time of year writhe convulsively in the coils of the females, thus inciting them to discharge their eggs, which the males promptly fertilize. Many molluscs, for example the common garden snail, are hermaphrodite, that is, they possess both male and female sex organs, yet these creatures show a dim foreshadowing of courtship, mutually exciting each other's reproductive instincts by plunging crystalline objects of appreciable size, known as " love darts," into each other's bodies.

Amongst the serried legions of the jointed animals, the crustaceans and insects, courtship becomes a more recognizable affair. Many of the crabs and lobsters show colourings and ornaments, or weapons that, as strictly male appurtenances, can mean but one thing. The craw-fish " grunts " by rubbing its feelers against its beak, and the male of the little snap lobster found on the southern coasts of England can snap the finger of its big right claw with a quite appreciable report—equal to that made by slapping the palm of one hand with two fingers of the other.

Still more picturesque is the wooing of the fiddler crab that swarms on every tropic and sub-tropic shore. The male has one claw double its body bulk, and most gorgeously coloured. This it flourishes before the dowdy little female with tireless persistency, until a satisfactory reply is vouchsafed.

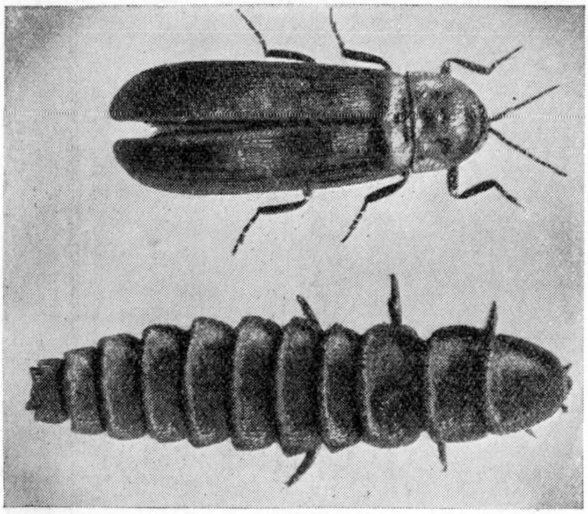

HAROLD BASTIN

GLOW-WORM LOVE-MAKING

Male (top) and female, who lures the former by a light emitted from the extremity of her abdomen.

The scorpion has a bad name, but he shows a certain old-world elegance in affairs of the heart. The lady is approached and taken by both her claws, these being held in the larger pincers of the male, who then, walking backwards, conducts her on a love walk of considerable length.

In the minute " false " or " book " scorpion which infests linen and library shelves, we can see the reason for this strange conduct. The male, which is a miniature of the true tropic scorpion, without the sting-tipped tail, places the fertilizing agent in a minute crystalline cup, poised on a slender stalk. He has then to find the lady and, having won her consent, he leads her by the claws until the cup is reached, and her eggs are fertilized. He may thus court half a dozen possibles before meeting with success.

Among the spiders we meet with courtships of a gruesome kind. There are species, it is true, in which both sexes live, for a time at least, in perfect harmony, but this is not the rule. Generally the male is to the female as might be a human dwarf to a cannibalistic giantess. He spends his wooing in alternately seeking to charm his lady with fantastic dances, or flying for his life. Sometimes he plays a sort of nightmare hide-and-seek amongst the lady's legs. One false step and her venomed jaws pierce him through and through.

HUSBAND AS WEDDING BREAKFAST

A dozen swains may thus pay for their temerity, and when at last one is accepted as a husband, as like as not he ends his career as a wedding breakfast for his bride.

It is likely that the female spider's ferocity is prompted by a blind urge to fortify herself against the strain involved by egg production. Possibly this instinct also animates the female praying mantis, who sometimes devours her husband even whilst their union is being consummated.

More attractive are some of the devices adopted by the higher insects when seeking each other to fulfil their destinies. The female glow-worm lights her lamp in the damp hedgerow, and the less brilliant but winged males

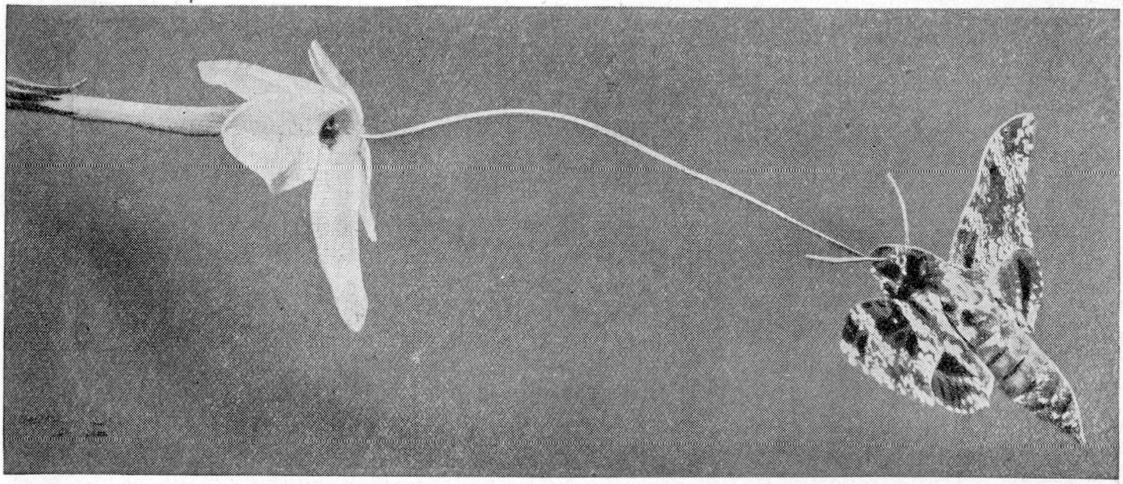

HAROLD BASTIN

PURSUING NECTAR BEFORE A MATE

Smell aids moths in finding a mate. A long-tongued Mexican hawk-moth visiting a tobacco flower before going courting. It can extract nectar from the depth of a floral tube of even greater length.

WIDE WORLD

FISH THAT FEEDS ON ITS PARTNER

Photocorynus spiniceps *is found in the Gulf of Mexico. The tiny male of this species attaches himself to the skin of the female and begins to feed upon the blood stream of his unfortunate partner.*

fly to her casement with all speed. Many moths have an extraordinary sense of smell which aids in finding a mate, and the wonderful nuptial flights of the bees and other insects have excited man's attention from early times.

More in the nature of true courtship is the behaviour of the little carnivorous flies called empids. The males actually offer their desired partners gifts of food, such as other minute insects, enclosed in little quicksilver-like bubbles of fine silk or other secreted material, the lover flying here and there seeking a mate who shall appreciate his offering. In some species the gift takes quite an æsthetic form, being composed of a scrap of gaudy feather, a flower petal, or even part of the discarded wrapper from a sweet or cigarette packet.

FISH IN COURTING DRESS

There are some pretty, and some lurid, courtships to be seen amongst the fishes. In those fishes which undeniably court, the male is always dressed for the part. The gallant not only exerts himself to the utmost to win his bride by blandishment, or, if need be, by force, but puts on a dress of magnificent though temporary finery. At such times all other males of his species and inoffensive strangers alike are hated rivals for his lady's favours.

Nobody, once having seen a stickleback in his courting dress—and mood, will easily forget the sight. The robin stickleback comports himself with a dash and verve worthy of a creature many times his bulk. Members of the growing band of tropical aquarists will know the courtship of the little Siamese fighting fish, who outshines even the robin stickleback in inspired fury and devotion. The fish glows with burning tints, as though illumined from within, and after a whirlwind courtship, tightly embraces the adored with his entire body.

PUGNACIOUS AT PAIRING TIME

The little goby waxes pugnacious at pairing time, and so also does the salmon, the male displaying an extraordinary hook-like development of the jaw at this season. The English dragonet shows the male at courting time as a fish equalling in bizarre form and vivid colouring any denizen of tropic seas.

The displays of some male fishes, and others of the lower vertebrates, though unquestionably passionate, are still in the nature of automatic reflexes. It would be a fatal error to humanize them, and to read into them anything approaching the loves of our own species. Once the fish courtier has won his bride, he is done with her. When, as sometimes happens, the male takes charge of the eggs, the mother may even prove a cannibalistic foe, to be driven off at all costs.

The amphibians are nearly related to the fishes, but the two main groups into which amphibians are divided—the frogs, toads, etc., and the newts, are as strikingly contrasted in courtship as in outward form. In the former the males simply advertise their presence by the well-known croaking chorus, and having seized the first available mate, courtship, such as it is, terminates.

POSTURINGS AND CONTORTIONS

With the newts matters are much more elaborate. The male extrudes the sperms in a little balloon-shaped capsule, which the female must take in her two hands, pass to her feet, and with these place the package in her oviduct. But it is not enough just to put the sperm case within sight of a female. To rouse her interest the male assumes a glaring dress of black spots on a chestnut and crimson ground with a saw-toothed crest running from nape to tail tip, and thus attired engages in extravagant posturings and contortions, until his offering meets with acceptance.

By all the laws of logic, reptiles should show an advance upon fishes in their love-making. It may be that they do, but up to the present so little attention has been given by scientists to the matter that no such assumption is justified. Turtles and terrapins often congregate in vast numbers to deposit their eggs in one specified area, but whether these assemblies involve any form of courtship we do not know. Many snakes gather at certain seasons to form huge inextricable tangles of both sexes.

MASS MEETINGS OF CROCODILES

Mass meetings of crocodiles are reported, and the males of the big monitor lizards are known to duel on their hind legs where the possession of a mate is in question. Probably the cumbersome and bizarre horns worn by some male chameleons are in the nature of adornments. Considering how these reptiles even when roused live in slow motion, they could scarcely be considered as weapons.

In the British Isles at least, no single phase of animal life in the entire Arcadian calendar has enlisted such general interest, sympathy and

K. STULCKEN (MONDIALE)

SHEDDING AN OLD SKIN FOR A NEW ONE

Female striped newt after sloughing skin, which can be seen hanging on the branch of the water-weed. When courting the male assumes a glaring dress with a saw-toothed crest running from nape to tail tip.

DORIEN LEIGH

TURTLES PREFER TO LAY EGGS IN COMPANY

Turtles often congregate in large numbers to deposit their eggs. This specimen carefully scanned the near horizon, covered her round white eggs, and crawled back to the swamp whence she had come.

imagination as the courtship of the birds. To most of us springtime is epitomized in the sparrows' noisy chatter, the cuckoo's note, the song of the mounting lark and the sweet warbling of the thrush and blackbird.

CEREMONIAL AND SONG

Song ranks but as an item in feathered love-making. Bird courtship implies also elaborate dress, and even more elaborate ceremonial. Though song and ceremonial may be as automatic as the sprouting of fine feathers, their wonder does not lessen when we consider the crude workmanship of the bird brain compared with that of the much higher but less æsthetically inspired mammals.

Bird song is often very obviously a love song, but is not always so. Recent observers have established that it is frequently a defiant declaiming of territorial rights, a challenge to rival cocks to enter the charmed circle of the nesting site, if they dare This is very apparent in the case of England's common warblers, the males of which arrive from winter quarters on the continent of Europe in advance of the females. When the hens arrive, song largely gives place to an invitation to collaborate in house building.

This is a device exhibited by many male birds. When a desired partner is found, she is approached with scraps of moss, leaves or twigs, and coaxed into partnership. Amongst some penguins, such as the Adélie of South Georgia, in the South Atlantic, stones make the nest, and selected pebbles are solemnly dropped by Benedict before his Beatrice.

As in other creatures love-making amongst the birds is largely controlled by physiological factors, and particularly in the female. Often the eggs forming within the hen bird must reach a certain stage of development before they are fit for fertilization, and when this point is arrived at, further efforts on the part of the male are required to inflame her to the pitch of actually mating.

THE ETERNAL TRIANGLE

Among the warblers, song is later augmented by pretty dances and posturing, spreading of wings and tail, and other antics played from the vantage point of some convenient twig, within full sight of the hen, and calculated to show the suitor at his best.

A strange feature in the courtship of many birds is the segregation of the males at breeding time. This gathering is no light-hearted bachelors' club, but a sort of mass meeting of male mannequins, each straining every faculty in a frenzy of display. To this assembly the females come in due course, walk round it, and eventually make their choice.

An instance of this seen in England is that of the ruff's " dance hall," usually a piece of waste ground rising from out an expanse of marsh. Here the males, in their wonderful ruffles, which look like judges' wigs, pirouette and twirl dizzily for hours on end. Anon come the sober-looking reeves (hen birds) to look for mates. When a cock is obviously selected, he changes his dance for an elaborate abasement, spreading his wings flat upon the ground, and placing his beak point down to the soil. Where the eternal triangle occurs, the two males concerned engage in savage conflict, their ruffles serving as shields against each other's stabbing beaks.

Even more striking is the dance hall of the prairie hen, one of the grouse tribe. Some grouse, like the red grouse, are monogamous,

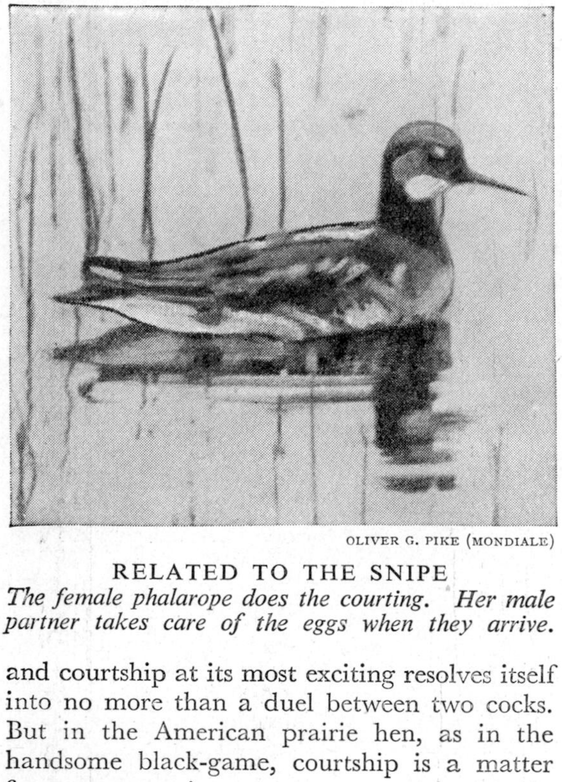

OLIVER G. PIKE (MONDIALE)

RELATED TO THE SNIPE

The female phalarope does the courting. Her male partner takes care of the eggs when they arrive.

and courtship at its most exciting resolves itself into no more than a duel between two cocks. But in the American prairie hen, as in the handsome black-game, courtship is a matter for a mass meeting.

From March to early May the prairie grouse assemble at some open space—its open quality largely the outcome of previous meetings which have stamped the ground clear. The cocks make a bold show, with horn-like tufts of feathers erect on either side of the head, and large bare sacks of skin puffed up to the size of golf balls. These augment the bird's voice, and help to produce a startling booming sound, which can be heard a mile or two distant. The cocks also loudly cackle, clash their wings, and leap high into the air. The ground becomes strewn with feathers, and the turmoil continues for an hour or more after sunrise, when suddenly it stops, the rivals feed peacefully side by side, and quiet reigns until another dawn breaks, when again they enter the lists.

Those extraordinary members of the crow family, the birds of paradise, outshine all other birds as male mannequins, but appear to have little idea of duelling. So elaborate are the plumes of many that duelling would probably be scarcely practicable. The males of each of the few score known species display distinctive crests, shields, or other adornments of dazzling metallic hues and almost incredible designs. Some when displaying are only recognizable as birds at all by their beaks and feet, and even these can be hidden by the voluminous finery.

MALE MANNEQUINS

A selection of typical paradise-crow gallants are shown in the picture. The Count Raggi, for example, has elaborate tail plumes, as also have many other kinds. The greater and lesser birds of paradise have waterfall-like cascades of orange plumes falling from what approximate to our armpits. The twelve-wired paradise-crow has exaggerated head ornaments, and the superb an immense distensible shield of burnished green and copper springing from its breast.

These dazzling inhabitants of the New Guinea jungle are precluded from such violent exercise as the grouse indulge in, but they still make display in a marked manner. The Prince Rudolf bird, for example, is one of the upside down school, as is also the superb paradise-crow. The Prince Rudolf bird completely inverts itself, spreads its wings, and trembles violently from head to foot. The first specimen ever brought to a zoo so horrified its keepers by these acrobatics that they thought the bird was in a fit, and treated it to a quite unwanted dose of physic.

BIRDS BUILD DANCE HALLS

Courtship perhaps reaches the summit of æsthetic refinement in another group of Australasian birds, the bower builders, which, like the birds of paradise, are members of the crow family. With few exceptions, the male bower birds are as unadorned and even dowdy as the inconspicuous hens of the paradise-crows. But they compensate for any lack of personal charm in the amazing dance halls, or assembly rooms, which they construct. So huge are some of these structures, that early travellers in Australia mistook them for aboriginal cradles.

BIRD OF PARADISE GALLANTS AND ARGUS PHEASANT

Top (left): Lesser superb bird of paradise, great bird of paradise, and (below) Prince Rudolf bird of paradise. On right, the same birds "in display" when courting. A typical hen is also shown. At bottom, Argus pheasant. When courting, the male in the background raises his wings to form a fan.

OLIVER G. PIKE (MONDIALE)

SEXES ALMOST IDENTICAL IN APPEARANCE

The hen bird of the great crested grebe meets her lover half-way when he is courting. In appearance the sexes are almost identical. They are more at home in water than on land.

Each species builds in characteristic style, using special materials, and putting them together with conservative ritual. No other animal structures, not even the most elaborate erections of beavers or social insects can approach in artistic discernment and downright workmanship these avian retreats secreted in the fastnesses of the Australian bush. Both sexes may collaborate in making the bower, which, whilst it is undoubtedly inspired by the pairing instinct, and is used as a love bower, may also apparently satisfy some æsthetic or social craving long after the fires of passion have burned low.

DECORATED WITH FLOWERS

New Guinea's gardener bower bird heads the list in artistic refinement. It builds out of twigs a two-feet-high hut at the base of a tree, crowning the roof with moss. In front of this structure is a lawn of moss, which is decorated with gay flowers and berries, the embellishments being renewed as often as they fade. Zoo captives invariably use what ornaments they can come by—glass marbles, new pennies, silver paper, and even bus tickets.

The golden bower bird is a mere amateur at decoration, but what it lacks in refinement it makes up for in size, for it constructs a big straggling dance hall fourteen feet long by six feet wide. Sometimes it builds on a more modest plan and crowds four or five huts into a space only ten feet square. Some kinds pile the hut up against a tree trunk until it reaches a quite imposing height, and often show a marked predilection for some special colour.

DANCE OF THE PHEASANTS

Perhaps the palm should go to the satin bower bird, which actually plasters the inside of its wooden hut with a sort of gesso or distemper made from chewed wood pulp. The bird has an unusual fondness for anything blue, a colour which matches its prominent eyes.

The bower birds are adepts in all kinds of dainty bobbings and curtsyings, but in this regard they are easily outshone by the pheasants. Each species of pheasant has its special dance, the outstanding performer of the clan being the Argus pheasant of Malaya. Like the so-called lyre pheasant of New Guinea, this bird shows wonderful skill in steering its enormous tail feathers through dense underbush.

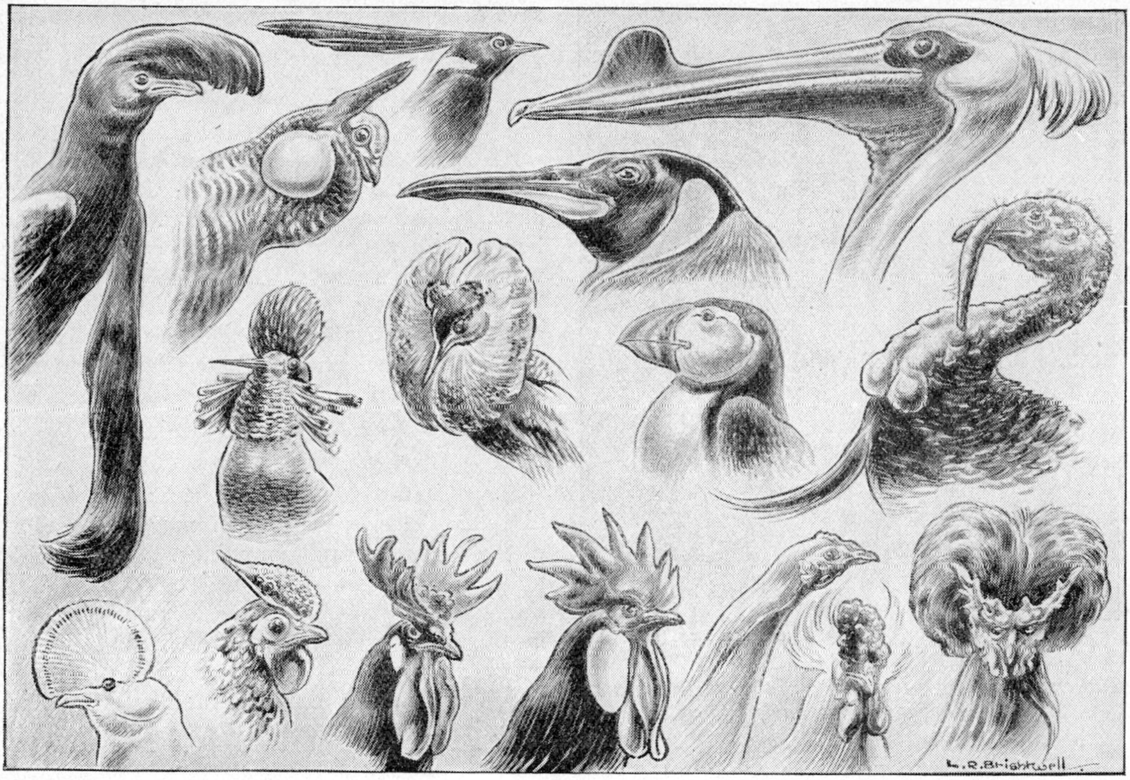

ATTRACTIONS DISPLAYED BY MALE BIRDS WHEN COURTING
Top: Umbrella bird, prairie grouse, jay shrike, king penguin, pelican. 2nd row: Humming bird, ruff, puffin, turkey. 3rd row: Cock of the rock ; domestic fowls—Hamburg, flower bird, Langshan, game, silky, Houdan.

In courting the male raises his wings to form a fan little less impressive than the peacock's famous tail coverts. The hundreds of eye spots on the wings face the hen in an unwinking stare, whilst their wearer peeps coyly between them to observe the effect he is making on the lady.

The largely automatic nature of bird courtship was strikingly evinced by a captive Argus pheasant mated to a hen of a related species. She failed apparently to understand his advances, and the bird, after exhausting himself in fruitless endeavours to please her, finally courted a metal feeding pan.

HEN MAKES ADVANCES

Courtship, usually the male prerogative, finds a reversal in the phalarope, a genus of wading and swimming birds related to the snipe. Larger and handsomer than the cocks, the hens do the courting, afterwards leaving the care of the eggs to their male partners. Among other orders the hen bird will meet her lover half-way. This is very noticeable in the almost identically dressed sexes of the great crested grebe, and also in the fulmar petrel, both sexes of this bird charming each other by amorously displaying the blue interiors of their mouths.

ACCESSORIES TO COURTING

Feathers by no means exhaust the catalogue of bird finery. The combs and wattles of farmyard cocks and turkeys at once come to mind, and these but touch the fringe of masculine magnificence. The love-sick puffin puts on a brightly striped over-beak, suggesting the nose of Mr. Punch, the king penguin wears salmon-coloured shields on his lower beak, and the male white pelican mounts upon his upper bill a big horny comb-like erection as big as the palm of one's hand. All these fripperies are shed when courting is over, and litter the mating grounds as thickly as autumn leaves in a lane.

Air-sacs, as seen in the prairie hen, are converted to erotic uses by many other birds. The frigate, or man-o'-war bird of the tropics, distends a huge scarlet bladder on its neck and a similar organ quite surrounds the

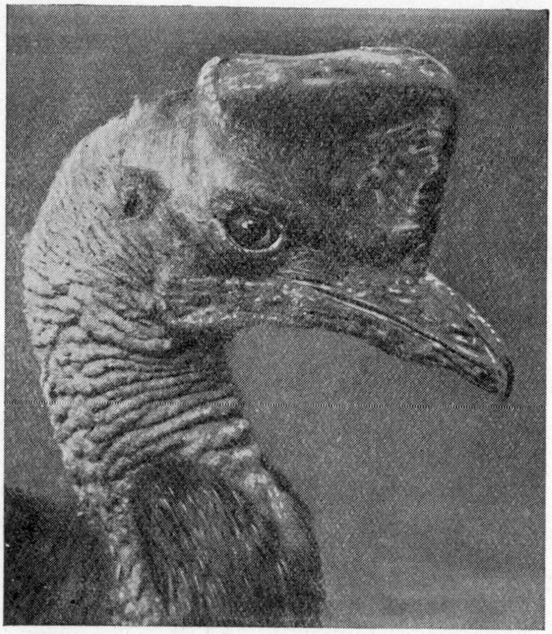

W. S. BERRIDGE, F.Z.S. (MONDIALE)

HELMETED BIRD

The cassowary, like the emu and the ostrich, has an air-sac which adds volume to his voice.

unlovely neck of the Indian adjutant stork. In the ostrich, emu and cassowary this air-sac helps to give the voice volume. Livingstone recalls how he once mistook the voice of a love-sick ostrich for the roar of a lion.

In these big ungainly birds the dance is an important feature of courtship, and such high kicks are indulged in that the performer is sometimes thrown upon his back.

CASTANETS OF THE STORKS

The greater wing power of the cranes and storks improves their foot play, and the storks in particular, masters of the *pas seul*, accompany themselves by a deafening castanet solo, rendered by clattering the two portions of the horn-covered beak together with incredible violence and rapidity.

Contradictorily enough the tender passion finds less poetic expression amongst the undeniably more highly-constituted mammals. In some the expressions of emotion may even, by the standards of civilization, seem actively repellent, though such expressions are often not without very obvious human parallels.

Voice plays a big part in mammalian love-making, the roof-concert of the cats bearing painful testimony to the fact. Many creatures, like the deer and porcupine, are virtually mute save at mating time, and in some creatures the normal vocal organs are enormously augmented by special devices. A male orang-utan, for example, wears a huge pouch upon its breast which gives great resonance to its voice.

All other animal voices, however, even the lion's roar, are as nothing compared with that of the Brazilian howler monkey. Though no larger than a cat it is undoubtedly the most vocal of all animals in relation to size. In both sexes, but especially in the male, the bones of the tongue are converted into a thin hollow shell of bone which may be as big as a man's fist. Scores of travellers have described the terrific sounds given out by this amplifier.

SCENT IN COURTSHIP

Scent is not without its erotic significance in our own species. Much more so does it play a part in animal courtships. Scent glands may serve as weapons, as do those of the skunk, or to blaze a trail, as for instance those in the hoofs of sheep and antelopes, but in many animals are found special scent glands which only make themselves manifest at pairing time.

Such glands are to be found above the eye in bull elephants, and behind the head in bull camels, and at certain seasons exude a thick,

LESLIE R. JONES (WIDE WORLD)

ADJUTANT STORK

A huge distensible bladder with a love-making significance adorns the ugly neck of the long-legged and ungainly adjutant stork.

OLIVER G. PIKE (MONDIALE)

LOVE DISCLOSED BY STRIPED BEAKS

Both male and female puffins have large sharp-pointed bills. The love-sick male puts on a brightly striped over-beak which is shed when courting is over.

powerfully odorous fluid. Even stranger is the "bloody sweat" of the hippopotamus, often responsible for the curious pinkish tint enlivening the normal drab colouring of the skin. The amorous bull hippopotamus exudes in great quantities this secretion, which dries to form a crystalline substance of unknown properties.

It is not so long ago since British manhood advertised itself in flowing locks, voluminous beards, pendant side-whiskers, and ferocious moustaches. Several nations still favour such adornments, and the animal world has never discarded them. In the wild at least, where brawn is at a premium, they stamp the male.

Darwin propounded the theory that such embellishments as the lion's and baboon's mane, or the bristling beards that cover some goats' frontal portions from chin to breast, were natural shields to protect the wearers when two males fought to the death for the love of a lady. But as we shall see when we

HORNED AND PLUMED FOR MATING

The male white pelican grows a large horny comb-like protuberance, as big as the palm of one's hand, on the upper bill during the mating season, but it drops off when courting days are over.

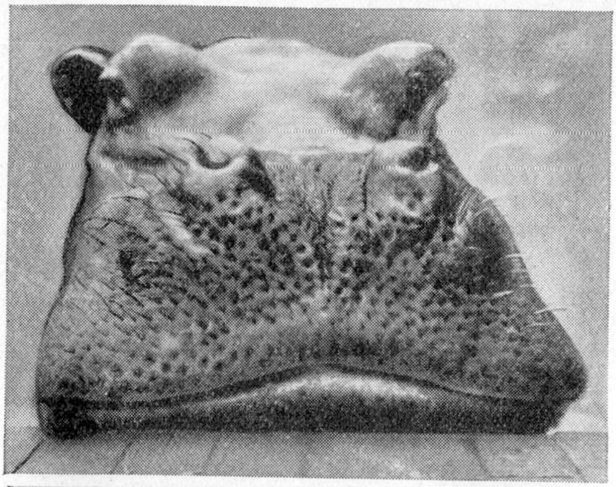

SEIDENSTUCKER; BRITISH MUSEUM (NATURAL HISTORY)

ANCIENT AND MODERN

Above: The hippopotamus as it really looks at close quarters. Below: As a medieval artist conceived it in a natural history book of the year 1491.

glance at animals in their relation to man, some of the most pugnacious creatures are entirely innocent of face trimmings.

DESIGNED TO CAPTURE THE EYE

The general consensus of opinion today regards such hairiness as male insignia designed to capture the eye of beauty quite as much as to withstand a foe. No other explanation can be offered regarding the wonderful moustaches of some male marmosets, or the bushy beards of certain little South American monkeys that seldom use their teeth on anything but nuts. The bare patches of vivid colour often seen on various monkeys undoubtedly tend to the same end.

As with some birds, many mammals congregate together in great numbers at courting time, and then only. Kipling has painted a vivid and accurate picture of this in his fine story *The White Seal*, which tells of how at rutting time the bull seals gather by hundreds on some secluded beach, and there fight out their differences, tearing each other's hides to ribbons in the process.

As we ascend the animal scale we find a marked tendency to make love, as does man, in secret. Having its well-springs in physiological processes, it is yet conducted as much with the brain as with the body. Personality tells, more and more. The finding and winning of a mate involves ever increasing subtleties denied the lower forms of life.

MYSTERY OF THE APES

We still know little or nothing of the home-life mysteries and intimacies of our next of kin, the man-like apes, but they possibly present more features in common with human behaviour than at the moment meets the eye. An interesting example was offered when the Zoological Society of London was seeking a mate for the female chimpanzee who later became the

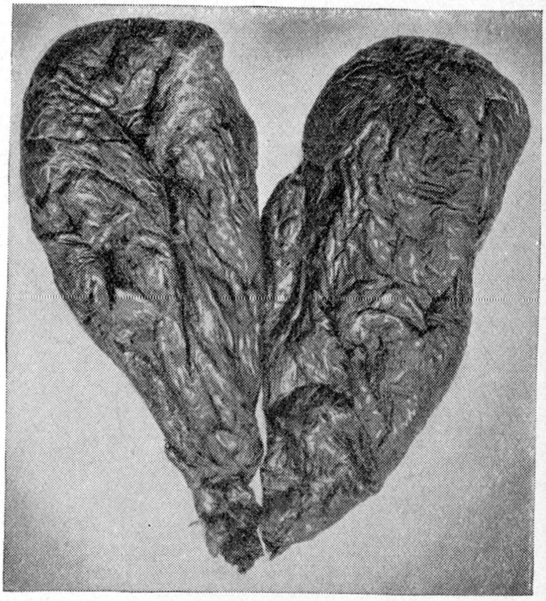

MONDIALE

SCENT GLANDS OF THE BEAVER

Many animals have special scent glands which only make themselves manifest at pairing time.

MARTIN JOHNSON (WIDE WORLD)

ORANG-UTANS IN A TREE-TOP

The courtship of man-like apes has many features in common with that of man. Most animals will mate with any member of the other sex, but not so the chimpanzees, who choose their partners with care.

W. S. BERRIDGE, F.Z.S. (MONDIALE)

NOISIEST OF ALL THE MONKEYS

Voice plays a large part in the love-making of mammals. The Brazilian howler monkey, seen above, has a louder voice than any other animal in relation to size.

WIDE WORLD

MAN OF THE WOODS

The orang-utan lives in Borneo and Sumatra. The males have a huge throat-sac on throat and chest.

mother of Jubilee, the first chimpanzee ever born within the metropolis.

For some time prior to the mother's successful mating, suitors had been sought throughout the many zoos, public and private, both in Great Britain and abroad, and also from various circuses and pet keepers. Boo-boo, the eventual mother of Jubilee, would have none of them. Finally, a middle-aged, but in all ways quite undistinguished male chimpanzee, Koko, was loaned from the Clifton Zoo, at Bristol.

CHARM IN A CHIMPANZEE

Without any apparent efforts on his part, Koko, the inferior of many of the rejected, at once walked into favour. At the time of writing he is the only father chimpanzee in Great Britain, with several children to his name, scattered up and down the country's zoos. Here then is a clear instance of that indefinable quality comprised in the terms charm and personality, manifesting itself in an animal whose possession of such many people would deny. Immeasurably less pleasing to the eye than the eagle, courting in the empyrean blue, or the peacock mincing on the lawn, Koko still knows far more about that force which, the poets tell us, makes the world go round.

BEHAVIOUR IN NATIVE HAUNTS

Chimpanzees in their native haunts would appear to have anything but a docile nature. There have been notable well-behaved individuals in the various zoological gardens of the world, and the fact that scores of thousands of persons have been photographed with young chimpanzees in Pets' Corner at the London Zoo is proof of the docility of the animal before it reaches maturity. Cases have been known in West Africa of these apes killing and devouring native children. It was for this reason that when a conference on the fauna and flora of Africa took place in the House of Lords in 1933, the chimpanzee, at first included in the list of animals recommended for the maximum of protection, was afforded less immunity.

FOX

DOG-FACED MONKEYS

On the posteriors of the baboons are patches of hardened skin which in some species are brightly coloured.

ARTHUR BROOK (MONDIALE)

ONE OF A PHEASANT'S FAMILY OF TWELVE

Most birds try to conceal their nests, and the female is often drably coloured. The pheasant builds its home on the ground, and is partial to a place where there are dead leaves.

HOW ANIMALS MAKE A HOME

COURTSHIP is the natural precursor of marriage, the making of a home and the bringing up of a family. To Nature's creatures of the wild the family is everything, the home only of importance in so far as it ministers to the family's needs and ensures the future of the race. Man stands alone in taking pride in the permanence of the structure he calls home, and even his pride in this is of comparatively recent development. Temples and tombs in plenty survive as evidence of the culture of ancient Egypt, but not a single private dwelling.

History shows that the status of the home has been in exact ratio to national advancement. We should therefore not expect to find pride in the home by any means a universal attribute of the human race. Morocco cheerfully avails itself of wireless and other refinements of civilization, but in matters domestic the people stand where they did in Bible times.

All over the world one meets tribes that have not changed their mode of living since first the white man stumbled upon them. Of none is this more true than of the numerous nomadic races.

Sometimes nomadism is the result of choice, sometimes of necessity. The latter applies to the Hausas of the Sudan, for ever wandering from one exhausted water supply to a fresh centre of sustenance; to the shiftless American Indian perpetually in search of game; and to certain coastal Esquimos, kept on the move by a climate that cramps and circumscribes all their activities.

It is not surprising to find that man's nearest relatives are similarly given to a nomadic existence. None of the apes or monkeys has any fixed abode. They favour certain areas, but never pitch camp in the same place twice. The man-like apes, it is true, build each night raft-like structures of twigs and branches well above ground, there to sleep immune from foes, but morning finds the place left far behind them and utterly forgotten. In the case of the gorilla, the head of the family or little clan sleeps at the tree foot. The purely arboreal orang-utan makes a temporary home even for an afternoon's siesta.

There is every reason for the unstable habits of these forest dwellers. Living in a land of plenty, with a climate inducive to anything but work, they have become care-free lotus eaters, much as have many humans in similar circumstances.

It is likely that the conception of a home, that is, of a structure made by an animal from substances outside itself, for its protection and possibly the shelter of a family, began far down the animal scale. It was a movable residence, as easily carried as an Indian's wigwam. The first such structures were made by the minute builders of the chalk hills, and the creatures whose shells now form the ooze covering vast areas of the sea bed. These infinitesimally small organisms made dwellings of mineral substances gathered from the surrounding water. Such homes are often of exquisite and most complex design and infinite variety.

WORMS IN TOWERS

A step higher in the scale we meet with homes the construction of which can be followed with comparative ease by means of a simple microscope. Ponds and rivers teem with a race of creatures which for want of a better assignation have been classed as worms, and are popularly known as rotifers, or wheel animalcula, so called because hair-fringed structures on the creatures' heads maintain a rapid oscillating movement which produces the illusion of rotating wheels.

Often these wheels are used only to aid respiration and to sweep eatables into the mouth, but in some species of fixed abode the wheels actually assist in the formation of circular bricks of mineral matter. These are placed side by side in rings piled one above another, the whole is cemented together and so gradually forms a tube or tower in which the animal rests secure, at least from foes of its own size.

The brickmaker is one of the larger of the rotifers, a clan whose members vary from one-twentieth to one-five-hundredth of an inch in length. Few unfortunately have popular names, but all who have read Charles Kingsley's *Water Babies* will remember "Floscularia," the beast which so excited the wonder of the little chimney sweep turned water sprite.

BRICKLAYERS OF THE SHORE

Among the higher worms tube-building becomes very elaborate. Hundreds of kinds of home-making worms infest the seas, and the shores of the British Isles abound in examples. Everyone knows the tubes of the peacock worm that protrude from the sand at low tide, suggesting stubble stalks after harvest. Just as familiar are the little limy worm tubes encrusting every blade of weed or dead shell; and the honeycomb worm that on some sandy shores

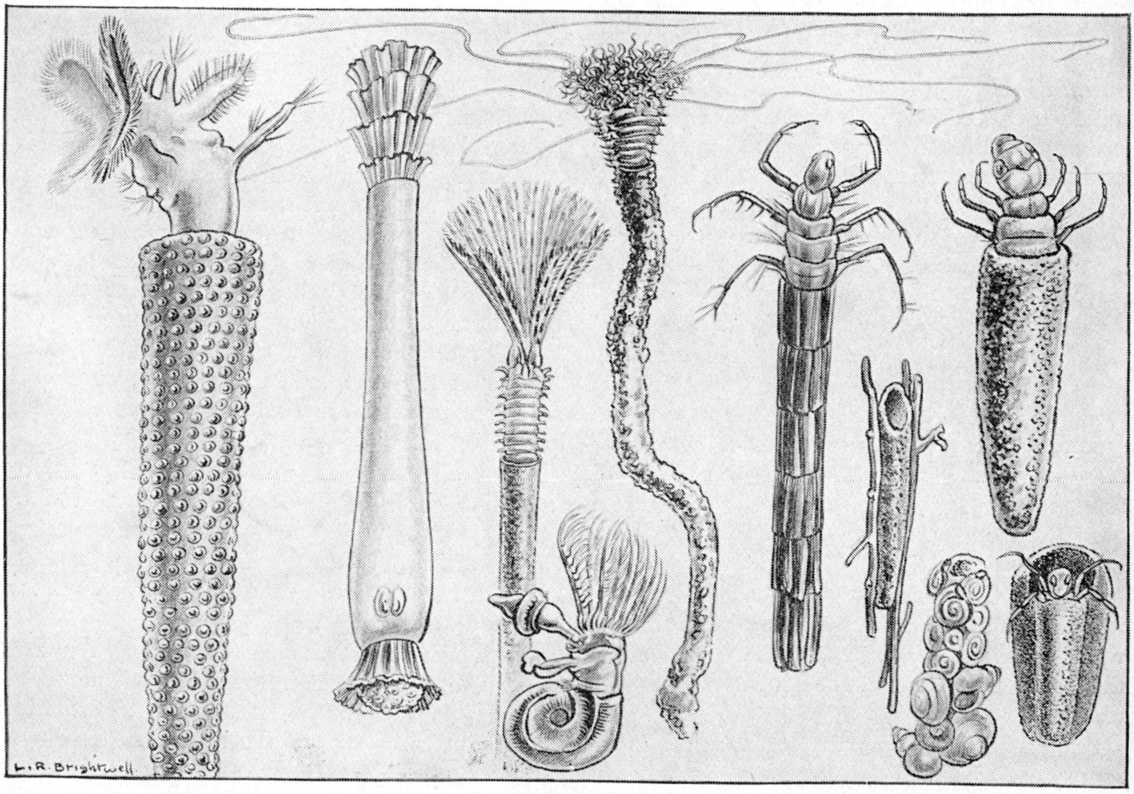

TUBE BUILDERS

Among the higher worms tube-building is very elaborate. From left to right: A rotifer, highly magnified; watering-pot shell; various species of marine worms; caddis fly larvæ and cases.

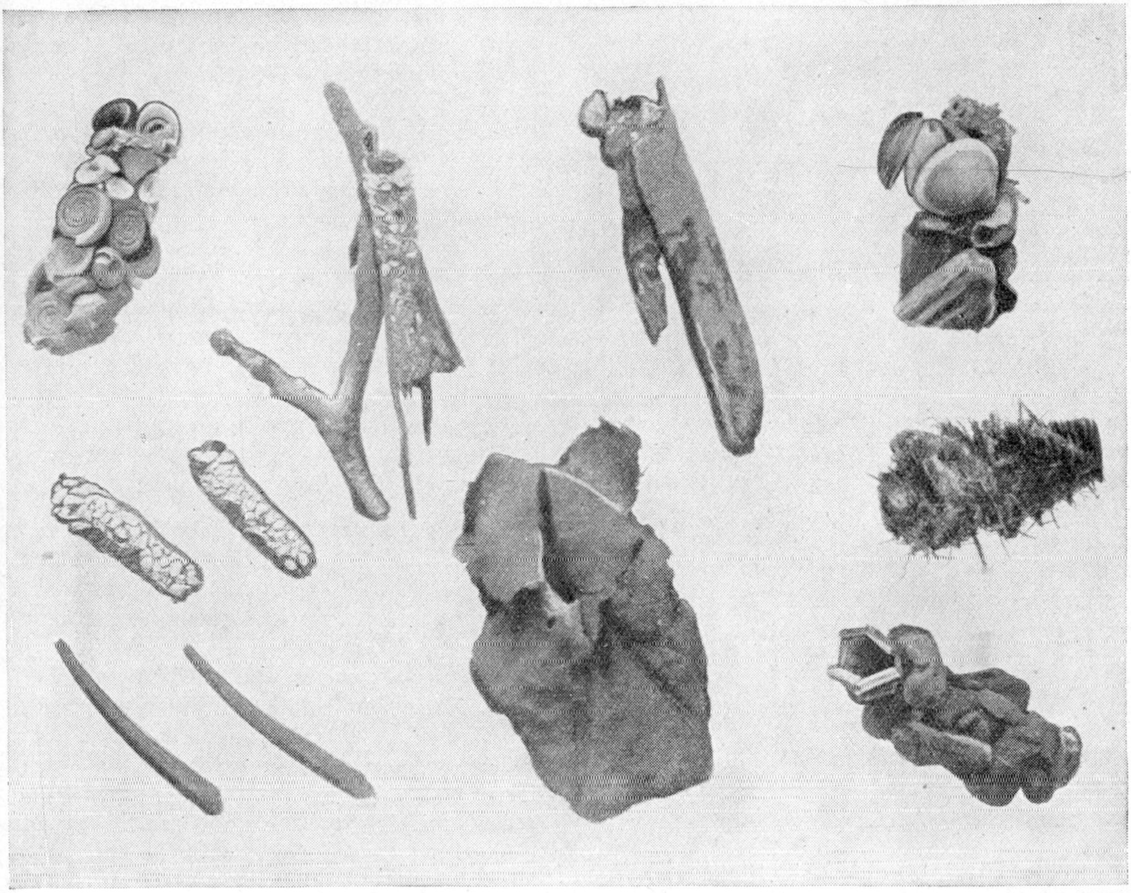

HAROLD BASTIN

STRANGE HOMES OF CADDIS WORMS

Cases made by caddis worms, the larvæ of the caddis fly. The cases are formed of various materials, including freshwater shells, sand, dead leaves and scraps of driftwood.

raises what look like miniature coral reefs, strong enough to bear a stranded boat.

An ordinary pocket lens shows that these sand tubes are made by superimposing grains of sand one upon another in circular tiers, like bricks in a tower or factory chimney. Special structures situated on the worm's head collect the sand particles and pass them along to the bricklaying organs at a terrific speed.

MOLLUSCAN ARCHITECTURE

The coiled tubes often seen encrusting weeds are built of lime, plastered whilst soft and mixed with a cement secreted by the worm upon the rim of its tube, the dwelling thus steadily increasing with the creature's bulk.

Here we see the beginnings of that wonderful architecture perfected by sixty thousand species of molluscs living today, and formerly practised by many more species now extinct. Special glands secrete colouring matter, and this, combined with the most varied architecture, results in those lovely forms so noticeable on a seaside ramble.

BUILDERS OF MIGHTY SHELLS

Since lime is the basis of all molluscan shells, land and freshwater species never produce such massive dwellings as do marine molluscs. Among the latter, pride of place goes to the three-feet-long shells of the giant clam of the Barrier Reef off the east coast of Australia, and the two-feet-long whelk of South Carolina, U.S.A., the world's largest snail.

Lime similarly forms the home of the so-called coral insects, the tiny sea anemone-like creatures that build huge stony reefs throughout tropic seas. For some reason coral animals, unlike molluscs, seem never to have colonized cold

HAROLD BASTIN

INSECT TUNNELLER

The mole cricket has developed shovel-shaped fore limbs not unlike those of higher burrowers.

waters to any extent. England boasts a single native species in the cup coral found fairly abundantly off deep water on the south-west coast of Devonshire.

All the univalves—that is one-piece shelled molluscs like the whelk and garden snail—are active, highly mobile animals. In them we see beginnings, not merely of home building, but of a homing instinct. Marked limpets have been found to return repeatedly to the same pitch, and apparently use it so persistently that the rock is often worn away by friction until a shallow depression is formed.

SNAILS COME BACK

Mark the shell of a garden snail—say with one's initials—and fling the snail over the garden wall; it will be found back in its old home twelve hours later. Though it be flung over half a dozen gardens—or as far as one's arm can carry—the result will be the same. Like the proverbial cat, the snail comes back.

If the shell suffers damage at the end of one of these aerial journeys the snail is equal to the occasion. It pours out an extra quantity of cement and repairs the damage, such repairs being obvious enough but still extremely serviceable.

All molluscan shells consist of several layers, and where the layers vary in colour, as in the tropic helmet shells, we get the materials for cameo cutting. The smooth iridescent mother-of-pearl layer lining many shells, both univalve and bivalve, is the basis of all commercial pearls, natural or cultured. Any foreign body irritating the animal is covered over with mother-of-pearl to prevent friction, much as one muffles an obstinate corn with a piece of lamb's wool. The big Roman snail of England's chalk hills makes a home within a home when winter comes by tunnelling into the ground, much as the piddock clam burrows into limestone.

In the jointed animals, house building develops in a dozen directions. Many soft-bodied defenceless larvæ, like those of the common caddis flies, emulate the tube-building worms and shell-making molluscs, though in much more clumsy fashion. Each species of caddis worm larva has its particular style of architecture. Some cover their nakedness with sticks placed endwise or in concentric layers, others use shells, stones and sand. The mineralogists amongst these insects, if dragged from their tubes and put in an aquarium well supplied with glass beads, produce very startling and picturesque residences.

SHIELD AND CRADLE

The caddis worm's home is at once a present shield against foes and a safe cradle in which it may tide over that hazardous period spent as a helpless chrysalis, awaiting the great change into the perfect caddis fly.

Every conceivable material has been pressed into service by insect ingenuity. The bees make wax from flower extracts, the wasps paper and cardboard from chewed wood, the tropical termites raise earth hillocks almost defying pick and shovel, and large enough to support big trees. Silk forms the temporary abodes of innumerable spiders and insect larvæ; tunnelling has been perfected by all kinds of spiders, insects and crustacea. Some tunnellers, like the burrowing prawns and the mole cricket, have developed shovel-shaped fore limbs that bear a striking resemblance to those of much higher burrowing animals

HAROLD BASTIN

IN A BORROWED HOME

A tiny crab that has taken up its quarters in the accommodating shell of a sea-mussel.

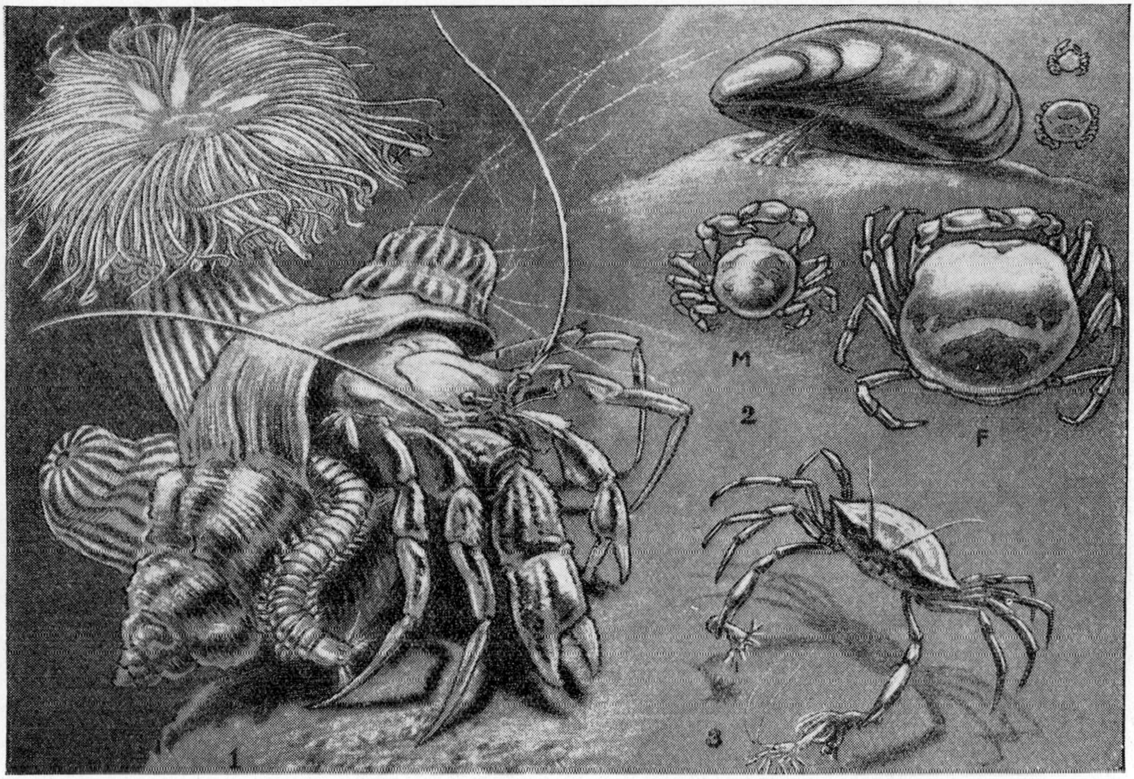

MESSMATES OF THE OCEAN FLOOR

1. *Hermit crab with anemones and a worm which share the crab's food.* 2. *Pea crabs, male* (M) *and female* (F), *which shelter in the mussel. Crabs to scale, and enlarged.* 3. *A tropical crab that employs anemones to catch food for it.*

such as the ant bear and the various moles.

As we ascend the animal scale, home-making increases in complexity, and reaches its grand climax in the birds, though always and only with a family in sight. If we except the bower birds, no animal delights in a residence for its own sake. The beautiful and intricate structures made by social wasps are as purely utilitarian as the makeshift residences of hermit crabs.

FORTRESSES OF THE CRUSTACEANS

Those diverting crustaceans, so abundant in all seas, show a wonderful adaptability in the choice of borrowed homes. Most tuck their defenceless rear portions into solid univalve shells (a whelk's, for example), but these unyielding castles need to be constantly changed to allow for the tenant's growth. When, as sometimes happens, a big anemone attaches itself to the residence, it dissolves the shell away, and encloses the hermit crab in an easy-fitting protective tunic of unlimited stretching capacity. Some species of hermit deliberately dress themselves in anemones, and one kind finds an equally accommodating fortress by tucking itself into the elastic tissues of a sponge.

FISH AS ARCHITECTS

Home-making amongst animals is usually so inextricably part and parcel of child welfare that here we will give our attention mainly to the mere materials and their utilization in accommodating a family.

Many fishes are painstaking architects, and often both sexes work together for the general weal. Wrasses thus make big ball-shaped nests of weed; salmon and trout clear spaces in the stream bed with their tails; and the lampreys, male and female, laboriously construct a nursery by removing heavy stones one by one with their suctorial mouths. Sometimes both householders and a few neighbours join forces where a particularly heavy stone is concerned. The American bowfins make a nursery clearing in a reed bed several yards in extent.

FOX

KINGFISHER'S RETREAT

Legend had it that the nests of kingfishers floated on water. They are in a hole in a bank.

In Great Britain at least the frog will never earn a reputation for tender motherhood. She light-heartedly dumps some hundreds of eggs in the nearest water and there the matter ends so far as she is concerned. Sometimes all goes well, but sometimes the water supply fights a losing match against a hot sun, and the eggs are dried up before they can hatch. Even the toad, though trekking at infinite pains year after year to the same ancestral pond, thinks no more of its rosary-like strings of eggs once they are deposited.

TREE FROG ENGINEERS

But there are frogs and frogs, and some members of this numerous tribe vie with the birds in care of their young. In Japan the male and female of a certain tree frog work together to make a snug underground nest for their spawn conveniently near to a well-filled irrigation ditch. They dig a tunnel from nest to ditch, and when at last the tadpoles emerge, they have but to wriggle down the sloping runway, always constructed at an angle, to launch themselves for life.

In Paraguay a wonderful little frog known as the wallunnkukk joins forces with his wife to wrap the eggs between two leaves overhanging a pool, so that when they hatch the tadpoles are only a step from the water which is to be their domain. Even this is outdone by a Brazilian tree frog which makes a veritable swimming pool for its infants by fashioning a basin-shaped structure of mud on the sides of a forest pool. The mud walls are neatly patted into position by the parents, and when the tadpoles wriggle clear of their gelatinous egg cases they are safe from hungry fish and water beetles.

SHARING A HOME

Judged by human ideals, reptiles are as unsatisfactory in their home interests as in their love making. A few are indifferent burrowers, the most thorough in this direction being the New Zealand tuatera, a lizard-like creature, last survivor of a now extinct group.

It makes a burrow some two feet long in soft earth, digging with its strong claws, and invariably laying its dozen or so eggs on the right-hand side. The left side is often allocated to a small species of petrel, bird and reptile living on good terms. For a reptile, the tuatera is quite a home lover, since it remains in residence throughout the whole of the incubatory period, a matter of thirteen months.

MONDIALE

BUILDERS OF MOSSY NESTS

Humming birds prefer to hover while feeding, when their wings move at nearly sixty beats a second.

DR. GRAF ZEDTWITZ (MONDIALE)

LITTLE ATTEMPT AT HOME-MAKING

A few wisps of grass or an accumulation of offal and fish scales form the nest of the gull. Elaborate architecture would be wasted on the wind-swept, spray-drenched edge of a cliff.

Remarkable as is the diversity of birds' nests, certain general principles seem to govern their construction. In almost all instances the builders seem to play for concealment, and there is amongst the more intelligent birds a marked tendency to build elaborate nests.

Some ostriches dump their eggs in the sand like lizards. At the opposite end of the scale we have the crow-like bower birds with their wonderful assembly rooms, and that still nearer relative of the crows, the common magpie, which not only builds a capacious nest strong enough to withstand many winters, but even provides it with a roof.

FAMILY IN A BOTTLE

All conceivable materials may be pressed into service, and the strangest sites are chosen. A blackbird has been known to build a nest entirely of watch-springs, a tom-tit to bring up a large and clamorous family in a ginger beer bottle, an old boot, or a discarded kettle. Only where weather or other conditions would make nesting a thankless task is there little attempt at home-making. The gulls and razorbills on the wind-swept, spray-drenched cliff edge would be wasting energy on elaborate architecture, and so a few wisps of grass at most, or an accumulation of offal and fish scales makes cradle enough for their hardy broods.

Burrowing birds there are in plenty, as witness the sheld duck and the puffin. The Argentine oven birds excel swallows as plasterers. They build relatively immense structures, very like old-fashioned earth ovens, placed in the most exposed situations, as on the top of a post or rock, where the sun bakes the material iron hard, and makes the oven a difficult object to break open.

IMMUNE FROM ENEMIES

The hornbills of Africa and Asia use clay to wall up the hen bird after she has clambered into a hollow tree trunk by way of a convenient hole. The orifice is reduced by means of clay until only a space big enough for the passage of food is left. Here the willing prisoner remains, fed by her mate and immune from snakes and monkeys until the eggs are hatched and the fledgelings big enough to take care of themselves. The so-called edible swallow of China, lacking clay, supplies its own cement in the form of a glutinous saliva, making with this and its own feathers a basin-like cradle on the face of a cliff.

As one might expect, home-making reaches a high pitch of perfection among arboreal birds, which must often use ingenuity not only in finding nesting materials but also in securely fastening the home amid the wind-rocked foliage. A triumph in this direction is achieved by the little Indian tailor bird, a species of warbler, which actually sews pendant leaves together with fibres, and in the cup so formed makes a nest proper of hair, down, lichens and grasses.

An eye for colour as well as for quality of nesting materials is very apparent amongst such perching birds as orioles. During the

WIDE WORLD

WALLED UP BY HER MATE

The hornbills of Africa and Asia use clay to wall up the hen bird when a hole has been found in a tree trunk. The opening is made smaller by means of clay until only a space big enough for the passage of food is left. Here the hen remains until the eggs are hatched and the birds ready to fly.

past ten years a wonderful series of experiments have been carried out at the famous Three Brooks Wild Life Sanctuary, near Roxburgh, Connecticut, U.S.A. The chief subjects of experiment have been orioles, birds which normally tend to build with strips of vegetable fibre, bark, scraps of vine, and so on.

BIRDS THAT LIKE BLUE

During the first eight years of offering the birds unusual materials, such as cotton, horsehair, and afterwards, coloured wools, the birds were chary of such innovations. But at last they took so kindly to the suggestions that they used nothing else, and produced nests of immense size and astonishing design. Late in the series of experiments other birds were apparently so struck by the rainbow-hued edifices of the orioles that they followed suit.

So here in this sanctuary are orioles with football-sized nests of flaring mauve, white and orange yarn; waxwings with scarlet nurseries; and king birds bringing up their babies amongst festoons of white cloth. Some birds acquired such a liking for blue that after introducing a few blue ribands into the general colour scheme of their nests, they elected in succeeding seasons to build with nothing else. Some of these nests glowed like orchids.

INGENIOUS NEST BUILDING

One might continue almost indefinitely listing the varieties of perching birds' nests, and the devices to make them and their fragile contents enemy proof. The helplessness of the young is the greatest of all incentives to ingenious nest building. Even when, as in the case of the common sparrow, several broods may be produced in a year, the family is always smaller than in ground-building types, which

NESTS FASHIONED OF LEAVES

Left: The nest of a Brazilian frog. Centre: The Indian tailor bird, which sews pendant leaves together with fibres, and in them builds a nest. Right: A tropical ant that uses its larvæ as shuttles.

WIDE WORLD

STORKS DO NOT LIKE CHANGING HOUSE

A stork returning to its nest, which is usually on the top of a building. Built of sticks, the bird uses the same home every year and adds a few more twigs and branches to the structure.

produce self-helpful young not so much in need of protection.

Some humming birds bind their mossy nests together with spiders' silk and hang them at the extreme tip of a leaf. The honey eaters hang their soup-tureen-shaped nests by both ends from a branch too slender to bear even a snake. The weaver birds and others find safety in numbers and build huge communal nests accommodating dozens of families, which unite to mob a common foe or give each other warning when danger threatens.

PROOF AGAINST NEST RAIDERS

The desert wrens of Arizona build homes in the fleshy stems of the big candelabra cacti, nightmare plants so densely clothed with needle-like spines as to daunt the hardiest bird-nester.

The hoatzin of Brazil always builds its nest upon a tree branch overhanging a stream. There is a reason for this. The fledgeling hoatzin can, almost from the first, scramble about the branches with beak, feet and wing fingers. But in Brazil danger in the form of monkeys or tree snakes may threaten from above. If this happens the baby hoatzin cheerfully takes a header into the water and strikes out with all four limbs together, using a stroke very like the crawl.

NEST TWENTY FEET HIGH

The remarkable homing instinct, so apparent in many migratory birds, often leads birds to repair an old nest and use it season after season. Mr. Cherry Kearton has recorded an instance of ospreys or fish hawks visiting the same nest for so many years in succession that the pile of sticks and fish offal of which it was composed eventually reached a height of twenty feet. It might have towered even beyond this but that it became lop-sided and collapsed in a gale.

Compared with these wonderful structures of the feathered world, mammalian homes are somewhat disappointing. The carnivora are chiefly content to select a cave or a clearing in dense scrub for the shelter of their young. A few of the smaller species show ingenuity in the art of burrowing, notably the moles, ant bears, and the rodents. The badger has little to learn in this regard. Some years ago a road collapsed as the result of two badgers driving their earth beneath it. At one point they had dug down through the solid chalk, full of large and sharp flints, to a depth of eighteen feet.

Small wonder that the fox is often glad to avail himself of this ready-made accommodation, the badger seeming to offer little resentment. Many burrowers line their innermost

MONDIALE

ANIMAL ENGINEER

The true beaver is the largest European aquatic rodent. His scaly tail has almost become a fin.

sleeping chambers with dried grass, even when no family is in evidence, and show a certain crude sense of hygiene. At the Whipsnade quarters of the London Zoological Society the prairie marmots can be seen every autumn drying freshly-cut hay for their winter quarters, and they periodically take advantage of a fine day to give this rough upholstery an airing, or even renew it altogether when it has become fouled past endurance.

Many squirrels and a few of the smaller lemurs make nests almost worthy of a bird's best efforts. The squirrel shows considerable forethought in providing two exits, with a view to effecting an escape at short notice.

The beaver stands in a class by itself among mammals as a home-maker, and has given rise to innumerable Indian legends as well as highly-coloured but inaccurate accounts in early natural history books.

The beaver forms pools in which to place its lodge and food stores, but not from any real appreciation of water finding its own level. It simply digs and digs until the stream it is seeking to divert at last runs the way it is required to go.

BEARS THAT NEVER COME

Innumerable instances can be quoted of the beaver being hoist with its own petard as a result of not fully appreciating the forces it is seeking to harness. It is true that it often fells a tree so that it falls conveniently for bark stripping, but the tree sometimes jams among other trees, and there are instances of beavers being crushed through the fall of a tree.

Beavers have lived in a wild " natural " sanctuary at Horsham, in Sussex, for forty years or so, but they still keep on the alert for the bear and wolverine that never come, and feverishly provide bark against each winter despite ample rations of all the foods they like best. Neither will storms nor floods induce them to forsake their water-logged lodges for comfortable sleeping boxes. Their natural sleeping chambers are dug deep in the lake's bank, just above water level, with two exits, one above, the other below water level.

PLUGGED WITH CLAY

One of the most ingenious of mammalian homes is that made by the aquatic duck mole of Australia, a beast which after all has more in common with birds than any other mammal. Its burrow shows more ingenuity than that of even a mole, for on retiring to rest it plugs the way in with a wad of stiff clay. Apart from the ingenious spring door of the tropical trapdoor spider, the average animal can think of no better device for excluding unwelcome callers than to fill the entrance to its home with a spine-covered head or an exaggerated claw.

As for the bears that fail to eventuate, the black variety is particularly partial to the neighbourhood of a fallen tree. With its powerful claws it digs a hole sufficiently large to accommodate its bulky body, the trunk forming a kind of roof which is also a measure of protection against enemies. If the timber is massive the animal will hunt for a hollow tree and make itself as comfortable as a night watchman in his hut. The female polar bear usually chooses a natural ice cave in which to rear her family.

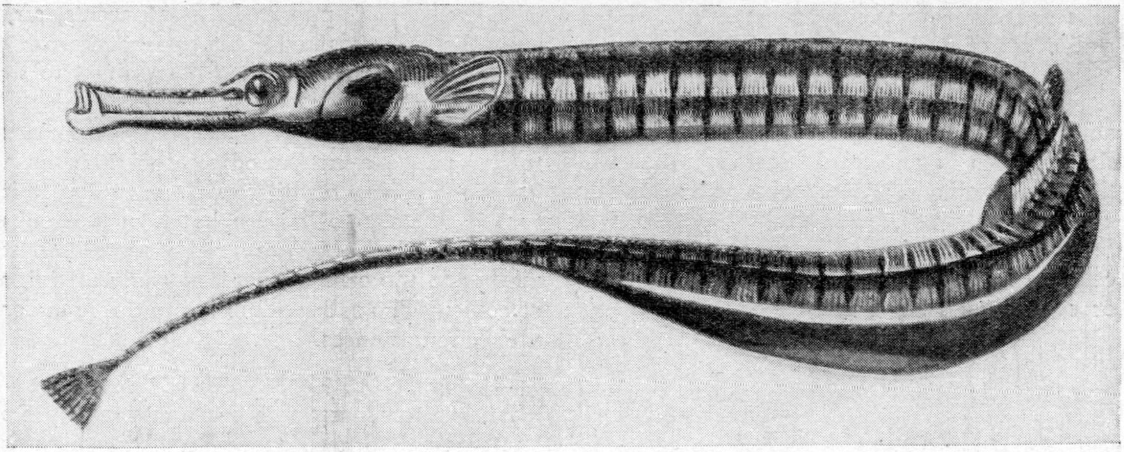

"NURSING" FATHER OF THE PIPE FISH FAMILY
Two flaps of skin on the under-surface of the male pipe fish fold one upon the other to form a pouch. In this the female deposits the eggs. The pipe fish is a very attenuated version of the famous sea horse.

BRINGING UP A FAMILY

The quality of mother love or parental devotion in animals is decided largely by the number of progeny. Anything like individual attention, or indeed concern of any kind, would scarcely be practicable in animals like the ling or the turtle, which count their families in multitudes. In the case of a communal insect, the mother, or queen, is a mere egg-laying machine, and her brood, numerous as the sands of the sea shore, is tended by a horde of neutral nurses, as passionless and mechanical in their ministrations as the robot-like El-women of Scandinavian legend.

Parental devotion might be assumed to reach a high standard in many mammals, birds, and fishes, if judged only by the pains taken to make a nursery, some examples of which have been outlined in the previous section. Devotion to young, however, is largely a matter of intelligence, and some of the world's most devoted animal mothers are creatures having little need or inclination to found an elaborate home.

Apes and monkeys, the most feckless and indifferent of home-makers, are not far behind our own species as nurses. Long after the infant has been weaned they test every mouthful of food before allowing the baby to swallow it. They also show wonderful patience in supervising baby's early attempts at climbing, lending their tails for the purpose. Not that foolish indulgence is the rule in monkey circles. A somewhat spartan discipline goes hand in hand with maternal tenderness, and where correction is deemed necessary the firm right hand is never spared. Bats similarly nurse their small families, and so do most of the rodents and the carnivora.

All who have seen it must have been impressed by the sight of a lioness inculcating the first principles of hunting by letting her cubs worry her tail tip. In the wild such lessons would be carried further by the bringing home of some small animal sufficiently maimed to give the family practice in the use of their weapons. Similar behaviour marks the family life of most birds of prey.

Large numbers of young mammals and birds pass through a rigorous schooling. The goat's kids find their mountain legs by staggering up and down the recumbent mother; the sea lion launches its youngster on the water, often when the little one is very loath to take the first plunge. Recent observers have given graphic accounts of how the golden eagle induces its young first to trust themselves to their wings, even dropping pieces of food in mid air, but within distance of the nest upon the cliff face, and so tempting the youngster to leap into the void.

Whilst many birds' nests become incredibly foul as the droppings of the brood accumulate, sea birds and some birds of prey remove such waste matters or coax the infants to deposit them hygienically over the edge of the nest, thus showing apparently some grasp of the rudiments of sanitation.

In our own species parental solicitude denied its natural outlets may find a substitute in adoption, or even in the keeping of pets. A similar state of affairs obtains with many of the higher animals. Recent observations of the gull have shown how blindly the bird will brood on almost anything once it has conceived the desire to sit. It will accept a ball, or even a tin box, if robbed of its eggs. We all know the readiness with which the domestic hen will accept a china substitute. The changeling which the cuckoo so successfully foists upon its dupes is another classical example that is worthy of note.

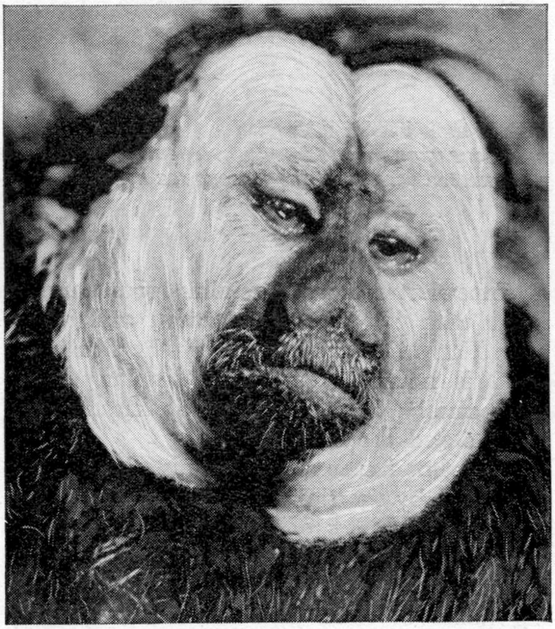

WIDE WORLD

NIGHT MONKEY OF GUIANA

Long after the infant monkey has been weaned its mother tests every mouthful of food.

In the bird market at Singapore, Mr. Walter Goodfellow, the famous collector, saw huge consignments of the popular Java sparrow cooped together in one cage. With each batch of some fifty nestlings there would be one or two adults, and these, when food was placed in the cage, literally wore themselves out dispensing it to the young with such devotion that the supply was exhausted long before they gave a thought to their own needs. In the Antarctic, an orphaned penguin chick is often literally killed by kindness by the joint efforts of a host of self-appointed foster parents, and an orphaned egg is invariably smashed between the would-be mothers, each determined to sit upon it.

From time to time the illustrated press brings to our notice a cat brooding ducklings, or a ferret mothering rabbits. In menageries it is very customary to hand a batch of lion cubs which have been born to a sickly or indifferent mother to the care of some matronly retriever or collie. The cubs seldom fail to thrive under such circumstances.

SHEEPDOG AS LION'S FOSTER MOTHER

An extraordinary case occurred many years ago at the Sydney Zoo when a lion cub was allowed to remain with its foster mother, a mongrel sheepdog, until it had reached full lion's estate. So complete was the dominance of its nurse that the lion, which could have effaced her with one tap from its paw, had eventually to be removed to ensure that it got its proper amount of food.

Records of the Anthropological Society in India show that the story of Romulus and Remus being suckled by a wolf was undoubtedly based upon actual fact, though the wolf-reared children of reality grow up into anything but woodland godlings. Such children indeed seldom survive for long when attempts are made at their reclamation to ordinary ways of life.

"NURSING" FATHERS

In glancing at the various ways in which animals make a home, it was noticed that the work was generally shared by both parents, but that responsibility for the family usually devolved upon the female. There are many cases in which the natural order is reversed. For reasons which are often obscure, responsibility for the future of the race, apart from the actual deposition of the eggs, is left to the male. The " nursing " father is an established institution in many widely different classes of animals.

Among mammals it is customary for father to bethink himself of bachelor joys as soon as the family appears. Unless he volunteers to walk out, the mother, knowing his irritable temperament, as often as not deserts him for the time being, in order to bring forth and nurse her young in peace.

Only one mammal apparently reverses this order. The male marmoset would seem to be

FOX

ENORMOUS NEST OF THE AUSTRALIAN BRUSH TURKEY

The one or more hens of a brush turkey household usually rest or hunt for food, whilst the cock raises a mound of impressive size. The hen or hens deposit eggs within the mound.

the partner of a frivolous wife, for he at once holds the baby as soon as it is born, handing it over to his partner only when its nourishment makes this imperative. Her duties having been very perfunctorily performed, she returns with all speed to more congenial employments.

MALE MARMOSET'S CHARGE

The father's job meantime is no sinecure. Laden like a miniature Sinbad, he toils about the tree branches bearing his precious burden, until its bulk and exuberant vitality must make its final relinquishment a very real relief.

A whole group of nursing fathers is provided by the ostrich tribe, nursery duties lying with the cock bird in the ostriches proper, the rheas, emus, cassowaries, kiwis and tinamous. The male ostrich may be called upon to take charge of as many as thirty eggs, and the emu nearly a score.

The South American cock ostrich or rhea appears to have its limits of endurance and willingness to be imposed upon. The ladies queue up to the saucer-shaped hollow in the sand which serves as a nest, and proceed to dump their eggs under the watchful eye of the nurse-to-be. When he decides that the nest is filled to capacity he intimates as much by kicking and pecking the still laden hens until they wander away disconsolate. Later the plain is strewn with orphaned eggs, and there they stay until cleared away by wild dogs or wandering gauchos.

INCUBATED BY THE SUN

The ostrich's wings, so impracticable for flight, are of great use when it comes to covering a score or so of eggs each equal in size to two dozen of the domestic fowl's. The cock bird subsides amongst his furbelows, like a seventeenth-century lady amongst her hooped skirts, and so stays for about forty days, the hens only under the rarest circumstances offering relief. In exceptionally hot localities the cock merely covers the eggs with sand, and, mounting guard over them, leaves the actual work of incubation to the sun.

With the evolutionary chain in mind, the ostrich's way of sometimes leaving eggs to hatch by the heat of the sun recalls the methods employed by most living reptiles, the last representatives of the forerunners of the birds. This reptilian trait finds its highest expression amongst birds in the remarkable brush turkeys of Australia.

These birds are not unlike the farmyard gobbler in general appearance, particularly the cock birds, who display resplendent wattles (fleshy lobes under the throat) in the nesting season. The one or more hens of a brush turkey household usually rest or hunt for food, whilst the cock by kicking leaves and rubbish backwards with his enormous feet, raises a mound of impressive size. Where several birds combine to make a communal mound, and build upon the same site several years in succession, it may measure one hundred and fifty feet in circumference, and be higher than a man. The efforts of a single bird will sometimes amount to as much as five tons of rubbish worked up into a compact pile. The ground round such an edifice looks as though it had been scoured with a vacuum cleaner.

HAROLD BASTIN

MALE MIDWIFE TOAD

It gathers the eggs, which are laid in long strings, and attends to them until the tadpoles arrive.

Within this mound the hen or hens deposit eggs, usually arranged in concentric tiers. There they remain for several weeks, the cock from time to time testing the mound's temperature by thrusting in his bare neck, and adding or removing débris as he deems advisable. The infant brush turkeys are extraordinarily precocious even for the young of ground-dwelling birds. They scramble their way to freedom, and are able to scratch for a living and even to use their wings as soon as they gain the light.

This reptilian mode of incubation brings its own difficulties. The snug mound commends itself to certain huge lizards known as monitors, and they hasten to deposit their own eggs in the nest so conveniently provided for them. The lizard eggs hatch quicker than do those of the birds, and the young reptiles make their first meals of embryo brush turkey.

CARRIED IN A POUCH

There are some paragon nursing fathers amongst the frogs. One, a minute species from Chile, known as Darwin's frog, swallows the eggs as fast as laid by his spouse and tucks them into a pouch beneath his throat. The eggs hatch, and the tadpoles feeding on their yolk sacs soon require more accommodation. Conveniently the pouch spreads, first down the underside of father's face, then along his sides, until it nearly covers his entire body. He is practically a walking nursery, and so remains until the last of his fifteen or so children have emerged as fully formed froglets.

A common continental amphibian is the well-named midwife toad. The male gathers the eggs, which are laid in long strings, winds them round his hind legs, and thus fettered struggles slowly to some underground retreat. At night he cautiously creeps forth and moistens the eggs in a convenient pond, or failing this bathes them in dew. Thus he continues until instinct tells him that the eggs are nearly ready to hatch, when he hurries to the nearest water and releases a swarm of tadpoles.

CANNIBALISTIC MOTHER

A cannibalistic mother would seem to explain the nursing father amongst many of the lower vertebrates. If the male giant Japanese salamander, for example, did not take charge of the strings of eggs laid by his partner, they would quickly be devoured by her.

In the long list of nursing fathers among fish can be numbered the little stickleback, already noticed amongst the nest builders. This fish, which abounds in ponds and ditches,

DORIEN LEIGH

FIRST AND LAST STAGES OF A BEAUTIFUL MOTH

This unusual photograph shows the Promethea moth depositing its eggs upon the beautiful Lady's Slipper. Pairing takes place in the air, and the female usually dies soon after the eggs are laid.

is wonderfully adaptable. It thrives also in brackish and in salt water, using whatever material is in season for its home-making.

When turning the boulders in search of shellfish, one often comes on hard clusters of beady objects of variable hue, white, pinkish or green. These are the eggs of gobies, or the little bullheads, and the male fish is usually to be found in the vicinity, putting a bold face on whatever odds may be against him in the defence of the eggs. The butterfly blenny and the butter gunnel, or nine eyes, generally tuck their eggs safely within an empty shell, blocking the entrance with their own persons, and glaring defiance at all comers.

Low down in the tide range during spring one meets the male lump sucker, a heavy dumpy fish ill-fitted for swimming, but clinging tightly to any anchorage by means of a big elliptical sucking disc upon its breast. This creature, whose brooding habits have earned it the name of hen fish, endeavours to keep free from harm some one hundred and thirty thousand eggs. It is a losing fight, for other fish, crabs and whelks take their toll from below, early spring gales dislodge masses of eggs from the rock cranny sheltering them, and sea birds attracted by the spoil in all probability also lay siege.

In the long bony pipe fish which always forms part of the shrimper's catch, nursing fatherhood reaches its peak. The pipe fish is simply a very attenuated version of the famous sea horse, and broods the young in precisely the same manner. Two flaps of skin on the male's under-surface fold one upon the other to form a pouch and in this the female deposits the eggs. A unique feature of this pouch is that it develops at this season a spongy lining, richly supplied with blood vessels; the eggs become partly embedded in this, and apparently draw nourishment therefrom, as do embryo mammals from the placenta.

Sea horse and pipe fish certainly need a good start in life, for they are the feeblest of swimmers. They are largely passive travellers, clinging by their prehensile tails to drifting weeds, and so wandering without a course or means of directing one, at the mercy of winds and currents. It would appear to be a very precarious existence.

ALMOST WITHOUT A BODY

Also in the shrimper's catch occurs the little crustacean known as a sea spider, a creature virtually without a body, for the internal organs are largely distributed through the basal segments of the exaggerated legs. In summer one finds the male of the sea spider carrying a little bag containing the eggs. He carries the bundle with him as he creeps about the rocks, plunging his long curved beak into sea anemones.

Worms might be regarded as the least likely to evince any parental care. Certain marine bristle worms, however, display something very like it, and again the male is the responsible party.

LIFE MEANS DEATH

On the shores of the English Channel lives a worm much prized by fishermen as bait, and not unlike the cat worm sold in fishing-tackle shops. Male and female share a tube made of sand, and when the female has laid her eggs, the male incubates them by causing a stream of water to pass continuously over them by rhythmic undulations of his body. The mother, having discharged the eggs, is so weakened as to be a mere encumbrance, so her practical helpmate philosophically devours her. To her the new life means death, but to him a presumably excellent meal.

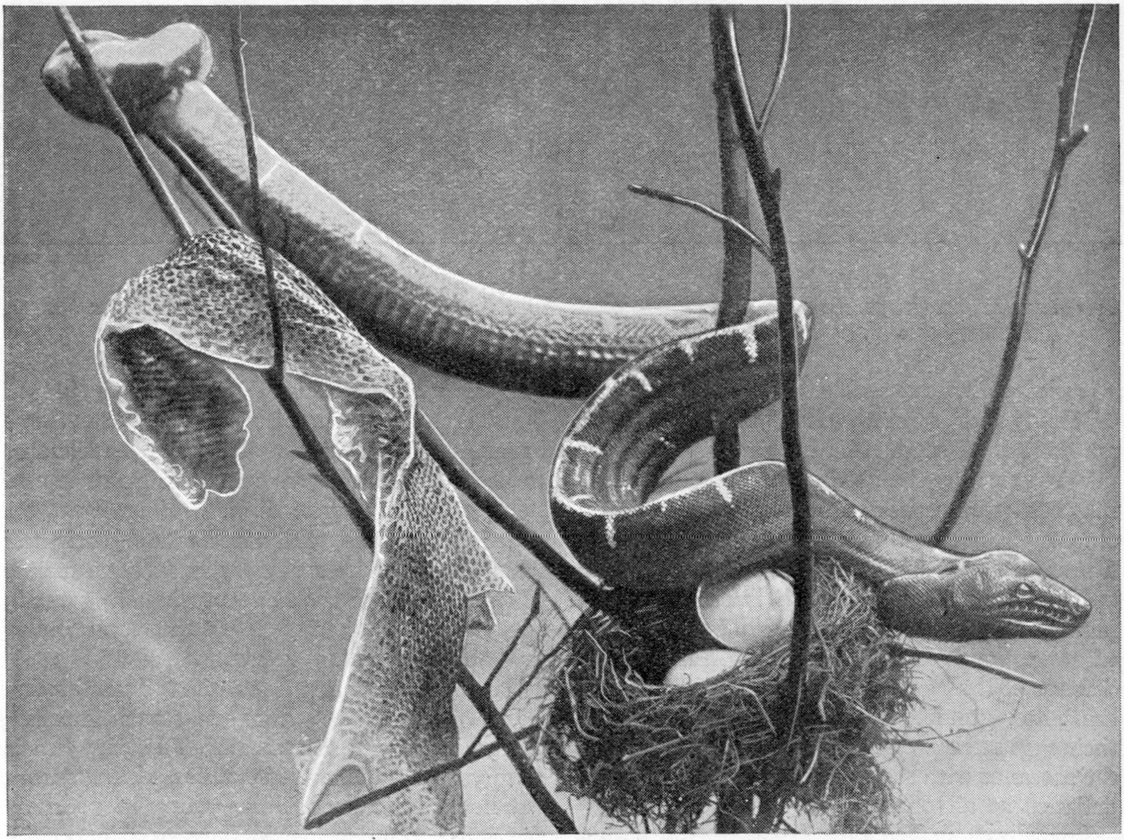

FOX

REPTILE THAT CRUSHES ITS PREY

The boa-constrictor produces its young from eggs, though those shown in the nest were laid by a bird. When this photograph was taken the snake had just shed a skin.

CHARLES ALFRED HAMILTON

LARGE ANIMALS LIVE LONGER THAN SMALL ONES

There is relationship between longevity and size. The larger machine usually takes longer to wear out than does the smaller one. Oxen, given good conditions, live about forty years.

DURATION OF LIFE

WHATEVER the nature of the animal—man, mouse or amœba—it is travelling to a goal of some kind, and the time it takes to run its course is always a matter of interest. Often the age limit of an animal may be of direct economic importance. If, for example, we knew the potential life spans of the various whales their conservation might be an easier matter. At present, legislation on their behalf must perforce be founded largely on assumptions.

Save where domestic creatures are concerned, exact knowledge of any particular animal's life span is hard to obtain. Major Stanley Flower and Sir Peter Chalmers Mitchell have amassed elaborate statistics of animal longevity based upon observation of captive specimens. But as the authors point out, such figures give comparatively little or no indication of the same animal's potential longevity under natural conditions.

Once a creature comes under human supervision it is sheltered from natural enemies, drought, famine and a hundred other dangers, as well as from ailments which might tend to shorten its career under normal conditions. Even so, such figures cast an interesting light on animal viability, as the life span is called, at the same time dispelling many popular illusions regarding the length of life of such animals as the raven, donkey and carp, which tradition has erroneously invested with Methuselah-like longevity.

In the first place, the longest-lived animal, regarded as a species and not as an isolated exception, is probably man, if we disregard for the moment the dwindling race of giant tortoises. Apart from wars and other disasters, the average man of today enjoys far better chances of attaining to a ripe old age than did his forbears of even a century ago. Improved sanitation, an increasing appreciation of the value of sunlight, fresh air and good food, and the wonderful advances made in medicine all tend to prolong life, and before very long perhaps the centenarian will cease to be an interesting curiosity.

The figures gathered to date tend to show that there is a marked correlation between longevity and size. The larger machine takes

FOX

GORILLA AT HOME

For their size the man-like apes are probably the longest-lived mammals next to ourselves.

longer to wear out than does the smaller one. Amongst mammals, statistics seem to show that vegetarian or mixed feeders wear out more gradually than do carnivores or flesh eaters, though it must be admitted they are obliged to spend much more time in feeding, a bigger bulk of fuel being required to obtain the same amount of power. On the other hand, they lead less strenuous and hazardous lives than do the flesh eaters.

EARLY MATURITY—EARLY DEATH

For their size the man-like apes, the gorilla, orang-utan and chimpanzee, are very likely the longest lived mammals next to ourselves. It is only recently that we discovered how to keep these delicate creatures successfully in confinement, so that exact information on this point is still very fragmentary. Chimpanzees and orangs have been known to live up to forty years in captivity. It may well be that, like the human beings native to tropical countries, they " burn out " much faster than do the people of the bleak but bracing northern hemisphere.

As we pass down the primate scale, there is a marked tendency to mature and die faster in accordance with diminishing size. A common rhesus monkey is senile earlier than a baboon, and a rhesus can generally be counted upon to outlive a marmoset. Yet here, as in all things else, the exception proves the rule. The honey-bear or kinkajou of tropic America may live for forty years, much longer than any monkey of the same size. The porcupine ant eater or echidna may also live to be over forty, but this is one of the lowest of all mammals, and has so much in common with reptiles as to be outside present considerations of size in relation to longevity.

SOMETIMES A CENTENARIAN

Contrary to popular belief, the elephant does not live for centuries and all stories of its extreme longevity are of such a hearsay or traditional nature as to be at best unconvincing. An elephant can breed when just turned ten years old, and though it may occasionally see a century out it usually develops signs of senility at about half that age.

The hippopotamus and rhinoceros can breed up to forty years of age, and most of the bigger grazers and browsers—camels, giraffes, horses, oxen, sheep, etc.—will, given good conditions,

FOX

FORTY YEARS IN CAPTIVITY

Chimpanzees have lived forty years in captivity. They probably die younger in their native haunts.

MARCUSWELL MAXWELL (MONDIALE)

PREFERS TO HUNT AT NIGHT

The rhinoceros can breed up to forty years of age. It prefers to live singly or in pairs and to do its hunting for food when the heat of the day is over.

live till about forty. A camel can be worked hard for over thirty years, and there are a few donkeys of this age still in harness in our own country. In the East a donkey's years seldom measure a quarter of a century.

DONKEY'S BURDEN

This is hardly surprising, seeing that the Oriental donkey, though smaller and slighter than the British breed, is normally saddled with loads that would appear stupendous to western eyes. There is a saying in the Near East that " a merchant first makes up his load and then goes out to hire an animal to carry it." As donkeys are far more numerous in the Near East than any other beast of burden, they usually have to bear the brunt. And, whatever the weight of the load, the eastern merchant invariably adds to it his own usually bulky person. By way of consideration for his pack animal, he makes his wife (or wives) walk !

Cats, bears and sea lions may live from fifteen to forty years, according to size. Lions, at least in zoological gardens, are easily the longest lived of all the cat tribe. But taking size for size the mammals certainly read an eloquent brief for vegetarianism. A fruit bat half the size of a fox enjoys twice the fox's age. A common insect-eating bat runs a dead heat with the omnivorous mouse or rat, namely two and a half years. Whales, as stated above, are largely an unknown quantity as regards their potential life spans. The mystery may one day be cleared up, thanks to the recent device of marking them with nickel darts or miniature harpoons, much as fish are marked with discs, or birds are ringed.

DIET OF CARRION

The known age limits of birds discount the meat versus vegetables theory of longevity. The ostrich, eight feet high and two hundred pounds in weight, is far behind the vulture, which on a diet of carrion often lives for nearly half a century. The raven, popularly supposed to outlive the centuries, is, according to the authorities of the Tower of London, where ravens have long formed part of the " garrison," a very old bird at less than half the vulture's age.

Owls and their near relatives the parrots, are probably the longest-lived birds. The big eagle owl of northern Europe has lived in confinement for over sixty-eight years, and there are many authentic cases of parrots and cockatoos exceeding even this. Parrots not only evince great age in the condition of beak and claws, and an unbecoming poverty of feathers, but also by sometimes glibly using the catch phrases of a long-departed generation.

REPTILES GROW RAPIDLY

Reptiles, akin though they are to beasts and birds, present entirely different problems as regards their age limits. Like amphibians and fishes they tend to grow very rapidly during their earlier years, and then settle down to increase their bulk slowly but continuously throughout life. Great size is not necessarily a criterion of reptilian age, although the oldest known reptiles are usually of impressive proportions.

Lord Rothschild at one time made a cult of giant tortoises. Several in his famous museum at Tring weigh over five hundred and fifty pounds each, and one of this weight can safely be estimated to have seen at least two centuries. One monster still living on St. Helena is known to have been almost the same size when it was a contemporary of Napoleon in his exile. In Peterborough Museum is the shell of a little Grecian garden tortoise which is said to have graced the cathedral close for two hundred and twenty years.

ARCHBISHOP LAUD'S TORTOISE

Almost as famous is the tortoise once owned by Archbishop Laud, the shell of which is now in the library of Lambeth Palace. The reptile is reputed to have ambled about the palace lawns for one hundred and twenty-three years, and was then, as a label attached to the shell quaintly says, " mortally killed " through the curiosity of a gardener who dug it out of its winter retreat in order to settle a wager regarding the creature's age.

All available figures show forty years to be a very ripe age for a crocodilian of any kind, and much the same applies to giant snakes.

WIDE WORLD

SOME BEARS ARE OLD AT FIFTEEN

Bears (right) may live from fifteen to forty years, according to size, and provided they are not confronted by a hyena (left) or other enemy who proves the stronger in a contest.

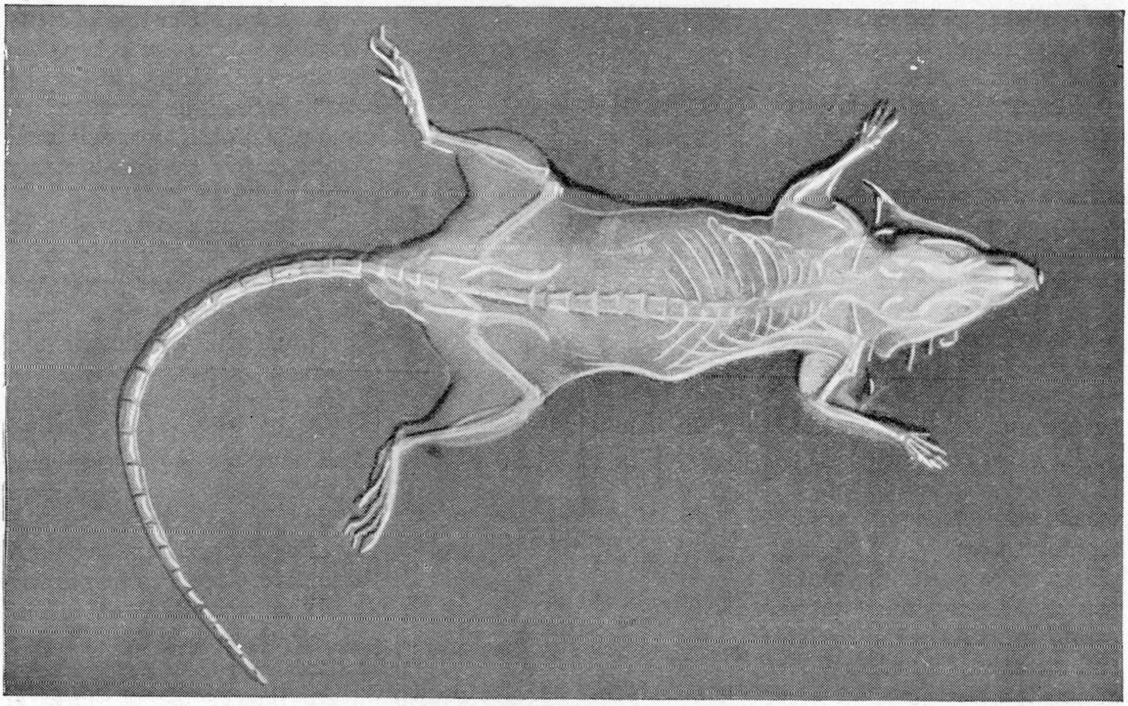

MONDIALE

X-RAY PHOTOGRAPH OF A MOUSE

The omnivorous mouse runs a dead heat as regards length of life with the rat and the common insect-eating bat, namely two and a half years.

Records of the ages of amphibians show that the giant salamander of Japan, which reaches five feet in length, may live for half a century. This is not long in proportion to its size, for many newts of only a few inches in length have lived in aquaria for more than twenty-five years. The toad, another creature reputed to outlive the centuries, is not known to live any longer than the common newt.

Possibly many fishermen's tales have centred round the age as round the size of the catch. A classic example is the story of the rustic who claimed to have caught a pike " centuries old " because he had found an Elizabethan coin inside it.

TELLING THE AGE OF A FISH

Today science leaves no ground for picturesque assumptions regarding a fish's age, provided it is of the kind having a hard bony skeleton and well-formed scales, features distinguishing the bulk of living fishes. Within the skulls of such fishes are two flattened bones, often suggesting porcelain, and having clearly marked upon them a series of concentric rings. These so-called ear bones are easily found in the ling and bream, being there exceptionally large.

The rings mark periods of summer growth, and correspond with similar rings marked upon the scales. Here then are two reliable age indicators, and they tend to show that, as in most animals, great size implies a correspondingly generous fill of years.

SHORT-LIVED STICKLEBACKS

The golden orfe, goldfish, plaice, bow-fin, bass, mirror carp, and halibut live from twenty-five to forty years. Often some fishes, particularly carp, suffer from a fungoid disease giving them a spurious " rime of age." Skate, herring, pike-perch, bass, trout and the Australian lungfish live for fifteen to twenty years. All records show that the little shore fishes of Great Britain such as blennies, gobies and sticklebacks live for a few years only.

Amongst the various groups of invertebrates, life spans so far as they have been ascertainable vary considerably. Shore crabs kept in aquariums have taken three years to attain full size, changing their shells seventeen times in the process. A lobster will change its clothes fourteen times in the first three years of life, then slow down to half this number of changes in the next five years, for shell casting becomes a more difficult and exhausting business with each successive effort.

A lobster's eggs hatch out in the course of some months. The eggs of the equally aquatic brine shrimp, so largely used as a fish food by aquarists, will keep fresh in a perfectly dry condition for a year at least, perhaps much longer. Few insects survive more than a year in the mature form, but many may spend years in the larval form, the goat moth and stag beetle being familiar examples.

The shelled molluscs like the whelk and the oyster provide tangible records of their ages by piling up deposits of mineral matter during the warmer months when food is abundant, and the animal at its maximum of activity. Any snail or clam shell presents a series of ridges, lines of growth, each of which marks a year's increase in size. Again size and longevity go hand in hand, as may be seen in quite a hurried survey of any fairly extensive collection of shells, whether land, freshwater or marine.

Two factors may serve to mar the record, but both are exceptional. Some desert snails, faced with famine, can sleep through a time of scarcity—even though it lasts for a year or more. Again, extensive injury may cause the shell to be so patched and plastered that the original sculpturing, largely provided by the lines of growth, is almost entirely effaced.

In such soft-bodied creatures as sea anemones and coral animals the life span varies enormously. The tiny builders of the Great Barrier Reefs and atolls may each live for a few days only. The sea firs of English waters, near relatives of the reef builders, are largely annuals, the main growth dying in autumn but ensuring next year's supply by disseminating eggs.

The sea anemones might be regarded as equally ephemeral, but here a surprise awaits us. The exact limitations of a sea anemone's life are not known, perhaps they never will be. The oldest aquariums in the world, institutions of just under half a century's establishment, shelter sea anemones that were placed in the tanks on the opening day and have remained there ever since, growing slowly and imperceptibly, as full of vigour apparently as when first prised from their native rocks.

An insect's life is short. A mayfly, for instance, is old four hours after it has ceased to be a pupa, and a dragon-fly lives no more than seven weeks. The risks run by the insect world are obvious. As Prof. J. B. S. Haldane points out, "A man coming out of a bath carries with him a film of water of about one-fiftieth of an inch in thickness. This weighs about a pound." That is not a serious matter to a human being, but "A wet fly has to lift many times its own weight, and, as everyone knows, a fly, once wetted by water or any other liquid, is in a very serious position indeed. An insect going for a drink is in as great danger as a man leaning over a precipice in search of food. If a fly gets wet it is likely to remain so until it drowns."

A short life, it would seem, and by no means necessarily a particularly happy one.

DORIEN LEIGH

A DRAGON-FLY LIVES FOR SEVEN WEEKS

Reading from top; The larva case breaks. Head, back and legs work themselves out. The dragon-fly has stripped off the whole of its former covering. A tentative raising of the wings. Fully developed. Ready to fly.

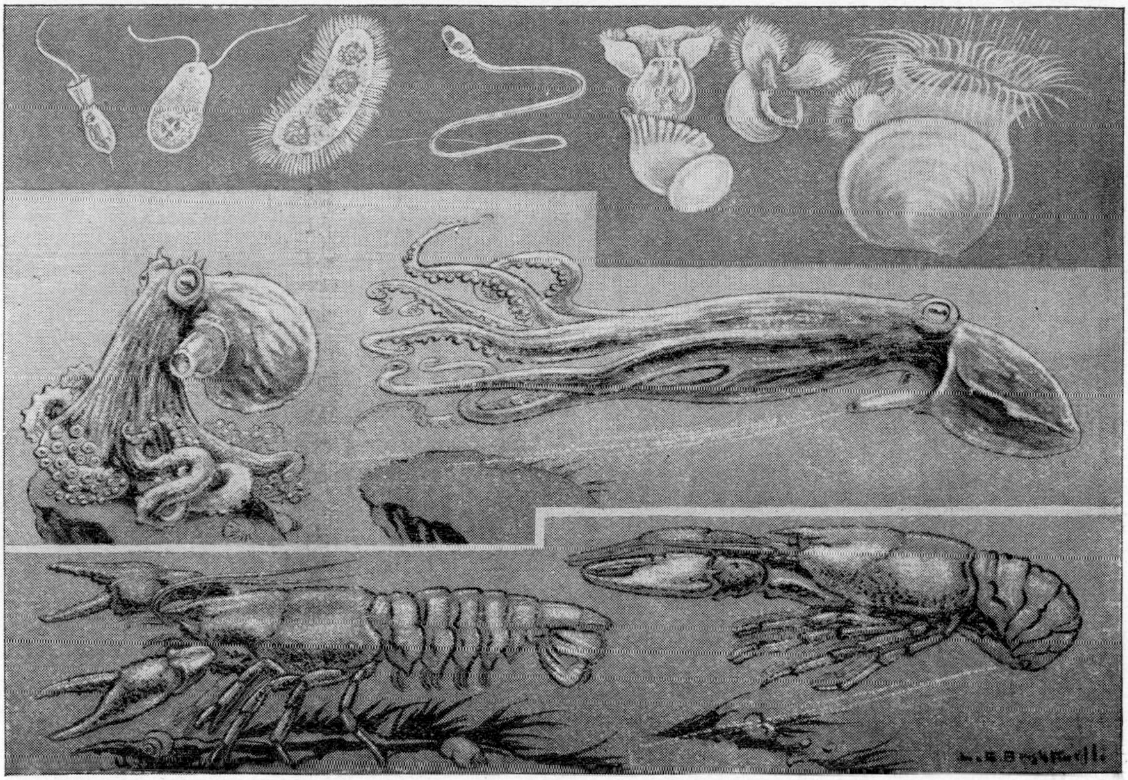

SWIMMING BY HAIRS AND JETS OF WATER

Top row: Swimming by means of hairs ; flagellates, a sperm, larval sea snails and an oyster. Middle and bottom rows: Swimming by means of a jet of water ; two octopuses and two crayfish.

MANY MODES OF TRAVEL

Animal travel of any kind consists in pushing the body forward by using limbs or their counterparts as levers, which shove against air, earth or water and so force their owner along.

One of the earliest means of locomotion was by means of fine hairs, or cilia, much like those which circulate the lubricating fluids of our nasal membranes, and in other parts of our body. Rows of lashing hairs punt millions of microscopic organisms and even young oysters and sea gooseberries through the water. But though hairs may be useful enough in setting up circulatory currents in the vital organs of such bulky creatures as the giant clam, they soon find their limitations as a means of locomotion. No really big animals move by means of hairs; they rely upon muscles.

Aquatic creatures thrust the fluid behind them by all kinds of means. Jelly-fishes contract and expand like an umbrella being shaken free of moisture, and so push themselves forward, or rather backward, since the mouth is on the underside of the jelly-fish's " umbrella." The octopus and cuttle fish, although much higher animals, also travel backward when swimming, for then they force the water which they have breathed out through a siphon pipe with such force as to drive themselves backward at high speed. It is a blind and blundering method of travel just like that of a lobster when it uses its tail fin, and such travel often leads to a crash or other disaster.

The first semi-vertebrates found a better means of progress in their tails, and though this mode of travel had its beginnings in the worms, or even earlier, the vertebrate's brain gave more direction to the force at its command. The advent of limbs, as seen in fishes, still left most of the work to the tail. When such a semi-aquatic creature as an otter or a crocodile takes to the water, it plants its limbs close to its sides and then rows itself ahead with the tail only.

WIDE WORLD

SMALLEST ANTELOPE

The dik-dik, found in East Africa from Abyssinia to Tanganyika, is the smallest African antelope. It stands no more than thirteen inches high at the shoulder when fully grown, and is a rotatory runner. When pressed it can travel at great speed.

When the conquest of the land was effected all quadrupedal creatures fell into two categories, the rotatory walkers and the diagonal walkers. The authorities of the New York Natural History Museum, by far the most wonderful place of its kind in the world, have set up a gallery of skeletons in action. To ensure the accuracy of these miles of film were taken of all kinds of animals running. Not only were they filmed in profile, but also from above, the cameraman swinging in a sort of trapeze high above the track.

ROTATORY AND DIAGONAL RUNNERS

The dog is a rotatory, the horse a diagonal runner. If a dog starts off with its left hind foot, then the right hind foot strikes the ground next, and after that the right fore foot followed by the left fore foot. So the feet move round and round, and at two moments in each stride, when the legs are bunched beneath the body, and again stretched in full stride, all four are completely free of the earth.

Either class of runner may reverse this action. In the accompanying picture the dog starts off with the left foot, so his legs move anti-clockwise.

FOX

DEER IN THE SCOTTISH HIGHLANDS

There are several different schools of progression among animals. Deer, like dogs, wolves and foxes, belong to the rotatory school, the method of which is shown in detail in the next picture.

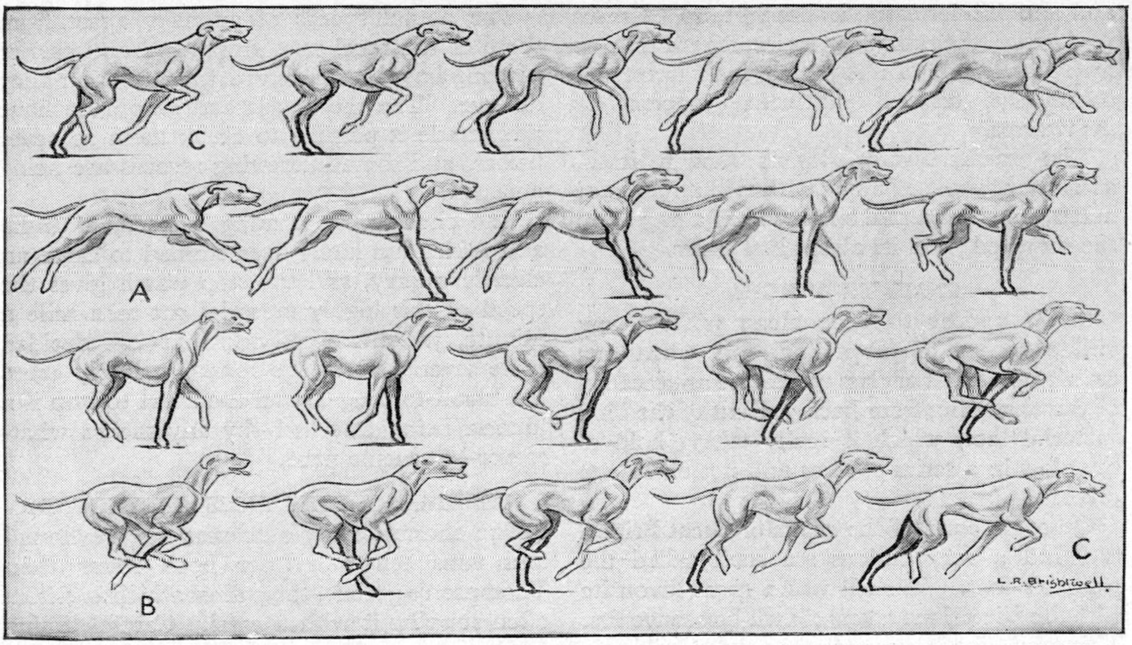

HOW DOGS RUN

Dogs belong to the rotatory school of progression. At two points (A *and* B) *of its stride, the animal is completely clear of the ground. This means that when going flat out it spends half the time in the air.* (C) *Beginning and end of a stride.*

This, however, is a matter of chance. He may just as likely lead off with the right leg, followed by the left leg, and so on.

The horse moves first the left and then the right hind leg, but follows not with the right, but the left fore leg. A dog is free of the ground about one-half of the time when going flat out, the horse is in mid-air for about a quarter of its career upon the racing track. Dogs, wolves, foxes, deer, elk and antelope are rotators; horses, cows, buffalo, goats and bears belong to the diagonal school of progression.

RELIEVING THE STRAIN

Another thing which the suspended camera-man revealed was that a quadruped in action tends to spread its hind legs much wider than it does the fore legs, and in this direction the bulldog, caused by fashion to violate all the laws of nature, is obliged to make pathetic efforts. It is small wonder the misshapen animal is soon blown.

In achieving the wonderful speeds of which some quadrupeds are capable, great strain is put upon the muscles and tendons. The latter are accordingly fortified by special little bones set in pairs near the various foot and hand joints. These bones are virtually knee caps, and the dog has between fifty and sixty of them. In our own fingers and toes such bones are little larger than wheat grains, but in many mammals they attain to the dimensions of hazel nuts.

INSECT MOVEMENT

To many people insects appear to scramble along anyhow, but this is by no means the case, as can easily be seen if some convenient species, such as the common garden beetle, has the leg tips on one side smeared with blue paint and those on the other with red. Then it becomes clear that two legs on one side and one on the other come into action simultaneously; a cockroach that is scurrying for shelter, for example, is continuously poised upon alternating tripods.

The caterpillar, despite its worm-like shape, uses its six legs as do perfect insects. Their action is augmented by the four claspers at the hinder end of the body. Caterpillar action can be roughly divided into two groups, the straightforward walk and the looper method. The latter is employed by many larvæ, notably the various stick caterpillars. They move in the manner of leeches, i.e., the forward portion takes a firm hold of the surface to be traversed and the hinder part is brought up to meet it, forcing the animal's entire length into a loop formation. In America such larvæ are commonly termed measures, loopers or inchworms.

The garden worm, legless though it is, actually punts itself along with minute poles or hooks, much as a snake levers itself along upon the sharp edges of its abdominal scales.

SNAIL THAT HOPS

Snails appear to glide along without any visible means of propulsion, but when one crawls up a sheet of glass we can see a succession of waves passing from back to front of the long suctorial foot, which is really taking hold of the glass in a series of steps and not all in one piece.

On some parts of the coasts of Great Britain is found a very curious sea snail called the pelican's foot. Its shell was a great favourite with the Victorian makers of shell-box souvenirs. This snail, like its near relatives the huge tropic fountain shells often seen on cottage window-sills, has such a small foot that gliding is impossible. Instead it hops and scrambles along in a fashion suggestive of a man trying to hurry with his legs in a sack and a watchman's shelter strapped on his back.

The actual speeds of animals, apart from those of the racehorse, greyhound and carrier pigeon, have not received the attention they deserve. The motor car and aeroplane have now made it possible to check them as never before, and some interesting records are being amassed.

The cheetah, or hunting leopard, of India and Africa has lately been trained to chase an electric quarry, and the stop watch gives the speed of this highly cursorial cat as a mile a minute, just the speed which it was decided some seventy years ago must inevitably cause the blood to congeal and the heart to stop if a human being travelled—by any means whatsoever—at such a pace.

CHEETAH OUTDISTANCES GREYHOUND

The cheetah easily outclasses the greyhound and runs ten miles per hour faster than Thompson's gazelle, the animal which in Africa often supplies it with a meal. Careful timing with a car speedometer has shown the giraffe's best pace not to exceed thirty-five miles per hour, which is also the limit for the ostrich's spring or the charge of the Cape buffalo. The elephant and rhinoceros can charge at twenty-five miles per hour, a little more than half the average speed at which the Derby is run.

SPENCER ARNOLD

AMERICAN BISON OR BUFFALO

Like the horse, the buffalo is a diagonal runner. It moves first the left and then the right hind leg, and follows not with the right but with the left foreleg. The buffalo has longer legs than ordinary oxen.

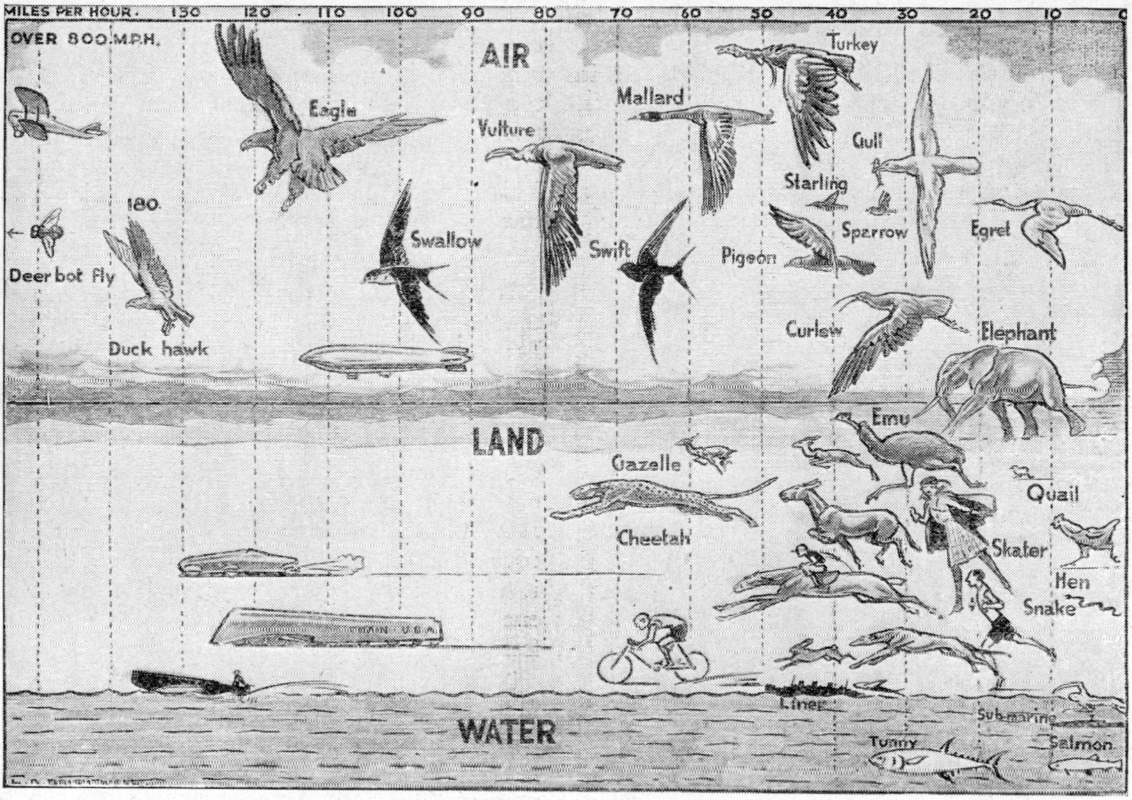

SPEED CHART OF THE ANIMALS

Eventually aeroplanes may travel at eight hundred miles per hour. This chart shows the approximate rates of travel of various human and animal champions. In many cases the speed is for a short distance only.

The advent of the submarine naturally directed attention to the speeds of fishes. Here the tunny, a giant mackerel, may with the sword fish claim the world's record. A thousand pound tunny is estimated to be capable of travelling at thirty-five miles per hour for a short distance. A salmon when terrified, as upon being hooked, can rush through the water for a short time at twenty-five miles per hour, a pike fifteen, and a large eel at about the same rate.

SPEED LIMITS OF BIRDS

Much more research has been expended on the speed limits of various birds, and the list of records increases proportionately with the general advancement in aerodynamics. The duck hawk and the eagle are regarded at the moment as the fastest birds on the wing, the latter having been timed to travel at over one hundred and ten miles per hour. The falcon's flight is a record by tradition rather than scientific proof. The stoop (falling vertically through the air) may touch eighty, but the level flight does not exceed sixty-five miles per hour—forty-five miles slower than the eagle.

HALF A MILE A MINUTE

The hawks, ducks and partridge-like birds generally show an average speed of forty-five miles per hour, and even the relatively clumsy heron can equal this if pursued by a falcon. The small size of the swallow renders its flight deceptive; its normal speed probably does not exceed half a mile a minute.

Some animals that have become bywords for slowness travel much faster than is generally supposed. The sloth lives up to its name in the tree tops but, rather surprisingly, cuts quite a presentable figure in water. No creature travelling head downwards two hundred feet perhaps above the earth can afford to make a false step when the road consists of slippery branches and creepers. Threading its way amongst moss-draped foliage, the sloth does not cover more than fourteen feet a minute, but in the Amazon, the waters of which it often crosses from one feeding ground to another, it swims at a rate of not far short of two miles an hour.

Snails are regarded as equal to the sloths in hastening slowly. This is not true in all cases. On the coast of the Channel Islands there lives a big oval-shelled sea snail, related to the limpet, much prized for market, and known

HAROLD BASTIN

GIANT AND DWARF

An elephant beetle and a ladybird, also a beetle. Beetles appear to spread four pairs of wings in flight.

as the ormer or ear shell. Allowing for the fact that the animal generally travels under water and lubricates its path with slime, it progresses at the very presentable pace of five to six yards a minute, or about one fifth of a mile an hour. As the ear shell is only some four inches long it no doubt seems to itself to move at quite a dizzy speed.

Speed, as we all realize nowadays, is not only a matter of fine mechanism as regards the actual apparatus for movement, but also a question of fuel. It is very noticeable that all the speediest animals are prodigious eaters; otherwise their engines could never achieve the efforts often demanded of them. As regards terrestrial animals at least, warm surroundings rather than cold ones make for fast movement. This is particularly noticeable in cold-blooded creatures such as reptiles and insects.

HEAT ENGENDERS ENERGY

It can be put to the test by a once popular schoolboy sport, the maggot race. If two larvæ of the blowfly are put on a sheet of glass resting upon a tray of hot sand and the light of an electric torch is shone on them, the grubs will put up quite a vigorous speed in order to escape the light. This simple experiment is, of course, best carried out in a dark room. It will soon be apparent that the course is covered much more slowly as the sand beneath it cools, the runners regaining vigour and energy as soon as the sand is brought up to its former temperature.

Not much more than thirty years ago a London newspaper offered £1,000 to anyone who made a non-stop flight from London to Manchester. When *Punch* followed with an offer of £1,000,000 to anyone who would dig down to Australia and report by speaking tube on the cricket match, most people were inclined to side with the humorist. Shortly afterwards the £1,000 was claimed.

MAN'S CONQUEST OF THE AIR

We can scarcely doubt that we have seen little more than the birth of man's conquest of the air. The triumphs of today will probably be viewed by future generations much as we look back upon the world-shaking trial run of Stephenson's " Rocket " in 1829. In less than half a century we have made man's dream of flight, as typified in the Greek legend of the attempt of Icarus to fly, come true, and have outstripped the efforts of the animals by perhaps sixty million years, if we count flight as dating from the first bird, and possibly five times that period if we award the honours to the insects.

To give the animals their due, they achieved flight on totally different lines from those now being so swiftly developed by ourselves. Though we are still learning much from the mechanics of animal flight, it was not until experimenters abandoned a slavish imitation of them that they found success. The actual

FOX

FASTEST LAND ANIMAL

The cheetah or hunting leopard of India and Africa can travel at a speed of sixty miles an hour, thus beating Thompson's gazelle, which is often its prey, by ten miles an hour. It leaves the greyhound far behind.

machinery by which we fly, though intimately related to them, is entirely separate from the structures it may carry; in animals the machinery is necessarily incorporated with the animal itself.

INSECT FLIGHT

Animal flight has been achieved by two sharply defined routes: in vertebrates by special adaptations of the fore limbs, and in invertebrates by peculiar outgrowths from the body, entirely separate from the limbs proper.

The very first efforts at spasmodic ventures into the air may have begun with certain minute crustaceans called copepods, or even the small molluscs that form the whale food of the Arctic seas; but at best such flights can only be regarded as prolonged jumps. The insects found a way to real air command when they developed wings.

The full story of insect flight cannot yet be told, owing to the rarity and fragmentary nature of fossil remains. It is likely that primitive insects may have developed special outgrowths from three instead of only two body segments. Some owl moths show hints at these extra wings in little movable plates projecting from the first ring or segment of the thorax; certain extinct insects that once lived in the coal forests show similar plates. Modern beetles appear to spread four pairs of wings when in flight, but two, though no doubt useful as planes, function chiefly as covers for the true organs of flight.

Thanks to the insect's respiratory system—which consists of a complex maze of tubes through which air is pumped—size is extremely limited. The largest insect known, an extinct species of dragon fly, spanned eighteen inches across the wings. The Atlas moth of India measures six inches short of this, and so, although the flight of insects may be relatively great, it can never compete in actual achievement with that of the much larger vertebrates.

COLD AS A HANDICAP

Long migratory flights are quite impossible at high altitudes owing to the inability of insects to withstand cold. The heavily haired bees are exceptional in this regard, but even with them flights at any great height are of rare occurrence and short duration.

The insects reached their limitations of achievement in the air at a relatively early date in the earth's history. But meantime other creatures were endeavouring to emulate them. Some have gone far beyond the insects, others remain where they began, the merest beginners.

Certain small tropic cuttle fishes learnt to

W. S. BERRIDGE, F.Z.S. (MONDIALE)

GREAT WHITE HERON

The heron is a fairly clumsy bird, but it can fly at forty-five miles an hour when pursued by a falcon.

volplane through the air by means of side expansions of the body wall. Later came the flying fish, with the shark and dolphin in pursuit.

FIRST VERTEBRATES TO FLY

The flying fishes were no doubt the first vertebrates to fly, but of the many very beautiful species known none has been able to direct its efforts to any appreciable extent. All attempts avail little against a smart breeze. There is a vigorous take-off with the tail, a feverish winnowing of the exaggerated breast and anal fins for a matter of yards only, and then back goes the fish into the water. Some dragon fish and gurnards of the coral seas, and one small freshwater fish of West Africa have developed on similar lines, but with indifferent success.

These attempts at flight, which have ended in little more than parachuting, are eclipsed by those of certain small spiders. Mounting a grass stem, one of these spiders lets out several strands of silk from its spinnerets, and away it goes upon the breeze. It can lessen speed or alight at will by just " hauling in the slack."

Probably after the fishes had acquired flight of a kind, some tropical frogs adventured in like manner. The flying frogs of Borneo make long hops by spreading the huge webs which extend to the extreme tips of their fingers and toes.

The far-eastern jungles, like eastern seas, have developed an unusual number of animal aeronauts. In the jungles of Malaya and the East Indies are also tiny flying lizards that plane by spreading enormous skin-covered expansions of their ribs, and even a tree snake has learnt to volplane from tree to tree by drawing in its stomach and converting itself for the moment into the likeness of a split bamboo. From the same regions also come the largest flying mammals, enormous bats, and the so-called flying lemur or cobego, which is really a cousin of the shrews, but as big as a domestic cat.

FLYING DRAGONS

Reptiles learnt to fly once only in their history, during the Age of Reptiles, when the dinosaurs owned the earth. The flying dragons or pterodactyls (literally " wing fingers ") were evolved, and contemporary with them must have been the " almost birds."

The flying lizards, far outnumbering the bird-like pioneers, developed on semi-avian lines. They had prominent breast bones for the attachment of wing muscles and, like birds, had hollow air-filled bones, communicating no doubt, as in the true birds, with the respiratory apparatus. But the skin-covered wings were attached to the creature's little fingers only, leaving the rest of the hand free as a very useful implement for scrambling about rocks and trees, and perhaps for holding and tearing food.

The flying lizards varied in size from that of a thrush to monsters with a twenty-five-feet wing span, more than twice that of the condor, the largest flying bird. They must have enjoyed great ascendancy over all save the very largest and most active earth-bound reptiles, but like these and the fish on which they are believed to have largely preyed, they were cold blooded and the climatic changes which

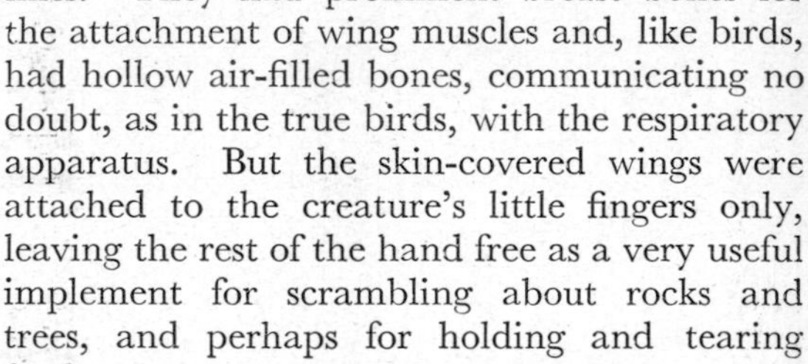

WIDE WORLD

WINGS OF A DOVE

This photograph, taken in the one-fifty-thousandth part of a second, shows a dove gaining altitude.

DORIEN LEIGH, FOX

THE SPEED OF BIRDS

Above: Female hawk carrying material with which to build her nest. Below: A baby African crane lying against its mother's wing. Hawks, like ducks and birds of the partridge type, show an average speed of forty-five miles an hour. Despite the fact that much time and money have been spent in research on the subject of the speed of birds, no exact statistics are yet available, owing to the difficulties attendant on experiments in this field. Present information indicates that the fastest birds are the duck hawk and the eagle. The latter has been timed at over one hundred and ten miles an hour.

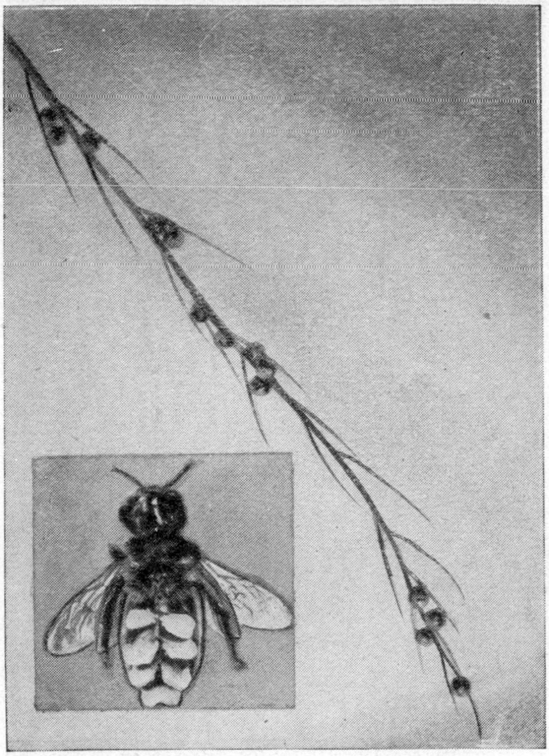

HAROLD BASTIN

FERTILIZER OF FLOWERS

Pollen grains on the feathered hair of a bee. Insects long ago attained the limit of their aerial capacity.

brought about the sunset of the dinosaurs effaced them also.

The little archeopteryx or half-bird, though very unlike any bird we know today, had all the essentials for life in the tree tops and the air. It had feathers with which to face the cold of high altitudes, and its wings were built on true avian lines. Other reptile-birds must have lived before it, but their efforts at flight were no doubt little more than desperate flutterings to evade some foe, or exaggerated leaps towards some desired object.

RUDDER OF FEATHERS

In archeopteryx the " hand " of the wing was more functional than in modern birds, save the nestling hoatzin, and the long lizard-like tail with a row of feathers on each side must have been a clumsy steering organ beside the neat, extensile rudder of feathers seen in all flying birds today.

As mentioned when dealing with the size limitations of animals, the very mechanism of bird flight precludes its exponents attaining to beyond a certain weight and dimensions. One has only to watch various birds take off to appreciate the difficulties which present themselves as the living flying machine gains in bulk.

The crane and the condor, though perfectly at ease once they are fairly launched, engage in much cumbrous flapping and struggling before they are well away upon the upper air currents. In marked contrast is the effortless take-off of the swallow, or even of the ground-dwelling partridge. The bird's breast bone is the key to its owner's prowess as an aviator.

HIGH SPEED OF BATS

For lack of the qualities essential to vertebrate flight—hollow bones and a covering of feathers to serve as planes and keep the engine warm—no mammals have ever become complete masters of the air. Were this not so, some of the carnivorous bats, like the fish-eating and cannibal bats of South America, might reach terrifying proportions. As things are, no bats can compare with the more specialized flying birds. They fly adroitly and often at high speed, but at infinitely greater expenditure of energy, and the nature of their diet confines the largest species to relatively few and restricted areas within the tropic belt.

Like many birds, bats feed while flying. They must consume an amazing total of insects, for they sometimes make an appearance during daylight as well as at night. Various experimenters have endeavoured to trace the source of the skill which enables the animals to avoid objects during their flight. One observer notes that a long-eared bat flew about a room lighted only by a candle, and although various obstacles were placed in its

FOX

INSECT-WINGS

The wing-scales of a peacock butterfly. Insects found a way to real command of the air when they developed wings. Their fossil remains are rare.

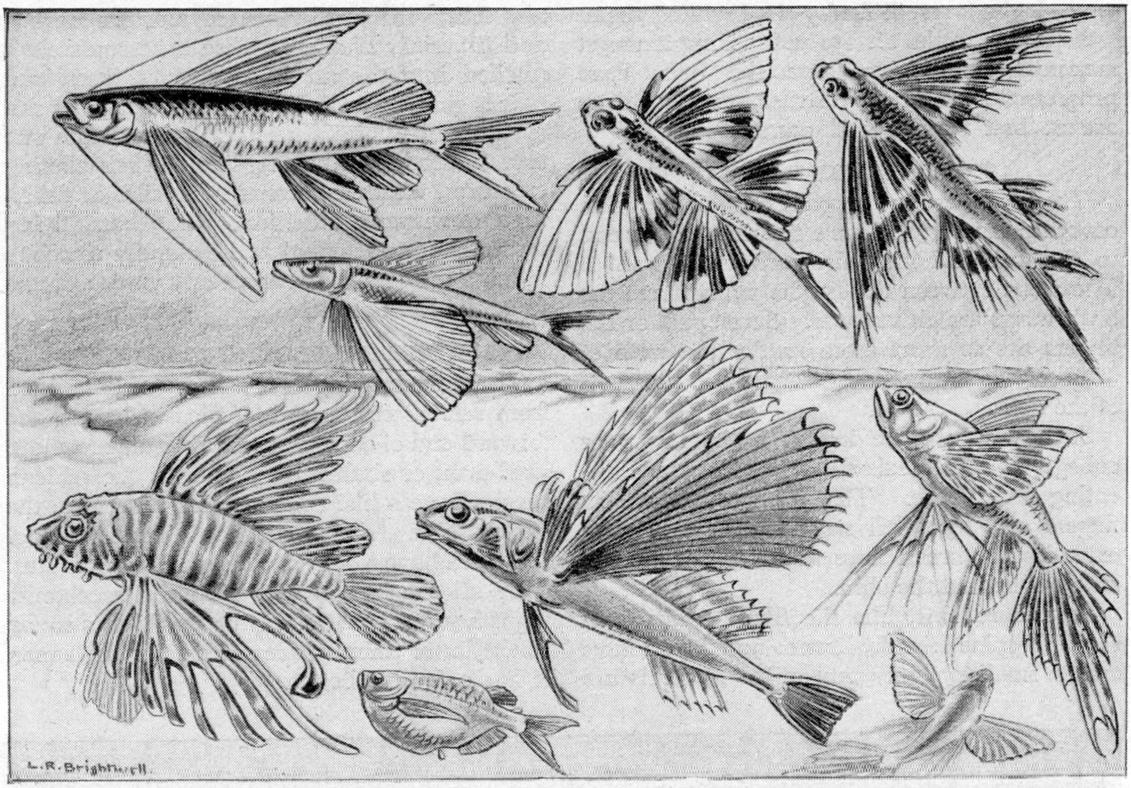

FISHES THAT TAKE TO THE AIR

Above: (*top*) *Tropical marine flying fishes skimming the water;* (*below*) *Extinct flying fish, East Indian dragon fish, South American flying fish, Mediterranean flying gurnard, Congo flying fish. Bottom: Close-up of flying fish. Its flights are a matter of yards only.*

way, it had no difficulty in avoiding them.

Aspirants to the air are not lacking amongst mammals, but none, save the bats, have progressed beyond the learner stage. Others are at best planers and parachutists.

SQUIRRELS THAT PLANE

Their planes are expansions of the skin covering the ribs, and are attached at either end to the fore and hind limbs in various ways. The webs between the fingers which form the bat's wings are either poorly developed, or the fingers are so short as to render the webs of little service even when extending to the roots of the nails.

Such webs we see in the flying lemur or cobego of the Malay Archipelago, a fruit-eating insectivore. The cobego has all its fingers and toes well webbed, the skin even extending in broad flaps to the tip of the tail and just behind the chin.

Several rodents, like the flying squirrels of the Philippine Islands, Borneo and Japan have rather smaller planes and allied squirrels are also found in North America, Eastern Europe and Siberia. If one of these little squirrels is pitched into the air it soon rights itself and planes gently as a falling leaf to safety. It can even give its baby a ride on its back from one tree to another, travelling like all such planing creatures, whether mammals, reptiles or fishes, in a downward direction. Like bats, flying squirrels are nocturnal and generally associate in large colonies. About seventy yards appears to be the limit of their gliding powers.

FURTHER DEVELOPMENT UNLIKELY

The Asiatic flying squirrels are distinguished from related creatures of Africa in having the forward end of each plane fixed to an enormous yard-arm, or sixth finger, whereas the African species have a like addition sprouting from the elbow joint. Numerous small marsupials of Australia have a very similar gliding apparatus.

By all the known laws of animal mechanics flight has reached the end of possibilities so far as the lower animals are concerned; with man it has only just begun.

PARACHUTING ANIMALS

Top row: A frog and a squirrel. Bottom row: A lizard and two lemurs or cobegos. All these animals are natives of the Far East. The lemurs, though primates, are neither monkeys nor apes.

FOX

TEETH IN THE WALLS OF THE STOMACH

The lobster's pincers are more effective than the rasp-like teeth of the sea urchin. They can chop up a mussel shell into small pieces which pass to three teeth fitted to the walls of the stomach.

FEEDING AND SLEEP

SCARCELY any known plant or animal is inedible—to somebody. It is probable that even the tropical trigger fishes with their highly poisonous alkaline flesh have natural enemies. There are certainly not many plants or animals which man does not use for food in some part of the world. Shellfish of all kinds, worms, insects and insect larvæ, eggs and mice all figure on the menu of civilized man. The kinds of food which can be eaten are so multitudinous that we shall here consider rather the different ways of absorbing them.

" All flesh is grass " said the sage of old, and it is literally true that all animal life is in the first instance dependent upon vegetables, which largely derive their sustenance from sunlight, air and soil. The leopard that lives on cattle eats grass by proxy so to speak, just as does the tiger shark, devouring fishes which in the first instance were nourished on the minute plant life collectively known as plankton.

All animals can be roughly gathered into two great gastronomic armies, one living on minute organisms in bulk, the other selecting larger food and eating it as a bolus or piecemeal. Feeders of the first order were the earliest of all diners. They thronged the seas in the persons of the minute chalk animals, the rotifers and other microscopic or semi-microscopic forms. They took their food by sweeping all that the surrounding water contained into their maws by violently lashing hairs, or cilia, and though some selection may have been observed when the food reached the diner's interior, it was brought there haphazard in the first place, with much that was waste.

In this way the minute animals already mentioned still feed, and so also do many worms, all sponges, sea squirts, barnacles and the vast army of bivalve molluscs—clams, oysters and scallops. Even the giant three-feet-long clams of the Great Barrier Reef feed thus on minute plants which are swept into their crops by means of countless microscopic whips.

Quite recently it was discovered that the giant clam had a special provision for getting enough of this food to sustain its enormous bulk—and one giant clam may make a meal for six men. It appears that certain portions of the clam's soft body form breeding grounds for the microscopic plants, so that the monster has always a reserve on the premises, apart from what it sweeps into its interior in the ordinary course of feeding.

Early in the world's history—early, that is to say, as regards animal life—there appeared another class of feeders which ate minute organisms but in a different way. Many worms and other soft-bodied creatures burrow into soil, and as they burrow, swallow all that crosses their path and force it down their simple digestive tracts. This heterogeneous mass of stuff is sorted out in the process, nutritive matter passing into the blood stream and the

AMERICAN MUSEUM OF NATURAL HISTORY, NEW YORK

CUNNING HUNTER

The leopard, or panther, is not fussy about its diet, being willing to devour anything it can catch.

waste being cast out via the vent. Familiar examples of such waste are the worm castings usually seen on every sandy beach and garden lawn.

Long before the first vertebrates appeared an advance was made upon these two simple ways of taking food, both of which permitted only relatively soft material to be dealt with.

BRITISH MUSEUM (NATURAL HISTORY)

IN LESS LEARNED DAYS

The leopard as pictured in a volume published in 1491. *The animal's head is almost human.*

A sea anemone may swallow a whole whelk shell, but it can only absorb the whelk. The shell must be cast forth, or at most only slightly dissolved. But some molluscs developed an internal shell made in several pieces, working one upon the other, and forming a very effective grinding mill. One can find such a mill, about as big as a runner bean, in the bubble snail, found on the sandy south coast beaches of England.

TEETH IN THE STOMACH

The sea urchins also developed fine sharp teeth, working one upon the other, but they could still only serve the purpose of a rasp, much as do the horny tongue teeth noticed when glancing at the snail's tongue. More effective grinding organs appeared in the complex tongs, forceps, scissors and brushes seen in the many modified limbs, or mouth parts, of insects, crabs and lobsters. A lobster can chop up a mussel shell into small pieces which pass to three teeth fitted to the walls of the stomach, and known as " the lady in the chair."

True teeth appeared first in the fishes, but not until the group was already well established. The first fishes had suctorial mouths, or at most sucking mouths ringed with file-like horny teeth, as in the common lamprey.

ASTONISHING SWALLOWING FEATS

True teeth are seen at their simplest in the sharks and rays as a roughening of the skin forming a series of sharp plates covering the lips. It must be admitted that this roughening was very impressive at times. One extinct shark known as carcharodon had a mouth big enough to accommodate a man, and ringed with rows of saw-edged teeth each about four inches long.

In the bony fishes which evolved later, teeth have assumed an infinity of forms. Often they are so long as to protrude far beyond the fish's face even when its mouth is shut. The common rock salmon, really a giant blenny, has teeth strong enough to break oyster shells. The angler's teeth work on hinges, forming a bristling barrier which no fish, once swallowed, can hope to repass. The wrasse can nibble hard barnacle shells off the rocks, and pass them on to other teeth in its throat, where they are ground to powder.

A large percentage of fishes bolt their food whole, and some are capable of astonishing swallowing feats. The pike and angler fish

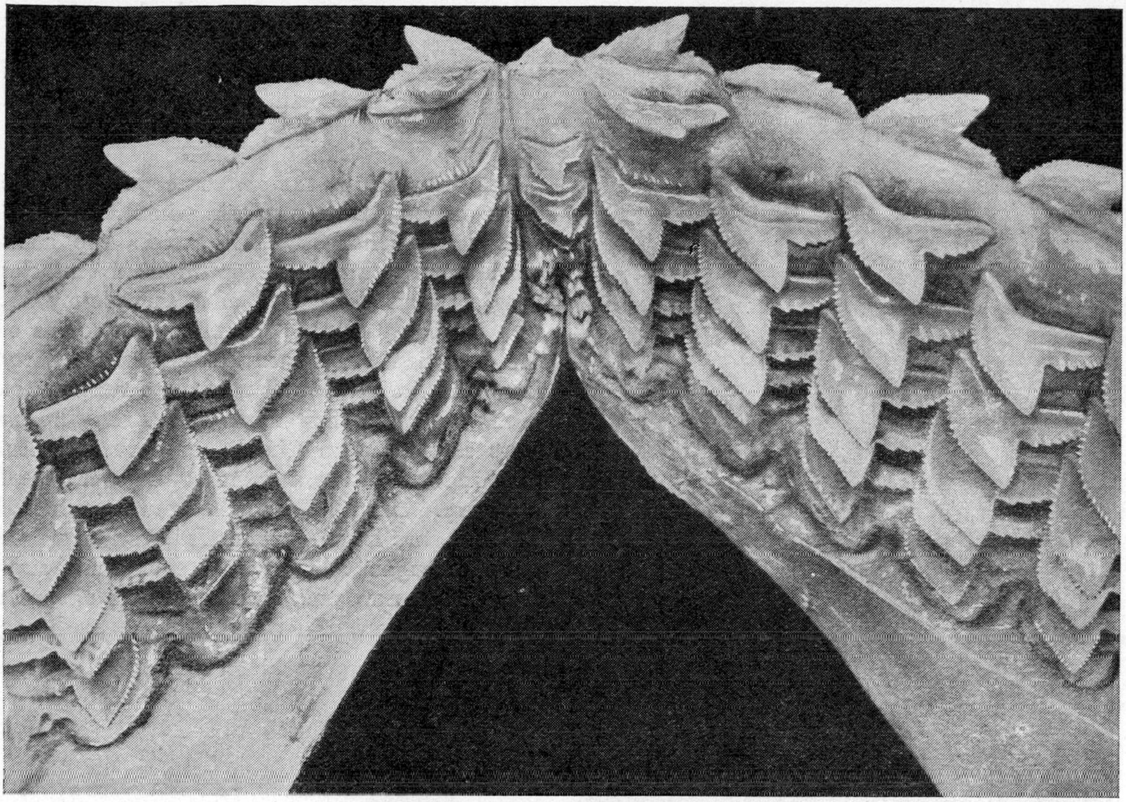

WIDE WORLD

SHARK'S DENTAL ARMOURY

Upper jaw of a tiger shark. As soon as a tooth on the upright row is lost or broken another springs erect to replace it. The fish to which these teeth belonged was captured by the Bermuda Oceanographic Expedition.

often choke to death as a result of swallowing prey too large for them. A fish of the deeps, however, though not so large as a herring, can swallow a fish three times its own length, the stomach conveniently stretching to accommodate the mouthful. It sometimes happens that the mouthful protests to such purpose that both diner and dinner are carried up to the sea surface, where some passing sea bird plays a last part in the tragedy. In spite of this fish's swallowing abilities, its teeth are little more than a fence to prevent the prey, once caught, from escaping.

MAIMED BY MILLIONS

Some fishes literally use their teeth-filled jaws as mincing machines. A shoal of piranha (a Brazilian fish no bigger than a roach) have been known to destroy a man and his horse. The edible blue fish of America follows shoals of sea perches, chopping off their tail portions as neatly as one might with a pair of shears. Some of the fishes live to swim minus their tails, the dorsal and anal fins closing in behind to replace the missing tail fin, but it is estimated that hundreds of thousands of millions of fishes are maimed past recovery within a blue fish season of about one hundred days.

LOBSTER'S AUXILIARY PINCERS

With all the advantages which the fishes enjoyed as regards organs of propulsion, circulatory system and breathing over the invertebrates, the latter had anticipated them in tactile organs. Crustacea are better off for hands than many mammals. The common lobster can utilize its pincers with almost the neatness and finesse of a watchmaker manipulating his tweezers, and in addition has two auxiliary pairs of pincers among its walking legs. A crab will take a carrot in one claw and eat it whilst keeping off would-be participants in the meal with the disengaged claw.

Apart from vertebrates and arthropods or jointed animals—crustacea, insects, etc.—only one other group of creatures seems to have developed satisfactory tactile organs. The octopods and cuttle fishes, highest of the mollusca,

WIDE WORLD

BABY OCTOPUS

The octopus eats crabs and oysters. It does not crush their shells, but pulls them apart with its tentacles.

have developed the molluscan " foot," as seen in the snail and pond mussel, into eight or ten long arms covered with sucking discs. The cuttle fish, a typical ten-armed mollusc, tucks two extra long arms into pockets, one on either side of the head, when not in use. These can be shot out at lightning speed, and the tips attached to passing prey—usually a fish.

LAIR OF THE OCTOPUS

The octopus, unlike the squid and cuttle fish, seldom hunts in open water. Instead it lies hidden in a rock fissure, and when a crab comes within range, unrolls one tentacle and attaches the tip to the front of the crab's shell. Only the lobster and a few species of crab offer any resistance; the victim generally appears conscious that fighting is futile, and a big octopus will thus catch a score of crabs in succession, storing them amongst its coils until wanted.

The arms, tapering to whip-lash tips, are deftly used to dismember the crabs and extract the meat; the shells are never broken, as each arm bears some three hundred tentacles, a terrific pull can be exerted; even the valves of a big oyster shell can be successfully forced apart.

GIANT SQUIDS

One may gauge the awesome power of the giant octopods of Australasia when it is stated that a specimen forty feet across the arms has about two thousand five hundred tentacles ranging in size from that of a threepenny bit to a breakfast saucer. In the giant squids of the Atlantic the long arms may measure thirty feet, and in all squids the large suckers are reinforced as to their rims with strong horny rings set with sharp hooks, or curved spines.

In reptiles we see a great advance in dental structure. Always the teeth grow from below upwards, are heavily enamelled, and as a rule grow throughout life, worn teeth being supplanted by new ones ever thrusting upwards from the socket. In crocodiles the teeth are

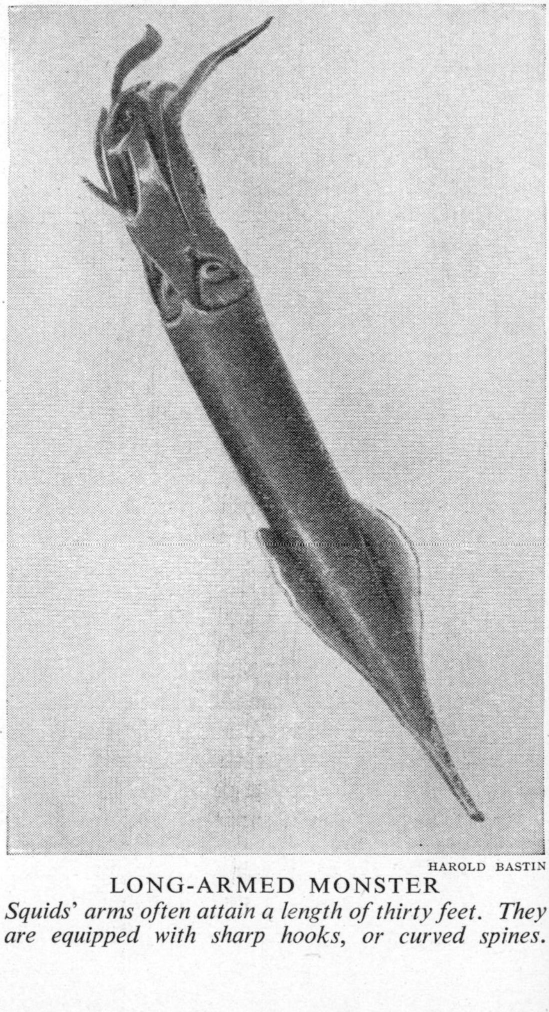

HAROLD BASTIN

LONG-ARMED MONSTER

Squids' arms often attain a length of thirty feet. They are equipped with sharp hooks, or curved spines.

WIDE WORLD

ALLIGATORS BURSTING FROM THEIR SHELLS

The alligator's denture differs from that of the crocodile in having the fourth tooth of the under jaw projecting into a hollow in the upper jaw. Crocodiles have this tooth fitted into an external notch.

fitted one on top of the other, like the hats of a circus clown. Usually the sockets are very shallow compared with those of mammals, and in many reptiles the teeth merely lean up against a ridge on the jaw bone, where they are simply held in position by the gums.

The hollow teeth which convey the poison of venomous snakes are ranged one behind the other, so that when one is dislodged by accident, as not infrequently happens, another immediately takes its place. In all snakes the teeth point throatwards, and though this may very effectually prevent the escape of a lively dinner, as in many fish, it can also lead to the diner's untimely end. Once a snake has gripped its prey, it must swallow it entire. There is no relinquishing its hold and ejecting an undesirable mouthful seized in haste. Each movement of the jaws only forces the bolus further into the interior.

This accounts for a snake sometimes choking to death. Its " eye has been bigger than its stomach " as we say, and if another snake almost its own size has similarly gripped the other end of the same victim, disaster is bound to follow.

In one snake there is an extraordinary development of tooth-like structures where such would not be expected. The true teeth of the African egg-eating snake are almost negligible, but the inner surfaces of the neck vertebræ have

WIDE WORLD

GREEK TORTOISE IN ITS NATIVE HAUNTS

Turtles and tortoises discarded their teeth for horny sheaths at the edges of their jaws. Other animals find teeth a disadvantage; duckbills and some whales are born with teeth which they lose in adulthood.

sharp enamel-tipped points. The snake's head, though no thicker than one's finger, can stretch to accommodate a hen's egg, and when this reaches the neck teeth they crack the shell and release the yolk into the snake's interior. There are cases known of this snake attempting to crack a china nest egg, such a meal invariably proving fatal.

MONDIALE

DEADLY HAMADRYAD

The poison of venomous snakes is passed through hollow teeth, which when broken are immediately replaced. In all snakes the teeth point throatwards.

In the long chain of evidence establishing the reptilian ancestry of birds, a very important item is the possession of teeth by many birds in the prehistoric past. Veritable teeth set in sockets were present in both jaws of the " almost bird " archeopteryx, and were in vogue amongst the true birds which followed after for many millions of years. Gradually they disappeared, at first from the front upper jaw and later entirely, being represented only by serrations of the bony structure and covered by a thin horny sheath, in which state they persist amongst some birds to the present time.

For some reason, teeth persisted in all but one or two of the mammalian groups which developed parallel with the birds. At first mammalian teeth presented the same curious uniformity as did the general make-up of the creatures wearing them. Amongst the earliest mammals none was obviously carnivorous or obviously herbivorous. But as the hairy creatures pioneered and steadily widened their range of activities, their teeth altered to suit each fresh exigence as it occurred, and today mammalian teeth present a far wider range of size, shape and function than do those of reptiles.

A few mammals have discarded teeth, just as the turtles and tortoises amongst reptiles abandoned them, for horny sheaths to the edges of the jaws. The very young duckbill has functional teeth, and there are milk teeth present in the jaws of embryo whalebone whales, though these vanish in later life as being detriments rather than assistants to the animal's peculiar mode of feeding.

ANIMALS WITHOUT TEETH

The whalebone whales mimic the oyster in gulping down vast quantities of minute food after passing it through a sieve, the sieve in the case of the whale being those horny curtains of whalebone or baleen which are really a peculiar development of the palate. The insect diet of the ant eaters has eliminated the necessity for teeth, although there is evidence, particularly in the case of the South African earth bear, that these strange creatures are the descendants of toothed ancestors.

Teeth are among the surest clues to an animal's way of life, and our own bear eloquent testimony to the fact that almost everything is grist to the human mill in matters of diet. Increasing reliance on soft prepared foods is tending to eliminate our back teeth, and to reduce the size of our canines, but in most other primates these last remain well developed, either for use as weapons or as effective nut crackers.

TUSKS THIRTEEN FEET LONG

Any of the teeth, like limbs or other features, are liable to extravagant exaggeration to meet peculiar requirements. In rodents the incisors are powerful chisels; in the elephant, tusks for stabbing a foe or uprooting trees. An extinct Indian elephant had tusks each thirteen feet long, and the two together weighed over four hundred pounds. Much more frequently it is the canine teeth that are prolonged to form tusks, and the upper are more often thus developed than the lower. The walrus uses its upper canines to haul itself on to ice floes, the water

BEEBE UNDERSEA EXPEDITION (WIDE WORLD)

BLACK ASTRONESTHES PURSUING LUMINOUS PREY

Many fish bolt their prey whole, being capable of amazing swallowing feats. A deep-sea fish, not so large as a herring, can gulp down a fish three times its own length, its stomach being extremely distensible.

deer and muntjac employ similar teeth for fighting other deer or unearthing roots and bulbs.

In the pig tribe both upper and lower canines attain tusk dimension, and the lower teeth only reach a large size in the horse, camel, rhinoceros and some other herbivores, who utilize such weapons only in duelling during the mating season.

ANIMALS THAT USE SHEARS

One race of animals, the kangaroo, has put the incisor teeth to a unique use, quite contrary to the general purpose of such teeth, which is chiselling hard substances. The two lower incisors appear to have no kinship with the upper incisors, which are numerous and peg-like. Instead, the lower pair are developed into two large blades, which being movable, work upon each other like the blades of a pair of shears, and are used in precisely the same manner for cutting grass.

The tusks of the hippopotamus are also in the nature of shears but function in a more usual manner, the lower pair merely cutting against two upper teeth. So great is their strength, that not only can they cut a whole truss of lush vegetation by a single snap, but in emergency even halve a native canoe or a man. They are also used with terrible effect in duelling.

Grinding teeth, which always occupy the hindermost parts of the jaw, usually present complex sculptured surfaces, sometimes showing, as in the musk ox, intricate designs formed to grind the hardest food, and so extract the maximum nutriment from the least promising material. In the elephant these teeth, reduced to two in each jaw bone, grow from behind forward, the rearmost teeth gradually supplanting the forward grinders as they are worn away.

Once a tooth is formed it is usually a completed structure, but an exception is provided by the horse. The roots of its teeth remain open for eight years or more, and so draw more than usual support from the blood stream, enabling them the better to cope with a hard, dry, farinaceous diet. Such teeth may remain in full vigour for forty years.

ENIGMA OF THE NARWHAL

Mammalian teeth, however strange or complex, usually yield the secret of their peculiar functions to patient study. The teeth of the narwhal or sea unicorn are exceptions, for they remain enigmas. In the male these present two spirally twisted rods of ivory, growing side by side from the front of the upper jaw, the left-hand tusk usually being the longer. They are quite inexplicable since the animal seldom seems to need them either for duelling or repulsing foes, and they can certainly be of no service in obtaining food, the creature's diet consisting chiefly of cuttle fish and small crustacea found swimming in mid-water.

The old adage that we dig our graves with our teeth need no longer apply to man.

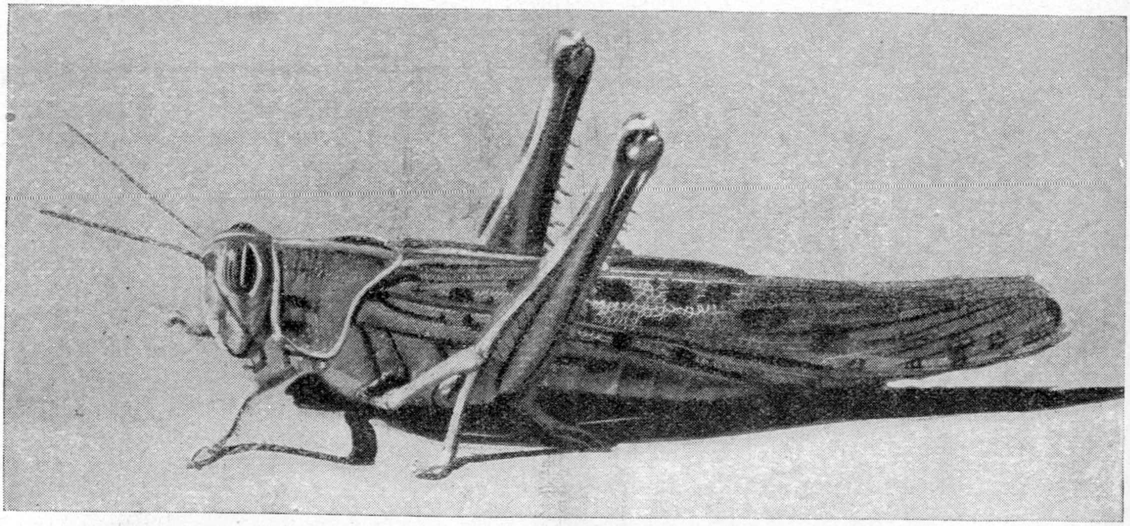

WIDE WORLD

SILVER GREY DESERT LOCUST

The eternal search for food inspires vast mass movements of animals, which, as in the case of locusts and grasshoppers, quite frequently cause enormous damage to human food supplies.

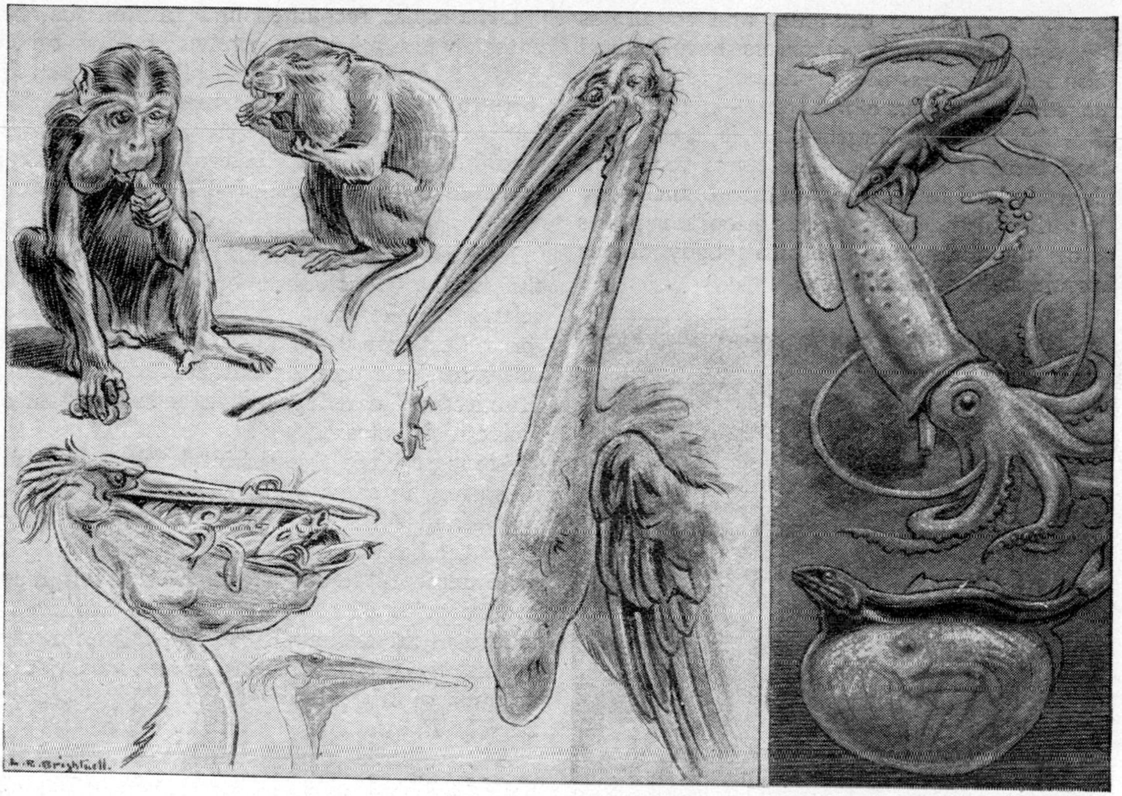

METHODS OF FOOD STORAGE
(Left) Pouched animals: monkey, gopher-rat, pelican and adjutant stork. (Right) Animal with distensible stomach: the black swallower, a deep-sea fish, before and after attacking a squid several times its own size.

Painless dentistry has rendered the phrase meaningless. It still holds good with the wild animals, however, and when once a creature's teeth decay, their owner is doomed. Accidents and abnormalities in an animal's dental armature, though not frequent, usually spell disaster.

Occasionally, elephants are met with having six or seven small tusks growing in one socket. The immense curved tusks of the wart-hog, if deflected from the normal curve in early life, grow straight out in front of the animal's head, making it difficult to root and feed. In still worse case is the rodent which snaps one or both of its lower incisors.

VAST MASS MOVEMENTS

Only continual use enables these teeth to be kept within reasonable bounds, and once gnawing is made impossible by the loss of their bevelled tips the teeth literally run riot. Rodents of all kinds have been found with these teeth curving right up over the creature's head and penetrating the eyes or ears.

The eternal search for food has largely determined the distribution of animals, including man. It inspires also vast mass movements of animals which, as in the case of locusts and grasshoppers, not infrequently result in vast damage to human interests.

FOOD STORERS

Most animals eat as they go, and most carry reserves of food stored about their bodies in the form of fat, but only those of the northern hemisphere seem to have emulated man's well-designed granaries and other food stores. The habit is confined to a few groups of animals only, and to social insects with which food stores are a natural part of the general régime. Some monkeys certainly store food in their cheek pouches, but this is only a very temporary measure, the outcome of living in a riotous society which makes it imperative to grab all one can when opportunity offers and then enjoy it at leisure when some measure of privacy is possible.

The chief mammalian food storers are rodents, though the rule is by no means universal, even amongst northern species. The beaver is a classic example, and so also is the squirrel. Recent observers have proved that not only does the Canadian grey squirrel make large numbers of nut stores—the locations of which it often forgets—but it even stores dead birds and fungi. These are very cunningly lodged in the forks of tree branches, so that the bird's head or toadstool's cap lies across the forks and the bird's body or the fungoid stalk dangles below.

MONDIALE

FEATHERED HOARDER

Some magpies, like ravens and jackdaws, have a passion for collecting bright or ornamental objects.

Nuts and berries are invariably carried to the dump in the animal's mouth, and generations of mouth cramming have stretched the cheeks of the American gophers till they present pouches rivalling those of the monkeys. When a gopher's pouches are crammed to capacity the animal is obliged to unload by squeezing its face with its clenched fists.

The habit many creatures have acquired of collecting all kinds of objects which can be of no possible service to them is possibly a perverted outcome of this food storing. Rats have long been famous as secretors of bright objects, and a tame rat introduced to a heap of coins will almost certainly first select the silver for concealment in its lair.

Darwin has recounted how in America the natives when missing a revolver, belt, or other small piece of property, would first make search in the nearest viscacha warren, and there the lost property would almost certainly be found amongst the other heterogeneous objects gathered by the guinea-pig-like rodents.

COLLECTOR OF CARTRIDGES

Hoarding is rare amongst carnivores, but the northern wolverine or glutton, a large relative of the stoat, not only stores carcasses for future consumption, but if opportunity offers, collects coins, weapons and what not. Hundreds of cartridges have been found in a wolverine's retreat.

Amongst birds this quaint habit may have its springs in some dim æsthetic sense, for the raven and other members of the crow tribe share the bower bird's love of collecting bright or ornamental objects. Sometimes this may lead to quite a little human drama, as immortalized in the famous Ingoldsby Legend of the *Jackdaw of Rheims*, and in Dickens's delightful account of his pet ravens in the preface to *Barnaby Rudge*.

A few birds are genuine food hoarders, notably the butcher shrikes, which impale insects, small birds and even lizards upon thorns, with an eye to the demands of a hungry family. The little owl has been observed deliberately to kill small partridges and then revisit the corpses after they have attracted a hoard of carrion beetles, which the owl much prefers to game.

MONKEY'S TREASURE TROVE

Cecil Aldin, in his book *Dogs of Character*, recalls an instance of a monkey who collected not only reserves of food but dogs' teeth. The milk teeth shed by the artist's numerous puppies had an irresistible fascination for the monkey. He collected them as they appeared and stowed them secretly in a particular cranny by a chimney corner.

For weeks together he might apparently forget his treasure trove, but every now and then the urge to gloat over his hoard would come upon him. Then, creeping away with utmost stealth, he would unearth his museum, and ranging the teeth before him devour them with his eyes, as might a miser his gold. After a " session " of variable length, he would return his trinkets to their hiding-place, and then rejoin society, apparently much refreshed and in a condition of " uplift."

INGENIOUS WAYS OF CAPTURING PREY
(Left) Mata-mata terrapin with artificial worm. (Middle) Deep-sea angler, with rod, line, luminous bulb and hooks. (Right, top) Archer fish shooting fly with water. (Bottom) Ant-lion larva with pitfall for ants.

In the scattering of their waste products animals disseminate seeds, circulate and purge the soil, and perform many other useful services in distributing matter. Vast amounts of useful fertilizer, however, go to waste, as may be witnessed by the huge guano cliffs which stood for centuries on lonely islets until discovered and exploited by man.

VALUABLE WASTE PRODUCTS

The possible exhaustion of a soil's fertility is now beginning to draw serious attention to the utility of the waste products from food consumed by animals of all kinds. Through sheer wastage of sewage over two hundred thousand tons of phosphorus are annually lost to the United States alone, and this at a time when there is increasing need for the element, which is rare in a natural state.

In their manners and methods of obtaining food, many animals show considerable finesse, and this is often the more surprising when we find devices suggesting almost human dexterity in animals of relatively lowly origin. Mammals and birds tend to feed by very direct methods; at most the obtaining of a meal implies an arduous chase or a certain degree of strategy in stalking. But in some fishes and reptiles the means of getting the next meal involves what can only be described as apparatus, of a complexity and delicacy quite disproportionate to its user's intelligence, which is generally of the lowest order.

TURTLE AS ANGLER

In Brazil there is an unlovely looking river turtle known as the mata-mata which literally angles for its prey. Whereas most predacious reptiles merely rely upon their resemblance to their surroundings, such as stranded logs, weedy stones, or mud banks, whereby to take the quarry by surprise, the mata-mata quite deliberately fishes for its dinner. On the creature's very deficient chin is a worm-like filament of skin which is gently waved in the water. Sooner or later a fish mistakes it for a worm, and such is the turtle's quickness of movement that the victim usually discovers its mistake too late.

Fishing for a living finds its highest expression

amongst the angler fishes, abundant in all seas and at all depths. The angler which comes to market as rock salmon is a typical fisherman of this order. The forward fin rays on its back and head are hinged so that they can be raised or depressed at will, and one or two of the longest bear skinny appendages very suggestive of small fishes. These lures, as they are called, seem to be used with some real understanding of their value, and once a fish bites, the angler's immense mouth plays the part of a very efficient landing net.

In the various deep-sea anglers the lure may be jointed, or dangled at the end of a sort of living fishing line. In the blackness of the abyss such a device might pass unnoticed, but it frequently bears a luminous bulb, so that the angler actually fishes as do many West Indian fishermen, who cut out the light organs from certain fishes and impale them on hooks in place of the more conventional worm.

WIDE WORLD

WORLD'S UGLIEST BIRD

The frog-mouth, said to be the world's ugliest bird, sleeps so heavily that lifting it will not awaken it.

What we call sleep is most apparent in the vertebrates, and it varies enormously not only in species but in individuals.

The old adage, "Six hours for a man, seven for a woman, and eight for a fool," is not to be taken too literally. When some scores of celebrities were asked how much sleep they required, the results were surprising. Some of the best brains apparently needed but four hours' sleep in every twenty-four, others demanded twice as long.

BRAIN NEVER STOPS WORKING

Marconi declared that quality of sleep was more important than quantity; Mr. H. G. Wells stated that eight hours was a minimum, and Mr. Henry Ford confessed that he slept six hours but was in bed nine. Napoleon would work for twenty-four hours without sign of fatigue, and seldom slept for more than two hours at a time.

Modern investigators such as Pavlov, have clearly demonstrated that though one is apparently quite unconscious even in so-called dreamless sleep, the brain never stops working altogether. The sensation of activity ebbs and flows in the brain continuously. We sleep chiefly at night simply because that is a convenient time. The work of many demands that they sleep during the day, and they do so readily enough. Similarly animals can be trained to reverse their normal hours for sleep, and they appear to suffer no more than any human worker on a night shift.

WHEN ANIMALS SLEEP

For this reason, a walk round a zoo at night is generally a somewhat disappointing experience. A high percentage of night prowlers are anything but prowling, since to do so would be purposeless. A few mammals, such as small lemurs, ant eaters and bats refuse to show themselves or feed until the last visitor has gone, but this is largely because, since they are not particularly good show beasts, no effort is made to exploit them. "The lions are fed at 4 p.m." proclaim zoo notices throughout the world, but this is a concession to a sensation-loving public, not to the lions.

Broadly speaking, mammals tend to sleep by day, birds by night. There are exceptions, and some of these rank amongst the profoundest slumberers. The night-flying birds

FOX

TRIGGER FISH

This long-faced fish has highly poisonous alkaline flesh, but probably some species find it edible.

known as frog-mouths, for example, sleep very heavily. No part of the brain seems to be in that semi-active state responsible for " sleeping with one eye open " as we say. A sleeping frog-mouth will suffer itself to be lifted from the branch, or even to have a companion next to it shot down, yet never show the slightest consciousness of anything untoward.

Sleep is a natural restorative of worn tissues and may come to the individual's aid when no means of refuelling the body machine is available. Intense cold or drought may both cut off food supplies for the time being, and the best way to tide over such lean times is to sleep. In the northern hemisphere many small mammals and all reptiles thus evade working extra hard for a living, as must such as elect to keep awake. The circulation falls and all the body machinery slows down, drawing what little fuel it needs from the fat accumulated in spring and summer.

ASLEEP FOR SIX MONTHS

The sleeping capacity of such creatures as the bear, hedgehog and dormouse seems to be much less than that of some desert animals. Many snails can sleep for half a year with ease, and there is one remarkable instance of a desert snail remaining quiescent for two and a half years in a museum case, at the end of which time it woke up, notified its presence by smearing slime on its exhibition label, and after being given a warm bath enjoyed a hearty meal.

The African lungfish digs itself into the river bed on the approach of the annual summer drought, and there remains within an earthen cell until the rains release it months later. For this reason, both lungfish and snails commend themselves to the natives as convenient iron rations, to be carried on long treks in inhospitable country.

Do fishes sleep? So far as recent observations in large aquaria cast light on the subject, most fishes remain in a dormant condition for some period in every twenty-four hours. Bottom feeding fishes such as dogfish and skate, sturgeon, lungfish, catfish and flat fish of all kinds are active at night, but by day usually lie half hidden in sand or mud.

A large number of other fishes are semi-dormant at night, resting amongst weeds, leaning against rocks, or lying motionless near the surface. The wrasses actually lie flat upon one side, almost like mammals. The various perches, breams, cichlids, trigger fishes and some kinds of trout rest on the floor. Sun-fishes, rock and sea bass, lean wearily against rocks, or perch amongst plants.

MULLETS' STRANGE BEHAVIOUR

Most striking of all is the behaviour of the grey mullet: as shown by experiments in aquaria, by day this fish moves steadily forwards in mid-water in solid shoal formation. At night the shoal is broken up; each fish rests horizontally on the tank floor, and each faces a different point of the compass. But the moment daylight is called up in the form of a powerful electric torch, or by switching on the lights above the tank, the fishes instantly come together again with almost military precision, all head the same way, and in a moment are off again upon their long trek.

W. S. BERRIDGE, F.Z.S. (MONDIALE)

FISH AND SLEEP

Most fish maintain a state of sleep-like immobility for a certain period during the day or the night.

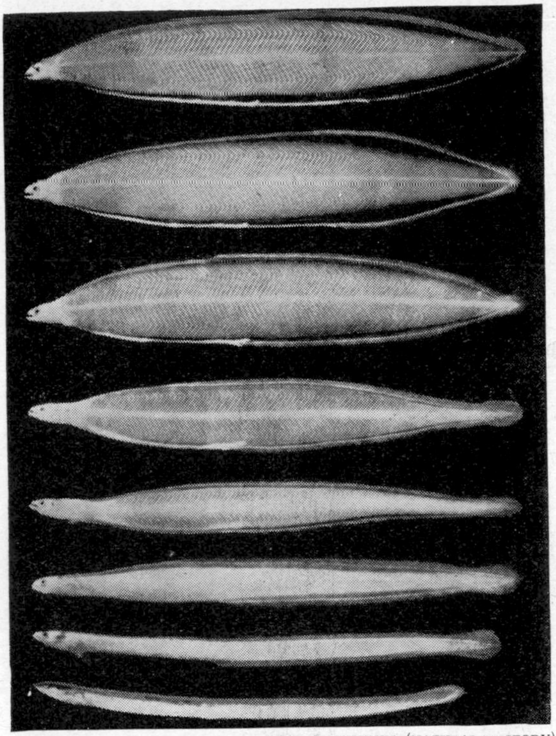

BRITISH MUSEUM (NATURAL HISTORY)

EEL'S DEVELOPMENT

Eight stages in the development of the eel. Note the reduction in depth and length during the change.

Perhaps the most remarkable fish in the world is the eel, which undergoes no fewer than eight changes in its life and seems to suffer from a perpetual wanderlust. In one of the phases it is a voracious feeder; in another it apparently ceases to eat at all for a time.

Dr. Johannes Schmidt, a Danish naturalist, found after extensive research lasting several years that the eels of both Europe and America journeyed thousands of miles to breed in the neighbourhood of Bermuda, where the Atlantic is deepest. He also discovered that the eels which frequented the rivers of East and South Africa, India, the Dutch East Indies and North Australia spawned in the Indian Ocean.

The young transparent fry, which hatch from eggs and mature very slowly, eventually make their way to the freshwater rivers, though perhaps thousands of miles have to be traversed. Doubtless, many millions of them fall prey to larger creatures.

For long enough the tiny specks of life which hatch from the eel's eggs were not recognized as having any connection with that fish, for the good and sufficient reason that none knew their source of origin. The larval form was therefore regarded as a separate and distinct species until 1896, when a scientist discovered in the Straits of Messina a series of specimens which revealed the truth.

AT THE MERCY OF OCEAN CURRENTS

The *leptocephali*, as they are called, are entirely at the mercy of the ocean currents. At the end of three years the fishes, now known as elvers, undergo a transformation which makes them more like an adult in appearance. Vast multitudes reach the shores of Europe and make their way up rivers, some even travelling overland in their urge to discover fresh water. The eels hibernate during the winter, and when they arrive at the age of puberty travel once again to the sea and the spawning ground two thousand or more miles away.

The story of Dr. Johannes Schmidt's researches since he discovered one of the larvæ near the surface some distance west of the bleak and desolate Faroes is one of the quiet romances of science that is not sufficiently spectacular to attract much attention. He followed his tiny clue all over the North Atlantic.

WIDE WORLD

ONE OF THE PUFFER FISHES

When it meets an enemy it blows itself out so as to make the short spines stand on end and present a very threatening appearance.

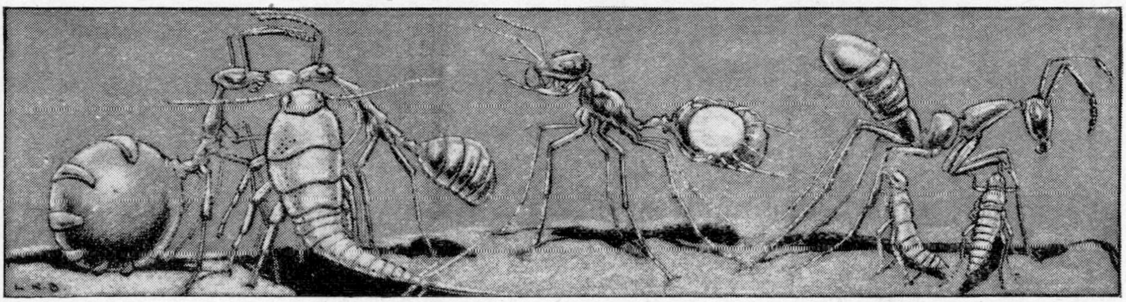

ANT CAMP FOLLOWERS

From left to right: A silver fish insect stealing food from honey pot ants; a mite riding on a soldier ant; beetles grooming the legs of an ant in exchange for food.

ANIMAL SOCIETY

FROM late spring to early autumn one often sees slow-running rivers or large tracts of stagnant water dyed a rusty brown, the mass coloration of uncountable legions of water fleas. Great areas of the sea are frequently discoloured in like manner by vast congregations of minute animals, and at night the waves appear to burn with a bluish fire. This also marks the presence of abundant life, that heterogeneous gathering of larval animals summed up in the word *plankton*, which is derived from the Greek *plagktos*, wandering.

Though all these gatherings of animals represent life as not even the most overcrowded city knows it, none of them can in the strict sense of the term be called societies. Society implies a certain co-operation and mutual tolerance, a coming-together for the general benefit, a quite selfish realization perhaps that No. 1 will stand more chance of prosperity in the proximity of No. 2 and No. 3, than if the individual remained in isolation.

By society one means a different gathering even from those immense periodic congresses of animals which occur during a breeding season, or when circumstances dictate a mass migration. Society implies a certain permanence, a lasting realization of the benefit to be derived from contact with one's fellows.

The water fleas, which dye the pond for yards around, are jammed side by side merely as the result of mass production. The scores of snails which one may rake out of some cranny during an autumnal clean-up in the back garden, are there, not from fellowship, but because the place appeals to each individual as an eligible spot for hibernation.

Animal society can be fairly sharply divided into two categories, the complex civilizations of certain sociable insects, and the much more general love of society which can be traced right through the whole series of vertebrates, advancing in complexity as we ascend the scale, until we reach that mass of social, legislative and political machinery which has become essential to the bulk of mankind.

Many volumes have been already devoted to the social insects, and the reader will find a world of entertainment in the works of Tickner Edwards, Henri Fabre, Dr. Julian Huxley, and a dozen other writers of distinction. Here we can only roughly outline the civilization of the ants and termites, bees and wasps.

Before doing so let us warn the reader not to attempt to find in the lives of insects any parallel with those of human beings. Some authors have done so in all seriousness, to the detriment of science, and the obscuration of clear thinking. In another class are H. G. Wells's *First Men in the Moon*, and C. Capek's no less famous *Insect Play*. These are sharp-edged satires and are not intended as anything else.

The old tendency to humanize insects no doubt originated in the Eastern sage's exhortation to " go to the ant." Dickens dealt a shrewd blow at the false philosophy built up on that adage when in *Our Mutual Friend* he made the West-end lounger, Mr. Eugene Wrayburn, languidly protest :

" I object on principle, as a two-footed creature, to being constantly referred to insects. . . . For the whole case is assumed. Conceding for a moment that there is any analogy between a bee and a man in a shirt and trousers (which I deny), and that it is settled that the man is to learn from the bee (which I also

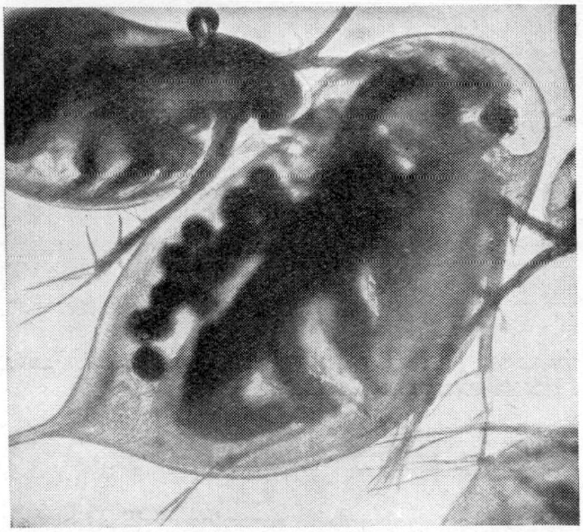

WIDE WORLD

WATER FLEAS

Water fleas, which are lower crustaceans, in a pond jammed side by side as the result of mass production.

deny) the question still remains, what is he to learn? To imitate? Or to avoid? When your friends the bees worry themselves to that highly fluttered extent about their sovereign, and become perfectly distracted touching the slightest monarchical movement, are we men to learn the greatness of tuft hunting, or the littleness of the Court Circular? . . . Are human labourers to have no holidays because of the bees? And am I never to have change of air because the bees don't? . . . I think honey excellent at breakfast, but regarded in the light of my conventional schoolmaster and moralist, I protest against the tyrannical humbug of your friend the bee."

An insect of any kind is for all practical purposes a machine to do certain things, and none other, throughout life. In the social insects we find the society having its main springs in a queen, which is little more than an egg-laying machine, and a number of males, one of which is destined to fertilize the eggs. Between these two are various grades of sexless creatures fitted, usually from the time they hatch, to perform certain functions, which however complex, however strikingly suggestive of human purpose and ingenuity, aim in the long run solely at the support of the living egg-factory—the queen.

LESSONS SLOWLY LEARNED

One can no more hope to inspire an insect to cope with a sudden emergency, or adapt itself to swiftly changing circumstances, than expect a clothes-wringer to undertake a job of printing when the typewriter breaks down. Be it remembered that whereas a few centuries or much less may induce a mammal or a bird to bring about some changes in its ways of life, the insects had trudged on within their narrow grooves for possibly millions of years before the first mammals saw the light. Circumstances have planned the insects' programme, teaching them their little lessons by infinitely slow instalments.

ANT'S NUPTIAL FLIGHT

Ants present the greatest variety in their forms of society and modes of life of any social insects. Between three thousand and four thousand species of ants are scattered over the earth, reaching their maximum in size and numbers within the tropic belt.

In ants, as in bees and wasps, the female mates once only, during a "nuptial flight," and thenceforward settles down to lay eggs as required. The sperms with which she is impregnated during her brief matrimonial experience are stored within her, and passed on to fertilize the eggs in relays—over a period of perhaps nearly a score of years. The sex of an egg is determined by the number of

WIDE WORLD

BATTLE OF THE ANTS

Left to right: At death grips; a casualty; sparring for an opening; the end of a struggle. Between three thousand and four thousand species of ants are scattered over the earth.

HAROLD BASTIN

ARDUOUS LABOUR IN THE ANT WORLD

Wood ant workers struggling with a twig to be used as building material. An ant community may number a few hundreds or scores of thousands according to the species.

sperms—or complete absence of sperms—allotted to it.

Ant communities are frequently subterranean, and all ants, once free of the chrysalis, should step on to the stage of life ready to work till they drop. A community may number a few hundreds or scores of thousands, according to the species. Infinite are the ways of the various communities.

ANTS AS FARMERS

The tropic battlement-ants build on steep hill-sides, and throw up concentric ridges or walls, which serve to divert water rushing downhill during storms, and so protect the nest from flooding. In striking contrast to the tortuous subways with which so many ants riddle flower beds are the homes of the leaf builder ants. One set of workers pulls the edges of two adjacent leaves together, whilst another cements them by squeezing an adhesive from ant grubs, using them as seccotine tubes. Other tropic ants build nests of various materials on trees, causing the big outgrowths known as negro heads.

Amazing devices are resorted to for storing food. English gardens too often suffer from the cowboy ants which farm the destructive aphis for the sake of the sweet secretion it exudes. Some foreign ants similarly farm various scale insects. The honey-pot ants use specially modified workers to retain huge stores of nectar within their abdomens, such ants becoming swollen to the bigness of peas. Even this is eclipsed by the mushroom farmer ants, who actually build fungus beds out of cut leaves, and sedulously cultivate vegetable moulds thereon.

Many readers have probably beguiled a summer afternoon in some woodland watching a party of slave-raider ants bearing off struggling victims from another tribe, later to train them to their own purposes, a bondage to which the witless captives raise no objection. For sheer aggressiveness, however, the raiders are quite outclassed by the terrible driver ants of tropical Africa.

MORE TERRIBLE THAN THE HUNS

These ants make foraging marches more terrible in their way than those of the ancient Huns. Everything falls before their serried ranks, and a regiment may take days to pass through a district. All kinds of insects, and even reptiles, small mammals and birds are devoured. A regiment consists of variously

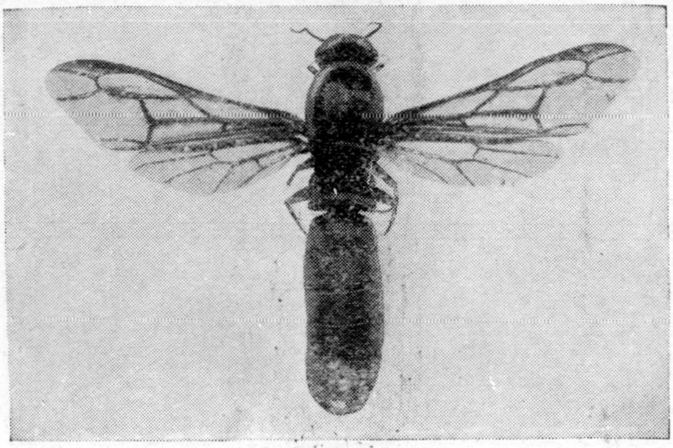

MOST TERRIBLE OF ANTS
A winged male driver ant. Lions give the road to a contingent of these insects on the march.

graded individuals. Some, known as soldiers, have enormous heads bearing razor-edged jaws. Even the lion and elephant give the road to a driver-ant contingent on the march.

Bees differ essentially from ants in that never more than one male fertilizes the queen, and the nest always consists of wax-built cells for the storage of eggs, grubs and food. This last is generally only nectar. Ants and wasps show a much wider range of comestibles, the former—according to species—favouring anything from corn to a dead horse.

Bee communities number only the queen, males or drones, and a single grade of worker, as against the various workers and soldiers of ant society. Further a bee society may range from the many thousands constituting a swarm to a mere family party, as in the bank-burrowing humble-bees.

COMMUNISTIC ANTS

Ants seem to hold together, to keep to their own sets largely by a sense of smell, but bees also evince a certain eye for colour, as is evident by the " honey-guide " markings on flower petals which lead them to the nectar. In large apiaries hives are coloured in groups, and this serves to keep the bees from wandering to neighbouring hives, and spreading disease.

An ant colony is communistic : the individual has literally no existence apart from the body corporate. Many kinds of bee, however, show considerable independence. Some few are quite solitary, lay their eggs, dump a certain quantity of food beside them and then leave them to shift for themselves. Bees have much higher intelligence on the whole than ants. They can be trained to couple a particular colour with a certain food, and with that only, the knowledge remaining with them till they die.

Wasps show still more individuality. Nearly all build beautifully fashioned combs, deep underground or attached to tree branches and grass stems. The material used is not wax but paper made from chewed wood. A wasp is a little living paper mill. The sting which, as in the bee, is a development of the queen's egg-laying tool, is used not only for attack but often to paralyse insects, which can thus be kept in the nest, in cold storage, so to speak, till the wasp grubs are ready to devour them. It is largely a matter of chance as regards the effectiveness of the poison administered. Sometimes a caterpillar may be killed outright and decompose, or so slightly paralysed as to give the wasp grub some trouble when dinner time arrives.

EARTHWORKS OF THE TERMITES

The so-called white ants or termites belong to a tribe quite different from and more primitive than that of the ants, bees and wasps. Termites are purely tropic or sub-tropic insects, and they live underground. Their excavations may upraise huge earthworks, supporting large trees, but the real life of the community is deep below. As in ants there is an egg-laying queen and a male, but the neuters are either sterilized males or females, not as in ants of one sterilized sex only.

FOUNDING A COLONY

A white-ant colony is founded by a queen and a king, who meet on the wing, then descend below ground, shed their wings, build a nest and finally found a colony. As in ants, this consists of the same tireless workers and

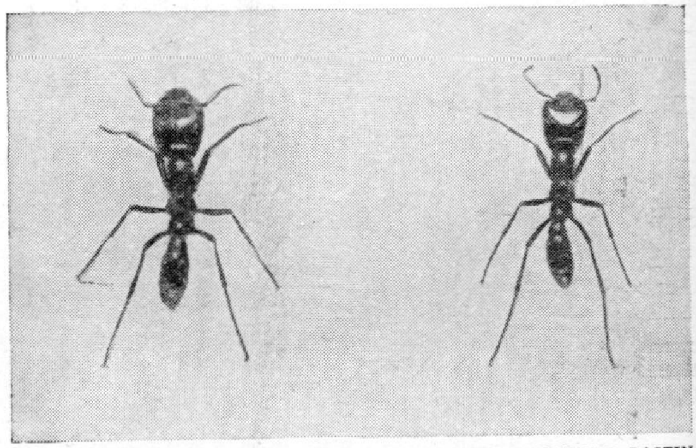

HAROLD BASTIN

WORKER DRIVER ANTS
A regiment of driver ants consists of variously graded individuals. Everything falls before them.

nurses and formidable poison-squirting or scissor-toothed soldiers. But whereas the ants show great diversity of diet, the termites of whatever species know one menu only—wood. Human life in the tropics is one long battle against the insatiable appetite of the termites for anything made of wood, be it a clothes peg or a house.

Herein the termites are unique. Few creatures can digest hard wood—the beaver attacks only a tree's soft, sap-filled outer layer—but a termite digests tough wood fibre by means of innumerable protozoa (single-celled organisms) that swarm in its interior. Nowadays efforts are being made to protect all natural enemies of the termite such as birds, ant eaters and armadillos.

SCOURGE BUT NOT USELESS

Scourge though the termite is, this bleached and light-shunning dweller underground is of some economic use. Wood is not easily converted into fertilizer, but after treatment in the termite's strangely populated interior, it is broken down and returned to the earth for its replenishment and the ultimate benefit of plant life, and as a natural corollary, animal life also.

With that relatively enormous increase of

FOX

WORKER-BEE'S POCKET

Leg of the worker-bee, showing pollen pocket. Workers act as charwomen, nurses and food collectors.

HAROLD BASTIN

HONEY GUIDES

Honey guides on a violet. Bees often confine their attentions to one species of flower.

brain power which marks even the lower vertebrates, society takes on an entirely different meaning. A lobster can live sixteen years in solitary confinement in an aquarium, and provided it is well fed, never realize it is solitary. When we read of a spider saving a medieval prisoner's sanity merely by offering him companionship, it is well to remember that the spider would offer the benefits of its society just as readily to a musical box or a piccolo solo rendered on a gramophone.

SOCIAL URGE IN VERTEBRATES

The vertebrates are in different case. Though fish will live many years in isolation, it is noticeable that most do better if given the society of their own kind, and this is particularly apparent in the many hundreds of shoaling species. If a herring is introduced into a tank which has hitherto housed but a single herring, the two fishes meet, and are very soon both heading the same way, side by side. If a shark plunges into the centre of a shoal, or the shoal leaders suddenly come in contact with a cliff face or other obstruction, there is temporary confusion. But before long, the shoal will have surmounted or circumnavigated the obstacle, and so proceed on its orderly way.

The extent to which even the many kinds of herding reptiles are really appreciative of each other's society, and not merely brought together by mass production or the mutual appreciation of common feeding grounds still needs further investigation. But amongst the birds and the even more highly constituted mammals, society is a very real thing, quite apart from the periodic meetings occasioned by courtship.

To many birds and still more mammals, solitary confinement is almost the worst cruelty that can be inflicted on them. So great is the social urge that a bird or beast denied the comradeship of its own species, will often go to extraordinary lengths to find a substitute. The newspapers frequently bring to our notice a strange friendship, as between a goose and a cat, and a dog and a badger. Zoos are full of queer partnerships. Apes and monkeys will joyfully accept almost any kind of cage-mate rather than none.

FOX

BUILT BY TERMITES

Termites, often called white ants, build homes which may reach a height of twenty-five feet.

Quite recently London's Zoo could show a green monkey fast friends with a wombat, and a young orang inseparable from a tree kangaroo. In the old days, when all the Zoo's service traffic was equine, an old horse which hauled the fodder cart could not be induced to proceed with the day's work until he had had his morning " chat " with a reindeer. Another horse similarly never failed to pass the time of day with a zebra. A famous zoo lion spent his cubhood in the society of a hutch full of rabbits. These instances of the social urge might be continued almost indefinitely.

ANIMAL DICTATORS

The flocking instinct of birds seems to have more in common with the communistic shoaling or schooling of fish than the gregariousness of mammals. Birds certainly derive great benefit from mass formation since the whole of a flock seldom sleeps simultaneously. Hence there are always some members in various degrees of wakefulness, and so able to give warning of approaching danger, though modern observers tend to doubt the old stories of deliberately posted sentinels.

Among mammals we have the first crude foreshadowings of councils, watch committees, government, and sometimes even of dictatorship. Most of the hoofed animals go either in small parties or great communities under the dominance of a leader and a number of aides-de-camp, one or more of which sooner or later evinces aspirations towards command. One may trace the parallel to much higher society without strain or undue humanizing.

In the pack and the herd there are command and intrigue—and co-operation. An old dog-wolf and a handful of seniors lead the whole pack in crescent formation towards a herd of musk oxen or deer. The grazers retaliate by bunching cows and calves together, the bulls forming a wall around them, and with heads down and horns at the ready, prepare for the attack.

BATTLE CODE OF SHEEP

Sheep, particularly wild sheep, have a well-established battle code. If only a solitary dog, of any size, threatens the lambs, they, together with the ewes, go to the rear. The rams then advance in succeeding ranks, those composed of seniors being to the fore. Thus arranged, the whole contingent slowly advances, and as the rams go to meet the foe they stamp with their forefeet—in unison. The effect can be highly

FOX

GANNETS PROVE THE FLOCKING INSTINCT

Gannets nesting on the island of Grassholme, off the Welsh coast. Birds derive benefit from mass formation since the whole of a flock seldom sleeps at the same time. The female gannet is careful of its eggs and will sit on its nest and defy anyone who dares to approach.

dramatic, and if the dog lacks the moral support of an accomplice he almost invariably decides to leave the flock in possession of the field.

REVELRIES OF CHIMPANZEES

Dr. Zuckermann, in his exhaustive study of monkey society, did not find a single instance of apes or monkeys living in anything but a social state, which might vary from a family party to a troop of some hundreds strong, the troop in its turn comprising a large number of family gatherings and cliques. The baboons, notorious as social monkeys, offer a striking instance of the strength that lies in numbers. The enemy of one automatically becomes the enemy of all. Many authentic stories are told of young or crippled baboons being left behind during a retreat, but only temporarily. Invariably a number of elders turn back, and by their ferocious demeanour hold the pursuers in check whilst the laggard regains the main body.

The chimpanzees, highest of all the lower primates, are even more strikingly human in their social traits. They recognize not only large family groups, or aggregations of family groups, but also a kind of club life. Chimpanzees emancipated from the nursery, but not yet arrived at maturity, form unruly mobs which racket through the jungle, enjoying themselves at the general expense. The hooligan revelries of one of these " mixed clubs " leave a trail of devastation and disgruntled would-be slumberers in its train, and it may so happen that the ringleader of one of these parties is a purposeful member of the gentler sex.

BREEDING STORMS

The rollicking, nomadic bands of adolescent chimpanzees naturally suggest one of the most striking aspects of animal society, namely migration. It has been already pointed out that vast periodic migrations may be inspired by the mating instinct, as in the march of the land crabs across great tracts of Africa, or the strange tree-top congresses of Brazilian sloths.

But migration, as with the nomadic American Indians or the wandering Hausas of the Sudan, may also be the result of hunger or disease. Astonishing tales of undoubted authenticity are told concerning the migrations of some hoofed animals in the days before the advent of the high velocity rifle.

There was a time when, as winter approached,

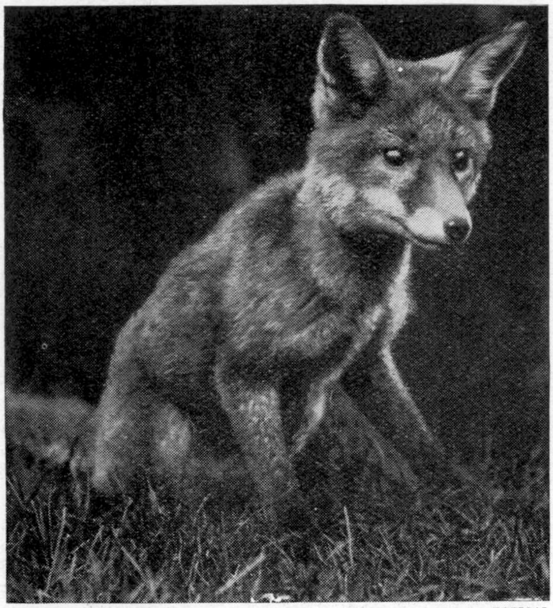

TOPICAL

FOX FIGHTER OF MOUSE PLAGUE

On an Australian farm seventy thousand mice were destroyed in a few hours by owls, foxes and ferrets.

the Canadian caribou passed to their cold-weather quarters in an unbroken procession, streaming through a district for several days on end. Less than a century ago, the South African springbok antelope migrated in such uncountable numbers that the very veldt seemed to move, as did the forest in *Macbeth*, and a lion caught in the close-locked ranks had no choice but to march with them until new grazing grounds were reached, and open order became once more possible.

A veracious tale is told of the big snub-nosed monkeys of mountainous China, migrating from one range to another. Entire villages turned out, spell-bound, to watch the march-past. Public enthusiasm at last caused the monkeys to stampede. They left behind them various jars of home-made wine which had been tightly clasped to the dense fur of their bellies —the said wine having been mourned as missing from a neighbouring hamlet for many months.

These regulated seasonal migrations usually have a happy ending. The promised land, hoped for by the leaders, is reached at last. But there are other less regular migrations occasioned by overcrowding, and then disaster follows. All animals are liable to what scientists call breeding storms.

Multiplication, unchecked by natural influences, reaches a climax, and there results a vast hunger march. The plagues of Egypt have been repeated with variations many times the world over. In 1907 three-quarters of Nevada's alfalfa crop were wiped out by mice, the burrows of which made the country look like a great sieve.

OVERCROWDING BRINGS DISEASE

Ten years later such a mouse plague swept a large area of Australia, and on one farm alone seventy thousand mice were destroyed in a few hours. Owls, foxes and ferrets gorged to repletion, without making any appreciable impression on the flood of rodents. None can doubt that the legends of the Pied Piper and the Wicked Bishop in the Rhine tower have their roots in fact.

In medieval times the Church was not infrequently called in to exorcise the animals causing a plague, and when the pests happened to be rodents the horde made for the sea and were drowned. The apparent miracle thus performed really had a simple, natural explanation. Unchecked breeding means overcrowding, and sooner or later overcrowding inevitably spells migration and disease.

This is how the periodic lemming plagues of Scandinavia always end. One such occurred only a few years ago, and it so far upset what is loosely and misleadingly called the balance of Nature that repercussions of the plague were felt as far south as Yorkshire.

NATURE'S UNSTABLE BALANCE

The little rodents known as lemmings form a staple diet of the Arctic owl. The owls, together with foxes, lived riotously on the lemming hordes making blindly for the coast. When, finally, the lemmings met a watery end, the foxes, more resourceful than the owls perhaps, and in any case unable to proceed farther, turned back to live as best they could. The owls, however, embarked in sheer desperation on a hunger flight. Some perished, no doubt, some made the Scottish peaks or Yorkshire coast, and some few, sinking exhausted upon the decks of chance vessels, eventually gravitated to zoological collections.

Animal society, indeed, is not so very far removed in its essentials from our own. The same motives inspire the bower birds' assembly hut and the dance music which the B.B.C. retails. There is much in common with the march of the caribou and the posters offering "special facilities to intending colonists" displayed in our shipping offices. When animal and human conceptions of an ideal state come into conflict then the complexities of Nature's most unstable balance are increased a hundred-fold.

There is no need to insist upon the interdependence of animals, but dependence is a matter of degree, and some kinds of dependence are more intimate than others. In olden times any animal obviously deriving some benefit from another was dubbed a parasite, but modern naturalists now make fine distinctions between the many animal associations and partnerships.

PARASITIC GATE-CRASHERS

In parasitism pure and simple the benefit is entirely one-sided, the guest being in the nature of a gate-crasher, and giving nothing in return for whatever it may gain from its host. Often an apparent parasite and its host are really messmates. Such cases are now placed in subdivisions according to the precise nature of the partnership.

Symbiosis (from *syn* together and *bios* life) describes any two creatures living in unison for mutual benefit. Inquilism is a more recent addition to scientific language, borrowed from the Italian *inquilenus*, a lodger who comes and goes at will without paying rent. Commensalism implies animals sharing a common table, and in some way describes a certain modern ideal of human society, though not an ideal necessarily finding universal acceptance.

WORRIES OF THE MARMOT

Very often an animal partnership is not easily classified correctly at a cursory glance. A classic example of this kind is offered by the prairie marmot, a little guinea-pig-like rodent living in large communities on the plains of North America. This busy little rodent drives long and deep burrows in the sun-baked soil, and in a land where enemies are many and cover scarce such subways offer ideal homes to animals less industrious or unformed by Nature for such navvy work.

The marmot is soon honoured by callers, the rattlesnake and burrowing owl. Victorian school-readers and popular natural history books used to paint a charming picture of this colonial life. It was invariably represented as a sort of Utopian commonwealth, a Wild West paradise. Bird and reptile were presented as friends and playmates of the paunchy marmot. Closer observation has revealed the sordid truth. Rattlesnake and owl vary their menus

DR. GRAF ZEDTWITZ (MONDIALE)

ARCTIC OWL

Sworn foe—with foxes—of lemmings, of which there are periodic plagues in Scandinavia.

by eating each other's young, and those of the marmot.

The wretched rodent has no sort of redress or means of retaliation. Sooner or later it is forced to effect a moonlight flit from its hard-won home and dig elsewhere. A few days or weeks of peace may follow, but sooner or later the marmot returns from foraging only to find its self-advertised lodgings let on an indefinite lease.

In the northern coastal areas of Great Britain the rabbit knows something of the marmot's worries. The sheld duck finds its burrow a perfect home for her own youngsters, and so does the puffin. But whereas the sheld duck flies in to leave no tell-tale footprints and brings up her young in some secluded by-way, the puffin shows no such finesse. It oftens kills off the young rabbits to make room for its own. Winter may find the moorhen also sheltering in a rabbit's bower, but no rudeness is intended, and the bird just waits in the passage till the weather breaks.

Birds often billet themselves on larger creatures. Some species build in the matrix or outskirts of larger nests, whilst many kinds haunt big animals, and for ridding them of insect pests are entertained most willingly. Little snowy cattle egrets ride on bison and other big game and dig out ox-warbles and other horrors.

ADAPTABILITY TO CIRCUMSTANCES

It is interesting to recall that Captain W. P. Beale was the first to agitate for the organized protection of these little birds in the Sudan. When as a veterinary surgeon he was brought in daily contact with the wandering Hausa tribe of that region, he noticed how the egrets followed the flocks and herds up and down the hundreds of sun-scorched miles between water hole and water hole. To this day cattle egrets of the Sudan are spoken of by the natives as "Doketar Billie's Pigeons."

The cattle egret is a heron and should feed on fish, but frequent fish famines have converted it to largely an insect diet, an interesting case of adaptability and bowing to circumstances.

BIRD JOCKEY OF THE RHINOCEROS

The ox-pecker, rhinoceros bird, or African starling, lives on similar lines. It rides nonchalantly on the big two-horned rhinoceros, in which act the cave-man first noticed and depicted it. Its cool impudence and daring is only surpassed by the little plover-like crocodile-bird or courser of India. It serenely scuttles in and out of the open mouths of giant man-eaters as they lie basking on the mud flats, and picks scraps of past meals from between the teeth, besides removing leeches and other nuisances from the monster's jaws.

Some remarkable gate-crashers occur amongst fishes. Round the coasts of Great Britain in fine weather one may meet floating far out at sea large jelly-fish, two feet or more across. Beneath the "umbrella" of the jelly-fish hides a shoal of baby horse-mackerel securely hidden from the hungry eyes of gulls above and protected by

BARTLETT EXPEDITION TO THE ARCTIC (WIDE WORLD)

WANDERER IN ARCTIC WASTES

Once a rover in Europe and America, the musk-ox is now confined to the Arctic regions of North America. The animals live in herds, and are an important item of diet with the Eskimos.

LITTLE BIRD FRIEND OF A BIG BEAST
A cattle egret perched on a hippopotamus, although it also rides on other big animals. It scavenges for parasites, and thus performs a good deed for the unwieldy beast.

the accommodating stinging cells from foes in the surrounding water. That they sustain no injury from the jelly-fish is surprising.

MORE DREADED THAN THE SHARK

Yet their case is no more wonderful than that of some other fishes patronizing equally or more deadly relatives of the jelly-fish. In tropic seas lives a little fish that actually hides amongst the stinging cells of the Portuguese man-o'-war, a jelly-fish dreaded by sponge fishers even more than is the shark.

In a similar class we may put the gorgeous little coral fishes of the Netherlands Indies. These fishes hide within the body cavity of a huge sea anemone, two feet in diameter. Immune, they play amid its thousands of stinging tentacles, retiring deep into its interior on the least sign of danger. Perhaps their tough scales protect them from harm, though this is hard to believe because most small fishes easily succumb to giant anemones. The coral fishes share their home with a certain prawn, and both fishes and crustacean perfectly blend with the gorgeous colouring of their strange host.

Other instances of fish gate-crashers are small fishes living inside sea cucumbers and starfish, giant whelks and even the gill chambers of other fish. In return quite small fishes may themselves become hosts. Certain little tropical fishes carry on their bodies or spines colonies of hydroids—tree-like creatures allied to the coral animals. Here there is mutual benefit, for the hydroids are carried continuously to fresh feeding grounds, whilst their presence makes the fish an undesirable mouthful to creatures that would otherwise devour it.

HANGER-ON TO SHIPS

We have all read old stories of the wonderful pilot fish that befriends the shark, and whilst gratefully eating such crumbs as fall from the big fish's table, guide it to likely game and warn it of foes. The sagacity of the pilot fish has been in question now for some time. It shows little nicety of taste, and when no shark is available, will follow a ship and gulp down offal flung from the galley. Once two pilot fishes came thus into Falmouth harbour having accompanied a vessel for nearly three months.

The most famous of all fish gate-crashers and camp-followers is the classic remora or sucker fish. Somewhat resembling a mackerel in shape, it is a foot or two in length, with the dorsal fin converted into an immense sucking disc by which it adheres with extraordinary tenacity to anything it touches. Forcible detachment is only possible by a sliding movement. The fish will act as a hanger-on to shark, turtle, ship, indeed any large moving object.

Early naturalists, from Columbus's day onwards, made wonderful pictures of the fish, based on " eye-witness accounts," hauling whales and sea lions out of the water. More wonderful is the fact that West Indian fishermen still use the fish, as in remote antiquity. They tether it to a long line and then launch it at a turtle basking on the sea surface. The sucker or fisherman fish automatically holds on to the turtle, and both are easily hauled aboard. The shark sucker usually affixes itself to the back or belly of the temporary host, but when billeting itself upon a particularly large shark may even take up a position on the roof of the monster's mouth.

WIDE WORLD

PARASITIC INSECT

Lice are parasitic upon man and other animals, few of which are wholly free from pests.

ANCHORAGES FOR BARNACLES

Apart from the crocodile-birds already noticed, neither reptiles nor batrachians seem to offer many attractions to parasites. Marine turtles may be burdened with barnacles and other hangers-on, but merely because they offer convenient anchorages, as do harbour piles and ships' keels. Land tortoises, on the other hand, are much burdened with ticks, and even the little garden tortoise often harbours specimens as large as one's finger nail, clinging tightly to the reptile's rugose skin by means of their eight sharply hooked legs.

Fish are afflicted by immense numbers of parasites of all kinds. Flukes and other worms infest the gills, leeches tap the blood stream at all points, enormous lice, often half as big as the host, similarly drain a fish's energies. The common skate often comes to market bearing big green leeches some six inches in length.

A strange parallel is offered to the leech in the lamprey, once an important food item in Great Britain prior to the wholesale pollution of rivers by waste products from factories. The lamprey, with its tubular mouth ringed with scores of horny teeth, eats into the flesh of a fish such as a salmon, until it taps a vein, when it drinks its fill, usually causing the death of its unwilling entertainer.

Few animals are wholly free from pests of one kind or another. The horny-skinned starfish and the even more effectively armoured sea urchins are sometimes bothered by a small sea snail, known as astericola, that lives amongst their spines. The crab, well protected though it is, often falls victim to an insidious foe, which may be found fixed tightly to its under surface.

PRICE OF PARASITISM

The parasite when thus attached appears as a shapeless bag of tough skin, about as big as one's thumb nail. It offers a remarkable instance of degeneration for it is actually a barnacle, and when quite young is almost identical with the free-swimming, hard-shelled larvæ of the common acorn and goose barnacles. But when the time comes for it to settle down it does so upon a crab, and there, casting aside its armour for the last time, becomes little more than a stomach, sending threads into every portion of the crab's anatomy, and by these countless arteries deriving its sole source of nutriment.

It pays the price of all true parasitism in becoming more or less helpless, and finally exhausts its sole means of sustenance, for the crab, once attacked by sacculina, as the parasite is called, usually dies a premature death.

There is frequently found within the edible mussel a small crab, known as the pea crab, being not unlike a pea both in size and form. The crab is merely a messmate, and in America, where a larger species invades the oyster, it is even more prized than the bivalve. The female pea crab has feeble legs and is so helpless that she spends her whole life hiding within the mussel, this sheltered life having tended to soften her shell, and so render exposure to the world without inadvisable.

The male pea crab, though only half the size of his mate, is a much more vigorous

FISH PARTNERSHIPS

Coral fish of the Great Barrier Reef living in a giant anemone ; a little fish that hides amongst the stinging cells of the Portuguese man-o'-war ; Mediterranean fish living in a sea-cucumber.

creature, having a hard shell and serviceable legs and claws. He leads a roving, independent life, only at mating time visiting mussel after mussel in search of a partner. Having found a suspected shell fish he patiently waits until its shells gape, when he deftly sidles between their sharp edges and joins the female.

It is doubtful as to whether the mussel derives any special benefit from the crab's presence, but many other marine animals find in crabs very harmonious and profitable collaboration.

ANEMONES AS TONGS

A tropic crab carries one or two anemones in each claw, and uses them as living tongs whereby to obtain food and also to ward off enemies. The crab, of course, purloins much of the anemones' hard-won victuals, but the anemones, by being carried from place to place, derive undoubted benefit in commanding a wider range of hunting grounds than they would if anchored to one spot.

The lodgers which billet themselves on the common hermit crab were glanced at in the chapter on Home Building. It may here be pointed out that only the marine hermit crabs appear to be thus imposed upon. There is a noticeable absence of lodgers on the shells worn by the big tropic hermit crabs, who live largely on land and even scale cliff faces or go birds' nesting.

ANTS' NIGHTMARE WORLD

Semi-parasitism, both in human and animal society, reaches its maximum development in the large community. The lighthouse keeper and the little island community are practically immune from footpads, burglars, begging-letter writers, bogus company floaters, and all the other pests which permeate every grade and stratum of the human metropolis. Moralists the world over never tire of pointing parallels between human civilization and that of the social insects. As already mentioned, such parallels are superficial or based on faulty observation, but at least human and ant society groan together beneath a common curse in the enforced support of blood-suckers.

As a chosen victim of the unscrupulous adventurer, both the bee and the wasp are outclassed by the thrifty ant. As with ourselves, the very vastness and complexity of an ant community offers ideal conditions to the smash-and-grab ruffian, or the more insidious purloiner of the society's garnered wealth.

About four thousand different kinds of ants are known, and upon these batten some two thousand kinds of insects, mites, spiders and crustaceans. Some of these gate-crashers are got up to resemble their hosts, and so largely escape detection; others enjoy immunity from arrest—and execution—by sheer nimbleness of foot, others again achieve their own ends by

HAROLD BASTIN

ANTS AS FARMERS

Green fly are farmed by ants, who greatly appreciate the syrupy exudations of the aphides.

blandishment, caressing and petting the ants, or even pandering to the worker ant's insatiable appetite for sweet things.

It is this which has led the green fly or aphis to be so extensively farmed by ants, who find in the syrupy exudations of the aphis an ambrosia of which they never tire. It is a nightmare world on which we look, when probing the secrets of the ant community. As Dr. Julian Huxley has well expressed it :

" If we imagined that in England our houses were, against our wills, inhabited by cockroaches as big as wolves and house flies like hens, and that there were crickets to whose presence we were indifferent, although they were the size of our own children . . . and monstrous creatures which we allowed to eat our babies in their cots because they secreted hot rum punch or some equally fascinating liquid . . . then we should begin to get some idea of the ant's menagerie of guest animals.

" Apart from the aphis, or ' ant's cow ' as it has been called, about two hundred kinds of beetle offer sweetmeats to the ant—in exchange for the privilege of eating the ants' babies unchallenged."

GLANDULAR ATTRACTIONS

Professor Wheeler, in *Social Life Among the Insects*, has said of these interlopers : " Any insect possessed of these glandular attractions can induce the ants to adopt, feed and care for it, and thus become a member of the colony, just as an attractive and well-behaved foreigner can secure naturalization and nourishment in any human community. But the procedure among the ants is more striking, because the foreigners are so very foreign. . . . Were we to behave in an analogous manner we should live in a truly Alice-in-Wonderland society. We should delight in keeping porcupines, alligators, lobsters in our homes, insist on their sitting down to table with us, and (in some cases) feed them so solicitously that our children would either perish of neglect or grow up as hopeless rachitics."

This catering for the ant and systematic cultivating of its demoralization—for the ant's rapacity for sweetness is like the drunkard's lust for alcohol—finds its highest, or lowest, expression in a little beetle known as lomechusa. It supplies sweetstuff to the belligerent red slave-maker ant, and even the beetle's grub is a sort of perambulating bar.

DRONE FLY SCAVENGERS

Another beetle, oxysoma, takes its fill from the ant's store cupboard after having stroked and wheedled the ant into a sort of coma. This is a favourite trick with many ant guests, and is an imitation of the stroking of one worker ant by another when it wishes it to regurgitate food. Half a dozen oxysoma beetles may thus combine to coax an ant into giving them a dinner.

Cruder but bolder are the tactics of the silver fish insect, a creature which sometimes invades our larders. It waits until one ant is passing food to another and then, neatly intercepting the titbit, makes off at high speed in the most approved bag-snatcher manner. Only recently the larva of the large blue butterfly has been added to the list of ants' guests.

White ants, or termites, bees, wasps—all the

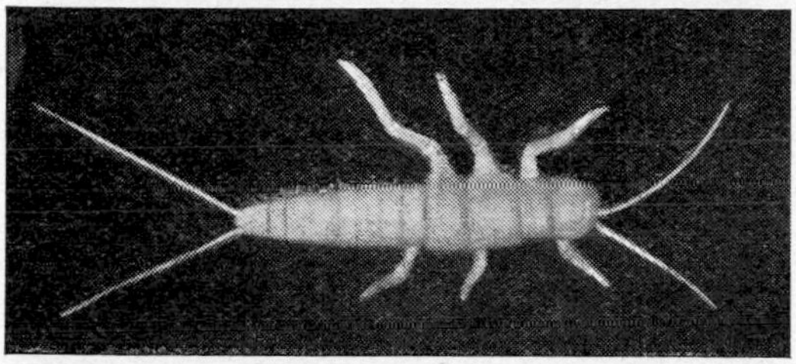

HAROLD BASTIN

SILVER FISH INSECT

This little creature snatches food when one ant is passing it to another and then makes off at high speed.

social insects, in fact—are thus to a greater or lesser degree victimized. Sometimes a nest-crasher is tolerated for genuine benefits conferred—as distinguished from gifts of sweetmeat offered as a cloak to mass murder of the host's progeny.

Some of the drone flies of Great Britain are got up very like wasps and enter wasp nests unchallenged, wherein they lay their eggs. These hatch into spiny grubs that assiduously eat up the dirt often encrusting the crowded cells of the comb, and even eat up the dejecta on the midden below the nest. The wasps seem well aware of the service rendered, for both fly and grub are treated with respect.

A less desirable lodger of the wasp is a little beetle known by no more popular name than *Rhipiphorus paradoxus*. The grub of this beetle has a sucker at the hinder end of its body, and with this it anchors itself to the top of a wooden post, and there waits until a wasp arrives in search of nest-building material. The beetle grub, reared up on end with its legs waving in the air, climbs on the back of the first wasp that appears, and in due course is carried to the nest.

WASP'S RELENTLESS ENEMY

Safely arrived at the nest, the beetle larva eats its way into the creature's interior until too large to find such cramped quarters comfortable, when it regains the open, plugging the hole in its victim's side with its own cast skin. The wasp grub still lives, and although the beetle larva continues to feast upon it, now from the exterior, enough vitality is permitted to remain in order to allow the luckless grub to spin its cocoon. The beetle's offspring then gobbles up the last of its host and lies snug in the ready-made cradle of silk until it turns into a chrysalis, and finally emerges as a perfect beetle.

This, to us, seemingly fiendish artifice is a variant of the ichneumon fly procedure, wherein the fly's egg is deposited in a living caterpillar and there metamorphoses, eventually creeping forth as a fly from the moth or butterfly chrysalis. We shall see later how, during the last few decades, man has learned to turn some of these insect parasites to his own advantage.

PLAYING TIT-FOR-TAT

Occasionally, there occur instances in which one animal makes use of another and is in return utilized without either party being conscious of deliberately playing tit-for-tat. In the fresh waters of Europe lives a small fish known as the bitterling. When the time comes for the fish to deposit its eggs, the female does so by inserting a long ovipositor—literally an egg gun—into the inhalant siphon of a fresh-water mussel, and the eggs being carried into the mollusc's gill chamber there remain secure from foes until hatched.

Here the fish appears to be making use of the mussel in a very one-sided manner, but in due season the mollusc plays a return match. Its young, like those of most molluscs, are minute organisms swimming by means of hairs. But in the freshwater mussel the two shells of the larva have each a strong hook, and the infant shell fish is further prepared for its peculiar start in life by means of one long sticky thread which floats loosely in the water. It may thus stay indefinitely until it dies, but all going well, in time there passes by a shoal of fish, as likely as not bitterling. By the convulsive opening

HAROLD BASTIN

ICHNEUMON FLY

Its egg is deposited in a living caterpillar such as that of the large white butterfly.

and shutting of its two shells the little mussel forces the thread upwards and, fortune favouring, it sticks into a passing fish.

For a while the shell fish, now launched, may be trailed behind, but soon it comes in contact with the fish, and then the hooks grip the skin, and this in time grows up around the little glassy shells. Here it stays, as secure as may have done its host before it in its own parent, and some three months later bursts through the

ANIMAL FRIENDSHIP
A chimpanzee at a zoological garden which took as its boon companion a tabby cat.

tightly stretched wall of its travelling home, to live its life out as a mussel driving a lonely furrow in the river bed.

As we descend the scale of life parasitism assumes more sinister forms, since the often minute size of the parasite renders its presence undetected until its ravages have passed beyond checking. The legions of the mites and ticks, those Lilliputian cousins of the spiders, inflict themselves upon every branch of the animal and vegetable kingdoms in innumerable ways.

They may be relatively harmless, petty polluters of foodstuffs, like the tiny mites which often swarm in flour or very matured cheese. Others, like the itch mite, find themselves in a sheep's bile duct, and having climbed up it into the liver banquet there some six weeks, eventually depositing eggs. So this strange history turns full cycle, launching another swarm of flukes upon the world and spelling ruin to the farmer.

ENEMIES OF MAN

The study of parasitic worms, or helminthology as it is called, now ranks amongst the most important of all branches of medical research. The study not only tracks down, and sometimes remedies, matters inimical to human welfare, but incidentally shows up many animals in a quite new and hitherto unsuspected light. Thus all kinds of browsing and grazing animals, numerous snails, insects and river crabs, though harmless or even useful in themselves, may under certain circumstances prove deadly foes by harbouring flukes in various stages of development.

A tropic fluke conveys via a small marsh snail the disease known as bilharziasis, in which the spiny eggs of the fluke perforate the human bladder and intestine. Allied to the flukes are the tapeworms, each segment of whose bodies can release myriads of eggs that being expelled with the fæces, carry on the race at the expense of man or beast. Often a tapeworm enters the human system via a meal of meat, the intermediary stages of the worm being spent imbedded in the muscles of an ox or a pig.

That most repellent ailment, elephantiasis, which may distort the affected areas of its victim almost beyond recognition, is due to a minute round worm, one of a too numerous clan known as the filaria. Another may infest man's muscles, being relayed via the muscles of the pig—a telling argument in favour of well-cooked meat.

VERMIN ERADICATORS

One might continue to review this rogues' gallery of the parasitic worms almost indefinitely, for the study is still in its infancy, but enough has been said to give some conception of its wide scope and ramifications. We will close this glimpse of animal partnerships and interactions with a prettier picture.

As already stated the more obvious partnerships amongst highly-constituted animals are relatively rare. Fox and badger sometimes share an underground flat, reptiles and birds the same burrow, or large beasts may tolerate small ones for their offices as "vermin eradicators," as up-to-date rat catchers call themselves.

AMERICAN MUSEUM OF NATURAL HISTORY (WIDE WORLD)

EVER ALERT FOR POSSIBLE ENEMIES

Vigilance is the price of life. The tense alertness which the jungle creatures must always keep is evident in this group of Indian bison, which is without the hump of the American species.

But none of these can compare with the ministrations of the little tropic birds known as honey guides. Here, once again, the victim is the long-suffering bee.

BIRD AND BADGER

Honey guides are dingy little birds, allied to the woodpecker and found chiefly in Africa, though one is recorded from the Himalayas and another from Malaya. Science has called one genus "indicator." A typical honey guide is the mayimba of Northern Rhodesia. Like the rest of its class, the mayimba feeds almost exclusively on the grubs of bees and wasps. It is no better provided than the average small bird for an attack upon a mob of several thousand furious bees, but it overcomes difficulties in its way by an extraordinary capacity for coupling cause with effect. It finds a partner to do the dirty work.

Usually this partner, in Rhodesia, is a small badger, whose capacity for hive-breaking has so won native respect as to cause him to be usually spoken of as Mr. Kambole. Kambole is a glutton for honey, but his legs are very short, and ill-suited for long treks from hive to hive. So he waits quietly until mayimba arrives, in great excitement, fluttering about his head and uttering shrill cries. Kambole bestirs himself and ambles off in the wake of the bird. The trek may be long and arduous, but the badger persists. He has never known the bird to let him down. It may also happen that some wily native notes the badger's businesslike progress and follows at a distance.

Before long the bees' nest, some distance up a tree bole perhaps, is reached. The badger, confident in his sting-proof hide and coat of coarse hair, attacks, and the bird feasts as the luckless larvæ are tumbled pell-mell into the open. The bird continues to gorge long after the badger, replete with honey, sinks to sleep amongst the havoc he has caused.

INTOXICATED ON HONEY

The partnership, like all other combines, has its ups and downs. Sometimes the bird leads the badger to one of the crude home-made bark hives erected by the natives, but reprisals are seldom if ever taken. The bird is much too valuable as an indicator, whilst the badger's onslaughts are forestalled by a contrivance similar to the rat-rings seen on ships' hawsers.

When a badger is not forthcoming, the bird

makes for the first native, who joyfully gets together some crude kind of bee-smoker, shoulders his shovel and falls into the train of his excited guide. In wet weather the spilt honey forms pools which quickly ferment, and then the badger, drinking deeply rather than wisely, behaves in regrettably human fashion.

BABOONS' RESPECT FOR THE DEAD

An ascending review of the animal scale is as though one walked through a dark tunnel with the light showing at first as a mere pin-point far ahead, but growing more insistent with each step taken until at last the walker finds himself in full daylight. The daylight we may here take to be our modern human society—if indeed we have already reached high noon.

Had space permitted, we might have dwelt at much greater length on the crude outlines of human society as seen in the animals most nearly related to ourselves—the apes and monkeys. When some years ago all the chief zoos were trying to keep—not too successfully—large gatherings of baboons, the " humanity " of these animals was illuminating, and to the ultra-conventional sometimes rather shocking. There was the same aggregation of cliquish family groups dominated by elders, with rebellious youth " knocking at the door." There were the beginnings of a kind of morality, and as in some higher gatherings, the female delinquent paid more heavily than the male for any irregularity. The intimate mutterings and interchanges of the elders when a crisis faced the community were reminiscent of the town council, and even of the senate. Baboon society was not without its hints at a crude respect for the dead. Whereas a cow whose calf has suddenly died will pass on after a brief lamentation, the baboon mother cherishes her lifeless babe until its remains have become mummified. The baboon colony was far above the machine-like " civilization " of the ants.

ANIMAL RECLUSES

The converse of society is solitude, and the higher mammals can provide many an example of the recluse. Here again the human analogy needs no forcing. The rogue elephant and man-eating tiger, solitaries both, are usually forced into their lone careers through disgruntled age coupled with failing health.

The fundamentals of society can be traced throughout the whole mammalian series.

SPENCER ARNOLD

MOUNTAIN SHEEP AS SENTRY

Sheep, particularly wild sheep, have a well-established battle code. When threatened, the ewes and lambs go to the rear and the rams advance on the enemy in succeeding ranks.

DORIEN LEIGH

UNIVERSAL PROVIDER OF THE FAR NORTH

The hardy reindeer supplies the Eskimos with transport, milk, meat and clothing. They live on tree lichens and reindeer-moss. Unlike other kinds of deer, both sexes have large antlers.

ANIMALS IN RELATION TO MAN

It is customary to regard this as a mechanized age. Petrol is supplanting the original horse-power by a mechanical counterfeit, and synthetic substitutes for homely commodities increase daily. Yet we are scarcely less dependent upon animals for our existence than was the cave man.

Human society still draws much of its food from flocks and herds and the teeming population of the waters. Animals continue to supply the bulk of our clothing from boots to headgear. As regards adornment, some folk incorporate in their attire a veritable zoo. Beasts provide furs, and birds, plumes; shell fish furnish pearls and buttons; insects are a source of dyes, pigments and trinkets of various kinds.

Necessity and luxury combined take a staggering toll of the world's animals. Often a harmless and beautiful creature, as for example the egret, will be driven to the verge of extinction at fashion's decree. Not infrequently Nemesis follows upon short-sighted exploitation of a creature's helplessness. Thus, in recent years, the trade in Central African monkey skins has been followed by plagues of locusts, insects which the monkeys previously kept in check. Similarly, the modern craze for snake and lizard skin commodities has seen in the home countries of these reptiles terrifying visitations of rats and mice, which have spelt ruin to the local farmers.

Animals have been drawn upon for drugs as liberally as for food and clothing. The modern pharmacopœia is almost as full of animal nostrums as was that of medieval times, though we may be glad that the preparation of such medicines has changed considerably. The physician no longer urges his patient to swallow live frogs for rheumatism, or " pill bugs " for colic. But we have derived insulin from the calf, isinglass from various fishes, blistering agents from divers insects, and beneficial oils from a variety of animal sources.

The ferret has been enlisted in the war against influenza, and a cure for hæmophilia or bleeders' disease found in the venom of Russell's viper, one of the world's most deadly snakes. It reduces the time taken for blood to clot from thirty-five minutes to seventeen seconds. Hundreds of patients have been treated successfully

TOPICAL

DANGEROUS BUT USEFUL

The python sometimes lays more than a hundred eggs at a time. Its skin is used for shoes.

since 1934, when the first practical test was made. Poisoning, cancer and epilepsy cases have been dealt with in a similar way.

Animals of every kind are enlisted to aid in medical research, and even the age-old quest for renewed youth has sought the means to its goal amongst animals. How wealthy senility has borrowed the " gland of hope and glory " from apes and monkeys is now ancient history. East of Suez there is still a thriving trade in rhinoceros horn, pangolin scales and monkey gall stones for a like purpose.

Where amusement is demanded, no animal is safe. The bull fight is by no means confined to Spain. In Great Britain bull-baiting has only just passed out of living memory, fox hunting, deerstalking and the annual slaughter of game are still as popular as ever, while the rise of greyhound racing proves how universal is the instinct for the chase.

Fish fights are to the Siamese what horse racing is to Englishmen and are controlled by equally elaborate legislation. In British India the demand for hunting-leopards (cheetahs) is so great that dealers are now scouring Africa to meet the market, the home supplies having grown inadequate.

Mechanised transport, despite its amazing development, is of so recent introduction that two-thirds of the world still largely depend on animals. They are the most cheaply fuelled form of transport in existence. Even in England draught dogs were abolished by law less than a hundred years ago, and not entirely on humanitarian grounds. They impeded horse traffic, particularly in London. Dogs continue to haul wheeled vehicles throughout the Continent.

CHINA'S FISHING CORMORANTS

Animals are used the world over in all kinds of curious side-lines of human activity. China has its fishing cats and cormorants; in Malaya monkeys are trained to harvest coconuts. The Florida turtle traders use that curious fish the remora to capture the slow-witted sea tortoise, as did their forbears eight hundred years ago. Fortunes are yet being piled up from the bee's honey, the cochineal bug's brilliant dye, and the guano of bats and sea birds.

Only today are we beginning to realize fully the vast possibilities of animals for human prosperity or the reverse. None is now regarded as insignificant, from the worm turning the soil, to the thrush which checks the worm's too lavish increase. As a result, we are seeking to make good the harm done by past centuries of ignorance and improvidence.

MAN THE DESTROYER

Animals all but exterminated by former exploitation are being reinstated on the game reservation, the bird sanctuary and the fur farm. The laws of animal life are being keenly studied in numerous up-to-date zoos. For the study of animal parasites, which promises to become an all-important branch of economic zoology, experimental farms and research laboratories are springing up all over the world. The systematic study and safeguarding of the world's fisheries has been placed on a sound footing during the last forty years.

Thus briefly we see how much we owe to the world's animals, the vast army of its unenfranchised citizens. The increase or decrease, improvement or the reverse of this army are largely under our control, and may well command the attention of all, since all are involved. Animals enter into almost every conceivable phase of man's activities, have inspired some

CHARLES ALFRED HAMILTON

DOG-CART IN MORE THAN NAME

Two-thirds of the world still largely depend on animals for transport. In England draught dogs were abolished by law less than a century ago; they continue to haul carts on the Continent.

of his most wonderful inventions, and have coloured his art and literature, folk lore and religious beliefs since first he attained to human estate.

Judged by cave drawings and bone carvings, which are the oldest human documents, man the world over was at first a destroyer and nothing more. He slew with crude stone spears and knives, slings, bows and pitfalls. Primarily man killed for food and raiment; later he began to slaughter for pleasure, a practice he still continues.

ANIMALS AS RELIGIOUS EMBLEMS

In his first primitive contacts with the lower animals, man learnt to dread some and admire others. These presently entered into his conceptions of religion and were deified. Animals figure as religious emblems in every nation to this day. Not that such deification always saved the animals from destruction.

Quite early in human history, the chase brought about automatically the semi-domestication, and later the intensified domestication of first (in all probability) the dog, then the cat and the horse. Later sheep, cattle, pigs and various birds joined the ranks of man's enforced servants, but apart from these more or less privileged creatures, the animal world had for countless centuries no reason to hold man in anything but dread.

TIDE OF DESTRUCTION

In his nomadic days man had but two major recreations, war and the hunting of wild animals. Both these recreations were adopted with avidity by the earliest civilized communities. Incredible numbers of animals were requisitioned to provide the blood baths in the circuses of ancient Rome, and though both the civilizations of ancient Rome and Egypt added fish and shell fish to their list of cultivated animals, man continued to destroy far more than he preserved. The earliest known zoos seem to have effected little as regards the encouragement of conservation, though the one founded by an early emperor of China about 1000 B.C. may have been an exception. At least it was given the encouraging title of the Intelligence Park.

Zoo or menagerie keeping of a kind became in time a cult with almost every monarch or his sufficiently wealthy henchmen. But the domesticated or specially protected "game" animals always excepted, the tide of destruction rolled on unchecked, and apparently

CHARLES ALFRED HAMILTON

BEASTS OF BURDEN

Descendants of wild asses, there is reason to believe that donkeys were domesticated before the horse.

uncheckable. So it continued the world over, until just over a century ago.

One might with ease compile a discouragingly lengthy list of creatures that have been blotted out of existence within the last hundred and fifty years. Amongst mammals may be cited Stella's sea cow, a creature three times as big as a porpoise. It went the road the whales are going; it was killed for its oil. Some mammals have fallen to collectors' mania. The last quagga died at the London Zoo in 1864.

At least a score of species of birds have been so ardently collected, or used as food, that they have disappeared from the face of the earth. The dodo and the solitaire are classic examples. The moa of New Zealand, an ostrich-like bird standing ten feet or more high, together with the great auk of Iceland, were believed to be alive as late as 1860, but though rewards were offered for living specimens no rewards were ever claimed. It is known that the mariners early in the last century used to drive the great auks like geese down gang planks into the holds of their ships for victualling during a long voyage. The giant tortoises of the Seychelles and Galapagos were used in the same way.

TOLL OF COMMERCE

Commodus, one of the more degraded of the Roman emperors, once killed one hundred lions in the Roman coliseum at a single performance. This was with the naked sword. Gunpowder soon after its invention made the orgies of Rome seem insignificant. Today even the largest bags by unintelligent trophy hunters are dwarfed by commercial slaughter with the most up-to-date weapons. Here are a few figures culled from recent official reports issued during the last few decades.

In 1906 Norwegian whaling companies killed nearly two thousand whales, but with improved methods quadrupled this by 1923. In ten years only, Japan, quite a novice, accounted for close upon twenty thousand leviathans, and seventeen years' whaling in the South Shetlands removed over one hundred and twenty-two thousand animals.

Whales have at least this advantage over the hunter, however efficient his equipment—they live in the sea, a vast and often unassailable sanctuary. The terrestrial fur bearers enjoy no such protection and have suffered accordingly. During the three years 1919–21 over ninety-one million skins, representing eighteen species of the more common fur-bearing animals, came into the market. Of the more valuable there were only eight and a half millions. Close upon two million kangaroos figure in the list, fourteen million squirrels, the same number of muskrats, and over two hundred thousand koalas.

SAVING THE KOALA

No reasonable objections, perhaps, can be raised to wolf, muskrat, squirrel or the various farmed creatures, such as nutria and foxes, figuring in the list; but the same cannot be said concerning the koala, the little arboreal marsupial that inspired the popular teddy bear. This animal is entirely harmless and subsists solely on the leaves of one or two only of Australia's two hundred kinds of gum tree.

In 1927 the then Queensland government

WIDE WORLD

FORMER INHABITANT OF ENGLAND

The wild boar was stamped out of Great Britain because it was harmful to agriculture and to the peaceable enjoyment of the countryside. It is still preserved in parts of Europe.

raised the ban placed upon the slaughter of the native "bear" or koala. In a month over half a million adults were killed, and two hundred thousand infants used for dog meat.

IMMUNITY AT A PRICE

At the end of 1937 there were only about five hundred thousand native bears left in Queensland, but by that time a bill had been passed prohibiting under severe penalties any further slaughter of these animals, while some hundreds had been captured and placed in reservations.

Timely propaganda succeeded in rousing public indignation against the plume trade, but the ultimate salvation of the fur bearers must be looked for in another direction. One by one many of the once most profitable species are virtually disappearing, so that the slaughter of the last survivors is not a business proposition—and so they gain immunity, at a price.

The figures quoted represent but a drop in the ocean of blood spilt for pleasure or profit within comparatively recent years. Much senseless butchery still continues, but something like an awakening to the possibilities of animal life wisely used and controlled is now taking place in all the more advanced nations. We will glance at some of the results achieved.

Many of man's greatest disasters, like his triumphs, have resulted from a too ready grasp at the needs of the moment, without due forethought to the possible consequences. Side by side with the indiscriminate slaughter of animals he has effected introductions of all kinds. We owe some of our most useful animals to such experiments, and sometimes we have lived to deplore them.

MENACE OF THE RABBIT

All too easily can man upset what is loosely called the balance of Nature. The balance is never the same for long : it sways back and forth as first one and then another plant or animal gains temporary mastery. The balance may be likened to that of an unsteady trapeze artiste—ever on the brink of a crash, but righting himself at the last moment, as by a miracle.

As the result of persistent endeavour, the wild boar was stamped out of Great Britain because it was harmful to agriculture and to the peaceable enjoyment of the countryside. Charles I, however, endeavoured to re-establish this ferocious and destructive animal in the New Forest, but we are told "the people rose against them." The people are rising against some other importations with less success.

We may regard the sparrow, rat, cockroach and other undesirables as accidental introductions for which no one is specially to blame. The rabbit ranks amongst our unfortunate experiments. Originally, the rodent probably

WIDE WORLD

GROWS NUTRIA FUR

The coypu lives in South America and the West Indies. It provides the world with nutria fur.

came to us after the Norman Conquest, and was kept within enclosure by the feudal landowners. But rabbits burrow, and there is no knowing where they will turn up next. The rabbits having broken bounds, reduced much pine forest by eating the seedlings, and so made way for heather in place of timber.

For centuries no other harm was done since the abundant stoats and foxes kept the rabbit in check. But for the last century or more the rabbit has been a steadily growing menace to agriculture, thanks to another importation, the pheasant. Where the pheasant is, none of the rabbit's natural foes—bar the fox—is allowed to exist. As a direct result of what we may term rabbit pressure, grass has now supplanted trees, heath and rushes on many acres : it can grow where the other plants have been eaten to vanishing point. With fewer stoats, hawks and owls to worry it, the rabbit turns from mere grass to young corn. Forty rabbits can eat in a day enough to maintain a cow or an ox.

The rabbit not only eats abundantly but spoils banks and riddles open ground, where valuable cattle may perhaps break their legs in its concealed holes. The rabbit supplies good and cheap food, its skin gelatine, and its hair such "luxury furs" as leopard gazelle, electric coney and other remarkable pelts unknown to nature. Rabbit fur also provides felt, and the animal's manure may be of some value. Yet the time has come when many are beginning to wonder if the animal pays for its keep. Looked at from its many facets, the rabbit problem is very real and daily growing more insistent. It is estimated that damage to the value of £50,000,000 a year is done by the wild rabbits of Great Britain.

REMEDIES IN NAME ONLY

Even if a war of extermination were practicable, it might find as many opponents as votaries. The rabbit is one of the mainstays of the fox's larder. Apart from the obvious effects which a rabbit famine would have on the already harassed poultry farmer, fox hunting —which also has its critics—circulates millions of pounds annually in England and provides more or less regular employment for a small army of people of every grade.

In Australia the rabbit, introduced much later than in England, of course, has long been such a scourge that every year scores of thousands of carcasses are burned as the only means of disposal.

The balance of Nature can never stay for long the same, once man, by elimination or addition to the existing state of things, sets the wheels of change in motion. Some remedies for the rabbit plague, for instance, have proved almost worse than the plague itself. On one sparsely inhabited island the human inhabitants introduced cats. The cats soon wiped out the rabbits, and their introducers were faced with eating cat in place of the rabbit of which they had already tired.

SPARROWS GIVE PLACE TO STARLINGS

Within living memory we have seen a radical change in the bird life of great towns, both in America and Great Britain. At home the motor has wiped out the trade in marsh birds from Norfolk in a curious manner. When London relied solely on horse buses, immense quantities of marsh grass were bought from East Anglia to feed the bus horses. Marsh grass areas regularly cut provide just the right nesting grounds for snipe and plover. Now the grass grows rank and high, the birds have migrated, and the trade in them, so far as

WIDE WORLD

SOME OF THE SPARROW RESIDENTS OF VIENNA

What appear to be leaves are sparrows. In Australia the bird, imported by ones and twos long ago from the Motherland, is a serious pest. In London the starling has partly supplanted it.

Norfolk is concerned, has come to an end.

The sparrow is gradually disappearing from London, and the starling is taking its place. This is another result of the motor age, which has cut off the London sparrow's main food supply—the droppings from horses' nose-bags. Something similar has occurred in America, where the starling is an introduction. Presently the birds may have to be kept within bounds, as have London's civic pigeons.

SEARCHING A TRAIN FOR A BIRD

Recently, a transcontinental train in Australia was subjected to a rigorous search—for one sparrow. In Eastern and Central Australia the sparrow, imported by ones and twos long ago from England, is a serious pest. A fine of £100 is imposed on anyone harbouring a sparrow. When, therefore, it became known that a stowaway sparrow had landed from a freighter at Fremantle and had boarded a train, committees were formed to track it down and prevent it reaching the west, an area hitherto kept sparrow-free by the barrier of the Great Central Desert.

This dread of the sparrow is very justified, for the bird has the hall-mark of a good colonist—adaptability. It is almost as great a world traveller as the common snail of English gardens, which can be met with in Morocco, feeding with customary gusto on the prickly pear cactus when nothing better offers.

We are only now realizing that it is not enough merely to deposit a foreign animal in our own country under conditions which promise to suit it; they may suit it too well.

SUPPRESSING THE MUSKRAT

When, a few years ago, it was realized that the muskrat would become a menace in Great Britain, the most drastic steps were taken for its suppression. Now the various fur farms—fox, nutria, mink, etc.—established to make good the havoc wrought by promiscuous massacre, are under the strictest supervision.

In the British Isles the grey squirrel, like the

rabbit, has also gone too far. The climate is not cold enough to make its fur of marketable value, and racial conservatism precludes its general use as food, though it is superior to rabbit in this regard. The animal is merely a nuisance and an expensive one.

Up to the year 1800, Great Britain was, as regards the general attitude towards animals, much where it was in medieval times, when

WIDE WORLD

VICTIM OF FASHION

The crested crane, once destroyed in great numbers because its feathers were demanded by fashion.

the only protective measures consisted in savage punishments meted out to those who stole the king's deer. Animals were tools and playthings, of use in crude agriculture, transport, sport and quackery.

There were only two zoos, as opposed to beast shows, in the world. One, of long standing, was at Vienna in Austria, the other and slightly younger institution was the scientific mecca of the period. Every biologist and scientific investigator sooner or later paid a visit to the Garden of Plants in Paris. Apart from the Royal Society for the elect few, England in 1800 was in a state of barbarism, and mightily amused at the efforts of a few fanatics struggling to establish a Society for the Prevention of Cruelty to Animals. In 1820 the Zoological Society of London was founded.

The story of this body has been told in detail in other books, and is only mentioned here as a conspicuous milestone on the road to better things. One of the Zoo's most energetic champions was founder of the famous Smithfield Club, England's oldest fat-stock show society. The Zoo had great hopes of introducing new food animals, and devoted its earlier years to their establishment without success save in one direction, poultry. It inaugurated the first poultry show, and helped to establish a huge network of poultry societies and agricultural research stations. It inspired the first dog shows, and incidentally the first homes for lost and starving dogs.

ZOOS INSPIRED BY LONDON

Apparently, the society, despite early predictions to the contrary, was founded at a fortunate time. The world was ripe for it. The amused curiosity it first aroused soon gave rise to enthusiasm. Within twenty years of its inception it was enjoying to full measure the sincerest form of flattery. One by one every other country followed in its wake, not only setting up zoos, but communicating with London, and establishing many other institutions similar to those the Zoo had inspired.

The London Zoo came too late to save some of the native animals, the great bustard for example, but other countries by vigorous action rescued from extinction valuable and interesting items of their fauna.

REINSTATING THE BISON

An outstanding instance is that of the American bison. Less than a century ago the animal was counted by hundreds of thousands. Greed decimated its ranks. There are even records of how American Indians and cowboys, in drunken frolics, stampeded whole herds of bison over precipices "for fun." Today the American Bison Society and scores of affiliated bodies have reinstated the animal and made it one of the country's most valuable natural resources.

Naturally enough man's attention as regards animals was primarily concentrated upon terrestrial species. He realized the necessity for their protection, but the flocks and herds of the sea he left largely to look after themselves, taking his toll of them as occasion served, confident in the soundness of the ancient maxim, "There's lots of good fish in the sea."

He believed much the same of freshwater fishes, bar the salmon, which he guarded with the same savagery as he did the royal venison. Even the far-sighted Thomas Henry Huxley shared the general attitude, and encouraged it by declaring, "Fish where you like, when you like, and how you like." Such was his confidence in the apparently inexhaustible fecundity of the seas.

FIGHTS CAUSED BY HERRINGS

Inconsistently enough, despite this childish faith in the sea's unbounded riches, extraordinary greed and jealousy were shown in the gathering of them. Many fierce naval engagements between European nations had their beginnings in a selfish desire on the part of each belligerent to monopolize the herring fishery.

It was in 1853 that the London Zoo opened its aquavivarium, the first exhibit of its kind. as opposed to the monkish stews and the Roman fish and oyster ponds. The aquavivarium, for want of those engineering devices indispensable to successful aquarium keeping, was in the end a dismal failure. But in its short lifetime it not only inspired the equally short lived aquarium craze of Victorian times, but the now highly organized safeguarding of the world's maritime resources. The Zoo's 1853 effort had in its turn been largely instigated by the books and other propaganda of P. M. Gosse, who little realized the vast machinery his ready pen and brush were to set in motion.

Less than twenty years after the aquavivarium opened, there was founded in Naples by Anton Dohrn, a German biologist, the first marine research station. This was established partly from his own private resources, aided by contributions from enthusiastic sympathizers, and grants from the Italian and German Governments. In England the only efforts to safeguard and control fisheries of any kind were in the hands of the indefatigable Frank Buckland, the father of fisheries so far as the United Kingdom is concerned.

WORK OF MARINE LABORATORIES

It was not until 1884 that Great Britain awakened to the parlous state of her ocean resources. In that year the Marine Biological Association of the United Kingdom was established, and an aquarium and research laboratory built on part of the old citadel site at the eastern end of Plymouth Hoe. Today there are about two hundred such stations scattered over the world, the nations with extensive coastlines, England, America and Japan, naturally having the greatest number of stations.

A marine laboratory deals with every conceivable phase of ocean life, from tracing the histories of the most obscure plants and animals to the study of wind, water and the formation of the sea bed. As in agriculture, the farmer of the seas can afford to neglect nothing; all is significant.

WIDE WORLD

ALLY OF THE CHINESE

The cormorant, which the Chinese have trained to catch fish without swallowing them.

When T. H. Huxley voiced his optimistic dictum, he spoke at a time when the leisurely sailing trawler and the seine net and long line could supply all the fishes the nation needed. But soon steam was harnessed to feed an ever-growing populace, and when the first steam trawler left harbour the security of the harvest of the sea was at an end. For in fishing one is reaping where one has not sown, and that can no more continue indefinitely at sea than on shore. The steam trawler, now vital to supplies, destroys at the lowest estimate a hundred times more than it brings to market.

Not only are countless young fishes killed and shovelled overboard, but in addition thousands of tons of the invertebrate life on which so many feed, and the roes of fishes which might otherwise ensure the harvests of many years to come are destroyed. Prejudice is so great that many wholesome kinds of fishes are automatically scrapped, and owing to the inevitable interdependence of all life, ashore or afloat, their loss is soon felt by the few fishes which meet with our unadventurous approval.

Apart from all this wastage the steam trawlers, now countable in thousands, carry devices for negotiating rocky ground that was closed to the old-style trawls, and by working winter and summer, and in almost any weather, scatter the fish when on their breeding grounds.

How greatly the game preserves in the seas may benefit from judicious resting periods was proved just after the World War, when for a short time fishes of all kinds were extraordinarily abundant, as a result of four years' comparative immunity from molestation. Regulating the mesh of nets, closing certain areas for recuperative periods and patrolling the seas to enforce observance of the fishery laws are useful measures still in their infancy. The difficulties are great, for the storm-torn and often fog-bound seas cannot be controlled as can a pheasant covert, or even great inland reservations like the Kruger, Yellowstone, Akeley and other animal parks now established in various parts of the world.

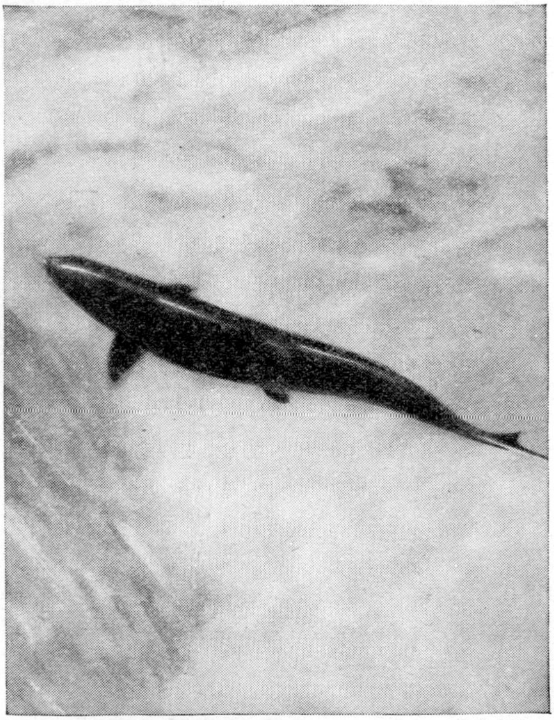

WIDE WORLD

SALMON LEAPING A FALL

The salmon spawns in fresh water, perhaps its original home. The Thames was a salmon river until pollution drove the fish away.

ROBBING THE OYSTER

River and coastal waters, though obviously much more patrollable than the open sea, have fared even worse. Just over a century ago the Thames boasted scores of fishing villages between the Nore and Teddington. Pollution of the waters has made them all no more than memories. Pollution has also rendered necessary the elaborate and costly purification tanks associated with England's oyster fisheries, established for the most part near or in estuaries.

Coastal waters may also be ruined, no less than the land, by hastily considered or accidental introductions. A case in point is the slipper limpet, the curious brazil-nut-sized shells of which may be gathered by the bushel on almost any beach in Great Britain. This sea snail was unknown in English waters prior to 1880, when it is believed to have been landed with a cargo of oysters from America.

The slipper limpet eats the same food as the oyster, and by multiplying at an amazing rate not only robs the valuable mollusc of its rightful nourishment but by sheer weight of numbers smothers it. Further, the creature appears to have few if any natural enemies in the waters of its adoption. Twenty tons a day are often dredged in the Essex estuaries alone.

SHELL-FISH SCOURGE

The sale of the shell for grit and other purposes offers small compensation for the expense of dredging, or the loss of oysters. The snail itself is both wholesome and tasty, but ranks with other good fare amongst the national taboos. Regarding this, Dr. J. H. Orton, the leading authority on oyster culture, writes: "One has the impression that if *Crepidula* (the slipper limpet) occurred in France . . . means would soon be found to convert it into a cheap source of food." One has only to remember that prior to 1903, when the government set about popularizing dogfish, now the mainstay of fried fish shops, this excellent dish was almost universally regarded as uneatable.

Another shell fish scourge, though of less

WIDE WORLD

DOGFISH AND THEIR VICTIMS

Previous to 1903 *dogfish were almost universally regarded as unfit for human food. They play havoc with young herrings, and sometimes content themselves by biting out small pieces as pictured above. Left: dogfish.*

import, is the zebra mussel, brought to Great Britain with timber from the Baltic some fifty years ago. The shell, which is about the size of an edible mussel, multiplies so fast as often to choke water mains. A three-foot conduit at Hampton had its bore reduced to nine inches as the result of this mollusc's fecundity.

NURSERIES FOR COD

Dr. Julian Huxley, in speaking of the balance of Nature, has referred to " the subtlety of the web's weaving, whereby a twitch on one life thread alters the whole fabric." This applies in like measure to the reactions of one plant or animal upon another, and man's control of them. Intensified methods of fishing have brought about intensified measures for propagating fish artificially. In Canada the salmon wheel catches the fish by thousands as they ascend the rivers, and hurls them straight into the cannery.

Parallel with this mass destruction has grown up a system of fish farming whereby ova and milt are taken from the living fish, intermingled, and the fertilized eggs eventually hatched in a special nursery. In America such sea animals as cod and lobster are now similarly farmed on the grand scale.

Study of the inhabitants of the seas no doubt increased the general interest in birds, their migratory movements coming under the observation of seafarers even more than landsmen. The value of birds as guides to fishing grounds, and their still greater importance to agriculture led, in 1889, to the foundation of the Royal Society for the Protection of Birds. Hitherto they were largely anybody's prey, and beneficial species suffered equally with the few pests, their alleged depredations being based largely on the observations of not too observant land workers and gamekeepers.

A year after the Society's foundation Lord William Percy made the first attempt at ringing birds for the purpose of checking their migrations. As a sportsman he confined his efforts to woodcock, but nine years later C. C. Mortensen, a Danish schoolmaster, began attaching numbered discs to the legs of such birds as he could catch. It is interesting to note how this device developed parallel with the idea of marking fish with metal or celluloid discs for a like purpose.

RECORD LONG DISTANCE FLIGHT

The practice of ringing birds was augmented by Messrs. H. F. Witherby and Sandsborough Thomas of Aberdeen University, with such fascinating and illuminating results that by 1909 the practice was common on both sides of the Atlantic.

Close upon a million birds have been thus marked during the last two and a half decades. From the records obtained it transpires that the Arctic tern holds the birds' record for long distance flight, leaving Labrador in July, and next appearing in South Africa, eight thousand miles distant. For its size the humming bird, though travelling only over land, comes next, whilst the swallow and the stork are almost equal in their annual journeyings.

BREEDING-SANCTUARIES

Other relatively recent activities on behalf of birds are the establishment of breeding sanctuaries, the immensely popular nesting box and food-table movement, the discouragement by broadcasting of pumping waste oil from ships, which kills diving birds, and the erection of resting racks on lighthouses. These devices, supplied by voluntary subscription, save tens of thousands of birds beneficial to agriculture during their hazardous migratory flights, which so often synchronize with the equinoctial gales.

Bird protection and study is so well organized in Great Britain today that by means of registered watchers all over the country, it has been found possible to take a census of such comparatively stationary birds as the barn owl. A similarly organized examination of the contents of the crops of various birds has resulted in many kinds once shot on sight being established as amongst the land workers' best friends and accorded the protection of the law.

IMPORTANCE OF INSECTS

In some respects the study of insects from an economic point of view is the most important of modern sciences, so far-reaching is it and so great its potentialities.

Honey, silk and cochineal dye have been appreciated, and in varying degree cultivated, by man since the dawn of history. But apart from these matters the significance of insects has only lately been realized or even suspected. Until comparatively recently all other insects were regarded as pests.

FOX

REAPING THE HARVEST OF THE SEA

When the first steam trawler left harbour the security of the harvest of the sea was at an end. Although the method of fishing which now obtains is vital to supplies, it also accounts for much wastage.

WIDE WORLD

PLAGUE OF LOCUSTS IN NORTH AFRICA

Locusts on the war path sometimes move on an immense front extending for many miles. Grass and leaves are devoured, and even boughs are broken down by the weight of the insects settling on them. During an attempt to defeat an invasion in Transjordan, two thousand four hundred and forty-seven tons of the insects were collected.

Today the study of insects is recognized as being far more vital to the interests of mankind at large than fur farming, game preservation, or even cattle breeding. Man's mainstay, the products of the soil, are at the mercy of the insect hosts as much as they are moulded by the elements. Here, as always, we learn by the expensive method of trial and error. Often a newly acquired scrap of knowledge must be discarded, or at least revised.

The gardener often uses " cures " that prove worse than the disease. Many of the deadly poisons with which we spray our crops to eradicate certain pests do as much harm as good, for friend and foe suffer alike. In North Africa the fighting of locusts by means of arsenic is now known to be largely responsible for the decimation of the European stork. The birds, enthusiastic scavengers, have fed on poisoned locusts and shared the fate of the insects. This has reduced their ranks quite as much as land reclamation and intensive drainage, which eliminates much insect life, besides frogs and water rats.

WIDE WORLD

AS USED IN GREECE

Honey has been of service to man since history began. A type of hive dating from remote times.

Comparatively few gardeners and farmers know one insect larva from another. There is some excuse for this. The British Isles alone harbour forty-odd kinds of butterflies, over two thousand kinds of moths and well over three thousand different kinds of beetles. All these produce grubs or caterpillars of a sort, and so do most of the other insect groups.

WARRING AGAINST INSECT PESTS

The economist cannot afford to be ignorant. This is why the Insect Department staff of the British Museum outnumbers that of all other departments by ten to one, and why all over the world there are now established State-supported colleges and laboratories for the study of insects similar to the Imperial Bureau of Entomology near London. It is now being realized that a safer and surer method of killing noxious insects than by sprays or poison gases is to pit their natural enemies against them. Much romance and high adventure is embodied in the cut-and-dried reports on some of these attempts to fight one insect with another. Not least of the difficulties involved lies in finding an insect to do the work required—and none other. We have already noted some of the dangers attending reckless introductions.

LADYBIRD FACTORIES

Let us take a typical triumph of the economic entomologist. At the beginning of this century Hawaii's sugar-cane crop was threatened by a weevil—a plant-boring beetle. After two years' search an entomologist found on the Pacific Island of Amboina a fly which preyed upon the weevil. Setting out on the four-thousand-mile voyage to Hawaii with a cargo of flies, the entomologist fell ill and all his hard-won insects died.

The fly had a short life cycle and was therefore difficult to breed in confinement. Eventually, it was realized that the only way to get the flies in bulk to Hawaii was to breed successive generations *en route*. By bringing off " crops " of flies first at Queensland, then at Fiji, they at last reached the scene of operations, and the weevil was doomed.

The earwig is a plague in some countries where it has been introduced, and in America —another introduction from England—the gipsy moth threatened vast areas with ruin until its parasites were discovered and sent to join it. The ladybird's now known voracity for greenfly has given rise to what are literally

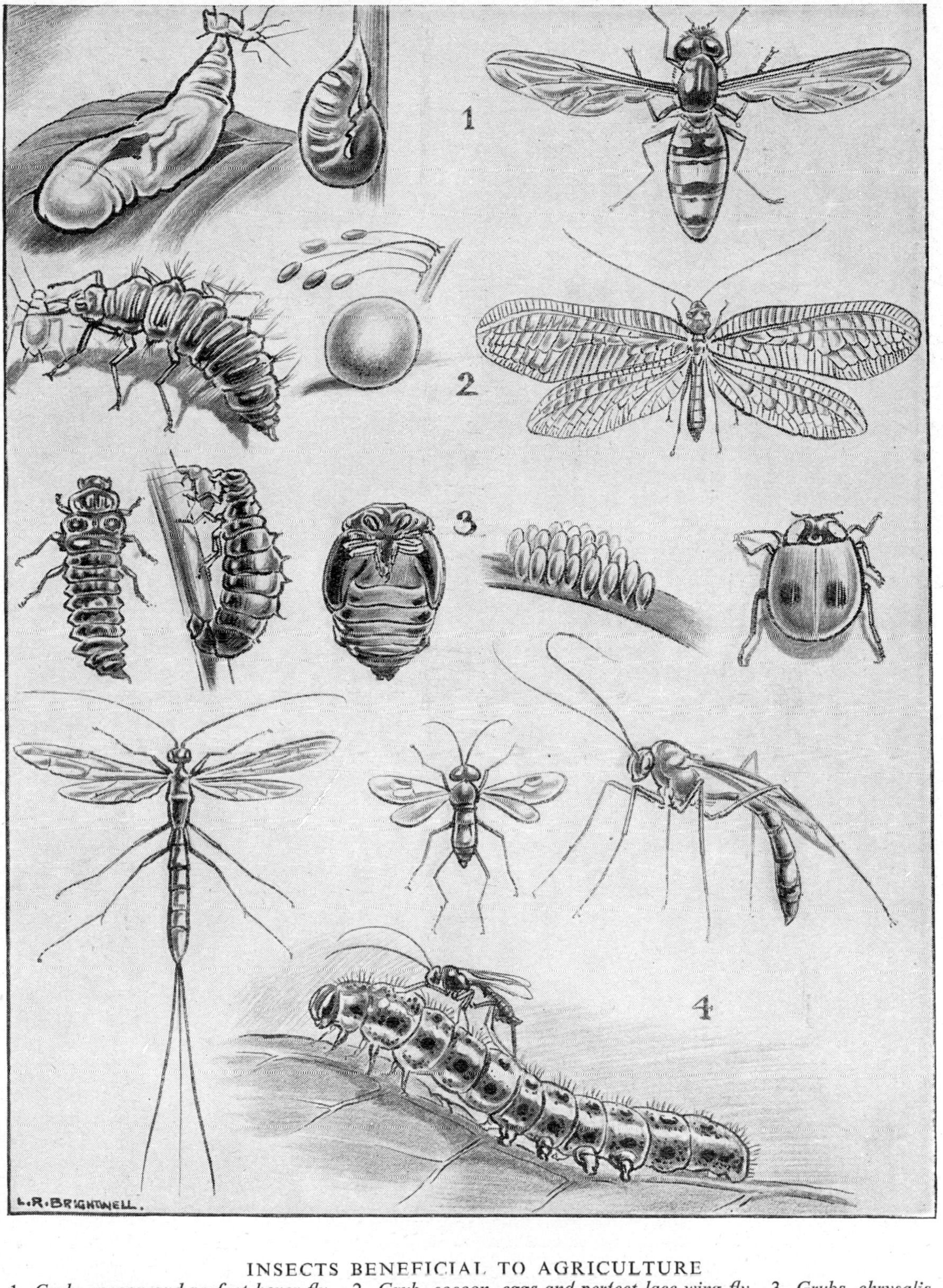

INSECTS BENEFICIAL TO AGRICULTURE

1. *Grub, cocoon and perfect hover fly.* 2. *Grub, cocoon, eggs and perfect lace-wing fly.* 3. *Grubs, chrysalis, eggs and perfect ladybird. All these are enemies of greenfly.* 4. *Ichneumon fly laying eggs in caterpillar.*

ladybird factories. Yet the average garden owner invariably mistakes the ladybird's voracious grub for " some sort of slug," and in killing it helps one of his garden's worst enemies.

APPLE-BLOSSOM WEEVIL

Many an apple farmer has been brought to the brink of bankruptcy by the apple blossom weevil. Often the affected buds are collected and burnt, and to the burning go not only the beetle grubs but the ichneumon flies that eat them. If the blooms are put into a muslin bag, the weevils can spread no farther and the flies can be released to save next year's crop.

Other friends of the gardener that everyone should know are the hover and lacewing flies, also among the foes of the aphides, the larger ichneumons which lay their eggs in living caterpillars, the caterpillar-killing technid flies, often mistaken for house flies, and the more important carnivorous beetles like the big blue ground beetle, the devil's coach horse and the snail-destroying glow worm.

In the United States ladybirds retire as winter comes to the hills, but their prey, the aphides, stay in the valley, and when spring returns again start feeding before the beetles can fly down to them. Today the ladybirds are saved a journey. They are collected by the basketful in their high winter retreats, sold at so much a pound, and given the freedom of the fields and orchards—with the farmer's blessing.

Prickly pear cactus makes good camel fodder, but when plant and beast were introduced into Australia, the cactus became so prolific that no number of camels could cope with it, for the camel is a slow breeder. The prickly growth promised to annex much of the island continent, until in 1920 an organized hunt was made for a prickly pear " pest " throughout America and the West Indies.

SPECIAL STEAMER FOR FLIES

At long last there emerged from scores of trial insects the caterpillars of a certain moth, various plant bugs and cochineal insects and the " red spider "—in Great Britain a pest to fruit trees. These creatures were produced in bulk at a special breeding station founded in Texas by the Australian Government, and the animals shipped to the affected areas as required.

A parallel victory to this was the discovery in Malaya of a fly which would attack the Fiji coco-nut moth, a scourge that throughout many islands converted fruitful palms into the

MAN TO THE RESCUE IN SOUTH AFRICA

Creatures of the wild drinking together in Kruger National Park, the great South African reservation where many animals which were dying out for various reasons are being preserved in their native haunts.

PROTECTING WILD LIFE IN THE UNITED STATES

A goat in Glacier National Park, Montana, which covers no fewer than one thousand four hundred and fifty square miles and is one of several reservations in the United States. Here American Indians live in tepees and wild animals rove about at large.

likeness of hop poles. After several years' search, the first consignment of three hundred flies was obtained and sent in 1925 from Malaya to Fiji in a specially chartered steamer. Their teeming descendants assure the valuable coco-nut's prosperity to this day.

As already stated, in introducing a parasite or anti-pest, the utmost precaution must be taken by experiment to make sure that it shall do the work required, and that only, and not in its turn become a menace. The mongoose, introduced into the West Indies to cope with a rat plague, itself became a pest when, tiring of rat slaughter, it found more toothsome fare in the local chickens and wild birds.

EGRETS THAT WENT A-ROAMING

Climate also must be taken into consideration. The African egrets introduced at Whipsnade kept down cattle parasites like the bot fly, but had to be collected and cosseted indoors as soon as autumn came. In the London Zoo the birds, given their liberty, found mere cattle-grooming a tame amusement with so many other distractions to offer. Before long some were discovered inspecting the possibilities of the Regent's Canal stickleback supply, and a few were even traced to the Temple Gardens, in the heart of London, purloining goldfish.

INSECT HELP FOR PLANTS

Whilst many insects are pests, or pest fighters, a high percentage are indispensable to the agriculturist in the cross-fertilization or pollination of plants. Geology proves that whereas plants no doubt anticipated animal life, none of the flowering and fruitful plants existed until after the insects had become well established. Some plants are self-fertilizing, others rely on the haphazard, wasteful method of broadcasting their pollen grains upon the wind, but insects offer a surer method and in flitting from flower to flower swell our crops and feed our cattle.

HAROLD BASTIN

TINY INSECT WHICH CAUSES MUCH DAMAGE

The destructive work of the beech leaf roller weevil told in three pictures which are self explanatory. The products of the soil are at the mercy of the insect hosts as much as they are moulded by the elements.

New Zealand, now literally the world's mutton factory, could at first make little success of sheep farming. Good mutton can only be raised on clover, but even when clover was introduced, little headway was made. The plants fared no better than the animals. Then it was realized that to propagate clover bumble bees are necessary, and New Zealand's prosperity dates from the day when a cargo of English bumble bees arrived. Thus mutton and beef, wool, hair, horn and leather, fertilizers, milk, cheese and butter are to a very large extent gifts from the bumble bee.

TUNNELLING LARVÆ

It has been estimated that in some years twenty per cent of the fruit crop of the United States is destroyed by insects, yet even so, as the Department of Agriculture points out, this may rightly be regarded as a tax paid on the successful production of the remaining eighty per cent. Not only are insects useful as fertilizers. Many tunnelling larvæ enrich the soil even more than do earth worms, by dragging down leaves and other rotting vegetable waste, and converting it into manure.

ANTI-GNAT FISH

Side by side with the march of agriculture and the opening up of new lands for tillage, has gone the study of insects as enemies to the colonizer's health—their potency as carriers of disease. In Great Britain flies are relatively merely a nuisance, and might be easily decreased in numbers by increased cleanliness. The cockroach, flea and louse are three more reminders that we are still some way from a hygienic Utopia, and the gnat and mosquito might be readily controlled by proper supervision of ponds and ditches and the encouragement of such easily bred fish as the stickleback and the golden orfe.

FUR FOR THE FAIR AND THE FORTUNATE

Animals continue to supply the bulk of our clothing from boots to headgear. The silver black fox is typical of Canada's fur industry. The pioneer business men of the future Dominion were fur-traders. The price of a pair of silver foxes for breeding purposes has reached as much as £2,800.

Italy is one of the few European countries to encourage scientifically anti-gnat fish. But within the tropic belt insects still vie with man's worst engines of destruction in the toll they take of life. Large tracts of land still defy the white man's best attempts at annexation; the mosquito and the tsetse fly hold them secure.

Forty per cent of India's death rate is still due to the malarial mosquito, once a scourge of ancient Rome and Greece. It was a dread broadcaster of ague in Great Britain until less than eighty years ago. The danger of mosquito bite lies not in the incision, or even blood letting, but the conveyance of the parasite of which the insect is an intermediary host. Fleas, working through the rat, are now known to have carried the plague or black death which so many times ravaged London.

MOSQUITOES AND YELLOW FEVER

Mosquitoes carry "yellow jack," the fever that used to kill one in five of the Jamaica garrison annually, and spreading via the slave trade to Africa, wreaked a fearful revenge on slave traders and slaves alike. It was only recently traced to the mosquito as the result of an expedition in which the investigators deliberately exposed themselves to the scourge in a manner that ranks amongst the most heroic epics of medical research. Here, as with malaria, the remedy lay in destroying the mosquito's breeding grounds, and so one day the awful history of "yellow jack" may be closed for ever.

PROBLEM OF THE TSETSE FLY

African relapsing fever is carried by lice, the intermediary hosts of the flagellate causing the disease. A tick carries red water fever to cattle in Northern Europe and Arabia, Japan and North America; another tick transmits the biliary fever to cattle and horses in East Africa, a third carries the typhus-like Rocky Mountain fever. The bed bug is now under suspicion of carrying not only typhus and relapsing fever but leprosy.

The tsetse fly, which causes sleeping sickness in man and nagara or tsetse fly disease in horses, dogs and domestic cattle, remains a largely unsolved problem. Its many natural enemies —insects, birds and reptiles—fail to produce any appreciable diminution of its numbers, but lately an ingenious device known as the Williamson trap has yielded some success.

The trap is a box, triangular in section, with a slit in the apex and a balloon fly trap mounted on the base. It is slung horizontally in shady places, which the flies always frequent, and is mistaken by the short-sighted insects for a cow. They attack the "belly"—in which is set the slit—and wander about in the " cow's " empty inside until they find a small hole giving access to the fly trap, and once inside they remain.

What havoc insects may work with stored as well as growing foods is known to all. Quite as spectacular are their onslaughts upon dead timber incorporated in furniture and architectural structures. The termite's insatiable appetite for wood has been already noticed. In London two famous buildings, Westminster

PRODUCER OF WOOL AND WEALTH
Australia is the largest producer of wool, yet the sheep is not a native of the island continent. It was among the first animals to be domesticated.

Hall and Bow Church, were saved from the furniture beetle only in the nick of time. Huge oaken beams had been reduced to so much sponge.

On a lesser scale the wood-boring wasps obtrude themselves. When unseasoned wood is used, the pupæ within at last yield up the perfect insects, which may make a dramatic entry by appearing from an unsuspected spot in a living-room wall or even from a table leg. To gain its freedom, one of these wasps has been known to chew its way through half an inch of timber and a thickness of sheet lead.

Here we must close our summary of what has been done as regards the study of animals, and the application of the knowledge gained, during the last hundred and thirty-odd years. Much unchecked slaughter has continued parallel with the world-wide spread of scientific and humanitarian societies, great and small. We have travelled a long way since Richard Martin saw the Act for the suppression of Bull-baiting passed in England in 1835.

CONSERVING ANIMAL RESOURCES

A notable post-war movement is the foundation of the Empire Fauna Society, which controls established wild life reservations and aids the formation of new ones throughout the British possessions. Italy is amongst the latest recruits to the bird protection movement, and the development of her freshwater fisheries has gone forward on model lines. The world's newly awakened sense of responsibility regarding its animal resources is characterized by an international spirit. There is a growing tendency to pool knowledge and use it for the general benefit, which is one of the most encouraging features of our restless age.

Canada and the United States possess thousands of square miles of National Parks of great beauty, where wild life is encouraged to flourish under natural conditions. Bears, moose, deer and an almost infinite variety of animals and birds enjoy a charmed existence, protected from the inquisitive and acquisitive instincts of man.

Extensive territory in the Belgian Congo is devoted to the preservation of its natural fauna and flora, including species known or reputed to be harmful. Included in it is an extensive forest where the rare mountain gorilla roams at will. The pursuit, capture, killing or molesting of any creature, and the taking or destroying of eggs, is forbidden under heavy penalties.

TRESPASSERS WILL BE PROSECUTED

Only those who are provided with a pass are admitted to the sanctuary. This rule is strictly enforced by the conservators and native police. There is also a protective zone around the park, the inhabitants of which are not permitted to use firearms or to fish.

The wonderful Kruger National Park in the Transvaal has an area larger than Wales, over eight hundred miles of road for visitors, and several rest camps. " We, the animals of the Kruger National Park," writes the warden in their name, " appeal for your sympathy and friendship. You have been our bitter enemies for so long that it takes time to make us understand that a new and happier era has begun for us—do not betray our trust in you."

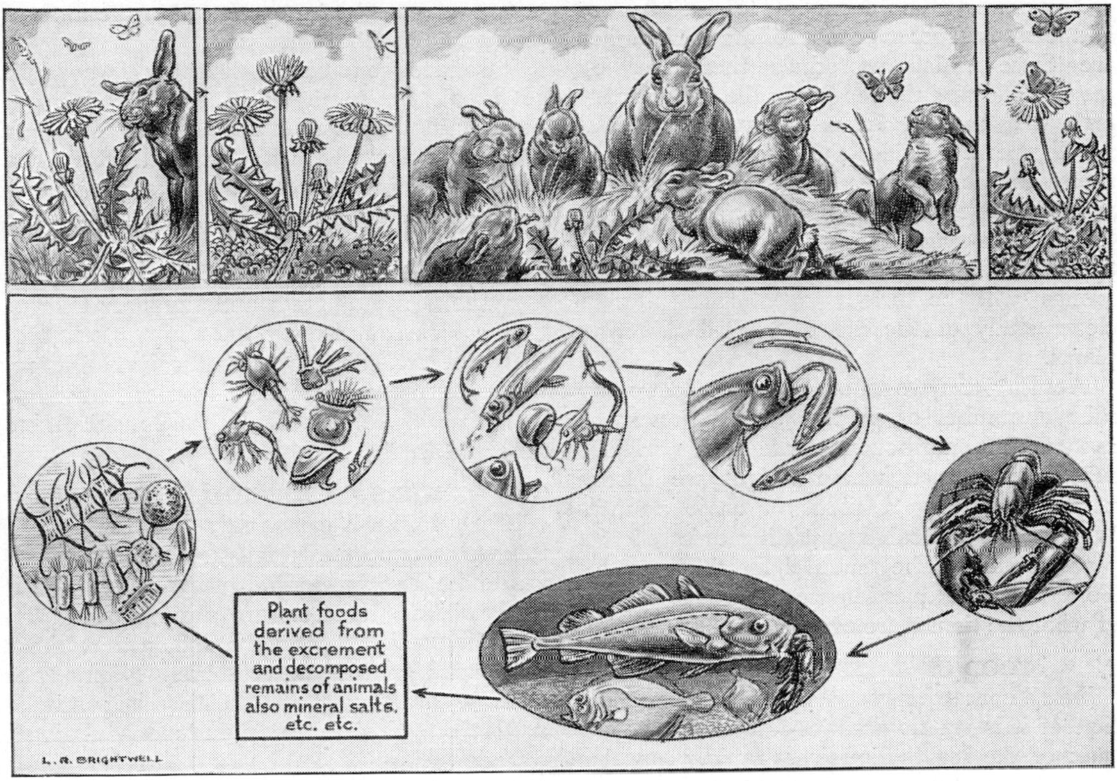

PLANT AND ANIMAL LIFE DEPEND ON EACH OTHER

Plants feed animals, whose waste products help to feed plants. Minute floating plants, fed by the chemical products of animals, form the basic food of animals in the sea until they prey on others.

THE PLANT KINGDOM

A VAST assembly of forms is included in the plant kingdom. There are at least two hundred and fifty thousand kinds of flowering plants. Fundamentally the living matter shows the same characteristics as in animals, but plants are mainly a sedentary group, they remain anchored in position by their roots and do not seem to us to display much activity, for all their movements are slow. One notices that at night daisy flowers have closed and the clover has folded up its leaflets. The same sleep movements are shown by the sensitive plant *Mimosa pudica*, which will also respond convulsively to a touch, the leaflets folding up and falling back. This is exceptional, for the pace of most plant life is much more gentle.

Slow-motion cinematography has aided the understanding of plant activity. Pictures of a plant are taken at intervals of perhaps a minute and are projected on a screen at the usual rate of sixteen a second. The speed of the movements is thus magnified tremendously. Roots writhing their way past the obstacles in the soil, shoots working spirally upwards and jostling their neighbours, and leaves fluttering up and down give an unforgettable picture of purposeful movement, making the verb " to vegetate " seem a libel on the plant kingdom.

The aerial parts of typical plants, particularly the leaves, are coloured green by the presence of a pigment called chlorophyll, which is really an intimate mixture of two green and two yellow substances. It is of the greatest importance in plant nutrition, and its presence is one of the main distinguishing features between plants and animals. The latter nourish themselves by taking in solid matter derived from plants or other animals; plants, with the aid of chlorophyll, make their food inside their bodies from simple materials and may literally be said to live in part on air.

The plants which occur in greatest quantity and form a carpet over most of the land surface are those which reproduce themselves by means of flowers and seeds. In the evolutionary scale they are the latest and most successful development. Besides them there are simpler types, the ferns, mosses and liverworts, the algæ (pondweeds and seaweeds) and the fungi (mushrooms and their relatives). Something of the life and reproduction of these groups will be briefly mentioned after a closer study of the life of typical flowering plants.

From a pennyworth of cabbage seed we can raise a number of plants which represent at maturity an enormous increase on the original substance—a seed whose weight we hardly notice producing a plant of some pounds. Whence has the cabbage, sitting quietly in its place, obtained the material for this growth? To answer the question we must first inquire of what the tissues are composed.

FOOD OF GASES AND LIQUIDS

Every housewife knows that a large proportion of it is water, perhaps four-fifths, for the bulk of the leaves diminishes rapidly as water is extracted in the cooking process. If by heating more strongly all the water is driven off (" the saucepan boils dry "), the leaves char and turn black, just as a burnt match does; the substance produced is charcoal, one of the forms of carbon. Still greater heating would reduce the leaves to a little heap of ashes, in which the chemist could detect various mineral elements, such as potash, calcium and iron. Besides these he would have found that part of the leaves vanished into the air in the form of gases, among them nitrogen.

If we cared so to treat a joint of beef we should get much the same results, for the chemical compositions of living plant and animal tissues are fundamentally very similar. Now the bullock obtained its material for growth by eating grass and other fodder, but plants have no mouths and stomachs and cannot take in solid matter. The only possibility then is that they make use of gases and liquids. Like us they are surrounded by the air, a mixture of the gases nitrogen, oxygen and carbon dioxide, while we know that there is water in the soil and that there are likely to be substances dissolved in it.

WORK OF THE ROOT-HAIRS

If a hyacinth is grown in a glass the level of the water continually falls below that which would be lost by simple evaporation. It is obvious that the roots are absorbing it. So, too, they take it from the soil, although we rarely can see the water there. Normally it forms a thin film round the tiny soil particles and is only visible to us in poorly drained, waterlogged soil.

Only a part of the root can absorb water. Cress seeds, grown on damp flannel and kept covered, will show a fine fringe of delicate hairs surrounding the rootlets from close behind the tip to an inch or so farther up. These so-called root-hairs consist of a single cell with a very delicate wall, which in nature comes into the closest possible contact with the soil particles and their water films.

To understand the way in which the root

HAROLD BASTIN

ACACIA AWAKE AND ASLEEP

Left: an acacia with its leaves responding to the sunlight of the early morning. Right: the same plant " going to sleep " at sunset on the same day.

HAROLD BASTIN

WELL NAMED THE SENSITIVE PLANT

Nearly all the movements of plants are slow, but the sensitive plant will respond convulsively to a touch. Left: leaves expanded. Right: immediately after having been touched.

hairs allow water to pass in through their walls we may think of a limp cucumber which has been put in a basin of water. It will not be long before it has been made plump and stiff by the entry of water. But suppose we were preparing one for pickling and put a fresh cucumber into brine, we should find it soon become limp and wrinkled as water was withdrawn from it by the strong salt solution. When two solutions are separated by a membrane which permits the passage of water, the stronger of the two tends to draw water from the other until the concentrations of each are equal.

MILLIONS OF MINUTE PORES

The soil water contains salts in solution, but it is much weaker than the sap of the root-hairs, and so water passes through their walls into the plant. The reverse would happen if the soil were watered with brine; water would be drawn from the plant and it would wilt.

Root-hairs are extremely important to plants. They are present in large numbers, so that the total absorbing area of the plant's roots is probably about equal to that of the leaves above ground. Normally we see them rarely. They are in such close contact with the soil particles that when a plant is uprooted and the soil shaken off they are torn away. For this reason when transplanting is done care must be taken to keep a ball of soil adhering round the roots, and to shade the plant for a few days to prevent excessive evaporation before the new root-hairs have grown to replace those which are sure to have been lost.

Plants, like all living things, are continually losing water. Sometimes this appears as liquid drops, as may be seen on the tips and margins of some leaves in early morning after a warm damp night. But most of the water passes away from the leaves in the form of vapour. As a rule it is given out largely from the lower leaf surface. Examination with a microscope shows that here the skin of the leaf is perforated by minute pores. Although so tiny they are present in enormous numbers; there are as many as eleven millions on a medium-sized cabbage leaf. Through them nearly all the water vapour passes, for the rest of the leaf is covered by a thin film that may be likened to a waterproof varnish.

To some extent loss of water can be regulated. Each pore is surrounded by two sausage-shaped cells. If these lose water, as when the plant begins to wilt, they change their shape and in so doing come closer together and shut the opening.

TREES AND RAINFALL

A surprising amount of water vapour is given off by forest trees, and its effects are not inconsiderable. It has been calculated that two and a half acres of leafy beech wood lose forty thousand gallons of water daily. This means that the air just above the canopy of leaves will be kept cool and damp, and clouds are more likely to deposit their moisture there as rain. This will drip slowly through the leaves to the soil, where it can be gradually absorbed.

When, as so often has happened, virgin forests are ruthlessly felled over large areas and not replanted, the rainfall is likely to be reduced. When sudden storms occur the bare soil will not be able to take all the water at

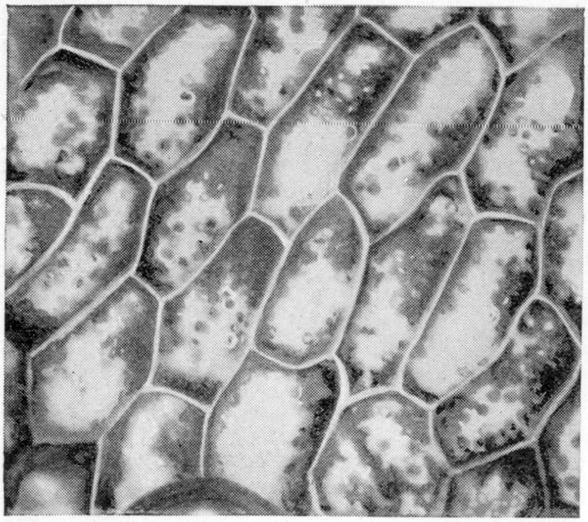

HAROLD BASTIN

WHY LEAVES ARE GREEN

Cells with the granular bodies containing the pigment known as chlorophyll.

once and there may be floods, while if the land slopes steeply the soil may be washed away.

With the water, the root-hairs also allow to pass in small quantities of the essential minerals present in the soil, especially the sulphates, nitrates and phosphates of sodium, calcium and magnesium. There is a possibility that plants obtain from the soil minute traces of unknown substances, which may be compared with the vitamins essential to animal welfare. The presence of these may account for the greater value of farmyard manure and leaf-mould as compared with artificial fertilizers.

RETURNED TO THE SOIL

Under natural conditions the roots of dead plants remain in the ground, the leaves and stems fall there, and in the end much of the substance is returned to the soil to be used again by other plants. But in agriculture large crops are being continually lifted, and it is necessary to manure the soil to keep up its fertility. Different plants vary in their requirements. Thus the sea kale likes a dressing of common salt, wallflowers and pinks need lime. It is therefore profitable for farmers to rotate their crops, growing on one piece of land in successive years plants which have different wants.

A good plan for vegetables would be potatoes, followed by peas, root crops and cabbages. The tobacco demands potash in quantity; before plant physiology was understood the original Virginian plantations were worked out and prosperity passed to new soils. Now the American farmers do not attempt to grow tobacco on the same plot every year, but sow successively wheat, grass, clover, maize and tobacco, returning the waste stems and leaves of the latter to the soil.

PLANT CHEMICAL FACTORIES

The pea family, which includes such valuable plants as clover, beans, lucerne and lupin, is remarkable in that its members actually enrich the soil with nitrogen instead of depleting it. On their roots will be found little nodules which are inhabited by bacteria. These have entered originally from the soil and, like others there, are able to take up the nitrogen of the air and manufacture chemical compounds from it. In some way these are passed on to the pea plant, which has thus no need for nitrogenous soil fertilizers. When it dies and decays a store of nitrogenous food is released for other plants. With few exceptions the pea family are

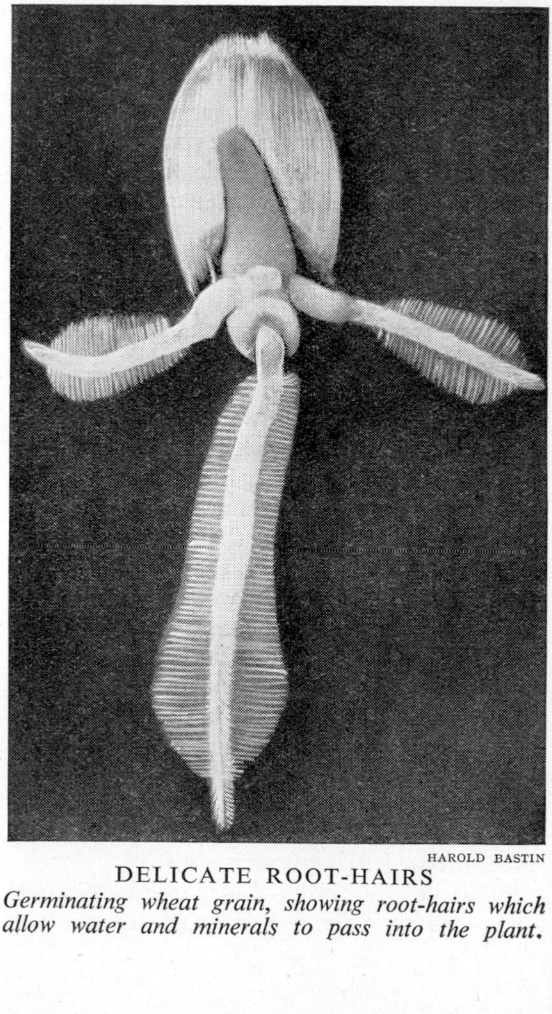

HAROLD BASTIN

DELICATE ROOT-HAIRS

Germinating wheat grain, showing root-hairs which allow water and minerals to pass into the plant.

FOX

WHAT HAPPENS WHEN FORESTS ARE DESTROYED

A surprising amount of water vapour is given off by forest trees. When, as so often happens, virgin forests are ruthlessly felled over large areas and not replanted, the rainfall is likely to be reduced. Above: a dust storm in the United States. Below: freshly-planted farm land being whirled away. The reckless destruction of forests has also much to do with the causing of floods. Liability to erosion and other wearing-away processes which help to silt up a waterway is increased.

the only plants which can use the vast stores of nitrogen in the air, and they do so only by the agency of bacteria.

The good effect of a crop of this type had been known for centuries, though the reason was not understood. It has now been found that actually when the plants are still growing they pass out nitrogenous compounds to the soil, and so the benefit is at once appreciated by neighbouring plants. Pasture land is much improved if sown with a mixture of grass and clover. The food value is considerably increased and nitrogenous fertilizer for the grass is unnecessary.

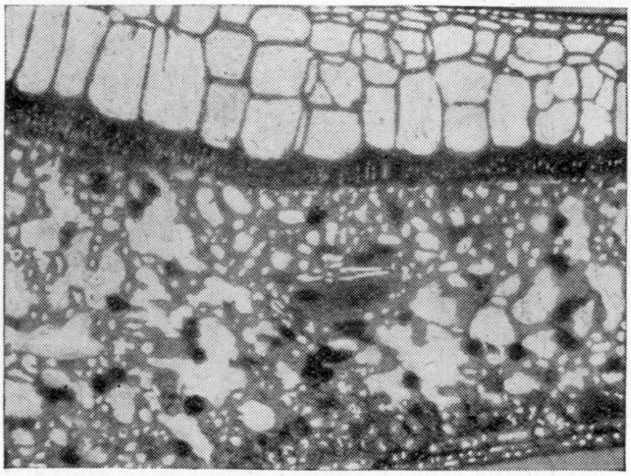

HAROLD BASTIN

CELLS IN A LEAF

Highly magnified section of leaf showing the diversity of cells and tissues.

Although its store of nitrogen is not touched, the air furnishes a vital part of the plant's food. Carbon dioxide, a gas which we know best as the bubbles in soda water and cider, is present in very small amount, about one in four hundred parts. In sunlight or suitable artificial light the green parts of plants are continually taking in this carbon dioxide and giving out oxygen in its place, exactly the reverse of what happens when we breathe.

In the plant the gas is decomposed, the oxygen released, and the carbon combined with the hydrogen and oxygen of water to form a sugar. To split carbon dioxide into its elements in the laboratory requires a large amount of energy. In the plant it is done through the agency of the green pigment chlorophyll, which in some remarkable way is able to trap the energy of light and use it to build up sugars with effortless ease from water and carbon dioxide. We should be astonished if a glass of soda water, left in the sun, was found to have become a sweet liquid, yet this is the transformation continually being made by the green plant.

Generally the sugar is at once converted into solid granules of starch, which are stored for future use. When a plant is preparing for a resting period food may be stored in special organs, such as swollen bulbs and tubers or seed leaves. That is why the leaves should not be cut from bulbous plants until they have finished their work and are yellowing, otherwise they will not have made sufficient food to build up a good flowering bulb for the next season.

WASTE OF THE PLANT LABORATORY

Not all the sugar is converted to starch. Some may be used to form oils and fats, especially in seeds, and more important still are the proteins which are necessary for building new tissues. In them carbon, hydrogen and oxygen are combined with the nitrogen taken up by the roots to make substances of complex structure. Many of the plant products which are of use to us, such as resins and aromatic substances, and various drugs, seem to be the waste materials of the plant laboratory. All but the sugars can be manufactured without sunlight.

The tremendous activity of the leaf factories may be realized when one is told that a rough estimate of the annual world increase in dry weight of plants is eighty billion pounds. It is on this that the lives of the whole animal kingdom depend. Much of our own food is vegetable in origin, while the animal portion of it can be traced in a very few steps back to plant material. Thus milk, butter, beef and mutton are built up from grass and clover, and hens' eggs are a product of their cereal foods.

FOOD PRODUCERS OF THE SEA

Even in the sea it is the same. The herring principally feeds on little shrimp-like creatures, and the latter on the tiny microscopic floating plants which are extremely numerous in the upper waters. There they find sufficient light to manufacture sugar and build that up into other substances. Without them the sea would be barren; there is, it is true, a fringe of seaweeds round the coasts but hardly any animals eat them. The little plants, whose presence we hardly suspect, are the real food producers of the sea. From their store of sunshine the cod and halibut derive the vitamin A which they store in their livers, and with which children are dosed in winter to keep them in healthy growth.

It is safe to say that without green plants the animal life which we know could never have evolved. Without chlorophyll too the plant world could not exist. It is true that certain bacteria can obtain their foods by breaking down iron and sulphur compounds and so are independent of light and of the products of other forms of life. Organisms might have developed further on these lines, but they would have been very different from the forms of life we know on this planet.

TRAPS FOR SUNLIGHT

The need for light dominates the life of green plants. Flattened leaf surfaces provide the necessary large area to trap the rays. It can often be noted how leaves on the branch of a tree arrange themselves to form a mosaic, so that there is as little overlapping and shading as possible. So effective may this be that hardly anything can grow under a beech in summer.

Stems generally turn towards the brightest light and so place the leaves in a favourable position. In hedgerows we find climbers, such as clematis and bryony, scrambling up and up through the branches of hawthorn and hazel to the open. Many low-growing plants, such as primroses and bluebells, flower and complete their growth in the spring before the hedges and woods are thick with leaf to shade them. Fortunately plants vary in the amounts of light they require. One of the most modest in its demands is the aspidistra, which will generally survive, if not grow, in the darkest corner of a room.

When improved illumination has been installed in caves, such as those in the Cheddar Gorge and at Kent's Cavern, Torquay, a film of green has appeared round the lights, where previously was a barren surface. Young ferns gradually developed. Probably the spores were carried in by air currents and were able to grow as soon as there was sufficient light.

SOME PLANTS LIKE SHORT DAYS

The length of the daily exposure to light bears an interesting relation to the flowering of plants. In the tropics day and night are roughly equal all the year round. In higher latitudes a twelve-hour day only occurs at the equinoxes (March 21 and September 22); in summer the days are long, in winter short.

Some plants are unaffected by this. The tomato, though a native of the tropics of South America, will flower and fruit in the British Isles from the longest days down to one of only eight hours, though outdoors frost will check its activities before these short days are reached. So it can be profitably cultivated in glasshouses in the winter.

On the other hand, violets will only flower if the days are less than twelve hours long; normally they flower in spring but will do so at midsummer if the plants are covered for part of the day. *Coreopsis*, a common garden plant, needs a long day; it can be flowered in winter in a greenhouse with electric light to lengthen the day. Quite a weak light is sufficient.

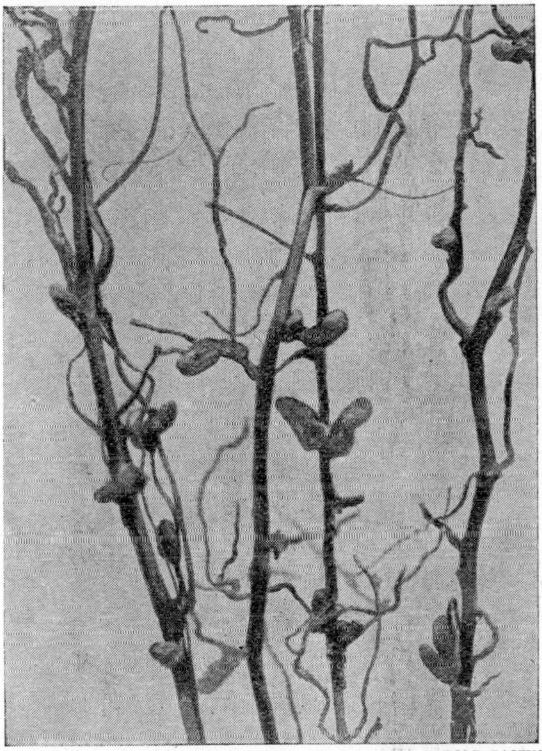

HAROLD BASTIN

LITTLE CHEMICAL WORKS

Nitrogen nodules on the roots of the red clover. They are inhabited by bacteria from the soil.

This reaction to length of day has to be considered when new plants are introduced to Great Britain. Thus Cosmos daisy is a short day plant. Early sowing will not make it flower faster; often the right day length is not reached until soon before the frosts take the plants. However, seedsmen are successfully

HAROLD BASTIN

LEAF MOSAIC

The house-leek arranges its leaves so as to take full advantage of the light.

finding strains which respond to a longer day and so flower earlier.

The formation of underground tubers is also related to day length. Dahlias and artichokes develop them when the day is short. Carrot requires a fourteen-hour day to make the roots swell, onions form normal bulbs with a fifteen-hour day. Fortunately for us our potato is indifferent to length of day. Its ancestors in South America only form tubers in a twelve-hour day, and in England might not be ready to dig before the frosts, which are fatal to them, have arrived.

PLANTS GIVE HEAT

For their living activities plants require a supply of energy; as in animals this is released for them by the breaking down, or digestion, of food materials. It may be likened to the burning of coal, which generates the power to drive a steam engine.

We have seen that in sunlight the green leaf gives out oxygen in return for carbon dioxide, but all living parts of plants are continually performing the reverse exchange of gases, just as we do when breathing. Oxygen is taken in, used to break down complex substances, and the carbon dioxide, which is produced in this process, is given out. Even so apparently lifeless an object as a dried pea is respiring, though in its dormant state the fire of life burns so slowly that perhaps not more than one cubic centimetre of carbon dioxide would be given out in three years.

In plants the substance broken down to release energy is a sugar; carbon dioxide, and the water which also appears, are the waste products and are passed out. A certain amount of the energy appears in the form of heat, though we rarely notice this. Sometimes after a fall of snow it can be seen that it melts first round the plants, which peep up through it.

The sugar which the green leaf manufactures in sunlight is generally stored as starch grains, and these must be broken down again before the sugar can be used as food material. There are present in living cells certain ferments, which work on complex substances in a way which the chemist may find hard to imitate.

LIVING FERMENTS

The sight, thought or smell of appetizing food causes glands in our mouth to pour out saliva, a fluid containing a ferment which reduces starch to sugar; the gastric juices of the stomach digest proteins, such as meat and cheese. Plant ferments are similar. Thus there is a powerful starch-splitting ferment in sprouting barley, which gives the sweet taste to malt (grains dried after sprouting). Fresh pineapple juice can digest proteins. If jellies are flavoured with it they will not set because the ferment digests the gelatine (a protein). There is no action if the juice has previously been well boiled, for such heat destroys the activity of all these living ferments.

The constant exchange of gases between plant and atmosphere is not ordinarily obvious.

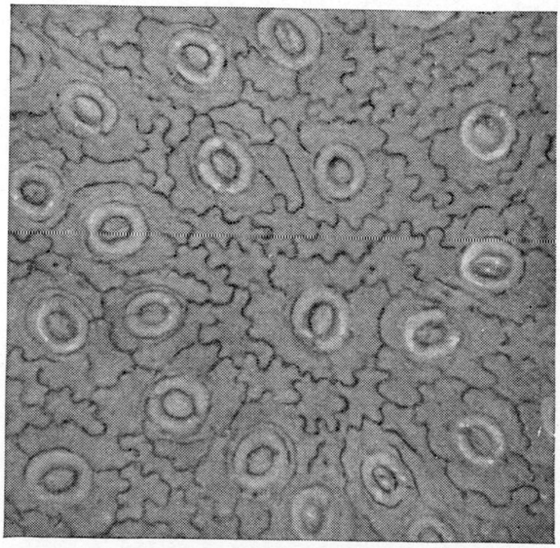

HAROLD BASTIN

HOW PLANTS BREATHE

In sunlight the green leaf gives out oxygen in return for carbon dioxide.

Plants left in a bedroom at night will not use enough oxygen to spoil the air, certainly not if the window is open, as it should be. But where there is a mass of actively respiring material, such as sprouting seeds, as in a ship's hold when grain has become damp, then quantities of carbon dioxide may be produced. This gas is heavy and so will tend to accumulate over the seeds, and may prove very dangerous to an unwary approacher.

Roots need oxygen for their respiration as much as do the parts above ground. So plants often do not thrive in heavy soils with few air spaces between the particles, and may be lost in winter if the ground is waterlogged for some time. Rolling lawns compacts the soil; there is greatly improved growth if the grass roots are aerated by spiking the ground systematically.

GAS RESPIRED BY APPLES

Some of the mangroves, which live in swamps on tropical seashores, have special breathing roots, which stick up out of the water instead of growing down into the ground. Their tissues are very loosely constructed so that gases can readily pass in and out.

Stored fruits, such as apples, are continuously respiring while still alive and ripening. The little spots in the skin are special pores of loose tissue, the rest of the skin being not easily penetrated by gases. If the fruit is kept without sufficient ventilation the accumulated carbon dioxide causes the injury to the flesh known as "brown heart." It is interesting that if the concentration is kept below the danger limit the apples are unharmed, and there is a delay in ripening which can be most profitable to growers, for it means that fruits can be put on the market long after their normal season.

FOX

MEASURING THE BREATHING OF APPLES
Stored fruits, such as apples, are continuously respiring while still alive and ripening.

MANGROVES
They have special breathing roots which stick up out of the water instead of growing down.

Storage at low temperatures in an atmosphere enriched with a certain amount of carbon dioxide is commercially successful in Great Britain for Bramley's Seedling and some other apples and is also used in ships' holds. By

HAROLD BASTIN

TRAPS FOR INSECTS

Frond of bladderwort, showing the numerous insect-trapping bladders that open inwards only.

1935 it was shown that pears could be kept in this way well into the next summer, and the development of gas storage is proceeding as fast as research workers can determine the right conditions for different fruits.

INSECT DIET FOR PLANTS

Mention of the gas respired by apples leads one to recall the observation made in 1932 that the presence of ripe apples in a potato clamp retarded sprouting of the tubers, and so assisted in their preservation. One knows the delicious scent of an apple loft. Apparently one of the ingredients of "apple air" is a minute amount of the gas ethylene, which is present also as an impurity in illuminating gas. It is this which checks the sprouting of the potatoes, but on the contrary it hastens the ripening of picked fruit, such as bananas, young apples, oranges and lemons, and is used for this purpose in America.

A small number of plants, most of them living in boggy places where supplies of nitrogen are often deficient, are an exception to the general rule, for they have adopted a partially animal diet, consisting principally of small insects. However, they still contain chlorophyll, and can manufacture some food for themselves.

SUNDEW'S STICKY TENTACLES

Perhaps the best known is the sundew (*Drosera*), a pretty little bog plant, whose reddish leaves are covered with glistening sticky tentacles. If a small animal touches the leaf it is held fast; quickly the tentacles bend towards it and cover it, pouring out a secretion similar to our gastric juice. The ferments partly digest the prey and the resultant liquid is absorbed. The sundew can be made to digest fragments of meat or egg white, but it will have nothing to do with bits of glass, cinders or paper, from which it could not obtain nutriment.

Also found in bogs is the butterwort (*Pinguicula*) with its pretty mauve flowers. The sticky leaves are a yellowish green with incurved edges. Tiny glands on the upper surface secrete a ferment which digests any insect that is caught. Milk in which a leaf is placed will be turned to curds and whey just as by the rennet from a cow's stomach.

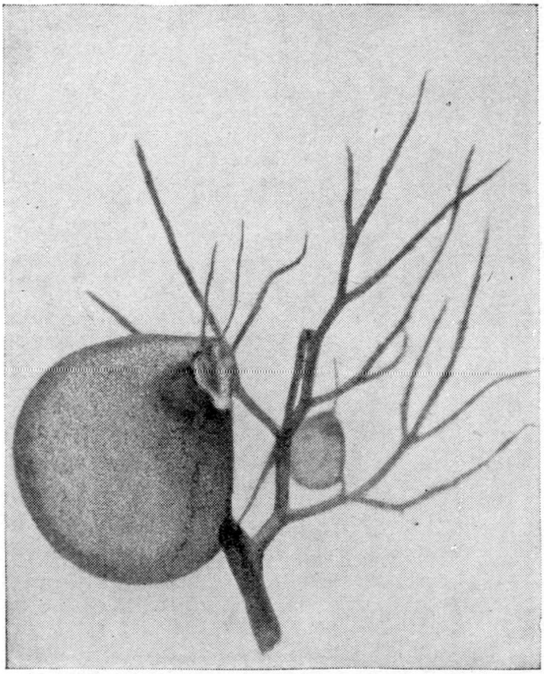

HAROLD BASTIN

BLADDERWORT'S CONDEMNED CELL

A bladder of the bladderwort magnified to show the little door at one end.

HAROLD BASTIN

BOG PLANT THAT DIGESTS MEAT

A remarkable series of photographs showing how a sundew leaf responded to the near presence of an atom of meat suspended by a hair from a needle. The sundew is a pretty little bog plant.

Of a very different type is the bladderwort (*Utricularia*) which is sometimes found in ponds. Among the very finely divided leaves are little bladders with a door at one end, opening inwards only. By some means the plant pumps water out of them and the walls collapse. The trap is then set. If some tiny swimming creature touches certain sensitive bristles round the entry, the door flies open and the side walls spring out. The change of shape causes water to be sucked in and the animal is drawn in with it. The door snaps back, and as it cannot be pushed open from within the prey is secured and later digested.

MISTLETOE IS A PARASITE

Despite their extra food supply the insect-eating plants of Great Britain do not wax fat, indeed they are far from conspicuous. Much more striking are some tropical forms, such as the pitcher plant (*Nepenthes*). The tip of the drooping leaves is prolonged into a tendril bearing a brightly coloured pitcher, complete with lid and a strengthened rim. Nectar is produced round the edge. Insects come to sip it, but as they walk in they find the surface becomes very slippery, and they are led to the bottom, where there is a copious secretion of liquid. Into this many slip and are drowned, and it seems that the plant absorbs the products of their decay. The pitchers of some forms may be as much as eighteen inches long, with liquid sufficient to drown a small bird.

Interesting though they are, the flowering plants which prey on animals are but an insignificant fraction of the whole. We may be glad that there has been no such development as the imaginary orchid of Mr. H. G. Wells's story, whose aerial roots fastened themselves like leeches to their grower and sucked his blood.

A small number of plants obtain their food from the activities of their neighbours. Compared with these they may be said to be degenerate, though they are only behaving as do many members of the animal kingdom. Mistletoe parasitic on apple trees is a familiar sight. It draws on the latter's sap, but its yellow-green leaves manufacture most of its food. Yellow rattle and the little eyebright are found in poor pastures. Although they are green they only develop normally when their roots have become attached by little suckers to those of grasses. There is no doubt of the purpose of these organs.

WORLD'S LARGEST FLOWER

More dangerous is the dodder, which is not uncommonly parasitic on gorse. It has no roots to draw supplies from the soil, but the slender stems, like a mat of red cotton, twine round the host, fastening suckers deep into its

HAROLD BASTIN

WITHOUT LEAVES

Dodder fixed to a stem of heath, on which it is parasitic. It has thread-like stems and no leaves.

tissues. Varieties which prey on crops do much damage and are hard to stamp out.

In the most advanced parasites the green colouring matter has been completely lost and the leaves are mere scales or missing. Perhaps the most remarkable is *Rafflesia Arnoldi*. It grows in the jungle of Sumatra, parasitic on the roots of a vine. The vegetative organs are reduced to underground threads, but the flower, with warty brown and white petals, surpasses all others in size, being quite a yard across and fifteen pounds in weight. Beautiful it is not: endowed with precisely the smell of tainted beef, it attracts swarms of carrion flies.

There are also a few flowering plants which, though colourless, are not parasitic, but live on the dead remains of organisms. The queer looking and evil smelling bird's nest orchis (*Neottia*), which is one of the few plants found in the shade of beech woods, obtains nourishment from the decaying leaf mould. However, it can only do this indirectly. The tangle of roots, from which it derives its name, is clothed with a mass of fungal threads. These pour out their ferments over the leaves, digest them and then absorb some of the products. Something is doubtless passed on to the plant, but the position of the fungus is one of insecurity, for where it penetrates into the cells of the orchis it often is digested itself.

The roots of most of Great Britain's forest trees have fungal threads similarly associated with them, which may help in their nutrition. When the fungal companion of the birch fruits above ground it proves to be the beautiful scarlet fly agaric. Illustrators of fairy tales are much given to introducing this mushroom into their pictures, but they rarely put it in its proper place under a birch tree.

A French fresco dating from 1291 depicts the Tree of Life as a fly agaric with Eve after having eaten of its forbidden fruit—a highly dangerous proceeding.

HAROLD BASTIN

SCARLET FLY AGARIC

The beautiful fungal companion of the birch, beloved of illustrators of fairy tales.

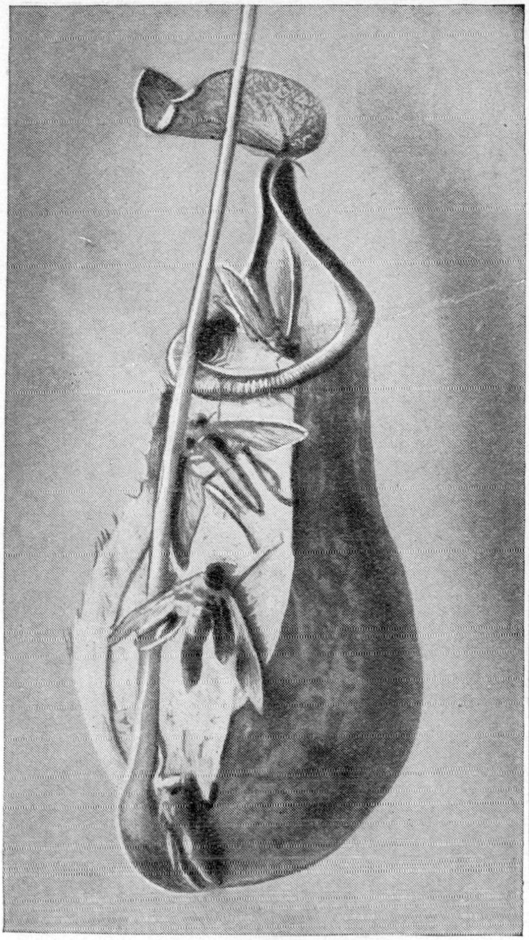

HAROLD BASTIN

PLANT WONDERS

Top: pitcher plant ; pitcher with insects creeping towards the fatal entrance. Below: mistletoe on apple tree ; epiphytic orchid, which roots on bark.

FOX

TREES THAT CRUSH MAN'S HANDIWORK

Of venerable age, this tree in a jungle of Sumatra has grown to such a tremendous extent that its powerful roots are slowly clamping the granite walls of the temple in a death-like grip.

HAROLD BASTIN

WORLD'S MOST WONDERFUL PLANT

The Venus fly-trap, which Darwin designated " the most wonderful plant in the world." When an insect is caught the plant slowly absorbs the nitrogenous matter in its victim.

THE REPRODUCTION OF FLOWERING PLANTS

THE span of life of flowering plants varies greatly, from the chickweeds and groundsel, which can grow, seed and die in a few weeks, to the tremendous " Big Trees " (*Sequoia*) of California, some of which are certainly over fifteen hundred years old and have even been estimated at four thousand years.

Many plants are of annual duration, growing and fruiting in summer and passing the winter as seeds. Most of the crop plants of Great Britain conveniently are in this group. Some, such as carrots, are really biennials, not flowering until the second season, but for the purpose of the consumer the first year's growth is sufficient. A great many trees and herbaceous plants fall into the class of perennials and may live a number of years, though some do not naturally have a very long life. Flowering brooms do not usually last more than about eight years ; gardeners have been known to suspect enemies of poisoning these plants when they have really reached the end of their term of years.

When death, natural or otherwise, comes there must be a means of carrying on the generations. Increase may take place by a form of division. Perhaps it is simplest of all in the bacteria, where the cells at a certain stage divide into two equal halves, a process which is sometimes repeated as frequently as every twenty minutes. In the yeasts the products are unequal; a tiny nipple-like cell is budded off from the parent but soon grows to equal it. This kind of reproduction is known as vegetative, for though it occurs in some animals, as when the broken-off arm of a starfish grows into a complete new animal, yet it is much more characteristic of plants.

Many cultivated plants are constantly increased by means of "cuttings" — leafy shoots as in fuchsia and pink, which root readily in damp, porous soil; portions of root as in horse-radish; and in begonia cut leaves. This is done by man's agency, but something similar occurs naturally. In the "Hen and

HAROLD BASTIN

HEN AND CHICKENS FERN

So called because complete miniature fern plants are produced from the old fronds.

Chickens" fern (*Cystopteris bulbifera*) tiny leafy buds develop on the fronds and root when they reach the ground. In the related "Walking Fern" the tips of the fronds regularly arch over and root and so it spreads to some distance. Shoots of blackberry will do the same.

Many plants send out creeping stems—above ground as in strawberry runners, or below as in perennial sunflower—from which new shoots arise at some distance and form their own roots. Bulbs and tubers are other familiar methods of vegetative reproduction.

This type of increase is often highly successful, as witness for example the invasion of untended grasslands of the dry type by the spreading underground stems of the bracken; the vast crops from "seed" potato tubers; the groves of the seedless orange produced by grafting. In 1906 there were in existence only three bulbs of the well-known narcissus "Bath's Flame"; thirty years later it was estimated that there were about nine and a half millions, all descended by vegetative reproduction from the original three.

In 1842 the Canadian waterweed (*Elodea*) first appeared in England. Only plants of one sex were present so seed could not form, but vegetative reproduction by portions of the plant breaking off was so rapid that in a relatively short time it was choking the waterways; now there is probably no river in the country which does not contain it.

PARENTAGE BRINGS DEATH

However, it does seem that sometimes continued vegetative reproduction weakens the vigour of the plant, and it is anyhow true that nearly all plants possess, like animall, a means of sexual reproduction. In flowering plants this precedes the formation of seeds. Often it leads to the death of the parent, as in annuals. In order to prolong the life of their plants gardeners pick off the "dead" flowers: these are very often those which are setting seed and are really very actively forming new living units. After long years of slow vegetative growth the century plant (*Agave Americana*) in a few weeks throws up its immense spire of creamy flowers and after fruiting dies.

Some butterflies never even feed; they emerge from the chrysalis, pair, and with the laying of the eggs their lives are ended. Many examples, from high to low in the scale of evolution, could be drawn to show the truth of Sir J. Arthur Thomson's statement that "In the dawn of life immortality was pawned for love." Shorn of the emotional complications of human parentage, sexual reproduction appears as an unselfish proceeding.

PRODUCTION OF NEW TYPES

Biologically its most important significance is the possibility it gives of the production of new types from the union of two parents with different characteristics, which may be re-combined in their offspring. Thus if a choice pansy is to be preserved, cuttings must be taken; if grown under the same conditions these will repeat exactly the original type. If the seeds it sets were sown, there would almost certainly result a variety of forms, none necessarily the desired one.

The essential feature of sexual reproduction

HAROLD BASTIN

LUXURIANT GROWTH OF THE CENTURY PLANT

The century plant, or American aloe, which after long years of slow vegetative growth throws up an immense spire of creamy flowers, and after fruiting dies. Its native home is Mexico and Central America.

is the union of two distinct male and female elements, from which the next generation arises. The sex-cells are very tiny, and it is rarely possible to see them or their union in flowering plants. Other lower forms of life are more simply constructed, and in them the details are more easily observable. Few objects are more favourable in this respect than the common bladder-wrack, a brown seaweed characterized by the air-bladders on its fronds and frequently found in abundance on rocky sea shores.

SPERMS OF THE BLADDER-WRACK

The reproductive elements are formed in the fat juicy tips. If plants are collected and kept out of water overnight it will be found that slime of two different colours has oozed from some of the tips. The orange contains the male sperms, the other is coloured olive-green or brown by the eggs. As always, the sex-cells are very small, but those fortunate enough to have the use of a microscope can now observe an enthralling biologic drama.

Drops of the slime are added to a little sea-water on a glass slip; even with the naked eye it can be seen that they at once mingle intimately. Under magnification the eggs appear as relatively large, rounded bodies, floating passively. Round each rages a furious commotion as a crowd of tiny sperms besiege it, lashing to and fro the little beating hairs by means of which they drive themselves through the water. As they swim actively over its surface and wriggle against it they even cause the egg to spin round.

ARTIFICIAL STIMULATION OF EGGS

Suddenly all is quiet, the sperms move off elsewhere; that particular egg has ceased to attract them, and we know then that a male element has penetrated into it. The two have become united and the egg is said to be fertilized. It can now begin to divide and produce a new plant. Artificial stimulation of the eggs of the bladder-wrack sometimes induces them to start growth without fertilization by the male, but this never proceeds very far.

HAROLD BASTIN

BLADDER-WRACKS

Fronds of these seaweeds, showing the air-containing bladders by which they are supported in the water.

Particularly interesting is this to watch, for our own origins are not dissimilar. The human egg-cell is a little motionless speck of jelly of about the same size, that is to say just visible to the naked eye. It is, however, sheltered in the body of the mother, into which are introduced the swarms of sperms, again minute bodies swimming actively. It is somewhat humiliating to consider our small beginnings, but there is plenty of food for thought in the problem of how these little globules, almost structureless to our eyes, can grow into such complicated and different organisms.

MALE AND FEMALE CELLS

Like the bladder-wrack, flowering plants have their male and female cells, but they are not so easily seen inside the flower. Typically the latter consists of four different kinds of structures. Outside are the green sepals which protect the rest in the bud stage. Then come the petals, often large and brightly coloured. Within are a number of stamens, delicate stalked structures with heads full of tiny pollen grains which generally look like golden dust. In the centre is the ovary which encloses the embryo seeds. At its tip is the sticky stigma, often borne on a little stalk.

By various means the pollen grains are conveyed to the stigma, where they adhere. There they are stimulated to put out each a little tube, which grows down into the ovary and makes its way to an egg-cell. Then from the tip of the tube the male cell emerges and fuses with the female; from their union a seed grows.

FERTILIZING PARTNERS

At least one pollen grain must be provided for each seed, more to allow for wastage. Compared with their size the pollen grains put out very long tubes, and it is remarkable that they are able to find their way to the right spot. In crocus flowers they have to go from the feathery stigma perhaps four or five inches down to the ovary, which is underground close to the corm. On their journey they are nourished by cells secreting a sugary substance.

A glance round a garden will show what varied types of flower there are. One may

HAROLD BASTIN

FLOWERS AND FRUITS

Left: fruits of the plane tree. Middle: male flower. Right: female flower.

see the open cups of poppy and anemone with their clusters of stamens, the funnel-shaped convolvulus, the nasturtium with a long spur, evening primroses and night-scented stock which do not unfold their petals until dusk, pansies prettily marked like kittens' faces, the butterfly flowers of sweet pea, the daisy-like marigold, and perhaps here and there among the wealth of colour and beauty of form the inconspicuous and unwelcome flowers of the prolific nettle and groundsel.

The differing characters of these and other flowers can largely be related to the methods by which the pollen is conveyed to the stigma. Often the two are so close together in the flower that it might be imagined the mere trembling in the breeze would effect it, and indeed this sometimes happens. But it seems to be a general rule in nature that better results are obtained if the pollen comes from another flower (of course of the same kind) and cross-pollination takes place. Many flowers are so

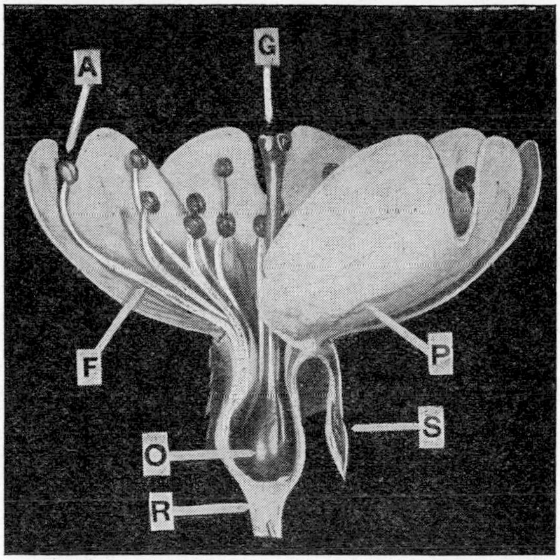

HAROLD BASTIN

PARTS OF A FLOWER

A—*Anther of stamen.* F—*Stalk.* G—*Stigma of pistil.* O—*Ovary.* P—*Petal.* S—*Sepal.* R—*Receptacle.*

HAROLD BASTIN

EMBRYO SEEDS IN THE OVARY

The flower of a narcissus bisected so as to show the essential organs. Note the ovules or embryo seeds in the ovary close to the sheath of the stalk.

constructed that it is impossible for them to fertilize themselves, either because of the relative positions of the organs or because stamens and stigma are not ripe at the same time.

Some cultivated fruit trees are completely self-sterile and are so particular in their matings that only a few other varieties can fertilize them. Thus if the black cherry Early

HAROLD BASTIN

WIND-CARRIED FRUIT

Top; Norway maple. Below (*left*) *sycamore ;* (*right*) *lime. Bottom* (*left*) *field maple ;* (*right*) *ash.*

Rivers is planted it must have a suitable partner, such as the yellow Governor Wood. If there is room for only one cherry in the garden it must be the self-fertile Morello. If a Cox's Orange Pippin does not fruit it may not be the fault of the weather, the tree or the soil but only that a suitable pollinator is not present. So it is recommended that orchards should be planted with a number of different varieties of apples, so that there will be in flower at the same time types which can fertilize each other.

The light dusty pollen of many trees and grasses is carried by the wind from plant to plant. With this haphazard method there is bound to be great wastage, and large quantities must be produced. Sufferers from hay fever, to whom the grains are intensely irritating, find grass pollen so widespread in June that it is difficult to avoid getting it into the nose.

The pollination of the great majority of flowers is related to the visits of insects, especially bees, but also wasps, flies, moths, butterflies and others. Pollen adhering to the body of an insect may be carried from one plant to another, and if it reaches the stigma may enable good seed to be set. The animal plays no conscious part in the transfer; its visits are only occasioned by the search for food. Pollen forms a good source of proteins and fats, while many flowers also provide a secretion of nectar, a sugary fluid which after partial digestion in the bee's crop is pumped up again as honey.

GATHERED IN POLLEN BASKETS

Neither of the two groups of insects and flowering plants appeared until a relatively late stage in evolutionary history. It is remarkable how the structure of many of their representatives has developed together so that the one act serves the different purposes of both organisms.

Bees are by far the most important flower visitors. Pollen is collected by the jaws and front legs, as well as being picked up by the feathery body hairs. It is gathered up by the hind legs and finally pushed up into the pollen baskets formed by a hollow, walled in by curving hairs, on the outside of the shin of each hind leg. Humble-bees can be seen with bulging loads of pollen as big as their heads. Nectar is sucked up by a tubular structure which can be protruded at will from the mouth.

BEES ATTRACTED BY COLOUR

We may wonder how the bees manage to find the flowers. Although many appear conspicuous to us, we must remember that other animals may not have the same senses as we. Dogs for instance can appreciate different degrees of brightness, but are almost colour blind. Bees can distinguish blue from yellow, but red appears dark to them. In their visits they show a marked preference for blue flowers, yellow coming next in favour. Their sense of smell is much the same as ours, that is to say it is not very acute and nothing like so strongly marked as in dogs or in some moths, where the male can scent a female a mile away.

HAROLD BASTIN

INSECT VISITORS OF FLOWERS

Top (left): Painted lady butterfly on a thistle head; (right) hover fly stealing pollen from a wild rose. Bottom (left): Humming bird hawkmoth feeding on a garden nasturtium; (right) blue butterflies on the cross-leaved heath.

Thus the bee will first be attracted by the colour of the flower, scent will be an additional guide as it approaches, while when quite close there may be petal markings, such as a light eye, scattered spots or rays which will aid recognition of particular types of flowers.

Hive bees have evolved a remarkable kind of sign language by which they communicate news of the flowers. When a worker bee (sterile female) returns to the hive from a rich source of nectar she disgorges the honey, and then dances round in circles. She is excitedly watched by others which crowd round and "sniff" at her with their feelers. Then she departs.

HAROLD BASTIN

PLANT AND INSECT PARTNERS

The yucca can only be pollinated by its moth Pronuba, *whose caterpillars live only on the plant.*

The dancing has conveyed to the others that there is plenty of nectar to be found, while the particular flower scent clinging to her has given them a clue where to search. Besides this they may find later that she has left her own mark on the flowers visited by exuding over them a little "bee-scent" from special glands in the tail. If supplies are poor there will be no dancing and no more workers set out.

When the news is that pollen is abundant the dance is of quite a different type, rather a swaying to and fro, while the pollen grains which are carried have their own distinctive smell.

TRANSFERRING THE POLLEN

As an example of a flower visited by bees we may take the foxglove. Its spire of spotted bells is a conspicuous sight, and humble-bees visit it from dawn to dusk in fine weather. They alight, push their way into a flower and protrude the sucking organ to draw up nectar from the bottom of the tube. The four stamens stand pressed against the upper side of the tube and pollen from them will be rubbed off on to the bee's back. The stigma stands in much the same place as the stamens, but is slightly more forward, so that is likely to be the first to touch the insect and pollen from another plant may then stick to it. Of course, when departing, the bee might transfer the flower's own pollen to the stigma, but this is not likely because the latter is usually not ripe until the stamens have shed their pollen. If insect visits are prevented, seed is not set.

The tale of the fig and its wasp has been told many times. The cultivation of the Smyrna fig in the United States proved impossible until the right insect was brought there to effect pollination.

PLANT AND MOTH PARTNERSHIP

An even more remarkable example of plant and insect working together is probably that of the yucca and its moth *Pronuba*, for the flower can only be pollinated by this moth, while its caterpillars live only on the yucca. It forms a handsome rosette of stiff, pointed leaves with large branches of creamy bell-like flowers, which are scented at night. The female moth, after being fertilized, visits a flower and makes a big ball from its pollen; then she flies to another and deposits her eggs in its ovary, climbs up and places the pollen on the stigma. Fertilization is ensured, the seeds develop and with them the caterpillars, there being sufficient seeds to feed the latter and leave a few to ripen. Then the caterpillars fall to the ground, pupate there and the moths emerge next year just at the time the yucca flowers open.

There are many other wonderful arrangements, but one must admit that the serpent sometimes enters into this Eden. In many flowers the nectar is at the base of a long tube; theoretically only certain insects are able to reach it, and in so doing will pollinate the flower. The snapdragon can only be pollinated by large humble-bees whose weight is sufficient to open the closed lip of the flower. But other shorter-tongued bees have learnt to bite through the tube farther down and then reach the nectar from the side. The robbers do not touch either stamens or stigma, and so the mechanism of the flower is defeated.

WORK OF HUMMING BIRDS

It is astonishing to watch butterflies and moths visiting flowers and putting out tubes for sucking nectar. The tubes may be as long as their bodies, but can in an instant be coiled up like a watch spring. Moths mostly visit long-tubed flowers such as honeysuckle, which are strongly scented at night and generally pale coloured or white.

Butterflies live up to their proverbially roving disposition; they flit from convolvulus to pink and then perhaps to something quite different. The pollen they might carry from one to another would be of no use.

There are a few unusual pollinating agents. In the tropics many large, brightly coloured flowers, particularly red ones, are pollinated by the tiny humming birds as they hover in front of them and insert their long thin beaks in search of nectar.

Every year in the autumn there are reports of these birds appearing in England. They are doubtless confused with the humming bird hawk-moth. As the latter's long proboscis is pushed into a flower the wings flutter at great speed; the hairy body with flattened tail has the shape of a bird's and only the antennæ on the head betrays its nature.

GIANT ARUM'S PRISONERS

A few plants, many of the arum type, have an extremely unpleasant odour and livid colour. Flies are attracted to them as to rotting flesh. The wild arum is of this kind, though its smell is mild compared with many of its relatives. There is a green sheathing spathe with a cylindrical structure inside terminating in a purple spike. Small insects fly down the tube, past a ring of downward pointing hairs, and find themselves trapped at the base. The hairs prevent them from flying out, and although there would be room for them to crawl out they cannot apparently do so. At the bottom

DR. BERTRAM TRUSTEES

FLOWER SIX FEET HIGH

Amorphophallus titanum, *a giant arum with a flower about six feet high. Its stench is almost insupportable.*

HAROLD BASTIN

SEEDS AS TRAVELLERS

A seed of the spotted orchis weighs only one-fifteen-thousandth part of a grain. It may travel many miles.

of the spike are female flowers which may be pollinated if the flies have visited another arum. In a few days the sheath withers and the captives can emerge, in so doing becoming dusted with pollen from the male flowers, higher up the spike, which are now ripe. One giant arum, *Amorphophallus*, has a " flower " of this type about six feet high. Its stench to us is almost insupportable.

POLLINATED BY SNAILS

The domestic aspidistra, a native of the forests of Eastern Asia, sometimes produces quaint brown flowers, lying just above the surface of the earth. It is said that in nature they are pollinated by snails crawling over them.

Occasionally, man has to perform the marriage ceremony. So gardeners dust their peach flowers with a brush full of pollen in case insects do not enter the greenhouses. The cultivation of the vanilla orchid was introduced into Java, but the humming birds and bees which normally pollinate it were not there. When the flowers open, women go round pollinating as many as three thousand flowers each a day. The seed then sets and the scented pods form.

SEEDS THAT EXPLODE

A few exceptional plants can set seed without fertilization. This happens frequently in the hawkweeds. Cucumbers and some apples require to be pollinated before the fruit will develop, but the latter will continue to grow without seeds forming. A cucumber with seeds is no use for eating. This behaviour is not particularly desirable in apples for the shape of seedless fruits is not good.

A flowering plant usually produces many seeds, but such is the competition and wastage that the numbers of the different species remain

HAROLD BASTIN

WILLOW-HERB OR FIRE-WEED

The seeds of the willow-herb bear tufts of light hairs that enable it to be carried by air currents.

more or less the same. Overcrowding would soon choke them if the seeds were not dispersed some distance from the parent. A few plants are able to do this for themselves. On a hot summer's day one may hear the dry gorse pods suddenly splitting in half and thereby flinging the seeds several feet through the air. Incidentally, ants are said to find them attractive and may carry them still farther away. Ripe fruits of the touch-me-not balsam are in such a state of tension that if touched lightly they explode violently and the seeds shoot in all directions.

DISPERSAL BY WIND

The most usual agency of dispersal is wind. The seeds of orchids are very minute and float in the air for long distances, possibly hundreds of miles. So numerous are they that Darwin calculated that the great-grandchildren of a single plant of the spotted orchis would, if they all lived, cover the whole surface of the earth with a uniform green carpet. So light are the seeds that each weighs only one-fifteen-thousandth part of a grain.

Heavier seeds may be so constructed that they do not fall at once to the ground and are carried some way by air currents. The seeds of the willow-herb bear a tuft of light hairs. It has been noted several times that building sites in the heart of London have been invaded by sheets of this plant; the seeds must have been transported some distance. In America the willow-herb is known as the fire-weed, not on account of its colour, which is a somewhat puce pink, but because it appears so frequently on ground where the original vegetation has been destroyed by fire.

HAROLD BASTIN

NATURE'S OWN PARACHUTE

The parachute which supports the seed of the cat's-ear and secures its dispersal by air.

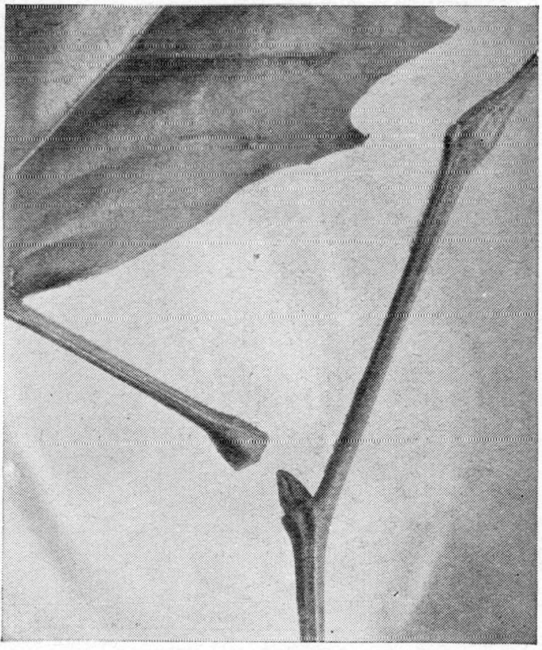

HAROLD BASTIN

FALL OF THE LEAF

A plane tree in the act of shedding a leaf, exposing the bud of its successor.

WINGS OF THE SYCAMORE

The hairy parachutes of the fruits of dandelion are well known, while the lightness of thistle-down is proverbial. The much heavier fruits of sycamore have two big wings and spin through the air. Seedlings often spring up in gardens some way from any tree.

Some fruits are carried by water. The coconut which we eat really corresponds to the stone of a plum. When shed it is surrounded by a thick fibrous coat, from which coir is derived. If it falls into the sea it can float many miles, and so we find the coconut palm is widespread on all tropical coasts.

Animals, too, play an important part, carrying seeds either inside or outside their bodies.

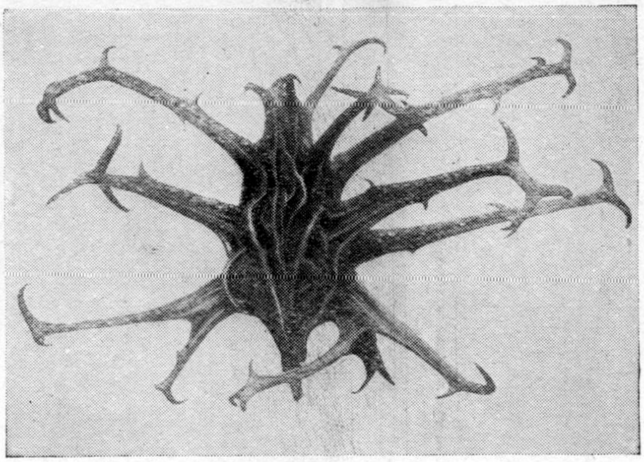

HAROLD BASTIN

HOOKED FRUIT

The fruit of the grapple plant hooks itself to any passing beast. The pod splits open when ripe.

The hooked fruits of goosegrass catch easily in furry coats and may be rubbed off later some distance away. Wading birds carry away the seeds of water plants in the mud adhering to their feet. Squirrels bury acorns and nuts and often forget their stores, which may later produce seedlings.

A plant which itself buries its fruit is the monkey- or pea-nut. Few of the millions who eat them realize that they have developed underground. The plant is low and bushy with small vetch-like flowers. After fertilization a stalk below the fruit elongates, grows down and buries the young fruit in the soil. It will not develop if kept in the light.

CARRIED INSIDE BIRDS

Juicy brightly coloured fruits, such as haws, make a special appeal to birds. The seeds inside them have a hard coat and pass unharmed through the digestive system. They may be carried a considerable distance before they are dropped. " Hurrah ! " wrote Darwin to a friend, " a seed has germinated after twenty-one-and-a-half hours in an owl's stomach. This . . . would carry it God knows how many miles."

The stork's-bill is so called because the long awn or beard attached to the seed pod resembles at a distance the beak of the bird after which the plant is named. When the seed falls to the ground the awn acts as a kind of auger, assisted by a number of flexible hairs that help to keep the seed in position. The varying conditions of the atmosphere make it twist and untwist, so that eventually it bores its way into the ground and the seeds germinate.

Man plays an important part in carrying seed to new places. Alien plants are often accidentally introduced from abroad with seed of other plants, or amongst cargo, ballast or packing. Many, such as the winter heliotrope, have escaped from gardens but have become thoroughly well established here in the wild. Sometimes well-meaning people try to beautify the countryside by sowing seed of some favourite cultivated plant. Usually the experiment fails, for conditions in a garden, where the plants are carefully nursed and competition eliminated by weeding, are quite unnatural. The practice is viewed with disfavour by botanists.

MENACE OF THE DANDELION

Occasionally it is successful. Every year the Northumbrian Roman Wall is brightened by the purple flowers of a little Spanish plant, *Erinus alpinus*. People have liked to imagine how some Spanish legionary centuries ago brought it there to remind him of home. In reality a local clergyman planted it and, conditions being to its liking, it has flourished.

Not uncommonly alien plants find the new surroundings so favourable, that with their

HAROLD BASTIN

CARRIED IN FUR

Another hooked fruit which is carried in the fur of beasts and thereby ensures wide distribution of the seeds. It may be taken a considerable distance.

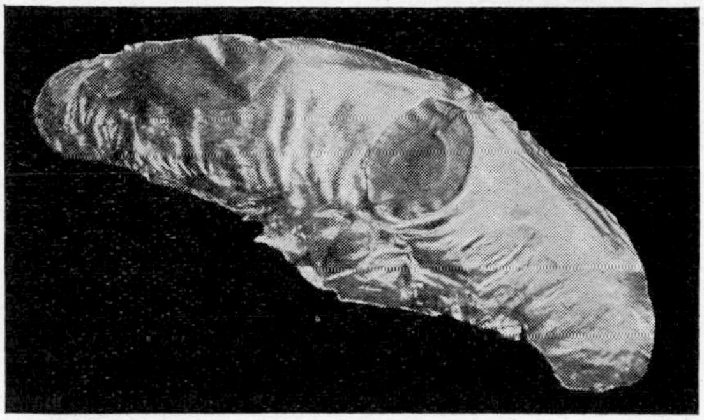

HAROLD BASTIN

PLANT GLIDER

Seed of Zanonia, which glides from the parent plant and sometimes is carried a considerable distance by air currents in its native Java.

natural enemies absent they increase by leaps and bounds. Daisies, plantains and dandelions are as common in North American lawns as in those of Great Britain, but all originated in Europe. The dandelion has spread so successfully as to be known as the yellow peril. In various parts of the world homesick Scottish colonists have grown and cherished plants of thistle and so added to the troubles of later years. Brambles, introduced into New Zealand, have become a gigantic menace.

USEFUL BUT OBNOXIOUS NETTLE

Many an alien plant flourishes on the banks or in the waters of England's slow-flowing rivers and canals. Mention has already been made of the Canadian pondweed, which first made itself known in Great Britain in Market Harborough some eighty years ago. Although it has never been known to produce seed in the country of its adoption, it manages to

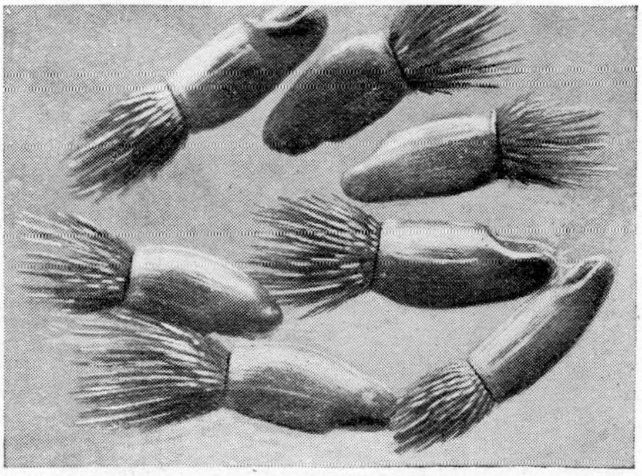

HAROLD BASTIN

LIKE SHAVING BRUSHES

Fruits of the corn-bluebottle plant. They resemble miniature shaving brushes.

flourish exceedingly and with even greater persistence than the proverbial bay tree.

A plant which is a native of Africa and India made its appearance all unsuspected in an English canal. Presumably, it had found its way by means of a consignment of Egyptian cotton sent to a mill. So far as is known it had secured a roothold on European soil only once before, in northern Italy. There it had been chaperoned by East Indian rice. Other

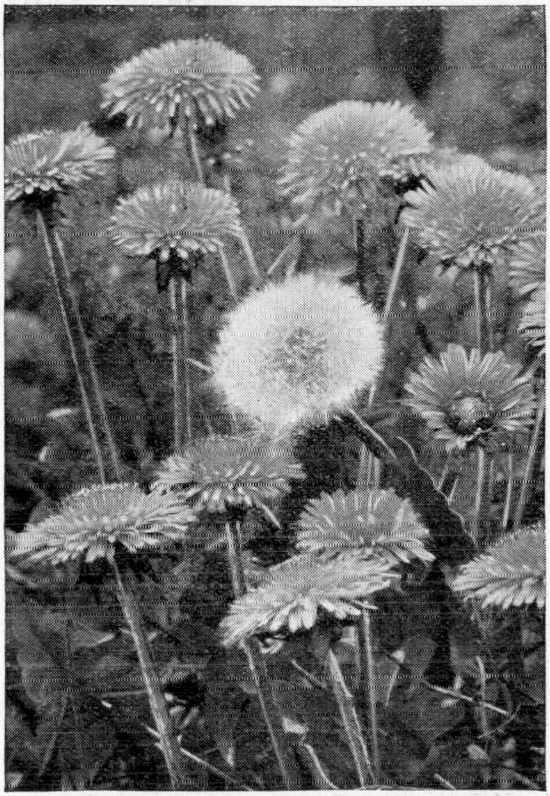

HAROLD BASTIN

KNOWN AS THE YELLOW PERIL

Dandelions are as common in North American lawns as in those of Great Britain. All originated in Europe.

importations have included algæ from America, again due in all probability to a bale of cotton, though on this occasion from the southern United States.

Nettles are by no means in the good books of the agriculturist and the gardener, yet they serve quite a number of useful purposes. Many species of birds which live on insects find their favourite food on the flowers and leaves, and the latter also afford excellent cover for their nests and eggs. The shade they give likewise secures a certain amount of moisture in the ground where they are rooted. This is appreciated by snails, which are eaten by birds that do not appreciate an insectivorous menu.

The caterpillars of various butterflies, including those of the red admiral, peacock and small tortoiseshell, and the tiger moths find the leaves of the common stinging nettle to their liking. Perhaps the most curious use to which this weed, at once so obnoxious and so useful, is put is for stopping leaks in barrels. The juice is rubbed between the staves, and when hard has the same effect as caulking on the wooden deck of a ship.

Many millions of acres in the north-western parts of the United States are covered with a plant called Australian saltbush. For long it was regarded as a weed that served no useful purpose; a mere encumberer of the ground on which it thrived all too well. As the earth was arid and nothing else seemed to thrive on it, little or no attention was paid to the plant until a rancher, finding by accident that his sheep took to it readily, decided to make an experiment and allow a flock to graze on it. The result was amazing, for he found that the animals flourished exceedingly. They produced considerably better wool and better mutton.

Another plant with good and bad qualities from a human point of view is spartina or rice grass. It is of considerable value on muddy flats, such as the sea invades and by slow degrees wrests from the land, because it helps to consolidate the soil and renders it valuable grazing land. It appeared apparently from nowhere in the neighbourhood of Southampton Water. Unfortunately, its excellent behaviour is not evident in navigable waterways, where it becomes a menace. Some years ago about a hundred cuttings of spartina were planted on the sea side of a wall which appeared to be doomed by the constant pounding of the waves. Although only a few of the plants survived the ordeal, they spread so rapidly that both the wall and the farm it protected were saved. The shrubby sea blite (*Suadba srutacosa*) is also an important beach strengthener, and there are kindly plants which bind together the sandhills.

" Nature," it has been said, " is conquered by obeying her, and man is but her puppet until he learns the lesson of obedience."

HAROLD BASTIN FOX

SPANISH PLANT ON THE ROMAN WALL

The Northumbrian Roman Wall is brightened by the purple flowers of a little Spanish plant called Erinus alpinus (*inset*). *It was not brought by a legionary centuries ago, but planted by a local clergyman.*

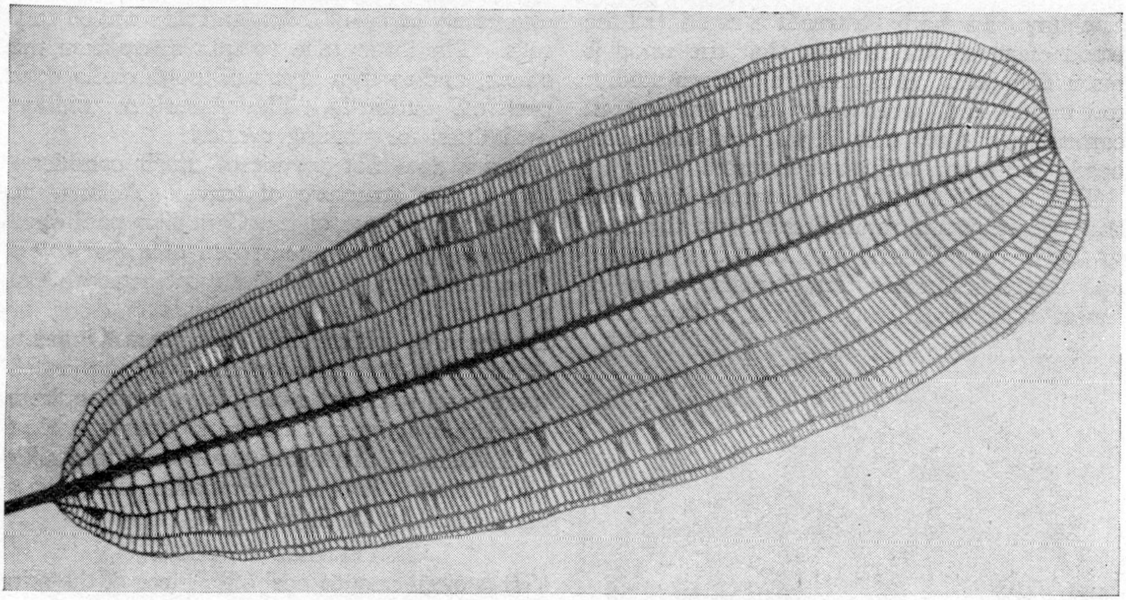

HAROLD BASTIN

WORLD'S MOST REMARKABLE LEAF

The exquisite leaf of the lattice plant, a native of Madagascar, which grows under water. The leaves grow to a length of some eighteen inches in the largest specimens, and consist for the most part of veins.

PLANT ANATOMY

PLANTS, like animals, are built up of a living substance, known as protoplasm, and its products. Protoplasm appears to be generally a semi-solid jelly; we can analyse it chemically and find its composition, but no one can put these substances together again and create living matter.

The plant body consists of many tiny units called cells; these when living contain sap surrounded by a layer of protoplasm in which is a special body, the nucleus, which controls the activities of the cell. Each is enclosed by a firm wall of a substance called cellulose. Cell walls make up much of the mass of plant tissue; human beings are unable to digest the cellulose, but the bulk it provides stimulates the movements of the intestines.

Cells may be considered the bricks of which the plant body is composed. At certain growing regions, particularly the tips of the roots and shoots, existing cells are continually dividing into two and producing new units. At first they are roughly cubical, but as they grow they develop on different lines according to the parts they have to play.

Some change their shape little. The pulp of fruits is formed of cells of this type. Besides cellulose there is present in the walls a gelatinous substance known as pectose. It is this which causes jam to set; it is most abundant in under-ripe fruit.

Other cells may become stretched out and develop thick walls. These form fibres, which strengthen the plant. When they are very long and strong, as in stems of flax and hemp, they are important to man.

Much of the bulk of stems and roots, the trunks of trees and the veins of leaves is made up of wood. The cells become drawn out lengthways, their living contents and the cross-walls between them disappear, so that long tubes are formed, as when drain-pipes are laid end to end. The walls are altered to a woody substance.

Growth in trees is more rapid in spring than in summer, and larger wood elements are formed then. The sudden transition from the close summer wood of one year to the open spring wood of the next is very marked, and shows up as a ring when a trunk is cut across. By counting the number of annual rings the age of the tree is found.

In the tropics, where there is little difference between the seasons, growth proceeds evenly and rings are hardly noticeable. Sometimes growth is slow, giving close, heavy wood such as ebony. In the balsa tree it is rapid and the wood elements are so light that the wood is more like cork. It is used in cinema studios to make the woodwork for knockabout comedies; a blow with it will not break any heads, but it can easily be shattered.

The tubes formed by the wood elements conduct water and mineral salts from the roots to the leaves. Exactly how they are pumped up, sometimes many feet, remains more or less of a mystery. In the spring at least there

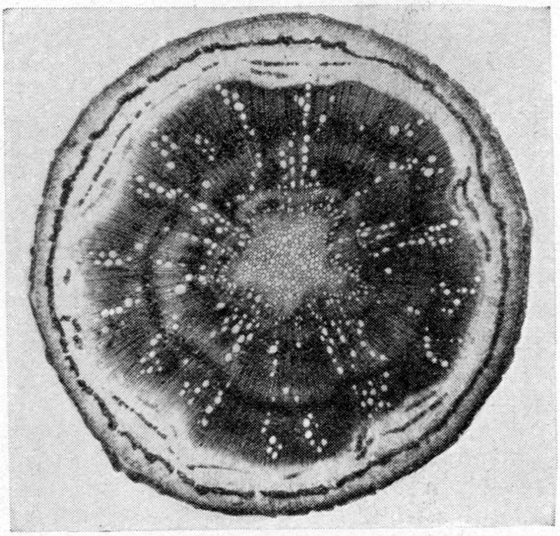

HAROLD BASTIN

SECTION OF YOUNG OAK

By counting the number of annual rings when timber is cut down the age of a tree is found

are also sugars in the rising sap; in the American sugar maple it is worth while collecting it.

Outside the wood is a tissue whose elements are formed in the same way from elongated cells placed end to end, but the cross walls do not disappear. They are perforated by tiny holes. It is thought that materials manufactured by the leaves pass down through these. Whether they make their way down to the roots through the wood also is a matter which is not yet decided.

Stems are often surrounded by a layer of cork. The cells here are compactly arranged and their walls contain a substance which makes them waterproof. They have no living contents. Potatoes have a corky skin which prevents them from losing water and also helps to keep fungi from attacking the food within.

The cork oak produces a great mass of tough elastic cork which is stripped off at intervals and finds many uses. In the birch there are alternately layers of thick- and thin-walled cork cells. The latter tend to split away from the others, and so thin layers of tough corky bark peel off naturally. The American Indians used them for making canoes.

Space does not permit of much consideration of the structure of leaves. Among the simplest are those of the Canadian pondweed (*Elodea*), which are composed of a few layers of brick-shaped cells. The most noticeable of their contents are numerous little discs, or chloroplasts, which hold the green pigment. Incidentally they are continually being jostled round and round the cells, for the protoplasm here shows active streaming movements. Most of the cells of other green leaves contain similar chloroplasts. It is in their bodies that sugars are formed in sunlight.

DEVELOPED IN CONES

It is often easy to peel off a piece of the skin from the under surface of a leaf. When one looks down on this through a microscope one can see the tiny scattered pores through which gases and water vapour pass in and out. Each is surrounded by two sausage-shaped cells.

The preceding pages have been devoted mainly to the plants which are most familiar to us, those which bear flowers and seeds and make up more than half of the plants known. Seeds are also found in the group of trees that includes pines, yews, cypresses, cycads and others, whose male and female organs are developed in cones. The male cells are produced from pollen grains; in the pine these are provided with two little wings to buoy them up. They are carried to the female by wind. The seeds are not enclosed within an ovary but are borne on the open cone-scales.

The group produces some very valuable timber trees, many being quick growing, with straight trunks and wood of even texture.

GIGANTIC FERNS

Besides the seed-plants there is a host of others of a simpler type. These never form seeds, that is to say large reproductive units produced as a result of fertilization and fitted to undergo a resting period, but have very varied methods of reproduction.

Ferns are found over much of the world; those of Great Britain are generally not very imposing. Bracken, of world-wide occurrence, attracts attention by the area it covers. Under a well-grown royal fern (*Osmunda*) a tall man can shelter, but this magnificent plant is now rarely allowed to survive in the wild in England.

In the tropics ferns are far more luxuriant. Some are like trees, a crown of fronds uncoiling at the top of a stout trunk. Fern-like plants were very abundant millions of years ago when much of our coal was laid down. Still preserved among it are the fossilized trunks of giant relatives of the present-day insignificant club-mosses.

ONE-CELLED SPORES

On the back of a fern frond one often finds little groups, apparently of brown dust. Here masses of tiny one-celled spores are produced. They are very light and may be carried far by the wind. If a bottle or jam-jar is inverted in damp soil it is very probable that ferns will in time appear under it, for the spores seem everywhere abundant.

They do not at once produce a fern plant, but instead a delicate little leaf appears whose under surface produces sex organs. From some burst out masses of tiny sperms, provided with

HAROLD BASTIN

LEAVES OF SIMPLE STRUCTURE
The leaves of the Canadian pondweed are composed of a few layers of brick-shaped cells.

beating hairs. The female, or egg-cells, are well protected, each being at the base of a flask-shaped structure. The sperms swim to them in the water which collects underneath, the fertilized egg grows to a new fern plant.

Lower in the scale of evolution are the mosses and liverworts. The latter are generally inconspicuous and restricted to damp places, but mosses are found all over the world, on rocks and dry land, in bogs and on tree-trunks, from the Arctic to the tropics.

MOSSES AS PIONEERS

Generally they grow in tufts of closely packed stems, covered with tiny leaves. At the tips of the shoots sex organs may be found. Though the details can only be seen with a microscope the groups are obvious in the common hair-moss (*Polytrichum*). The male organs make a little orange-red cluster surrounded by green leaves, the form of the whole recalling a daisy.

The sperms must have a film of water in which to swim to the groups of egg-cells, again housed in flask-shaped structures. The fertilized egg grows out to form the moss capsule,

HAROLD BASTIN

CONIFEROUS TREES
Top (left): Spruce and Douglas fir; (below): Scotch pine and Austrian pine; (right): Larch. Their male and female organs are developed in cones.

a little globular or urn-shaped body on a delicate stalk, not unlike a poppy seed-head. It is full of spores, which produce new plants.

Mosses are important pioneers in the colonization of bare ground, but we have little contact with them. One of the best known is the bog-moss (*Sphagnum*) which forms soft masses of bright green over dangerous mires. The dried fronds have the power of absorbing moisture very rapidly and have been used for wound dressings.

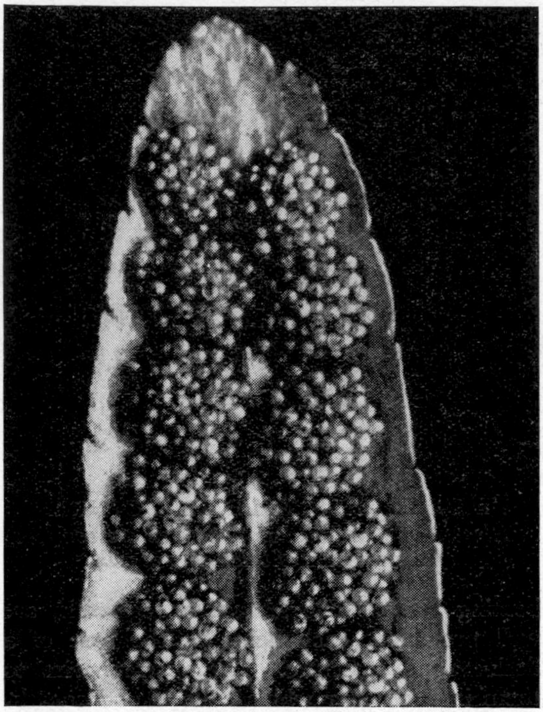

HAROLD BASTIN

"FERN SEED"

Underside of a magnified fern leaf, showing groups of tiny one-celled spores.

One moss (*Schizostega*) has the power of so collecting up light with its tiny cells that it appears to be luminous. It favours damp, dimly-lighted places, such as caves or rabbit burrows, and is said sometimes to have deluded miners. When it is carried out into the light the film of moss can no longer be seen and the false nugget is just a lump of earth.

The writer recalls visiting the stone tomb of some pre-historic Cornishman. With the body a golden beaker had been found many years ago and presented to Queen Victoria. Now the fairy gold of moss accompanies the chieftain's spirit, shining with a lovely greenish radiance on the walls of the hollow.

Among the algæ are seaweeds and the growths which form pond scum, together with many microscopic forms which include the simplest plants known. Nearly all live in water. Some consist of but a single cell; in others chains of cells form simple filaments or threads, while in many seaweeds these are woven together to form quite a solid body.

The tiny green algæ of ponds only reveal their beauty under the microscope. One of the loveliest is *Volvox*, whose cells form a hollow sphere, clearly visible to the naked eye. Each cell has a pair of beating hairs, and so the ball makes stately progress through the water.

WITH A FLINTY COAT

Diatoms are important members of the group. In the mass they are brown. Each consists of a single cell with a flinty coat, most delicately sculptured. Countless millions of them float in the upper waters of the oceans and provide food for many marine animals.

Among seaweeds the green pigment is often masked by red or brown. One red weed, the Irish moss (*Chondrus crispus*), contains much gelatinous substance. It is collected and dried by the Aran islanders and still finds some uses.

The brown weeds include the large kelps or oarweeds (*Laminaria*). They have a remarkable power of taking up the minute traces of iodine in sea water and storing it in their tissues. The plants make good soil fertilizers, while a certain amount of iodine is still extracted from them commercially.

Some red seaweeds take large amounts of lime from the sea and deposit it in their tissues so that they become hard as coral. They are found on the shores of the British Isles as a pink coating to rocks and stones; in tropical waters there are forms which help to build up reefs.

EVOLVED FROM ALGÆ

Sexual reproduction in the bladderwrack has already been described. There is great variety in the reproductive processes of the algæ, but nearly always the male and female cells are shed into the water and fusion takes place there.

One very large group, the fungi, is devoid of the green pigment chlorophyll. Included in it are the mushrooms and toadstools, moulds and blights, mildews, rusts and smuts, yeasts and bacteria. Although many are harmless, the presence of others is the cause of most plant and animal diseases.

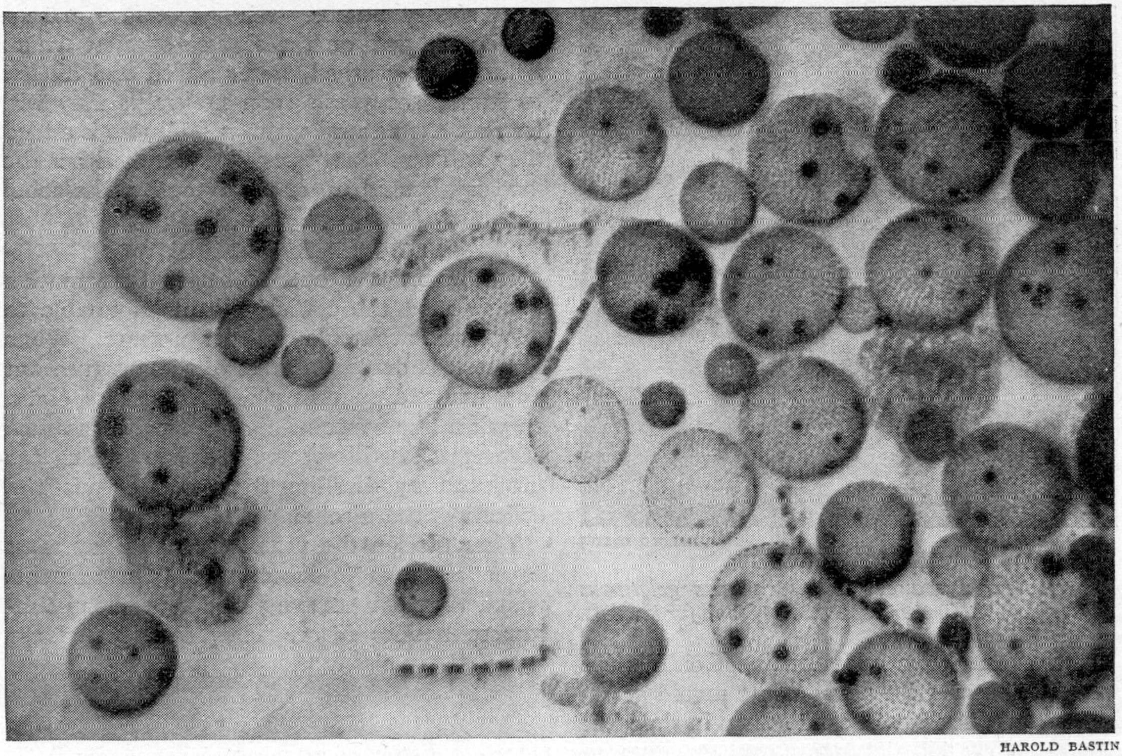

HAROLD BASTIN

FLOATING COLONY OF ALGÆ

Volvox, *one of the loveliest of the tiny green algæ to be found in ponds. Each cell has a pair of beating hairs which enable the ball to make stately progress through the water.*

They seem to have evolved at a very early stage of existence from algæ which lost their pigment and came to obtain food in various peculiar ways. The vegetative body usually consists of very fine branching threads, which may sometimes be woven together to make a solid body, as in the mushroom. It must be noted that the real mushroom plant is the fine underground threads, which when mixed with dung form " spawn "; the mushroom we eat is only the fruiting body.

FORTY MILLION SPORES A DAY

In many fungi there are no traces of a sexual process, but in almost all, tiny spores are produced in great quantity. A sunbeam reveals that the air is full of dust motes, but it cannot show the hosts of fungal spores and bacteria always present too; even many thousand feet above the earth a few can still be detected. Small wonder when we learn that a common mushroom produces forty million spores a day.

Many fungi live on dead organic matter, mushrooms on dung heaps, toadstools on tree stumps, black mould on bread, green mould on jam and cheese, in fact there is very little that some form will not find to its taste. Usually the substances have to be broken down in order to provide the simple compounds they need. Ferments are poured out and the threads then absorb the products of digestion.

RUSTS AND SMUTS

It is a small step from feeding on dead to living matter. Many have become parasitic, taking their food from the bodies of other plants and animals and thereby causing much damage. There is indeed hardly a plant which is not liable to be attacked by one or more kinds. There are various rusts and smuts on cereals, potato is affected by blight and wart disease and many others, plum by silver-leaf, rose by mildew and leaf-spot, and so the catalogue goes on. It is not an exaggeration to say that something like one-tenth of the crops are lost owing to their activities.

The fungus responsible for the damping-off of seedlings can vary its behaviour. It is at first parasitic on them, feeding on the stems just above the ground; then when they have been killed it lives on their dead tissues.

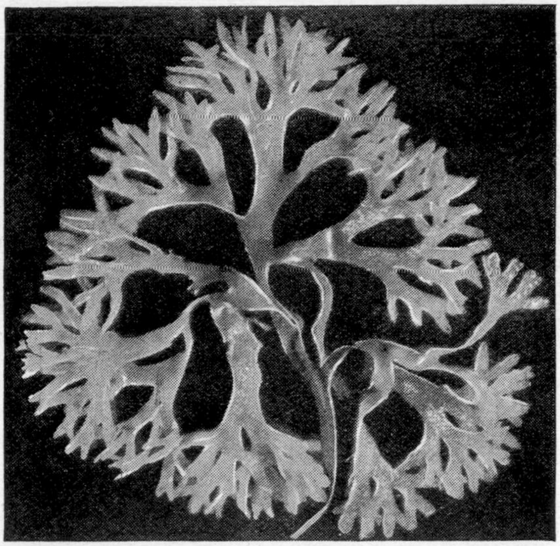

HAROLD BASTIN

IRISH MOSS

The edible red seaweed which contains gelatinous substances used in the preparation of food for invalids.

A few fungi live on animals. Goldfish are sometimes seen with a fine white mould growing on the gills; it will choke them in time but can easily be killed by dipping the fish into salt water. Ringworm and thrush in human beings are caused by fungi.

Yeasts are fungi with a very simple structure. The body is but a single ovoid cell, of which there are many millions in an ounce of compressed yeast. It can vary its mode of life according to the conditions. When supplied with food, in the form of sugar and plenty of oxygen, it proceeds as in a normal plant, converting it to water and carbon dioxide and using some of the energy released.

KILLED BY THEIR OWN PRODUCT

But if oxygen is absent, as at the bottom of a vat of liquid, it can live in a more extravagant way, known as fermentation, only partly breaking up the sugar and leaving as waste products carbon dioxide and alcohol. We might perhaps compare the process to a child eating the icing off a cake and throwing the rest away.

The action of yeast has been employed by man for centuries. If added to a stiff mixture of flour and water it digests the starch; the carbon dioxide produced is held by the elastic dough and the bubbles formed by the gas make a spongy texture, which gives palatable and digestible bread.

Also important is the production of alcohol from sugary liquids. Wild yeasts are present in the air and on the surface of most fruits; if these are crushed, water added and all left to stand, the yeasts soon multiply; they will ferment the natural sugar and if more is added they will continue " working " until either the food is all used up or the quantity of alcohol that they have produced kills them.

EXPLOSIVES FROM YEAST

If the brew is bottled before fermentation has finished the carbon dioxide is unable to escape and accumulates under pressure. When the cork is drawn bubbles of the gas rush out and make a sparkling drink, such as cider. In wines the concentration of alcohol is much higher; it is still greater in spirits, which are produced by distilling fermented liquids and collecting the alcohol.

Tiny though the yeast cells are, they must house a veritable laboratory. The ferments which they can secrete will act on many substances besides sugar. How complicated are

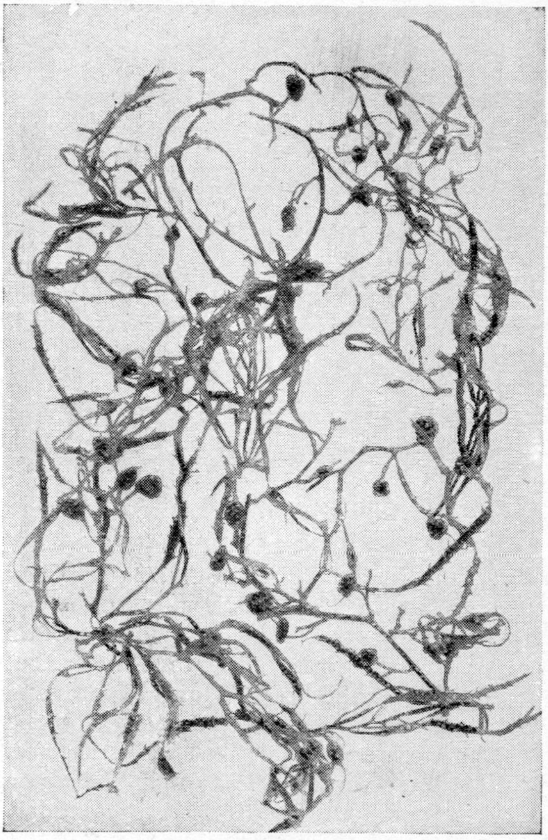

HAROLD BASTIN

FOUND IN THE SARGASSO SEA

Gulf weed, a seaweed with an evil reputation because it is found extensively in the Sargasso Sea.

the processes is shown by the fact that in the World War a clever chemist was able, by suitable treatment, to obtain in the fermentation glycerine instead of alcohol. This was a discovery of the greatest importance to his country at a time when there was such a shortage of the fats from which glycerine for high explosives is usually made.

INCREASING BY DIVIDING

Placed among the fungi are the bacteria (sometimes known as germs or microbes), whose structure is even simpler than that of the yeasts. The body is a single minute cell; it may be rod-like or spherical, and in some it is spirally twisted. One-twenty-five-thousandth part of an inch is an average length for these tiny beings. The smallest is only just visible under the microscope. Bacteria are colourless and have so little structure that to show them up it is necessary to stain them with various dyes.

They increase by dividing in half, sometimes as often as once every twenty minutes. There is no sexual process. When conditions are unfavourable the cells may tide themselves over a difficult period by turning into tough-walled spores. In this form they can resist drought and exposure to high temperatures.

Bacteria make their presence known to us by their activities, in particular their feeding methods. There is a whole host upon whose active life the processes of decay depend. They find their food supply in the dead tissues, breaking them down into simpler substances with the aid of their digestive ferments. The waste products of some of them are gases whose smells we dislike, and so decay has unpleasant associations, which it does not deserve. The soil is full of them, busy breaking down the substance of plants and dead animals. In fact, its fertility depends on their presence, for were they (and fungi too) not continually at work the minerals which plants take from the soil would be locked up and the available supplies soon exhausted.

BACTERIA AND TEA

The early stages of decay are utilized in several important instances. The leaves of the tea plant are picked and left in damp piles. Bacteria digest the starch and sugar and then the residue is dried. Green tea is prepared from unfermented leaves, dried at once in the sun; although the brew from them looks colourless it is much more stimulating than black tea.

An unpleasant bitter substance is removed from cocoa nibs by allowing them to ferment a little after shelling. Coffee owes nothing to bacterial action, for the beans are dried as soon as they are picked.

Tobacco leaves are put in layers and begin to decay; the action of different kinds of bacteria produces the varying flavours. Flax stems are steeped in water and the fibres freed from other tissues by allowing bacteria to digest part of the cell walls.

HAROLD BASTIN

KILLED BY DEADLY FUNGUS

A house-fly done to death by the spore of the Empusa *fungus, which may be seen on the glass.*

The lactic and butyric acid bacteria cause changes in milk which make it " turn sour." It is important for cheese makers to have the right strain of bacteria at work, for on the activity of particular kinds depend the distinctive flavours of cheeses from different parts.

About eighty years ago, when improvements in the microscope had made it possible to see bacteria clearly, it was noticed that if hay was steeped in water there were soon so many bacteria present that the water became cloudy. It was thought they had been produced in it either by the air or by the decaying matter.

That living bodies should appear suddenly from dead matter seemed quite possible, for it was held that the mud on river banks could

HAROLD BASTIN

STINKHORN FUNGUS

So called because it emits an unpleasant smell that attracts flies which disperse the spores.

breed fishes and frogs. It was even stated by a sixteenth-century scientist that if dirty linen was pressed down with some pieces of cheese, and left for three weeks, adult male and female mice would be produced !

The belief should not be laughed at, for even now superstition and ignorance are still widespread. There are many who are willing for their actions to be guided by what the stars are said to reveal; while magical practices, such as ill-wishing and charming of warts are still performed with faith in their efficacy.

BACTERIA ON MOUNTAIN TOPS

It was the great Frenchman Pasteur who finally proved that if the hay and water were first thoroughly boiled, so that living organisms were destroyed, and kept so that the bacteria in the air could not reach them, then they remained unchanged. Unless special care is taken bacteria from the air fall into the liquid and multiply there, for they are always present, even in the pure air of mountain tops

Pasteur also showed that most infectious diseases are caused by the presence in the body of certain bacteria; these are conveyed from one person to another in various ways, and so the diseases spread.

Very often it is not their actual presence which causes trouble. Thus our intestines house a varied collection of bacteria, whose bodies are so numerous that they make up about half of the contents. We feel no ill effects from them. But sometimes another kind, such as the cholera germ, enters and then there is likely to be grave disturbance, for its waste products are a poison to us.

CARRIERS OF DISEASE

Not all the disease-producing bacteria are solely dependent on the human body for their food. Typhoid germs can live in fresh water, where they may be carried with sewage. They may again infect human beings if they enter a water supply or are taken in with shell fish.

It is curious that some people, known as "carriers," can house these bacteria and still be perfectly well. They are very dangerous to their neighbours, for they will be continually passing on the germs of typhoid unknowingly. This applies to several other diseases.

Anthrax bacteria live and multiply in man and many other warm-blooded animals. In the soil, on animal skins and carcases, they can exist for years in the form of resting spores. Shaving brushes made from infected hair have been known to cause anthrax in the users, the bacteria entering through cuts and at once resuming their activities.

Many bacteria cannot endure long away from their living hosts, though they may not be restricted to one type. Thus the black death and the great plague of past centuries (still known in the East) were caused by an organism whose real home is in small animals such as rats. Sometimes infected

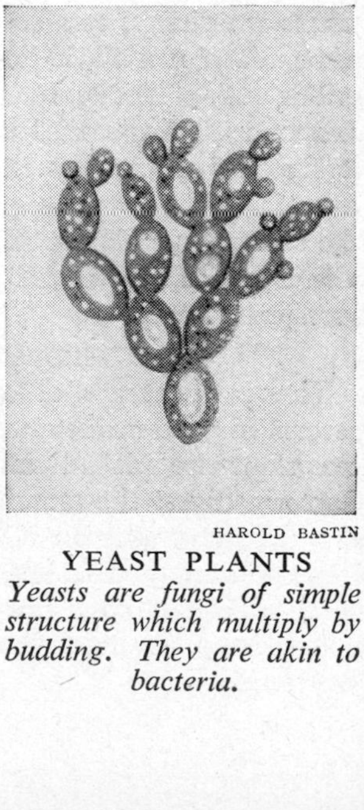

HAROLD BASTIN

YEAST PLANTS

Yeasts are fungi of simple structure which multiply by budding. They are akin to bacteria.

HAROLD BASTIN

NATURAL DEFENCE AGAINST ENEMIES

Three twigs of holly picked from the same tree at different heights, showing how the prickliness of the foliage decreases as it grows out of the reach of browsing animals.

animals die, their fleas leave them for another warm-blooded creature and may land on a human being. They live by sucking blood and are very likely to introduce the germs of plague into the bites.

LIVING WITHOUT OXYGEN

Like the yeast plant, some bacteria, such as the type that causes lockjaw, can live without oxygen. These are found deep in rich soil. If they enter a wound they multiply there and their waste products travel round the body in the blood stream, causing terrible muscular spasms.

Fortunately lockjaw is not very common, but all wounds are liable to become invaded by other bacteria, whose products cause blood poisoning and prevent healing. Previous to about 1870 the smallest wound was likely to become poisoned in this way, and the majority of surgical operations proved fatal. It was little wonder when we read that it was etiquette for the surgeon to wear an old frock coat stiff with the blood stains of years, while the same sponge might go the round of all the patients in a ward, infecting one with the germs from another.

It was Pasteur again who showed bacteria to be the cause of blood poisoning and pleaded for surgical methods which would keep their numbers down. He was ridiculed until Lord Lister heard of his work and put his methods into practice. The surgeon's hands, the instruments, sponges and bandages were soaked with a solution of carbolic acid, which destroyed any bacteria present; it was also sprayed round the wound. As a result only six out of his next forty amputation cases were fatal.

VALUE OF PASTEURIZATION

But carbolic acid and other so-called antiseptics are not particularly good for the living tissues of the body, and so nowadays heat is relied on largely for killing the bacteria. The instruments and the surgeon's rubber gloves are sterilized with steam, the garments and dressings are previously brought to a high temperature, and any water used is boiled.

Pasteur's name is remembered in the "pasteurization" process which much of our

HAROLD BASTIN

PROTECTED BY PRICKLES

By producing bunches of prickles on its main stem the climbing of the honey-locust is rendered impossible.

milk supply undergoes. It was originated for wines and beers. Sometimes they become "diseased" through certain bacteria getting in and spoiling the flavours. No one would drink beer which had been treated with carbolic to destroy bacteria, but Pasteur found that if it was heated for a short time at 55° C. (about midway between the freezing-point and boiling-point of water) the intruders were killed or so weakened that they caused no trouble.

WHERE THE MICROSCOPE FAILS

Milk is the perfect food not only for babies, but for many bacteria, which quickly turn it sour. Pasteurization (at a higher temperature than for wines) does not alter the flavour as does boiling, the food value is little affected and it keeps much longer. But it is by no means free from germs, for the standard of pasteurized milk fixed by law is that it must not contain more than thirty thousand bacteria in one cubic centimetre, that is about half a thimbleful ! Diseased cows may have passed the germs of tuberculosis into it, and so all who can afford the extra cost should give children certified milk, which comes from cows proved to be healthy.

There are a number of plant and animal diseases which cannot be attributed to bacterial attack, while if living organisms are the cause they are too small to be seen with any microscope. In plants affected with these so-called virus diseases the leaves become rolled or their green pigment may be partly destroyed so that they develop "streak" or "mosaic." Breaking in tulips is due to a virus which makes the self-coloured petals show white streaks.

REVERSION IN PLANTS

Though attacked plants rarely die, they are not improved in vigour, and if the leaves are the crop, as in tobacco, the trouble is serious. Plant viruses are principally spread by small insects such as aphides (or green-fly) which suck their juices and infect them through the bites. Here is, then, another reason for keeping these pests under control.

The two principal troubles of the black-currant grower are "big-bud" and "reversion."

TOBACCO AS GROWN

A healthy tobacco plant. The leaves when attacked by one of the virus diseases become rolled.

The former is caused by a mite which lays eggs in the buds and destroys the blossoms. When bushes are affected by reversion the leaves gradually change their form and finally are produced so abundantly that there are no flowers. It is thought that this is the plant's reaction to the presence of a virus, which is spread by the big-bud mite. In the early stages the leaf-form is little altered, and shoots for cuttings must be very carefully selected.

FILTER-PASSING ORGANISMS

When the juices of a plant infected with a virus disease are passed through a filter with pores so small that no bacteria can get through them, they are still capable of producing the disease if injected into a healthy plant. So it was thought that living organisms must be present. At the time of writing this seems doubtful, for the virus causing mosaic disease of tobacco and potato has been obtained in the form of crystals.

Smallpox, measles, scarlet fever and possibly influenza are caused by "filter-passing organisms." It remains to be seen whether these too will prove to be non-living substances.

SPENCER ARNOLD

FAMOUS BACTERIOLOGIST

Louis Pasteur (1822–95), *who showed that most infectious diseases are caused by bacteria.*

HAMILTON COLLECTION

SWEDISH CLASSIFIER OF PLANTS

Carl von Linnæus (1707 78), *whose classification of plants was used until the middle of the nineteenth century.*

Finally lichens may be mentioned. They are an extraordinary group, for they are not individual plants at all. Each is produced by the intimate union of an alga and a fungus of certain kinds, living together in such adjustment that between them they produce a structure of definite and characteristic form, such as the bright orange lichen often found on old walls.

LICHENS DISLIKE LONDON

Under the microscope it is seen that tiny green algal cells are enclosed in a felt of fungal threads. The fungus seems to keep the upper hand over them, for it alone produces the fruiting body and must derive food from that which the alga makes for itself. The latter receives shelter, moisture and mineral salts and is also enabled to grow in the bleak places which lichens often inhabit, and where normally the alga would not flourish.

On the other hand, the alga is not dependent on the fungus but can live alone if need be. Though the fungus appears to be master in the lichen, its spores can only grow if some of the right kind of algal cells are near by.

Lichens are exceedingly important as

colonizers of bare and stony ground. They may grow slowly, but in so doing they gradually break up rock surfaces and prepare the way for higher plants. They will accept the poorest conditions, but one thing they demand is pure air. In London and other big cities one looks in vain for them.

DYES FOR TWEEDS

The reactions between alga and fungus lead to the production in the lichen of peculiar acids; a number of these provide colouring matters. In the Highlands lichens are still used for dyeing wool. After somewhat crude preparations, sometimes involving long steeping in household slops, liquids are obtained which can give very pleasant dyes. They are used for genuine Harris tweeds.

A grey branching lichen known as *Cladonia rangiferina*, found on moors in Great Britain and elsewhere all over the world, attains importance in the Arctic tundra for it is the chief food of the reindeer. " Iceland moss " is a lichen containing much starch; when a bitter substance has been washed away it can be used to make bread of a kind.

The space that has been devoted to the different groups of plants has been very unequally divided among them, but most attention has been paid to those which most closely affect our lives. Thus our interest in the fern world may be restricted to the plant adorning the front window, but we are vitally concerned every day with the organisms which make our food go bad or mouldy or which may endanger our health.

TWO THOUSAND YEARS OLD

There is a tremendous range of size in plants, considerably greater than in animals. The big trees of California (*Sequoia gigantea*) have the distinction of being the largest living organisms, though it must be remembered that most of the wood is dead tissue. The tallest is over three hundred and twenty feet high with a trunk thirty-five feet thick ; it is certainly two thousand years old.

These figures are as nothing compared with

HAROLD BASTIN

ONE OF THE LARGEST FLOWERS

Flower buds and bloom of Aristolochia gigas, *one of the world's largest flowers. The species belongs to a genus of shrubs to be found in Europe, the United States, Central America and Mexico.*

FOX

FOREST TURNED TO STONE

A petrified forest in Arizona, U.S.A. Sections of trunks lie scattered in disorder, victims it may be of volcanic eruptions æons of ages ago. Water, carrying silica and other minerals in solution, turned the trees into stone. Some of the sections weigh many tons.

the length of the family history of these trees. Fossil records show that *Sequoia* has been flourishing for something like a hundred million years; its remains have been found all over the world and, though it is now confined to a narrow belt on the Pacific coast of North America, there is no lack of vigour in this remarkable link with the remote ages before man was known.

The redwoods of California (*Sequoia semper-*

HAROLD BASTIN

FOOD OF REINDEER

Iceland moss, a lichen which is widely distributed and the chief food of the reindeer.

virens) may be taller, though their trunks are not so thick, and the same applies to some of the Australian blue gum trees (*Eucalyptus*); they are much faster growing.

At the other end of the scale one of the smallest woody plants is the dwarf willow, a creeping alpine plant seldom more than two inches above the ground; the catkins are very small with only a few flowers.

The Japanese dwarf trees are, of course, not natural products; they are kept very small by allowing the roots little space and periodically pinching them off. Severe weather conditions have produced the dwarf oaks of Wistman's Wood on Dartmoor, with gnarled and twisted trunks centuries old and yet only a few feet high.

Smallest of all the flowering plants is a tiny duckweed, *Wolffia arrhiza*, said to be often present in ponds with the common duckweed but overlooked on account of its minuteness. The plant is merely a floating green disc, about a twenty-fifth of an inch across, without any roots or leaves. The flower, which is rarely produced, consists of a single tiny stamen and an ovary with one seed. This may be compared with the flower of *Rafflesia*, previously noted as the largest known.

SEA-SERPENT OF SEAWEED

Another water plant, *Victoria regia*, may be mentioned for the size of its floating leaves. They are circular with an upstanding rim, and may be more than six feet across. There are very large air-spaces inside the leaf; these give it something of the feel of a modern multi-spring mattress. The leaves of this water-lily of the Amazon can support a child's weight.

One giant among the lower plants must be mentioned, a brown seaweed, *Macrocystis pyrifera*, which grows in cold waters of the Southern Hemisphere. There is a tough stem which reaches the surface of the sea; from it hang long fronds, each buoyed up with an air bladder so that most of the plant is floating. It reaches a length of over two hundred feet, and on one occasion at least has been taken for a sea-serpent.

Since the filter-passing viruses are probably non-living, we must find the smallest plants among the bacteria.

Which of all these groups and forms were the first plants like?

GOLD IN SEA WATER

There can have been no life on this planet until the earth's crust had cooled sufficiently to allow water vapour to condense on it. This may have collected at first as a world-wide sea, or there may always have been oceans and land masses with rivers and lakes. The land would have revealed bare rock surfaces, for soil is largely a product of plant and animal life, and the nearest approach to it would have been sand, into which the rocks may have been broken up.

We can hardly imagine life originating elsewhere than in water, whose presence is essential to it. At first the ocean would have been fresh water; gradually minerals would have been washed down into it from the land.

HAROLD BASTIN

GIANT WATER-LILY OF THE AMAZONS

Victoria regia *in bloom. Note the immense leaf in the background, which measures six feet across, and the developing leaf to the left of the flower. Its original home was British Guiana.*

Nowadays common salt is the substance present in largest amount in the sea, but it also contains nearly every known element, although some, such as gold, are only in very small quantity.

GREEN PLANTS BEFORE ANIMALS

It has been possible under special conditions in the laboratory to produce a little sugar from water and carbon dioxide when exposed to light. Perhaps this might have happened too in the primeval ocean and a store of sugars and minerals been ready for the first life. We cannot tell, but certainly there must have been green plants of a kind before animals evolved.

The simplest green plants which we know now are found among the algæ. One common pool form, *Chlamydomonas*, will serve as an example. It is a single spherical or ovoid cell with a cellulose wall. Inside is a bowl-shaped chloroplast and a central nucleus. At the colourless front end are two delicate hairs which continually lash the water and drive the cell forwards. Close to them is a tiny red spot, which possibly has something to do with perceiving light and guiding the plant to swim to a suitably illuminated place.

When it multiplies it either divides into several smaller editions of itself or else individuals slip out of their coats, pairs of them become entangled by their lashing hairs and they mutually engulf each other in a primitive sexual process. We can see the beginnings of the separation of the two sexes, for sometimes the fusing cells are of two sizes. The larger is very sluggish, the smaller seeks it out actively and corresponds to the male.

FOOD FROM MINERAL SOURCES

Sometimes the cells lose their lashes and develop a thick mucilaginous wall. They contrive to multiply, but the cells stick together and a colony results. We can imagine it possible for this to lead to the evolution of a more complicated, many-celled plant body.

There are many of these tiny swimming forms in fresh and salt water. One of them (*Polytoma*) is colourless. It lives in water polluted with sewage, from which it obtains food. One might see in it a pointer towards

FOX

GIANT CONIFER

A Californian big tree, a species which has the distinction of being the largest living organism.

the origin of the fungi. Many others are more like animals in their behaviour.

Tiny little plants such as these are not preserved in fossil form, and we can only guess how they might have given up swimming and settled on the bottom in shallow water, have grown to more complicated bodies, which were gradually able to invade the seashore or margins of pools and so passed to living on dry land. We can only say that fungi and bacteria appeared very early in the history of plants. Bacteria are so peculiar in their habits that it is possible that they arose quite independently from other groups of plants. Some of them, such as the iron and sulphur bacteria, obtain their food from mineral sources and are not dependent upon any other forms of life; they might have existed even before there were green plants.

As Professor J. Lloyd Williams has pointed out, by elaboration of their bodies, by specialization of their functions, and by adaptation to, and improvement under, new conditions of life, the vegetation of the sea transformed itself into the green mantle of the earth. It was at first difficult to believe in the descent of the various members of the group from a common stock, so different are the life histories of the species, but there is now more or less agreement as to their close relationship in the remote past.

The seaweeds, to quote the opinion of Dr. Church, of Oxford, "illustrate in a manner beyond all other types of the plant kingdom the beginnings of plant anatomy and vegetable morphology"—the branch of biology dealing with the form of organisms.

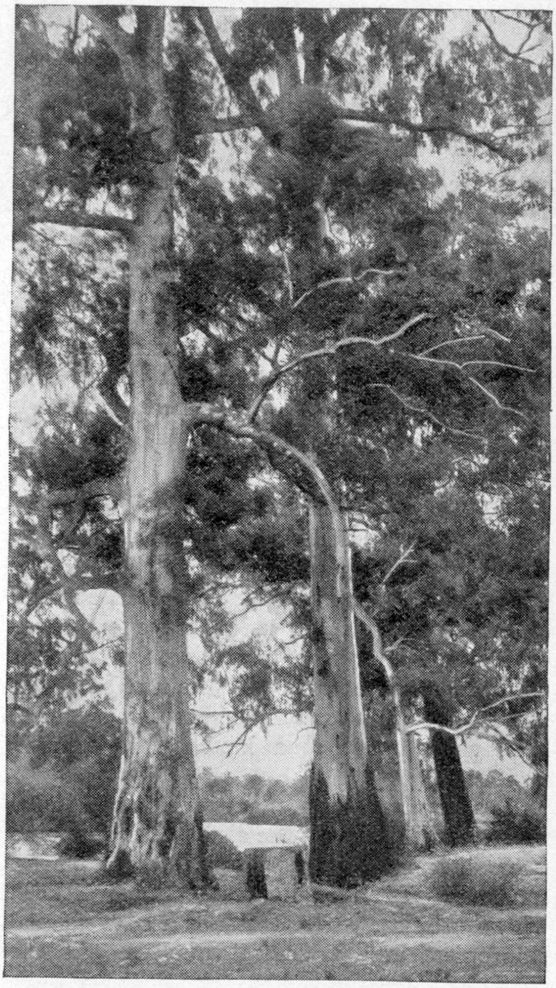

COMMONWEALTH OF AUSTRALIA

AUSTRALIAN GUM TREES

The tallest specimen of this magnificent tree grew in Victoria and reached a height of 470 feet.

KINELORSKY

WASTE LAND BEGINS TO BLOSSOM

A scientific worker in an experimental field in the Pamir Mountains. He is sprinkling potato plants with a fluid to protect them from insects. Not long ago the land was regarded as entirely unfit for cultivation.

PLANT BREEDING IN INFINITE VARIETY

UNTIL the nature of sex in flowering plants was understood, pollination was left to natural agencies and plant breeding was not practised. In the date palm male and female flowers are on separate plants, and as far back as the ancient Babylonians it was the custom, with religious ceremonial, to cut branches of male flowers and shake the dust over the females. It was known that this was necessary to ensure fruiting in the date, but the wonderful connection between pollination and seed production in other plants was not then appreciated.

After about 1700, when sex in plants had been revealed, several kinds of plant were successfully cross-pollinated. The progeny were named hybrids, from a Latin word meaning the offspring of a cross between a domestic sow and a wild boar.

Most of our cultivated plants differ widely from the wild forms and show many variations among themselves. For example, the small sour hard crab is the ancestor of the long list of orchard apples.

It is obvious that at some time man must have noted plants which were better than the normal types, and have deliberately selected them for cultivation. Often this is successful. Thus Vilmorin, a Frenchman, founder of the oldest existing seed establishment, set himself to make a useful plant of the sugar beet. By continuously taking for seed the plants whose roots showed the highest sugar content he more than doubled the average of this, without recourse to hybridization. Nowadays there is a whole science connected with the study of inheritance, and the specialist is able to give advice how best to tackle the problem of the production of new forms by hybridization.

The existence of heredity and variation are plain to us all. In our own families we notice that children resemble their parents in many of their characters, physical and mental, and yet none is exactly like another or either of its

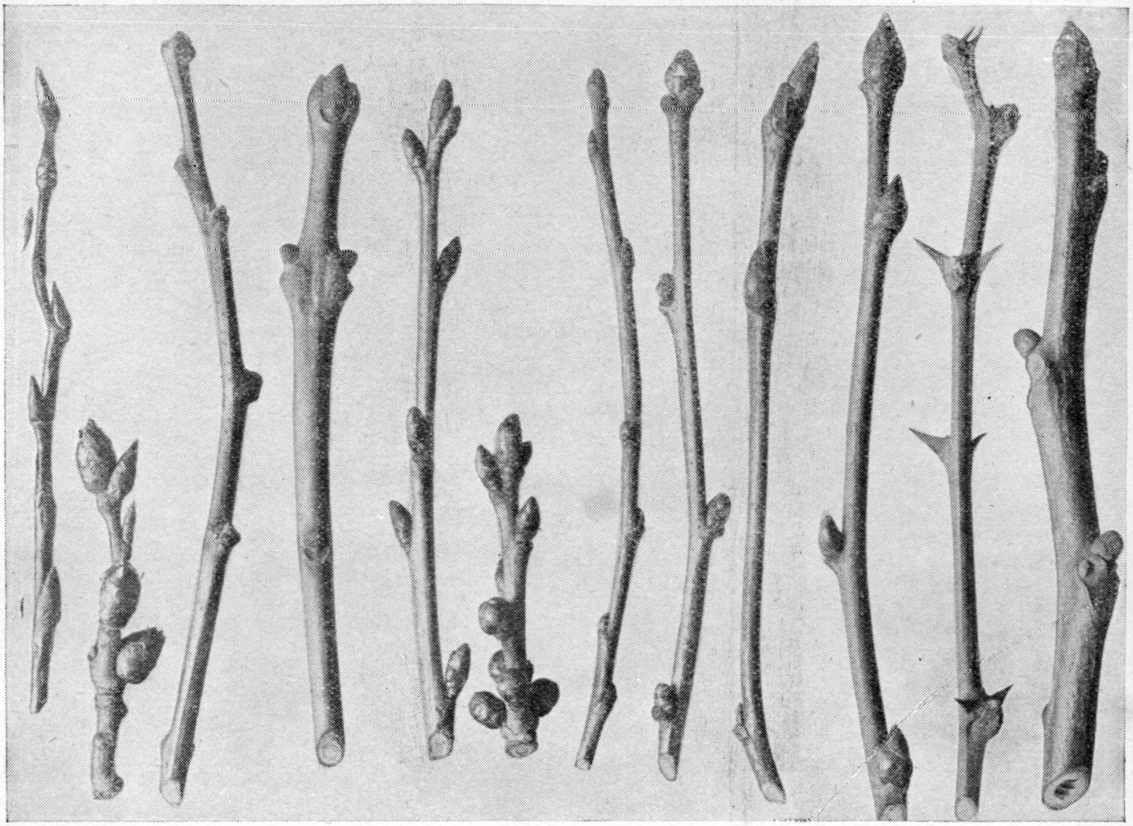

HAROLD BASTIN

HOW TO IDENTIFY WINTER TWIGS

Left to right: *Aspen* (2), *wych elm, ash, wild cherry* (2), *wild apple, wild service, rowan, whitebeam, locust and walnut.*

parents. Certain of these differences may not be inborn or heritable. Poor nutrition may prevent a child from attaining the height of which he was capable. A parent may have lost a limb, but his children will not resemble him in his one-legged condition.

INHERITANCE IN PLANTS

Similarly a pea plant of a tall variety may be kept very short by drought or poor soil, but its seeds, given normal cultivation, will produce tall plants. Again, the offspring of a pollarded elm will not resemble it but will show the usual type of branching.

The study of inheritance is best begun by considering a few clear-cut characters in particular examples and seeing how they appear in successive generations.

Suppose we take seed of a plant such as the bean, which is normally self-fertilized, choosing a variety which is known to come true from seed, then, no matter what are the conditions of cultivation, its characters will be handed on unchanged from generation to generation.

In one experiment the average weight of the seeds of such bean plants was recorded; although in each generation there was a wide range the average seed weight was always the same. When in each generation only the heaviest seed was taken and grown, it might have been expected that a strain would result whose average seed weight was higher than in the original type. In reality it did not alter. Nor did it change when instead the lightest seed from each generation was taken. The size the seed attains depends upon conditions around it when it is growing; these do not affect its hereditary constitution.

UNCHANGED BY OUTWARD CONDITIONS

The conclusion is that in true breeding strains, when there is no crossing, the heritage is unchanged by outward conditions throughout many generations. It is a different matter when two different strains are crossed; there

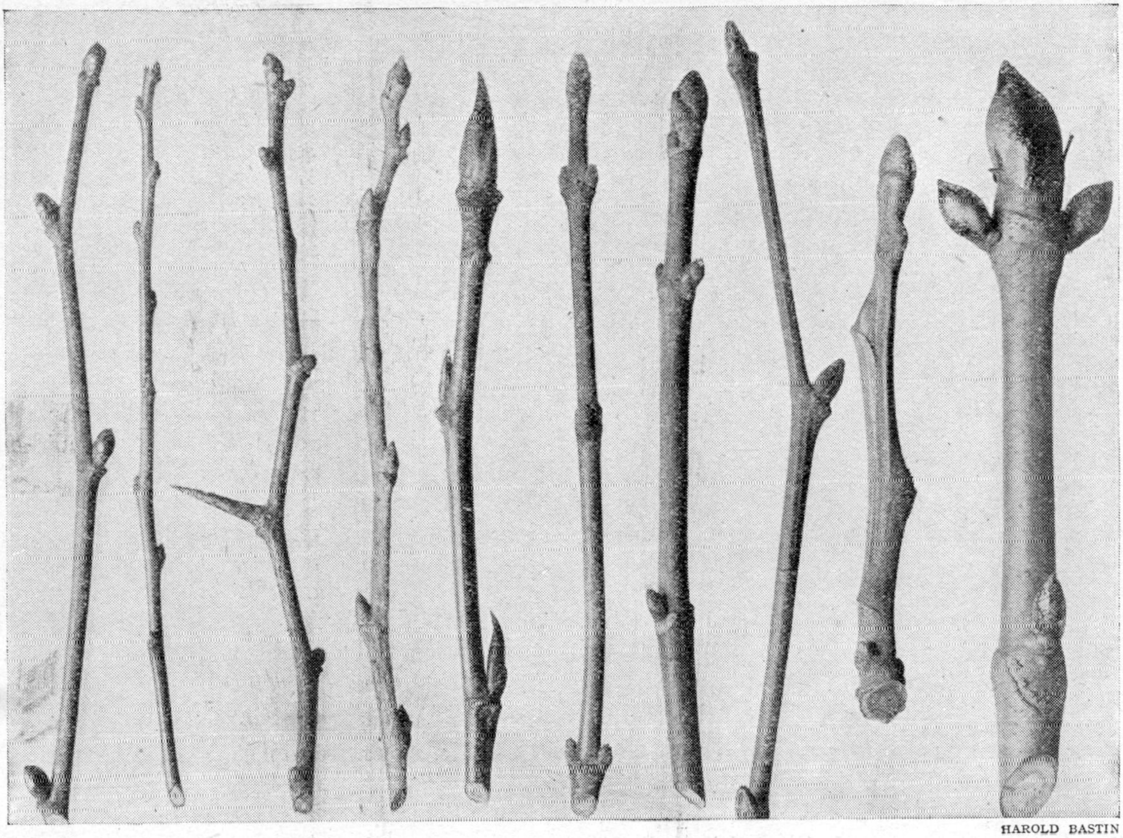

HAROLD BASTIN

—THAT GROW IN GREAT BRITAIN

Left to right: Hazel, blackthorn, hawthorn, white poplar, black poplar, maple, sycamore, plane, sweet chestnut and horse chestnut.

is much more to be learnt from the results of this operation.

The problem was first studied systematically by Gregor Mendel, an Austrian monk, whose conclusions were published in 1865. They are now recognized as having made a revolutionary step forward in biology, but at the time they were ignored. It was not until 1900, years after Mendel's death, that attention was redirected to his work and his name made famous.

DIFFERENT TYPES OF OFFSPRING

Mendel worked with garden peas, of which there are a number of well-marked varieties, such as tall and dwarf, yellow- and green-seeded, purple- and white-flowered. Having proved that his plants came true from seed, he studied the results of crossing forms with these clearly contrasted pairs of alternative characters and followed them through several generations. This was not a new line of work but Mendel was the first to make accurate counts of the numbers of the different types of offspring and to draw conclusions of general application from his results.

MASTERING AND DISAPPEARING FACTORS

When tall and dwarf strains were crossed the resultant seeds all produced tall plants. They were not intermediate in height, and there was no suggestion that anything which could govern dwarfness had been passed on from the other parent. But if the hybrid plants were allowed to set seed by self-pollination (the normal method in the pea), dwarfness reappeared in roughly a quarter of the offspring, the rest being tall. There must therefore have been concealed in the hybrids some factor which could make plants dwarf, otherwise they would not have been able to pass it on to some of their descendants. It can only have been derived from the dwarf parent of the hybrids.

Mendel described the factor which made for tallness in peas as being dominant (or mastering) with respect to its opposite factor which determines dwarfness. The latter he called recessive (or disappearing), because it apparently vanished in the first hybrid generation.

A great many simple characters in plants and animals have been found to be inherited in this fashion. Thus the peach and the nectarine only differ in one respect, the possession by the peach of a factor which makes the fruit hairy and is dominant to the smooth-skinned condition in the nectarine. If the two are crossed the hybrid plants bear hairy fruits and are apparently peaches, but when selfed, nectarines appear again as about a quarter of the offspring.

HAROLD BASTIN

VALUABLE SUGAR BEET

By taking for seed plants whose roots showed the highest sugar content, the average of this was doubled.

To find what was the meaning of this three to one proportion of the two types Mendel allowed the representatives of the second generation to be self-pollinated. He found that the dwarf plants bred true, as did one-third of the tall plants. The remaining tall plants behaved like the original hybrid, producing tall and dwarf plants in the proportion of three to one.

HEREDITARY FACTORS

As he saw, these results can only be explained on the theory that the sex-cells, which are the sole links between the two generations and whose union precedes seed formation, can only carry one or other of the alternative characters; there must be equal numbers carrying each of these. There must thus be an orderly arrangement whereby half the sex-cells receive the dominant factor and the other half the recessive.

The distribution of the hereditary factors in this cross is shown below; T is taken to represent that governing tallness and *t* is the corresponding factor producing dwarfness.

	Factors Present
Parents	TT *tt*
Sex-cells of parents	All T All *t*
Hybrid	T*t*—appear tall
Sex-cells of hybrid	Equal numbers of eggs—T and *t* ,, ,, sperms—T and *t*
Possible matings of egg and sperm when hybrid is self-pollinated	Equal numbers of— TT—tall } breed *t*' —dwarf } true T*t* } tall but are of same *t*T } nature as hybrid

Occasionally the dominance of one of the alternative characters is not complete and the hybrid is intermediate between its parents with respect to that character. Thus, if the radishes "Early Red" and "Early White" are crossed, the hybrid is purple-rooted. This when self-pollinated gives offspring of three types in the proportion of one red to two purple and one white. Of these the red and white breed true, and the purple, which plainly shows its mixed constitution, behaves like the original hybrid.

PRODUCING NEW FORMS

Mendel's principles can be applied to more complicated crosses between parents differing in more than one pair of contrasting characters. In the hybrid only the dominant characters of each pair will appear. Thus, the result of crossing a tall, yellow-seeded pea with a dwarf green-seeded pea is a tall and yellow-seeded pea. In this hybrid there will be equal numbers of sex-cells, male and female, carrying the dominant and recessive factors, while the factors for each pair are sorted among them independently of each other. Hence eggs and sperms will be of four types, carrying factors as follows: tall yellow-seeded, tall green-seeded, dwarf yellow-seeded, dwarf green-seeded.

The reader has perhaps by now done sufficient mental juggling with peas, so we will do no more than say that as a result of the possible matings of these sex-cells, plants of the four types mentioned will appear in the next generation. The important point to be noted is that the characters of the parents have been recombined to give two new types, tall green-seeded and dwarf yellow-seeded; indeed all the possible combinations of the parents' characters with respect to height and seed colour appear.

Practical breeders often cross plants differing

in a number of these pairs of alternative characters. The hybrids will be of a uniform type, only showing those of the pairs which are dominant, but on selfing them (i.e., letting them set seed with their own pollen) there will appear all possible combinations of the characters. When several are being considered this means that a great variety of new forms will be produced. Some will breed true, and from others pure breeding strains may be isolated by continually selfing them. This is the procedure often adopted, but it must not be supposed that the work is always straightforward or that the inheritance of all characters is clearly understood.

INCREASING THE ACREAGE OF WHEAT

Very soon after Mendel's principles had become widely known and had been confirmed it was found that they applied also to the inheritance of less easily-defined characters, such as resistance or susceptibility to disease, and early or late flowering. Planned efforts were made with wheat to combine desired features of this type with good yield. An important product was " Marquis," which was bred in Canada from a cross between " Red Fife " and a very early maturing Indian wheat known as " Hard Red Calcutta." " Marquis " is about a week earlier in ripening than " Red Fife," and so could be grown considerably farther north. It greatly increased the acreage of wheat in Canada. From " Marquis " still earlier maturing forms such as " Ruby " have been developed and cultivation spread still nearer the North Pole.

RESISTANCE TO RUST

Unfortunately " Marquis " is susceptible to the attack of the destructive rust fungus. In 1930 the bread wheat and another species which was resistant to rust were crossed; only one plant with shrivelled seeds resulted, but some grew and after a few generations a strain named " Hope " was produced which possesses a wonderful resistance to all types of rust disease and also has many desirable characteristics. It is solving the problems of many American growers.

In the same way the two varieties " Spratt-Archer " and " Plumage-Archer," which account for three-quarters of the barley grown in Britain, were bred so as to combine by hybridization of suitable forms the qualities most desired by farmers and brewers.

Natural hybrids sometimes occur and some have proved of importance. The cord-grass (*Spartina Townsendii*), which covers so much of the tidal mud in Southampton Water, appeared there in 1870. It was an entirely new plant and probably arose by the crossing of an insignificant native grass with a related species accidentally introduced from America. It was amazingly successful and has spread over hundreds of acres of sea flats. Its untidy looking tussocks of stiff leaves bind the mud and gradually raise its level so that the land may be reclaimed. During the World War some use was made of its fibres for paper, and it is not without value as herbage.

HAROLD BASTIN

PRODUCES HAIRY FRUIT

If the hairy peach and the smooth-skinned nectarine are crossed, the hybrid plants bear hairy fruits.

For years unsuccessful efforts were made to cross a blue delphinium with the red-flowered *Delphinium nudicaule*, sometimes seen in rock-gardens. One year, among the rows of the two kinds, a purple-flowered plant appeared. It proved to be a natural hybrid between them and from it many new shades have been derived. In 1937 the form " Pink Sensat on "

DOMINION OF CANADA

COMBINING DESIRED FEATURES

Red Fife wheat (left) introduced into Canada from Danzig; Ruby, a cross between Downy Riga and Red Fife.

was first shown in London. Some, who feel that blueness is the character for which the delphinium is most to be prized, will think that it is as little to be desired as a blue rose.

HOME OF THE PLUMS

Scientists have suggested that the cultivated plum may have arisen in the wild by the crossing of the red-skinned yellow-fleshed cherry plum with the sloe, which has a blue skin and green flesh. Russian botanists have recently found in the Northern Caucasus, which they think to be the home of the plums, that the sloe and cherry plum grow there and also a wealth of forms which they think are natural hybrids between the two.

It is well known that new varieties sometimes appear suddenly. Darwin's theory of the origin of species was that all members of a species showed slight variations. Some of these might be advantageous to the form possessing them and would favour its preservation in the struggle for existence. So he thought the variations best fitted to the conditions around them would survive and new species be gradually evolved by a continuation of this process. Nowadays it seems much more likely that new forms are produced by relatively large changes, the cause of which is generally unknown.

JUMPS IN EVOLUTION

When the sweet pea was first brought to England from Sicily in 1699 it had small, purple, scented flowers. It is normally self-pollinated but in the course of years several new types appeared, such as white, red and picotee flowers. Hybridization was not practised until 1880. Suddenly, in 1900, a most important advance occurred when the Spencer form with waved standards appeared in four different places among plants of the variety "Prima Donna." The Spencer type has now quite ousted the old-fashioned varieties, but many of the modern sweet peas lack the delicious fragrance of less showy types.

Such sudden sports or jumps in the evolution

DOMINION OF CANADA

INCREASING THE YIELD

Hard Red Calcutta wheat (left) and Marquis. The latter is bred from a cross between the former and Red Fife.

of new forms are common in horticulture. The dainty, free-flowering belladonna type of delphinium is of unknown origin but has been grown for years; it set no seed and was increased by cuttings or root division. In 1902 three seed-pods appeared on one plant and from them a whole race of belladonna hybrids have been raised, all setting seed normally.

PLANTS THAT CANNOT SEED

Many of our horticultural forms might have been produced in nature but they would never survive in competition with the original types. It is the practice of many breeders to spoil (or so some think) the purity of floral form by producing double varieties. Often the extra petals are transformed stamens and the plants cannot set seed. Many of our best apples, such as "Bramley's Seedling" and the crimson form which arose as a branch sport from it,

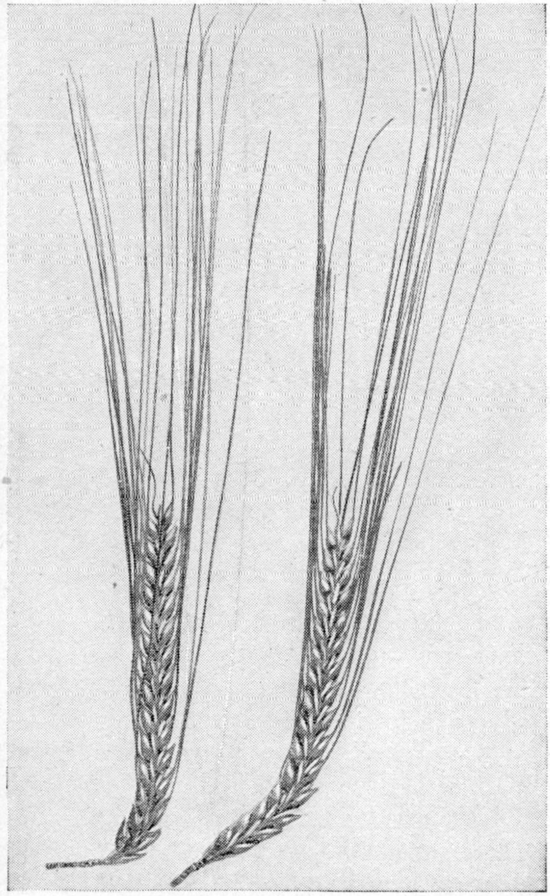

HAROLD BASTIN

SPRATT-ARCHER BARLEY

Spratt-Archer (left) and Plumage-Archer (right) account for three-quarters of the barley grown in Britain.

HAROLD BASTIN

PLUMAGE-ARCHER BARLEY

Bred with Spratt-Archer to combine by hybridization qualities desired by farmers and brewers.

are almost completely sterile and are only kept going by artificial budding and grafting.

PLANTED UPSIDE-DOWN

Curious results sometimes follow when plants of two species are united. Apples are normally grafted on stocks of a different type, sometimes pear or quince, but this does not radically change their nature. In 1825 a Frenchman grafted the small broom *Cytisus purpureus* on the common laburnum. From the union a bud developed which produced leaves and flowers intermediate between the two. This form is still kept in existence by vegetative reproduction. Occasionally shoots with the leaves and drooping clusters of yellow flowers of the laburnum appear, and there may be on the same plant others with the small leaves, stiff habit and scattered purple flowers of the broom. The so-called "graft-hybrid" seems to consist of a core of laburnum tissue surrounded by a skin of purple broom; every now and then the two separate.

Similar peculiar forms have been produced by grafting together the hawthorn and medlar. The variegated *Pelargonium* (the geranium of gardeners) with white-margined leaves is of a comparable nature, though its origin is unknown. There is a green core, surrounded by a white skin. That the interior of the plant is really different from the skin is proved by taking root cuttings. On these the buds arise deep in the tissues; they produce pure green shoots. The pollen grains and embryo seeds develop from the outer white skin layers and so, when such a *Pelargonium* is selfed, the seedlings which result are pure white. As they have no chlorophyll they cannot manufacture food for themselves and they soon die.

HAROLD BASTIN

ENEMY OF THE FARMER

The destructive rust fungus on barley. On the left is an ear before being attacked by the disease.

The pelargonium "Salmon Fringed" is a similar union of two types. Normally the leaves are funnel-shaped and smooth, and the flowers are salmon coloured with fringed petals. But often a branch shoots out with flat hairy leaves and normal flowers; this is supposed to constitute the core of the plant. Country people assent that if a primrose is planted upside-down the flowers will be pink. No one ever seems to test the truth of this statement, but it is certain that some geraniums, when treated like this, produce shoots (from root buds) of a very unexpected type.

BURNING FORTY THOUSAND PLANTS

One of the most famous plant breeders was the American Luther Burbank (1849–1926). Even in his cradle he showed his love for flowers. After great privations, when he was even reduced to sleeping in a chicken coop, he started a nursery garden in California. His first big order was for twenty thousand young prune trees to be delivered in nine months' time. Normally it would take at least two and a half years to rear the plants. With characteristic originality and resourcefulness Burbank sowed the quick-growing almond; soon the saplings were big enough for prune buds to be grafted on them and the order was successfully executed.

After a time he closed his business in order to devote himself to plant breeding, finally receiving government support. His experiments were conducted on a vast scale. As many as five hundred thousand lilies were grown in one test; their fragrance spread a mile away. In another, forty thousand blackberry-raspberry hybrids were grown to maturity. One single plant was chosen as the best, and the rest burnt in a pile twelve feet wide, fourteen feet high and twenty feet long.

Money meant little to him. The Burbank potato, which increased the wealth of the U.S.A. by millions of dollars, he sold to a nurseryman for a hundred and fifty dollars (£30). His plums and prunes were of great value in California. After years of work he produced a luscious plum without a trace of a stone. The "plumcot" was a union of plum and apricot.

TO MAKE THE DESERT FERTILE

The Shasta daisy, with blooms up to seven inches across, was derived from small-flowered wild varieties. One day he noticed a yellow Californian poppy (*Eschscholtzia*) with a tiny streak of red in the petals. This was seized and from it a pure red form developed. The origin of the famous Shirley poppies was somewhat similar; an English clergyman found a wild red poppy with a thin white margin to the petals and from its seeds and their offspring the many colours we know today arose.

As a little child Burbank would toddle round with a potted cactus as his dearest toy; in his maturity one of his greatest triumphs was the production of the edible thornless giant cactus. With this he hoped to make the desert fertile.

WALNUTS WITH THIN SHELLS

His "Paradox" walnut is well known in the United States. He crossed an English and a Californian walnut, and finally raised trees which in fourteen years grew six times as much as the Californian parent had in thirty years. The wood is close and fine-grained and is a valuable timber. To the nuts he paid little attention. One day he thought that a thinner shell would be an improvement, so he continually selected saplings pointing in this direction until the shells were so thin that birds pecked through them!

Burbank was no trained scientist. His method was to cross chosen forms and grow all the resultant seeds. Their progeny in turn would give him a large collection, from which he selected only those approaching the desired forms. Further large families would be grown from them.

He was scornful of the scientific principles of plant breeding and considered that his results completely disproved them. In this he was wrong. Mendel's laws teach that when two different forms are crossed the various hereditary characters will be recombined in all possible ways in the second generation after the cross; this is exactly what he found: he worked with forms differing in a number of characters and the very large families he raised would emphasize the variety of new types arising. From one cross he had two thousand poppy plants, among which the leaves of no two plants were alike in form. He would continually discard all but the most hopeful plant and try by breeding from that to obtain a pure strain. Intuition played a greater part than science in picking out the right plants, but the results justified it.

HAROLD BASTIN

SLOES

A wealth of forms probably hybrids between the sloe and cherry plum are found in the Northern Caucasus.

HAROLD BASTIN

PARENT OF THE PLUM

The crossing of the cherry plum (above) with the sloe probably gave the cultivated plum to the world.

PESTS OF THE VINE

Of late years breeding experiments on a scale even larger than those of Burbank have been carried out. The German vine industry is said to have been devastated by two pests, mildew and the vine-louse. A North American vine is resistant to their attacks, but its grapes are poor, so the European variety was crossed with it. By 1933 it was said that as many as

HAROLD BASTIN

BROOM IN FLOWER

The union of broom and laburnum produces leaves and flowers intermediate between the two.

ten million hybrid seedlings had been raised. These are all artificially infected with the mildew; any that resist it are handed over to the vine-louse. It was hoped that in ten years the problem would be solved.

EXPERIMENTS IN RUSSIA

The botanists of the Soviet Union are carrying out hybridization experiments on a magnificent scale, embracing all the plants commonly cultivated over their wide climatic range. The guiding principle has been to collect first all their known varieties, so that the different characters possible in each plant will be at hand for breeding experiments. Thus over five thousand different wheats are sown annually and the scientist will find amongst them the characters he desires to combine, if they exist at all in the wheat.

Plants have been gathered from all over the world and the places of origin of many cultivated plants found. These usually prove to be a few mountainous regions, where conditions are often severe. There is some evidence that the sudden sports which often produce new forms are more likely to occur in such circumstances.

In these regions are a great variety of forms and it seems that often the cultivated plants have been derived from only a few of them; there still exists in the wild a wealth of plants with valuable characters, which when combined with others by hybridization may solve many problems. Thus one wild wheat shows great resistance to mildew, smut and rust and to insect attack. This only needs to be combined with the good yield and baking qualities of cultivated wheats.

EDIBLE FRUITED HONEYSUCKLE

In the mountains of Central Asia and the Caucasus the Russians found a great variety of apples, plums, cherries, vines and other fruits. Many are very hardy and have been used to produce new types capable of fruiting much farther north than before, in lands that previously were barren. Frost resistant vines and apricots and edible fruited honeysuckle and mountain ash are some of the new forms produced from them.

Much attention is being paid to the potato. It has been cultivated in South America for centuries, but was unknown in Europe until

PRODUCER OF THE PLUMCOT

Luther Burbank, who did wonderful work in plant breeding and gave many new varieties to the world.

PLANET NEWS

MAKING THE POTATO FLOURISH IN THE ARCTIC

A research worker in the Arctic Murmansk region crossing potato flowers to cultivate a potato suited to the climate. Below: Gathering fruit in Alma-ata, Kazakhstan. Alma-ata is known as the "Father of Apples."

1587, when a tuber reached Vienna, and the next year England. They were evidently of hybrid origin for the seeds obtained from the plants produced a number of varieties and the strange vegetable gradually won favour.

ROMANCE OF THE POTATO

There is no certainty as to who introduced the tuber into England; even the date is disputed. Both Sir Francis Drake and Sir John Hawkins have had the honour thrust on them, and it has also been stated that returned colonists from Virginia took it to Ireland and not Sir Walter Raleigh. There is a tradition that the first crop was grown at Brixton, near London, and another that it was raised in Lord Burleigh's garden in the Strand. Certainly it was at first regarded with grave suspicion, and alarmist reports were spread that it caused leprosy and other dire diseases.

Some ten years following its arrival, the potato is described in Gerarde's *Herbal*, where it is stated that some of the roots " are as a ball, some oval or egg-fashion, some larger, some shorter, the which knobby roots are fastened into the stalks with an infinite number of thready strings. It groweth naturally in America, where it was first discovered, as report says, by Columbus, since which time I have received roots hereof from Virginia, otherwise called Nurenbega, which grow and prosper in my garden as in their own country."

Dr. Parmentier was ridiculed when he praised them in France, but he managed to interest Louis XVI. At a ball Queen Marie Antoinette wore a wreath of potato flowers and the king granted Parmentier a plot on which to grow them. A guard was provided for it and the people then thought there must be something valuable there; at night they stole the plants, cooked and ate the tubers and found them good.

Ireland came to make it the staple food and with its aid the population increased from two millions in 1785 to over eight in 1845. In that year the potato blight, a fungous disease, struck the crop. The nature of the attack was quite unknown and nothing could be done to stop its ravages. Several hundreds of thousands actually died of starvation and all who could emigrated to America.

EIGHT THOUSAND VARIETIES

Grieved by their sufferings, a New York clergyman, the Rev. Chauncey Goodrich, set himself to study the problem of the potato. He thought (though wrongly) that the disease arose because the constitution of the plants

PLANET NEWS

ELECTRICITY IN THE SERVICE OF AGRICULTURE

On the left is a cucumber leaf grown in a glasshouse with the help of electric light and heat, and next to it a leaf of the same kind of plant grown under ordinary conditions.

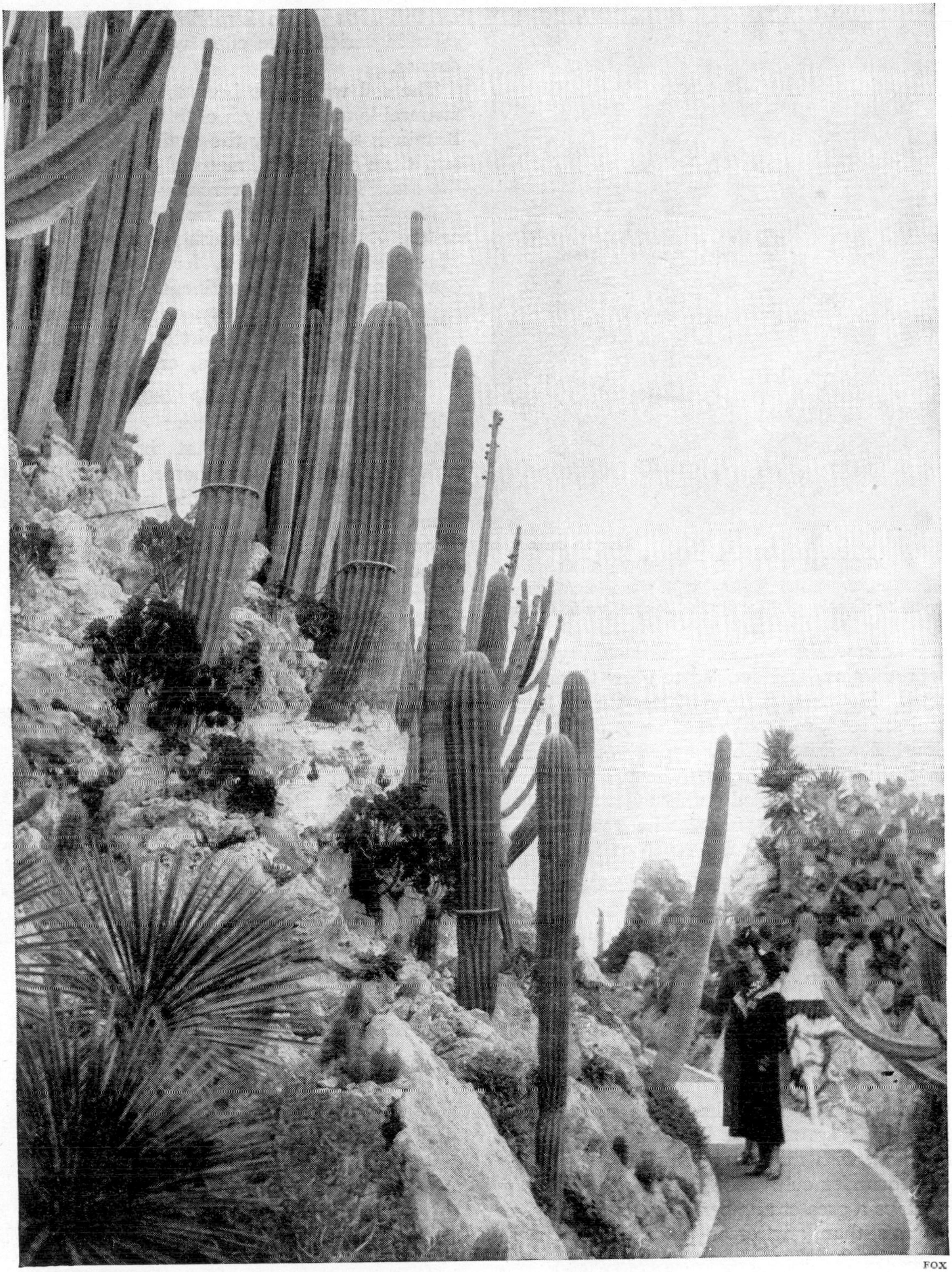

FOX

MOST WONDERFUL CACTI IN EUROPE

The exotic gardens at Monaco have the most wonderful collection of cacti in Europe. Some of them grow to a height of fifteen feet. Luther Burbank produced an edible thornless giant cactus.

RISCHGITZ COLLECTION

CHAMPION OF THE POTATO

Antoine Parmentier (1737–1813), *whose writings did much to dispel prejudice against the potato in France.*

had been weakened by the continued vegetative reproduction, and decided to grow them from seed. However, many potatoes rarely flower and set seed, so he obtained some plants from South America, which he hoped would " bring in fresh blood." Among them one with a rough purple-skinned tuber was the most hopeful, and with its aid he reared eight thousand different varieties.

GROWN IN EVERY CONTINENT

It was said of Goodrich that he was " so busy with experiments he had no time to make money." From his potatoes the famous " Early Rose " was derived. Burbank's potato was probably a sport from it, and it was used by English breeders.

By the beginning of the twentieth century the characters of the original varieties and of Goodrich's new strain had been combined in so many ways that the limit had nearly been reached, with many problems unsolved. The potato under cultivation is liable to attack by perhaps a greater number of fungous and virus diseases than any other plant, and resistant forms, with other characters that satisfy the requirements of growers, marketers and consumers are needed. Thus in Great Britain the shape and texture of the potato preferred by fish-friers is an important consideration; suitable varieties are often very susceptible to disease.

The soil which has been found particularly favourable to the growth of the potato in Great Britain is that left by the draining of the fens and the rich alluvial material reclaimed from the sea. For a similar reason the polders of Holland, also recovered from the North Sea or the Zuider Zee, furnish a valuable crop. The plant is cultivated under varying climatic conditions in every continent. Even in the region of the Andes, between nine thousand eight hundred feet and thirteen thousand feet above the level of the sea, crops are grown.

LARGEST FOOD CROP

The Russians in 1925 sent expeditions to South America to see what the potato was really like in its natural home. They found an astonishing range of wild and cultivated forms, some growing in tropical conditions, others near the snow-line (the English potato cannot stand frost); some forms are resistant to fungal attack, others to drought. With this wealth of new types it should be possible to make great advances in the production of good varieties for cultivation. One hopes that these may become generally available, for the potato is perhaps the largest of the world's food crops.

It is to be regretted that there is so little provision in Great Britain for work such as this, on the grand scale which is necessary if results are to be gained at all quickly.

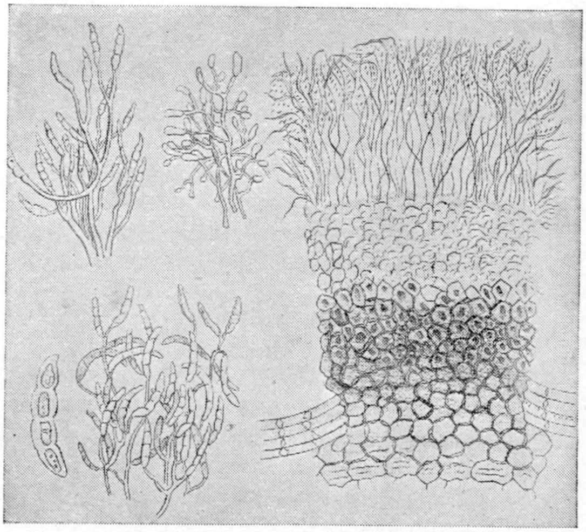

HAMILTON COLLECTION

POTATO BLIGHT

A fungus disease which resulted in hundreds of thousands of deaths from starvation in Ireland in 1845.

HAROLD EASTIN

FIRST STAGE IN THE MAKING OF COAL

Stacks of peat, which is decayed vegetation. It is invariably found in bogs, marshes and swamps. The decaying matter below is constantly added to by successive generations of plants until it becomes a form of coal.

PLANTS AND MAN

THE aim throughout this whole section on plants has been to deal with them as far as possible in their relation to man. It has been shown that we depend finally upon plants for our food. Much, of course, comes directly from them, and it is possible to live entirely on a vegetarian diet.

Cereals bulk largest in our meals. It was a great step forward when wandering tribes first began to cultivate them and collect their seeds for food. This meant that they had to settle down for the best part of a year in order to produce the crops; civilized arts had time to develop and homes were made.

It is thought that wheat was first cultivated in Central Asia, which is regarded by many authorities as the cradle of civilization. It is a region specially favoured, for it seems to have been the natural home of a great many valuable crop plants. Wheat has always been the food of the world's aristocrats. More millions depend upon rice than on any other cereal, while maize, barley, rye and oats feed others.

It is only within the last few centuries that cane and beet sugar have been available. Previously to that honey was the only sweetening agent known. It is questionable whether the large amounts of sugar we now eat are particularly good for us.

There are many valuable oils obtained from seeds and fruits of plants such as the olive, the pea-nut and above all the coco-nut palm, which provides most of the fat for margarine and soaps.

Nowadays pepper is the only important spice, but in the Middle Ages such flavourings as cinnamon, nutmeg and cloves were of fabulous value; a pound of the latter would buy seven sheep, and rents were sometimes paid in peppercorns. In their recipes spices are used so lavishly that the meats could not have been tasted. Probably the disguise was necessary, for there were no means of keeping it fresh, and in winter only salted meat was available.

Among other essentials which we obtain

from plants is coal, the fossilized remains of forests of distant ages. From trees too come our furniture and much of the structure of our houses. Wood pulp provides most of our paper and also the modern fabric "rayon." Silkworms feed on mulberry leaves and the transformed plant matter reappears from their spinnerets as threads of silk. Manufacturers imitate this by preparing a cellulose compound from wood pulp and forcing it through minute holes into a hardening liquid. Threads of rayon result.

TREE OF THE GODS

Flax fibres and cotton seed-hairs provide other material for weaving. These fabrics used to be dyed with plant products, such as madder and indigo, but the chemist now manufactures from coal-tar derivatives vastly superior and fast colours. But these can still be traced back to plants through the coal.

We rely on plants for nearly all our drinks. Our appreciation of them is largely due to the presence in them of drugs, among which alcohol must be included. Tea and coffee both contain caffein, which stimulates the nervous system, and there is a similar substance in cocoa, which Linnæus termed "the tree of the gods."

Many of the medicinal drugs, such as strychnine, digitalis and cascara, are of plant origin. Their use dates back centuries to when, by a painful process of trial and error, men learnt the properties of various plants. Valuable though they are, few drugs will in themselves cure disease, and faith is still one of the most important ingredients of the bottle of medicine. Quinine is an exception, for it actually destroys in the blood the parasites which cause malaria.

Its ravages were widespread, and to its weakening effect the fall of the Roman Empire has been attributed. In 1638 the Countess of Chinchon lay dying of malaria in her Peruvian palace. To her was sent a packet of a reddish bark with orders to the physician to administer it in powder form. The cure was miraculous, and the Countess took back to Spain the marvellous bark, whose uses the South American Indians had discovered. Its fame spread over the world.

SMUGGLED FROM PERU

The demand for quinine was great, but the Peruvians were lazy, and made no effort to cultivate the forests of cinchona trees. There was a danger of world shortage, yet it was

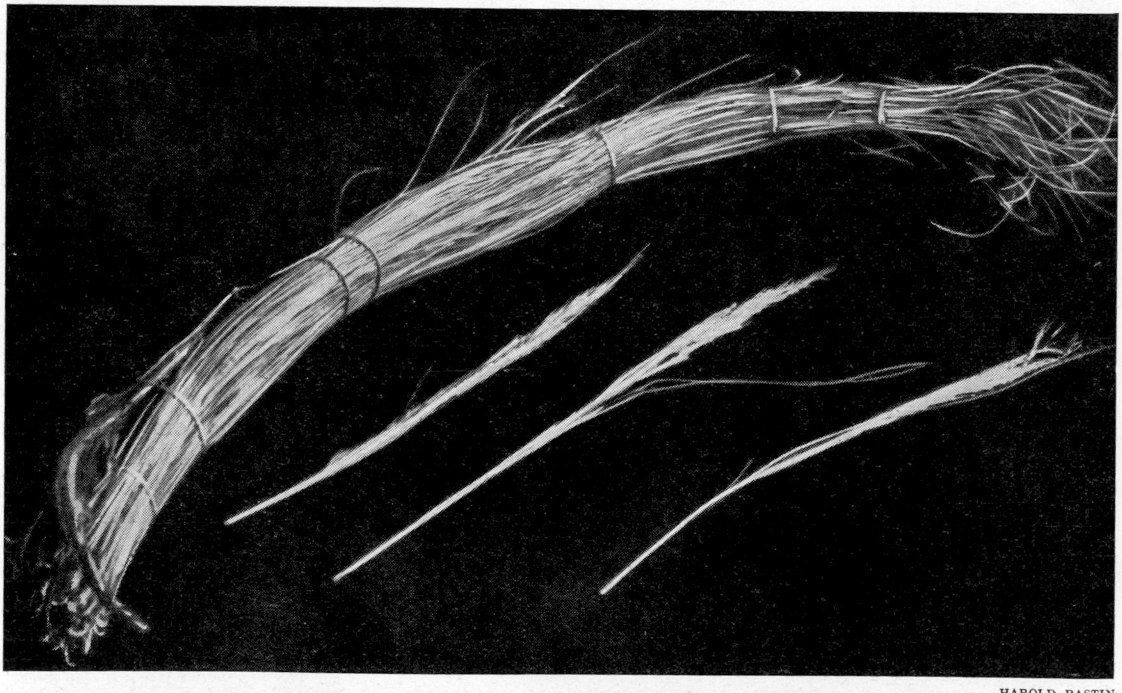

HAROLD BASTIN

ONE OF THE ALLIES OF CIVILIZATION

A bundle of esparto grass and three flowering heads. Esparto is used in the making of some of the better kinds of paper. Wood-pulp is more generally employed in the production of newspapers.

FOX

TREE OF DESTINY IN ANCIENT ATHENS

Scarcely two months after the tree has pushed its head above the soil it is ready to bloom. Sometimes reaching a height of eighteen feet, it grows vivid red blossoms and then dies.

with the greatest difficulty and hazard that seeds and seedlings were smuggled from Peru to India and Java. It is upon the labours of the Dutch in that island that we now depend.

Few plants have had more influence on mankind than the opium poppy. From the milky juice of its seed-heads is extracted morphia, which gives welcome relief from pain. But, in the East especially, over-indulgence in the drug has wrought havoc with millions.

Countless uses are found for another milky juice, that of the rubber trees. Columbus recorded his amazement when he saw Indians playing with balls which were elastic and bounced, but rubber was of little practical value until it was discovered that by mixing it with sulphur it was greatly strengthened and made more elastic. During the World War German chemists were able to manufacture a rubber substitute that closely approached the natural product.

Americans would not care to be without the juice of the sapodilla plum, from which they make chewing-gum. Of plant resins, gums, scented oils, of camphor, cork and many other products there is not space to tell. Suffice it to say that so varied are plant products that it is possible for the inhabitants of the tropics to supply nearly all their wants from one plant, the coco-nut palm.

COCOA AND CHOCOLATE IN THE RAW

The home of the cocoa tree is South America, but here natives are drying the beans or seeds on the Gold Coast. The trees grow to a height of thirty feet, and usually bear fruit for about twelve years. Each pod contains about forty beans.

EWING GALLOWAY, N.Y.

INVOKING THE GOD OF THE RAIN

Natives of Zululand invoking with solemn fervour and outstretched hands the god of the rain to send a plentiful supply of "cloud water" so that the land may be fertile and yield her increase to the tribe.

MAN'S FAMILY TREE

ALL the living races of mankind as they exist in the world of today belong to one species, *Homo sapiens* (from Latin *Homo*—man and *sapiens*—wise, possessing intelligence). This name expresses the fact that man is distinguished from other members of the animal kingdom, and more especially from the members of his own order and family—which include monkeys and the great apes—by the possession and habitual exercise of the specific quality of being able to reason.

In the days before Darwin wrote *The Origin of Species* (published in 1859), it was believed that all species in the world of nature, each in its respective kind, were fixed and as God had made them in the beginning. But when once the doctrine of evolution was formulated and applied to the origin and development of the various forms of life, it was natural and inevitable that further questions should be asked. Had man always been what he is now? If not, what was he like before he became modern man as we know him? And if he had evolved from an earlier and more primitive form, had he any near relations who could be shown to have a like ancestry?

Of these problems the last in particular raises an obvious issue. It is evident at even a casual glance that monkeys and the great apes bear a close resemblance to man, both in form and to a certain extent in behaviour. It is owing to this similarity of form that zoologists have classified man and the great apes—gorilla, chimpanzee, orang-utan—and the gibbon, the diminutive member of the group, in one family as being closely related.

So striking is this resemblance that it was believed by many in the early days of evolutionary theory that monkeys represented an ancestral form of man, and that man's family tree could be traced back to one or other of the great apes, preferably the gorilla or the chimpanzee. More carefully detailed comparison of the skeletons, brains, muscular and nervous systems of man and the great apes showed that such a line of descent was not possible.

It was found that instead of man's anatomical characters showing a greater likeness to any one member of the group, to the exclusion of all the others, as would be expected if he were descended from that form, the resemblances were distributed fairly evenly over all members of the group. In certain characters man was more like the gorilla than any other ape, in other characters more like the chimpanzee, and so on, the balance, if any, being rather in favour of the little gibbon, with the chimpanzee, perhaps, as second.

MAN'S PAINFUL PROGRESS

The conclusion to be drawn was not that man was descended from any one of the great apes as we know them, but that at some remote period in the history of the world, the monkeys, the great apes and man had had a common ancestor, from whom all members of the family were descended, and whose characters had been inherited in varying degree and with widely differing modifications and adaptations by each of the different members of the group. The apes were shown to be neither primitive nor rudimentary forms of man. Each in its kind, equally with man, is a highly developed type.

The superficial characters in which the apes and monkeys resemble man are too well known to need enumeration, while the resemblances in structure on which the comparative anatomists rely chiefly are of a highly technical nature. One distinguishing character of man, readily to be appreciated and most significant for the present purpose, is his ability to walk upright.

As we look back over the early phases of man's slow and painful progress towards a higher form of existence, three factors stand out as crucial in the stages of that advance. Of these the most important is the assumption of the upright posture. When man began habitually to stand and walk erect, as opposed to the occasional assumption of this position by the apes, it entailed an alteration in the position of the internal organs and the character of their muscular supports in the human abdomen. This changed the balance of the body and the carriage of the head on the vertebral column or backbone, while releasing the fore-paws and fore-limbs to acquire those functions of arm and hand which have played a predominant part in the development of the specifically human activities for which they are a necessity.

The upright mode of progression also conferred upon man the advantage in the struggle for existence of a greatly extended flexibility and range in vision and movement, and more especially a freedom in the employment of head, trunk and fore-limb. These advantages made it possible for him to use, adapt and fashion material aids for attack, defence or protection to counterbalance his weakness, as compared with other members of the animal kingdom, in natural means of defence against his enemies or the rigours of climatic conditions. They made up for his deficiency in tooth and claw as a fighter and the loss of his coat of fur which once had kept out the cold.

Secondly, and scarcely less important than the upright posture, was the change to full stereoscopic vision, a change which begins in the evolutionary scale in tarsius, the little tree shrew. By focusing both eyes on a single object, this alteration in range gave increased accuracy in sight and judgment, with a consequently increased stimulus to the development of the higher functions of the brain.

Thirdly came the opposable thumb, which by moving out of the plane of palm and fingers gave evolving man an inestimable advantage over the ape by making the human hand one of the most delicate and efficient mechanisms in nature. It provided an instrument for the accomplishment of the will and purpose of man which, as a supreme product of evolutionary adaptation, is capable with training, of making provision for all human needs and implementing most human desires.

These three factors have played preponderating rôles in the development of those qualities that have been responsible for the gradual building-up of man's civilization through the ages.

EVOLUTION AND CIVILIZATION

So much then is to be inferred from a comparative study of man and the great apes as they exist today. The salient fact which emerges is that if there are resemblances between them which point to a common ancestor, there are differences which are o even greater significance. In these differences are to be found the evidences of an evolutionary process, in the course of which a disparity in structure and function, and more especially in intellectual function, has developed between man and the great apes as a whole. By it man has been enabled to build up stage upon stage in the advancement of civilization, while his simian relatives have remained stationary in a

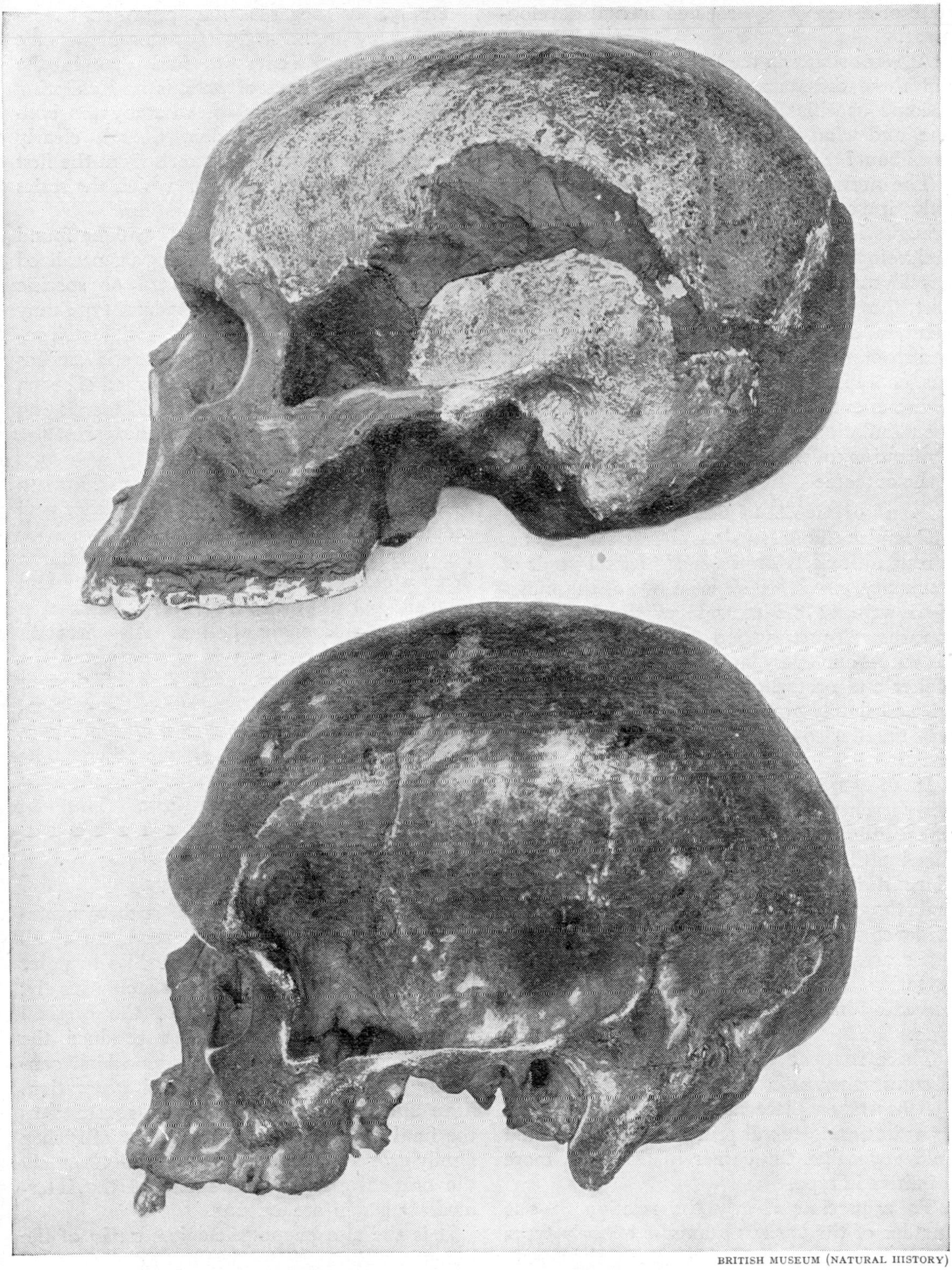

BRITISH MUSEUM (NATURAL HISTORY)

SKULLS ANCIENT AND MODERN

Skull of the Piltdown man (top) and of a modern man. The brain-case of the Piltdown man is shaped much like that of a young ape, and the brain must have been of a very low kind. There are no bony brow-ridges. The projection of bone in the lower jaw forming a chin does not appear before modern man.

state of arrested physical and mental development.

At what stages in the line of common descent did these differences arise? When did man become specifically man, as opposed to the ape, and what were the causes which brought this about?

The answers to these central problems are only imperfectly known as yet, but when brought into relation with the studies of the archæologist, who seeks to trace the growth and development of man's arts and industries in the past, they go far to explain how each development in the evolution of man's form, acting and reacting on the development of his intellect, has enabled him to modify and exploit his environment to meet his needs, and thus to lay the foundations and build up the early stages of civilization, of which this modern world of ours is the outcome.

CHANGES IN GENERATIONS

Complex though modern civilization may be, it rests ultimately on the fundamental needs of humanity, needs which arise out of the biological urge of the struggle of the individual towards self-preservation and perpetuation of his race—our everyday quest to provide food, shelter and protection from outside danger for self and family group, which no less insistently was the day-to-day problem of our remotest ancestor.

In the study of the evidence for the origin and descent of man, two classes of facts have to be taken into account, the data of morphology, showing the changes in form which have taken place in the course of the evolutionary process, and the data of chronology, in which the evidence is arranged in order of time. This latter arrangement should show, if the interpretation is correct, the primitive forms as preceding in time the forms of more advanced type.

There may be exceptions owing to special circumstances, as for example when a degeneration has taken place instead of an advance in type; but as a general principle the rule should hold good that the earlier in time, the more primitive in type.

To appreciate clearly the relation to one another of the various examples of early types of primitive man which have been discovered, it is necessary that the methods by which these two classes of facts are handled should be understood.

Firstly, as regards the argument from morphology or the study of form. If we take an evolutionary series we find that in the course of generations of parents and offspring certain changes take place whereby the end-products or last generation, though clearly related, differ in various respects from the first pair, or original parents from which the series begins, as well as from one another.

In examining such a series it will be found that change proceeds by modifying a generalized or generic type into specialized or specific forms. For example, a generalized type may have been modified to fit into a special environment, as the white coat of the Arctic fox has been evolved to match the background of snow, or the black skin of the negro is a differentiating character which affords protection against the actinic rays of the tropical sun.

A simple illustration will perhaps serve to make the meaning clearer. Let a father and mother of five children be taken to stand for the generalized type. Each of the children bears a certain resemblance to the father and mother, but they are more or less sharply differentiated from one another. As generation after generation is born in descent from the original five children, each line of descent becomes modified from the type of the original parents, and at the same time more and more clearly differentiated from all the others. The differences mark each line of descent as a specialized or differentiated form. This can be shown in various ways, as by measurement, by description, or by photographs.

DATING EARLY MAN

If we had a complete set of such measurements or photographs for all members of all the generations, it would be possible to point in detail to the morphological changes by which the generalized type of the original parents has been modified to produce the specialized or differentiated types which constitute the end-products or final generation. Man and the great apes may be regarded as the final generation or end-products of such a family group of lines of descent. Unfortunately the original parents and many of the intermediate stages are missing.

It is the aim of morphological study of the living members of the family and such fossil specimens of both apes and early man as have been discovered, to puzzle out and fill in the details of the family tree, and at the same

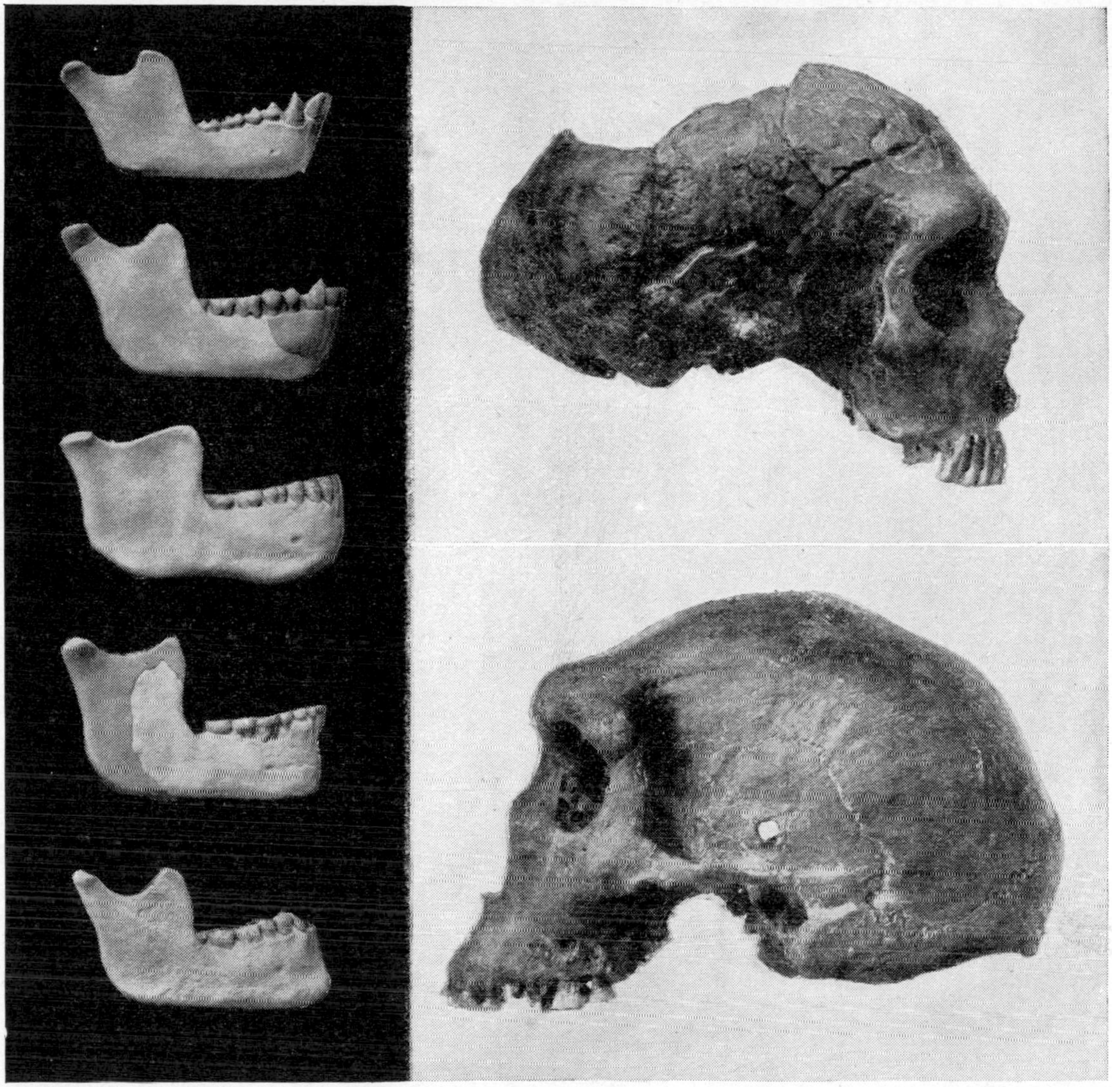

BRITISH MUSEUM (NATURAL HISTORY)

EVOLUTION OF THE HUMAN LOWER JAW

(*Left*) *Half of the lower jaw of a young chimpanzee, Piltdown man, Heidelberg man, Neanderthal man and modern man.* (*Top right*) *Neanderthal skull from Gibraltar ;* (*below*) *Rhodesian skull from north-west Rhodesia.*

time to arrive at some idea of how, in what way, and at what stages in development have arisen the differences by which the members of the family as we now know them are distinguished.

Let us turn now to the evidence of chronology. It is obvious that the various specimens of early man that are known—specimens that at one time or another have been found embedded in the gravels and clays which lie beneath the upper soils of the earth's surface, cannot by the circumstances of their discovery be dated by any usual system of chronology. Such systems require a fixed point from which to start, such as the Christian calendar possesses in the birth of Christ; a time measure, such as the year—solar, lunar or calendar—and a method of recording, such as a body of numerical symbols, perpetuated in writing.

None of these exists for dating early man. The only means available for arriving at some idea of the antiquity of any given specimen of early man, and its relation in time to other specimens, is by examining carefully the character of the deposits in which the specimen is found, and comparing these deposits with others, with a view to determining their relative age.

It is essential, of course, that the deposits should not have been disturbed, so as to ensure that the specimen is of the same age as the deposits, and that the bones have not been introduced into them at a later date, for example, by falling into a rift in the ground, as some think happened to the remains of Rhodesian man in South Africa, or by burial. When the relation of all the known deposits or strata one to another has been determined, this gives a time scale by stratification.

TREASURE-TROVE IN REFUSE

Let us take as a simple illustration the method by which the archæologist works when excavating the remains of a city which has long been destroyed, and of which there are no written records. Suppose that near a village there is a refuse pit into which the inhabitants of the village have been accustomed to throw all their refuse for a period of hundreds of years. The refuse will include not only scraps of food, but broken domestic utensils and furniture, broken pots, tools and the like, as well as old bones. If this pit has been undisturbed, when we dig down through its contents we come first of all on the refuse of yesterday, then in succession to that of last week, last month, last year, and so on back through the centuries, until we reach the time when the village was first founded in the virgin soil at the bottom of the pit.

Now if the contents are taken out carefully in separate layers and sifted, and the contents of each layer kept separate and arranged in the order in time in which they were thrown away, as shown by the order of the layers or strata, it is possible to reconstruct a more or less complete picture not only of the history of the settlement, but also of the manners, customs, industries and arts of the inhabitants of the village at different periods.

What kind of cattle they had and the nature of their food will be shown by the bones and food refuse. How they dressed, and what material they used for tools and implements, when new fashions in material and form were introduced, and when old fashions died out—all these can be traced; and if the layers are numbered in order these changes can be dated accurately in terms of the time scale afforded by the sequence of layers.

Further, if we can form any idea of the period of years covered by each layer, it is possible to translate this time scale into terms of years, and to say, for example, that a form of bowl which is found in the fourth to sixth layers was in use in a period extending from six hundred to four hundred years ago. The time series can be used also to date objects coming from another source altogether; for if any object can be matched with one in our series, it can be said to be contemporary with the layer from which the object from the pit was taken.

In dealing with the dating of the remains of early man the same procedure is followed, except that it is only in the later stages of his career that his remains are found preserved amid the refuse of human occupation, which affords us a clue to his way of life. This first occurs during the phases of what is known as the Old Stone Age, when man had learned how to flake flints to give them a keen edge, had taken to living in caves, and the bodies of the dead were either buried in the floor composed of the debris of occupation, or left there and abandoned to be worried by wild beasts and the remains covered by the wastage of time and later comers. A clue to the dating of the skeletal remains is then afforded by the character of the animal bones, implements and so on, which are found with them.

For most of the specimens of early man, and especially for the earlier examples, these aids to chronology found with the caveman are unfortunately lacking, and the clue to period must be deduced from the age of the undisturbed deposits in which the bones are found. These deposits, for the most part clays and gravels, often have been laid down by water, or by the action of the glaciers which formed the great ice cap covering the whole of the more northerly part of the globe in the Ice Age.

CALENDAR OF THE ROCKS

The rocks which compose the earth's surface, including these clays and gravels, have been studied by the geologist in the same way as the archæologist studies the layers of his refuse pit. They have been classified by him, according to the order in which the layers or strata lie one upon another, into great systems or groups, each group the equivalent of a geological epoch, representing a vast period of time, in which the deposits of that group were being formed.

Further, in each of these strata or deposits are found fossilized remains of animals and plants, many or most of which are now extinct. Not only do these show, according to their kind, what the climate was like at that time, hot or cold, wet or dry, but as many of them are "characteristic" or "type" fossils, that is they are found only in certain strata and in no others, whenever they occur with other remains they serve as an indication of date.

They show that the remains with which they are so found in association must belong to the same period in the geological time scale as themselves. Thus if the bones of early man are found in gravels in which also occur the bones of the mammoth or the woolly rhinoceros, it shows that that man must have lived in the same period of the Ice Age as those monsters.

THREE IMPORTANT EPOCHS

In this classification into epochs of the rocks and deposits the student of early man is concerned only with the latest in time, the Tertiary epoch, the Quaternary and the Recent, the last named covering the deposits of the present era.

Of these the Tertiary epoch is divided into periods or stages, according to the number of certain types of fossils they include, the number

PROF. J. H. MCGREGOR

MODELLED FROM FRAGMENTS

Modelled on a restoration of the skull of Piltdown man from cranial and jaw fragments.

FOX

PILTDOWN MAN RECONSTRUCTED

The resemblance of the mouth and jaw to those of a chimpanzee is particularly noticeable.

increasing as time progresses. Thus we get the Eocene or dawn stage, the Oligocene as these fossils appear in small numbers, the Miocene as they increase, the Pliocene when there are still more, and then as we enter the Quaternary epoch, the Pleistocene, when they reach their highest number, this stage in turn giving way to the "Recent" deposits as the Old Stone Age closes, perhaps eight to ten thousand years before the birth of Christ.

TIME SCALE OF MAN

This classification is of supreme importance to the study of early man because it gives the geological succession or time scale by which the antiquity of the remains of the different types of early man can be determined, according to the character of the deposits in which they have been found. Not only does this show how old they are in terms of geological time, but it also tells us which are earlier than others, and which lived at approximately the same time.

Up to the present no remains of early man have been found in the deposits of Tertiary age. It is in this period, however, that we should expect to find the common ancestor of man and the apes, for it is in the early phases of this period that fossil monkeys begin to appear. The remains of man actually known as the earliest come from the beginning of the Pleistocene stage.

For the greater part of this period much of the northern hemisphere was covered with an ice cap which oscillated or advanced and receded a number of times as the temperature varied. Accordingly we find that the remains of early man in Europe in this period are associated with fossil animals now extinct, some of which, such as an ancient type of elephant, must have demanded a hot climate, while others, such as the cave bear and the mammoth, belong to a period of intense cold.

BRITISH MUSEUM (NATURAL HISTORY)

MADE BY PILTDOWN MAN

Flint implements found with the Piltdown skull. One face is irregularly flaked round the edge.

Any attempt to translate these geological epochs into terms of years is little better than guess work; but it has been calculated that the earliest remains of man from the early or Lower Pleistocene, at the beginning of the Quaternary epoch, cannot be much less than half a million years old. Some geologists are inclined to regard this estimate as too high, while others would increase it to near a million years.

Before passing on to consideration of the principal types of early man which have been found in various parts of the world, and their relation to one another, two questions require attention. Where and at what stage of development does man first appear?

WHERE MAN FIRST APPEARED

As regards the place of man's origin there is a sharp difference of opinion. Some authorities would place that event in Africa, others favour Asia. On behalf of Africa it has been argued—and this is the view to which Darwin lent his support—that as it is the home of the great forest apes, the gorilla and the chimpanzee, it is the most probable region for man's first appearance. The mere fact that the great apes have survived here is sufficient indication that the conditions of place and climate were favourable for such a development.

Further support is afforded by the occurrence of fossil apes of primitive type and early age in the Egyptian Fayum, while *Australopithecus* (from Latin *australis*—southern and Greek *pithekos*—ape), usually referred to as the Taungs skull, discovered at Taungs, South Africa, in 1925 by Professor Raymond Dart, comes so near the human line as to have been considered by its discoverer to be the "missing link" between man and the apes. It may indeed represent a stage of development corresponding to that at which man's ancestors were ceasing to be tree-dwellers. A later and still more advanced form was found by Dr. R. Broom in the Transvaal in July, 1936. Although now generally held to be a chimpanzee-like form, some authorities still regard the Taungs skull as within the line of human descent.

GIANT AMONG FOSSIL APES

On the other hand, there is much to be said for Asia as the region in which man evolved. In the foothills of the Himalayas known as the Siwalik Hills, the Miocene deposits have produced a large number of bones, the remains of fossil apes of various types. Of these *Dryopithecus* (from Greek *drus*—tree and *pithekos*—ape), particularly in types recently found by an American expedition, comes very close to the human line. This is shown especially in the form of the teeth, which have been classified by

Professor W. K. Gregory, of New York, as ancestral in type to those of both man and the great apes. *Dryopithecus*, which in size is a giant among the fossil apes, has also been found in the Tertiary deposits of France and on the Rhine.

APE-MAN OF JAVA

From the geological evidence, as well as the evidence of the fossils, obtained in the Siwalik Hill region by the latest expedition from Yale University, it would appear that at some time in the Tertiary period with which we are dealing a great climatic change took place which caused the tropical belt to swing from north to south. As a result the mammals of India, of which the fossils are now being found, migrated towards the south-east of the continent. This migration, it is thought, also had a crucial effect on the development of man. It is therefore not without significance that it is in this south-eastern area, namely in Java, that one of the earliest known types of early man, *Pithecanthropus erectus*, the ape-man of Java, has been found. Further, at about the same time as the climatic change in India there was a similar change in climate in China. This change drove out the sub-tropical animals and plants which had previously populated that part of the world, but it offered favourable conditions for succeeding waves of immigration of new forms from the north-west and the south with which man appears, probably from the south. The famous Peking man, *Sinanthropus* (from Latin *Sinensis*—Chinese and Greek *anthropos*—man) is a result of this immigration.

EARLY MAN IN ENGLAND

For these and other reasons it would seem that the balance of the evidence is in favour of Asia, and more particularly the southern portion of Central Asia, being regarded as the scene of the crucial stage in man's evolution. Some authorities would link the event with the change in the environment which took place at the great uplift of the central ridge extending from east to west, of which the Alps, Hindu Kush and Himalayas form a part. This tremendous happening may well have forced man's precursors to change from an arboreal to a terrestrial mode of existence. The ape descended from the tree and became man.

The assumption of the upright posture, even as a permanent habit, does not completely differentiate man from the ape. Man has been defined as a tool-using animal, but the ape also will use a convenient stick, stone or other object with sufficient sense of purpose to justify the inclusion of the ape with man as at least an occasional tool-using animal. Man, however, is not only capable of making use of some material object to attain his purpose, but he alone of all living organisms also modifies the form of such object to his requirements. In

BRITISH MUSEUM (NATURAL HISTORY)

BONE IMPLEMENTS FROM PILTDOWN
The oldest known bone implement. It is made from a fragment of the thigh bone of a very large elephant.

other words, man is not only a tool-using animal; he is also a tool-making animal.

If this exercise of tool-making activity be accepted as the differentiating character of man it marks the stage of his transition from ape to man, as distinct from the sub-human. There is then reason to think that man came into existence and was widely distributed over the earth's surface long before the age of the earliest known human skeletal remains. These, as already noted, have not been found before the earliest phases of the Pleistocene. Stone implements, however, fashioned by purposive action to a definite shape and intended to meet a specific need, have been discovered in deposits of the Upper Pliocene. Some experts indeed would say, for example, of the implements found in the late Pliocene deposits of East Anglia, that they are derived from an even greater antiquity than the deposits in which they are found, having been washed out of their original site by later floods.

While these implements suggest the existence of man at a very early period and in the Tertiary Age, the violence of the convulsions of nature at this time affected geographical and climatic conditions to such an extent by the repeated rise and fall of the earth's surface, which changed the relative distribution of land and water, that it is improbable that such fragile relics as the bones of man would survive.

PROF. J. H. MCGREGOR

PITHECANTHROPUS

Head of Pithecanthropus *modelled by Prof. J. H. McGregor on the restored skull. The remains were discovered between* 1891 *and* 1894.

For one relic of early man, however, a claim for Tertiary Age has been advanced. Some of the gravels among which the fragments of the skull of Piltdown man, *Eoanthropus* (from Greek *eos*—dawn), were found in Sussex, as announced in 1912, were of Pliocene Age. But these relics came to light after the gravels had been dug out and removed from their beds, so that it had become impossible to say with certainty what the original position of the skull had been. It could not, therefore, be dated without question, and is now generally considered to be of early Pleistocene Age. If this is correct, the Piltdown skull is approximately of the same antiquity as the two relics from the Far East already mentioned, *Pithecanthropus*, which was found in early Quaternary gravels of the Pleistocene at Trinil in Java, and Peking man, who was found in the cave of Choukoutien, near Peking, in deposits in which it was associated with fossils pointing to an early Pleistocene dating.

SKULL OF PEKING MAN

The remains of *Pithecanthropus* first found by Dr. E. Dubois between 1891 and 1894 consisted of a skull cap, thigh bone and tooth. Other bones were also discovered, but not described until many years later, while some details are still unpublished. The skull cap is of so primitive a form that doubts were long felt whether it were human at all. Dr. Dubois himself is still inclined to regard it as a gigantic gibbon, but it is now generally accepted as a very primitive human type, while the character of the thigh bone shows that this being walked upright, hence the addition of the word *erectus* in the full title.

The human character of *Pithecanthropus* is now supported by its resemblances to the later discoveries of Piltdown man and Peking man. The first complete skull of the latter was found in 1929; the latest specimens are three skulls discovered in the same cave in 1936.

FORESHADOWING MODERN MAN

It has been claimed that of skulls of early man found in Kenya, in East Africa, one may be approximately of the same age as Peking man and *Pithecanthropus*, but it is of a different type, a precursor of " modern " man. The claim to a high antiquity for man in this region, resting as it does on evidence which at present lacks corroboration, must be regarded as " not proven."

It is a remarkable and significant fact that the most primitive examples of early man should be derived from localities so widely apart as the Far East and Western Europe. If the numbers were not so small, such a distribution in itself would suggest a dispersal from a common centre such as mid-Asia. The occurrence of an early specimen of man in East Africa, notwithstanding the difference in type, might also favour an Asiatic origin, as being within striking distance of a line of migration from Asia followed by other races in later times.

The three primitive types of early man—*Pithecanthropus*, Peking man and Piltdown man—show a striking agreement in certain general characteristics. All of them exhibit features in which they show marked resemblances to the apes; but in others both Peking man and Piltdown man approximate to or foreshadow characters in "modern" man. These latter characters are not entirely identical in the two types, and the differences are perhaps even more instructive than the identities. The result of a detailed comparison of these specimens of early man is, in fact, such as would appear had Nature been experimenting along now one, now another, line of advance towards modern man.

HEAVY AND MASSIVE SKULLS

All the skulls are heavy and massive, the bone being extremely thick, although in *Pithecanthropus* and in Peking man the skulls are small, especially the Peking man skull first discovered at Choukoutien. Measured in terms of cubic capacity, the skull of *Pithecanthropus*, so far as can be gauged from the skull cap, had a capacity of nine hundred cubic centimetres only, while the skull known as Peking Man I is about one thousand cubic centimetres. One of the three Peking skulls recently discovered reaches as high as one thousand two hundred cubic centimetres, but this is probably exceptional.

RESEMBLANCES TO THE APES

These measurements must be compared with the modern Australian aboriginal at one thousand two hundred and ninety cubic centimetres, though even that is low for a modern type. The modern European averages one thousand four hundred and fifty cubic centimetres. Piltdown probably stands at something over one thousand three hundred cubic centimetres. A comparison of plaster casts of the interior of the skulls which show the form and character of the brain indicates that while the brain of Peking man was one of the most primitive human brains known, that of Piltdown man shows a decided advance towards the "modern" type.

As regards the general appearance of the skulls, all agree in being low and having a low receding forehead, like that of the apes, but the most striking feature is the thick heavy ridge or torus of bone which runs across the forehead over the eyes, a mark of primitive man which reappears, as will be seen, in later types and gives a fierce and repellent cast of countenance, such as is evident, though in a less marked degree, in the Australian aborigines. It is a distinctly simian character.

Nothing can be said of the facial skeleton of *Pithecanthropus* because the skull cap only is present; but in the remaining two, as in later types, the lower part of the face and lower jaw project to form a heavy muzzle such as is seen in the apes, and almost forms a snout. The bone of the lower jaw falls away below the line of the projecting teeth, so that virtually there is no chin. The projection of bone in the lower jaw forming a chin does not appear before "modern" man.

In all these characters, as well as in others of a more technical kind, *Pithecanthropus*, Piltdown and Peking man agree in showing resemblances to the apes. Brief mention must now be made of certain significant differences, especially as between the two latter.

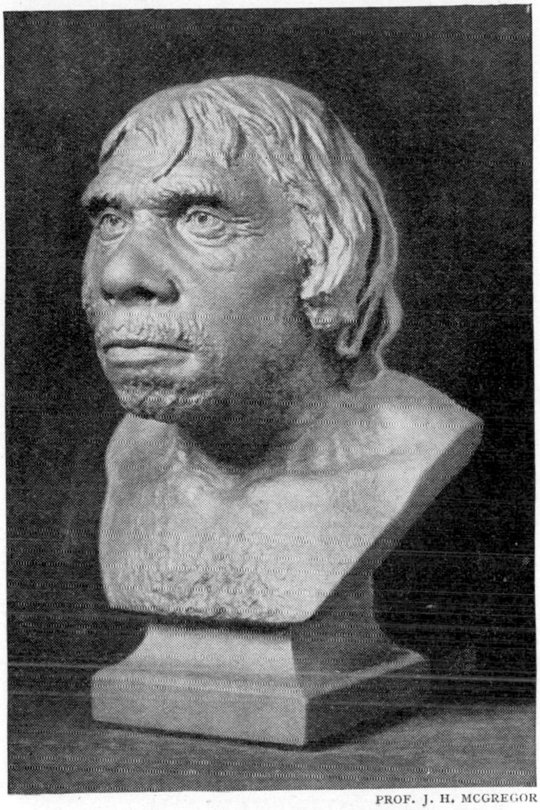

PROF. J. H. MCGREGOR

NEANDERTHAL MAN

Head modelled by Prof. J. H. McGregor on the skull found in 1908 at La Chapelle-aux-Saints, Corrèze, France.

The first and most important point is the difference in the character of the lower jaws of the two types. In Peking man the lower jaw, of which eleven specimens are now known, though still massive and primitive, in certain characters shows a distinct advance towards the type of " modern " man—in fact, it approaches that type more nearly than in any other primitive skull. The teeth, of which over a hundred examples have been found, also show certain " modern " characteristics.

HERBERT PHOTOS

NEANDERTHAL WOMAN

Neanderthal woman cleaning a reindeer skin. A model on exhibition in the Field Museum of Natural History, Chicago.

In both respects the evidence has been interpreted as revealing signs of development towards the modern Mongolian type. This resemblance is fortified by the fact that Peking man appears to have had a broad flat nose like that of the Mongolian races. Further, there seems to be no reason why Peking man should not have been able to talk, although it is inferred from the form of the jaw that some other types of primitive man—as, for example, Heidelberg man, a primitive form known only from a massive jaw found in Germany in 1907—may not have been able to use the tongue in such a way as to produce articulate speech.

The lower jaw of Piltdown man is a very different matter. It is the most ape-like jaw for which a human origin has been claimed. As the skull was found in fragments at different times, some authorities maintained that it was not possible for such a jaw to belong to a skull which, for a primitive type, was so advanced. They held that it had belonged to a fossil chimpanzee or even an orang-utan. They also pointed to the ape-like characters of the teeth, especially of a canine tooth which was found some time after the rest of the skull, and is distinctly simian.

DISCOVERED IN KENT

Further attempts at reconstruction of the skull from the fragments have brought it more into harmony with the character of the jaw, which is now generally, though not universally, accepted as belonging to the skull and as being a human jaw of very primitive type. The problem remains that an ape-like jaw is here united with a brain of an advanced type, while in the Far East, in Peking man, an extremely primitive brain is found with a jaw well advanced on the evolutionary track. The recent discovery at Swanscombe, Kent, of a skull similar to Piltdown but of a more primitive appearance in certain characters, yet possibly much later in date, has further complicated the issue. For the moment, however, and as a practical measure the evidence of Piltdown man as a primitive type may be accepted.

NEANDERTHAL MAN

When first Peking man was discovered it was thought by some that it was an ancestral type of Neanderthal or Mousterian man. Neanderthal man (*Homo Neanderthalensis*) is an important but extinct form of early man which for long was the only type more primitive than " modern " man known to science. Its name is derived from the fact that the type was first recognized in a skull found in 1857 in the Neanderthal Cave, Düsseldorf, Germany; but the Gibraltar skull found in a cave in Gibraltar in 1848 is now know to belong to the same group. When this type of man is found in association with stone implements these are invariably of the class of palæolithic or Old Stone Age implements known as Mousterian, first found in the cave of Le Moustier in the south of France. Hence Neanderthal man is sometimes called Mousterian man.

The chief reason for connecting Peking man with Neanderthal man lay in the general appearance of the skull, and more especially in the character of the jaw and the occurrence of the bony ridge or torus, characters in which at first sight it appeared to resemble these well-known features of the Neanderthal type. It is now generally agreed that the occurrence of these common features in the two types is due to a common heritage.

HUMAN CHARACTER QUESTIONED

For long after the first known skull of Neanderthal man was discovered its brutal and ape-like appearance caused its human character to be questioned. The verdict in favour of its humanity has been supported by a large number of later discoveries ranging from isolated teeth to complete skeletons, which have established this as a distinct form of early man, clearly differentiated in a number of characteristic features from " modern " man, *Homo sapiens*.

The numerous specimens which have been found in Pleistocene gravels and clays of the periods immediately preceding and during the last great advance of the glaciers over northern Europe in the Ice Age (the Würm glaciation) as well as in caves, show a considerable variability in type, but their main characteristics are constant.

These are a low skull, a low retreating forehead, showing the heavy ridge of bone across the brow found in the earlier primitive types of man, and a heavy and brutal countenance in which the lower part and heavy and massive jaw project like a muzzle. There is no chin. The teeth are large and of a distinctive character. The capacity of the skull, averaging one thousand four hundred cubic centimetres and approaching that of the modern European, shows that the brain was large, but it was primitive in form and character.

FIFTY THOUSAND YEARS AGO

Generally the skull and the bones of the rest of the skeleton of Neanderthal man have retained in a marked degree the ape-like characters which were noted in the earlier and more primitive types of early man, especially *Pithecanthropus* and Peking man. The ape-like appearance of Neanderthal man is further emphasized in the fact that the head was set on the vertebral column in such a way as to project forward, while the leg bones show that he could not stand completely upright. He walked with a slouch, recalling the attitude and gait of the ape when upright.

Neanderthal man evidently had a wide distribution in time as well as in space. Heidelberg man, known from the Mauer jaw, as this relic

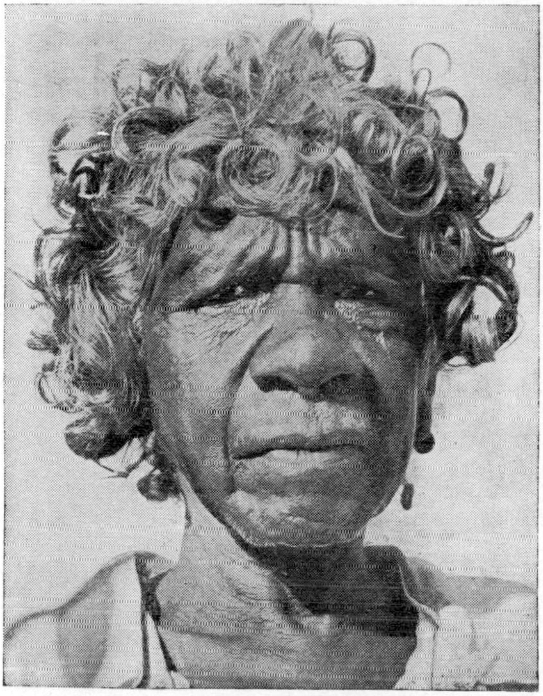

FOX

AUSTRALIAN ABORIGINAL

An Australian aboriginal woman. The likeness of the nose to that of the Neanderthal woman pictured opposite is striking.

is sometimes called from the sands outside Heidelberg in which it was found, is regarded as an ancestral form of Neanderthal man. He is placed by some authorities as very little if at all later than Piltdown man. The Neanderthal period is usually regarded as dating at about fifty thousand years ago.

The geographical distribution of Neanderthal man is of great interest. Most of the specimens known have been found in Central and Western Europe—Germany, Belgium and France; but relics of the type have been discovered in the Channel Islands, in Italy near Rome, and in Malta. From west to east the finds become less numerous, but specimens have come to light in the Caucasus and in Palestine. Outside this area, Solo man, human skeletal remains discovered in gravels on the Solo River in Java in 1932, show Neanderthaloid features and is considered by some to be a forerunner of Neanderthal man. Rhodesian man, found in South Africa in 1921, shows a close affinity to the Neanderthal type.

Rhodesian man is of special importance for the question of the descent of man. Its date is uncertain, but it is probably a late survival. It shows strong Neanderthal affinities, especially in the face and jaw, which in certain respects are markedly characteristic of that type. In other characters the rest of the skull more nearly approaches the modern type, and it is clear from the form of the base of the skull that Rhodesian man held his head more nearly erect and, as the leg bones also indicate, probably walked upright. In this specimen we see again a remarkable combination of primitive and "modern" characters.

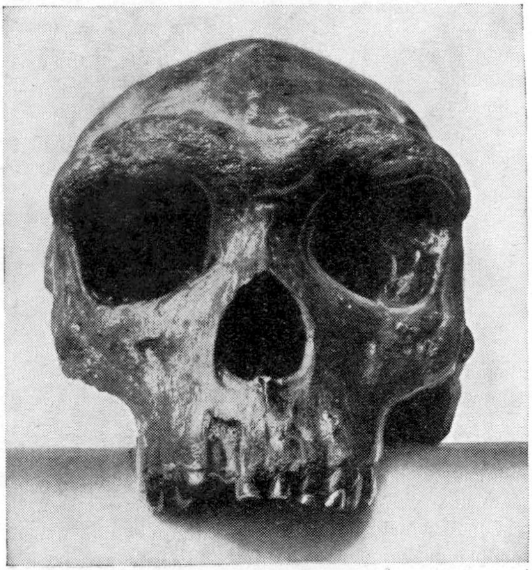

BRITISH MUSEUM (NATURAL HISTORY)

SKULL OF RHODESIAN MAN

Found with remains of a typical human skeleton and modern animals in a cave at Broken Hill, north-west Rhodesia.

At the close of the period in Europe known to archæologists as Mousterian, Neanderthal man seems to have died out. His place was taken by "modern" man, the Crô-Magnon man, as he is usually termed, of the later phases of the Palæolithic Age in Europe.

It was thought at one time that the line of descent of "modern" man might be traced through Neanderthal man, the connecting link being an ancestral form of the Australian, the most primitive of the modern races of man, but recent discoveries have shown that this type of early man stands quite apart and differs specifically, or even generically from *Homo sapiens*. It is evident, however, that just as has been shown in the line of descent of man and the apes, there must be a common ancestor of the two forms. Neanderthal man split off from the common stock, and specializing in certain directions reached his fullest development in Western Europe, where he died out, probably as the result of environmental change—possibly owing to the climatic and other changes which took place towards the close of the Ice Age.

LADY OF LLOYD'S

Certain lines of evidence support this view. When the Neanderthal type was the earliest form of man known to science, with the exception of *Pithecanthropus*, it was natural to seek in it the derivation of modern man. Now both Piltdown and Peking man have shown that the germs of the modern type are to be found in certain characters in primitive types. The evidence of Rhodesian man pointed in the same direction, as did also the Galilee skull, the Neanderthal form found in Palestine in 1925. These were little more than suggestive indications of a possible interpretation before it was recognized that the skull known as the Lady of Lloyd's, found in London in 1925, was not only essentially "modern" in type, but also belonged to a period which antedated Neanderthal man, or at least was contemporary with the earliest known examples of that type. A strong presumptive case was thus made out for the argument that the line of "modern" man was as old, if not older than Neanderthal.

PRECURSORS OF EUROPEAN MAN

The claim for a high antiquity for the line of descent of "modern" man has now been placed beyond question by recent discoveries in Palestine. Sir Arthur Keith and Mr. T. McCown, in a preliminary report on skeletons which were discovered in 1933 in caves on Mount Carmel, have identified two distinct races in this material.

The two races were contemporaries. Of them one is of the Neanderthal type, closely resembling though not identical with the Neanderthal of Western Europe, while the other, a very variable race, is virtually identical with the Crô-Magnon race of Europe—a form of "modern" man. They are tall, have the Crô-Magnon type of skull, and they show a chin. They may, in fact, be regarded as the precursors of European man. They have made substantial progress in development towards a form out of which modern races of Europe might evolve.

These two races also antedate or are contemporary with the earliest forms of Neanderthal man, as the fossil animals with which they are associated in the cave deposits belong to the period which preceded the last great glaciation in Europe, the heydey of Neanderthal man.

As has already been stated, this second and " modern " race is very variable. Some of the specimens show features which belong to Neanderthal man. It is evidence, therefore, that they are in process of development. It may be said, in fact, that we are here looking on the evolution of one of the earliest of the European races, not indeed from a Neanderthal form but from the form of a common ancestral type.

EVIDENCE FROM PALESTINE

The significance of this evidence from Palestine is brought out more clearly if it is brought into relation to the distribution of Neanderthal man to which reference was made above, when it was pointed out that the finds of Neanderthal became more rare in progressing from West to East. It is important to note also that the examples found in Eastern Europe, and farther East—as, for instance, the Galilee skull—show certain affinities with modern man which are not found in the more fully typical specimens. In the light of the evidence from Palestine this must now be taken, not as evidence of a modification of the Neanderthal type towards " modern " man, but rather as indicating that as we approach the location of origin of the type in the East, its form tends to show the more clearly evidence of a line of descent which is diverse from that of Neanderthal. In type, if not necessarily in time, they represent an earlier or less completely differentiated phase than the fully developed Neanderthal form of Western Europe.

AMERICA REACHED FROM ASIA

With the emergence of Crô-Magnon man on the European scene in the final phases of the Ice Age when Neanderthal man disappeared, we enter upon another aspect of the study of man. Confronted with this tall upstanding type, with modern form of skull and face, modern jaw, furnished with a chin and a modern brain, we are no longer dealing with the human race as an entity, but with the question of the origins of the modern races. It is true that little is known as yet as to how and where *Homo sapiens* as such originated, but before much light can be thrown on that problem we need to know much more of how, when and where the several varieties or races of *Homo sapiens* first began to be.

PROF. J. H. MCGREGOR

CRÔ-MAGNON MAN

Head modelled by Prof. J. H. McGregor on the skull found in 1868 *at Les Eyzies, Dordogne, France.*

In Europe alone, for example, although it is customary and convenient to speak in general terms of Crô-Magnon man as typical of the later Palæolithic period, yet in addition to Crô-Magnon man in the strict sense of the term there are at least three, and possibly more forms which can be distinguished among the skeletal remains of this Age which must be studied in their relation to the problem of the origins of the races of Europe.

Other forms of early " modern " man are known from North Africa, from East Africa and from South Africa, while Rhodesian man carries us on to early forms of "modern" man in Java, thence to those of Australia and so to the modern Australian; and from the later Palæolithic Age, or possibly the following Mesolithic or early Neolithic, some form of early man reached America from Asia.

A summary of the main line of argument in this chapter may serve some useful purpose.

RUSSELL

AUTHORITY ON EARLY MAN
Sir Arthur Keith, F.R.S., one of the world's leading authorities on all that concerns early man.

Man, apes and monkeys, it is maintained by most scientists, are descended from a common ancestor, who must be sought in the early phases of the Tertiary period in the geological time scale. Early in the line of descent, monkeys, then apes branch off from the family tree and by adaptation become so completely fitted for life in their respective environments that further development ceases. Some die out while others perpetuate their kind, to survive in the present-day monkeys and apes. Of the early forms which have died out, fossils have been found which show their affinity with the human line of descent.

Of the specifically human, early forms have been found in *Pithecanthropus*, Peking man and Piltdown man. These forms as such became extinct, but they exhibit characters which point in part in their ape-like form to their line of origin, while in their foreshadowings of the characters of "modern" man they point the direction which was being taken by the line of evolution.

FAILURE AND TRIUMPH

Neanderthal man, on the other hand, is an early form of specialization away from the line taken in the evolution of modern man. On attaining the fullest development of his special qualities he gained predominance for a time but failed to adapt himself to altered conditions of climate and surroundings and died out. The line of descent of modern man shows that he went further than his precursors in shedding characters held in common with the apes, while he refrained from developing those special attributes by which man's simian relatives effected an adaptation to their environment. Man developed his manipulative skill and his intellectual equipment, and thus succeeded in preserving his adaptability while fostering the specific qualities of *Homo sapiens* by which human civilization has been built up.

THINKERS WHO DIFFER

Although the majority of scientists are more or less agreed regarding the lines of man's development as outlined above, some thinkers do not see eye to eye with the evolutionists. On a famous occasion, Disraeli remarked : "Is man an ape or an angel? I, my lord, I am on the side of the angels." This was in 1864, but in 1935 Sir Ambrose Fleming vigorously protested against what he regarded as "one-sided teaching of the animal origin of man by imaginary or nightmare-like pictures, which attach importance merely to certain similarities in bones, body, blood and behaviour in man and ape, but ignore altogether the immense actual or potential dissimilarities mental and spiritual."

To quote another writer, Dr. W. H. P. Faunce : "The doctrine of evolution, rightly understood and interpreted, is to-day one of the most powerful aids to religious faith. It has delivered thousands from perplexity amounting to despair. It has supplanted the old paralysing conception of a 'world-machine,' a world mechanical and lifeless, grinding out human destiny without end. In place of that soulless mechanism we now have a growing organism. In the words of John Fiske, 'The simile of the watch has been replaced by the simile of the flower.' A developing world, still in the process, ceaselessly unfolding, still to be shaped by human purpose and effort—that is the inspiring conception now placed in the hands of the Church by modern science, a conception which formed the basis of the first Christian parable of the ' The Sower.' "

DOCTRINE OF DEVELOPMENT

" Science is not yet able to discern a world-soul or a Creator; it leaves that to religion. It has nothing to say about the purpose and goal of life or the spiritual presence in all things, which is the vital breath of religion. But it has shown us a universe alive, progressing, climbing with many backward steps towards ' one far-off divine event.' The doctrine of development has cleared away most of the difficulties in Old Testament ethics, and enabled us to reconcile teachings which, given in different centuries, are yet united in one Book. It has furnished the Church with a powerful apologetic, which many of our leaders are now using."

Dr. W. R. Inge is not altogether in agreement with the writer quoted above. " We must not deify evolution," he notes. " Evolution is always of finite things within a whole. We cannot infer from the fact of human progress within the historical period that the whole creation is in progress of development toward ' one far-off divine event.' . . . My conclusion is that evolution is only the method by which

FOX

GALLEY HILL MAN
Based on an early skull of indeterminate age found near the mouth of the Thames. Authorities differ as to its dating.

FOX

SPIENNES MAN
He lived during the later Stone Age, when early man used tools of stone, bone and horn.

the eternal God carries out most of His purposes in the world. Belief in gradual change is taking the place of the older belief in catastrophic Divine intervention."

Reference has been made in an earlier chapter to the controversy which took place when Darwin announced his theory of evolution. " I will not join in the chorus," Dr. W. R. Matthews told the members of the British Association in 1932, " and deride the theology of the Victorian Age for resisting Darwin's theory of evolution. The theologians did not oppose Darwin on the ground of imperfections in the theory. Their real reason was that they felt a revolutionary change was being threatened in the status of man."

FALLEN ANGEL OR RISEN APE ?

" A fallen angel or risen ape was the crude but not wholly false way of stating the antithesis between the traditional religious view of man and the new scientific conception. No change in scientific ideas, I suppose, will ever reverse the process or make it possible to return to the opinions of pre-scientific religion on the origin of man. Whatever be the details of the process, we must think of him as the product of an evolutionary process."

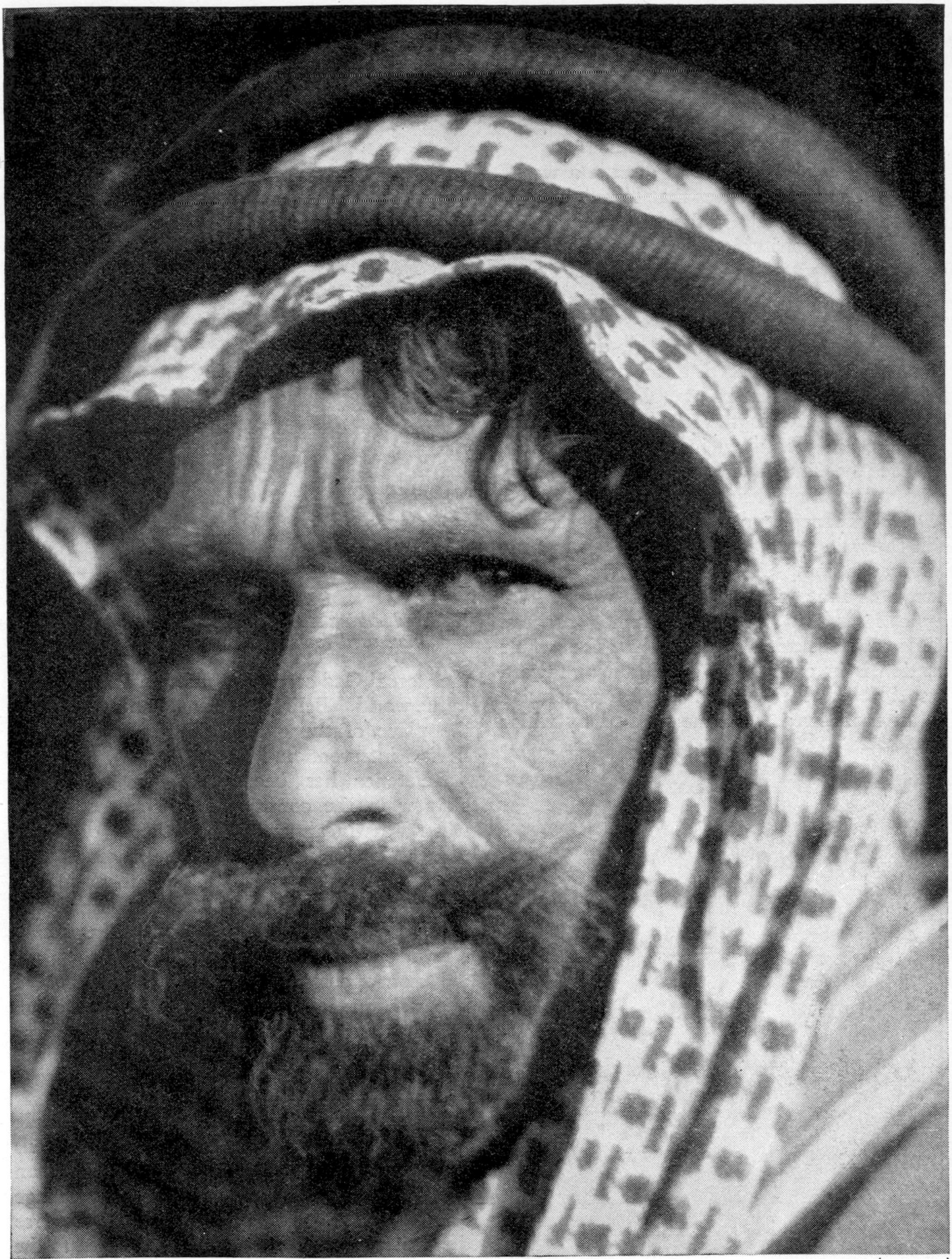

CARL R. RASWAN (MONDIALE)

SHEYKH OF THE SYRIAN DESERT

A sheykh of the Haddediyyin tribe, which is mainly located in the northern parts of Syria between Aleppo and Mosul and also north-east of Damascus, slightly west of the Sha'ban. The title "sheykh" indicates the head of a nomadic Arab family, tribe, or clan.

FOX

BLACKFOOT INDIANS ON THE WATCH

Many of the North American Indians display a distinctly Mongolian cast of feature, which indicates that their ancestors probably came from Eastern Asia. The Blackfoot group consists of three tribes.

RACES OF MANKIND

BEFORE it is possible to discuss the origin and distribution of modern races to any good purpose, it is necessary to have clearly in mind what is meant by " race."

This is a question on which there is apt to be much confusion in thought, and which unfortunately is sometimes made a warrant for injustice in action. Difference in race is wrongly held to imply a difference in character and status, such as to justify that section of society which regards itself as belonging to the superior race in inflicting political, social and economic disabilities on the race or races stigmatized as inferior. This has happened in Germany in the persecution of the Jews and so-called " non-Aryans."

In approaching the scientific study of " race " and the races of mankind, the first essential is to look at the facts and lay aside all preconceived ideas. When we were at school we were taught—or at least some of us were—that the Chinaman had a yellow skin, flat face, broad cheek-bones, lank black hair, and so forth; the Australian aboriginal a black skin, broad flat nose, beetling brows and so on, and the other races of the world were described in the same way and in similar terms. We gathered, or were left with the impression, that these " races " were more or less fixed types unchanging and absolutely distinct.

The anthropologist's view is far otherwise. He finds various characteristic associations of bodily features constantly recurring in groups among the peoples of the world, and to each of these groupings he applies a descriptive title for purposes of future identification and study.

He finds, for example, that a yellow skin, a broad flat face with broad cheek-bones, lank black hair and other characteristic features

DR. WELLER-BERLIN (MONDIALE)

TYPICAL ITALIAN

Most of the Italians are of the Mediterranean type: short, dark-haired, with dark eyes and a long head.

are constantly associated together, and so labels this constantly recurring association of characters " Chinese," or more strictly " Mongolian," because it occurs most frequently and is the predominant (but not the only) type found in Mongolia, China, and other parts of Eastern Asia.

Another grouping of characters, as will be seen later, is called the Mediterranean race, because although it occurs all over Europe, it is the type found most commonly in the countries around the Mediterranean and appears to have originated there.

The popular view of race begins from the wrong end. It begins with the type and tries to fit the people into it. The scientific concept of race collects the facts and from them constructs a generalized type.

Further, as all racial groups, however nearly approaching uniformity, in fact vary within certain limits, which can be calculated statistically, the anthropologist recognizes that his types or races are not " fixed," but are generalized descriptions to which the members of the race only tend to approximate. Not all Mongoloid peoples, including the Chinaman, are exactly like the Mongol type, and individuals may approach it more nearly in some characters than in others.

ONE SPECIES BUT MANY VARIETIES

The opinion most generally held by scientists is that the modern populations of the world all belong to one species (*Homo sapiens*) and spring from one stock. But man is the most variable of all the animals, and it is obvious that this single species includes many varieties. Variation has, in fact, been going on ever since the earliest days to which it has yet been possible to trace the history of " modern " man, as *Homo sapiens* is called to distinguish him from the other more primitive forms of man now extinct. These variations shade into one another, but as explained above, the variable characters tend to form distinctive " clusters," which are the anthropologist's " racial types."

In the later stages of the Old Stone Age, when, as was pointed out in the preceding chapter, Neanderthal man had apparently died out and " modern " man had become predominant, there were already several varieties of the latter type existing in Europe, while at the close of that period not only had the broad lines of the racial differences of the modern peoples of Europe begun to show themselves, but distinctive forms were appearing in North Africa, Palestine, East Africa, South Africa, Java, Australia—in fact in every part of the world in which human skeletal remains have been found associated with this phase of Stone Age civilization.

WHAT RACE MEANS

These facts point to the conclusion that variability is a very ancient characteristic of " modern " man. It raises an interesting question. Are we justified in regarding these variations as anything more than individual aberrations, or is there any sufficient reason why we should regard them as distinct races? The problem cannot be solved conclusively

D. CARRUTHERS (MONDIALE)

WOMAN OF THE CHARKHAR MONGOLS

Among the features characteristic of the Mongolian type of Eastern Asia are yellow skin ; straight, lank, coarse, black hair ; dark eyes, broad cheek-bones, flat noses and extreme scantiness of facial hair.

until we have arrived at a satisfactory definition of what we mean by "race."

In the strict sense of the term, "race" is a purely biological concept. In brief, it connotes "a group of people who have certain well-marked features in common," a definition which perhaps had better be somewhat expanded. The term "a race" should be

ELLIOTT AND FRY

NORDIC OF FAME

Dr. F. Nansen, the Norwegian explorer, was of the Nordic type, which predominates in Scandinavia.

used only of a group of individuals, adequate in number, exhibiting a number of physical (bodily) characters in common, which are usually constant, and by which the group is distinguished from all other groups, and which are transmitted by inheritance from parents to offspring, and as a rule have been so transmitted over a number of generations.

The numbers of the group must not be too small. Only in exceptional circumstances would so small a unit as a single family constitute a race. If the characters are not constant the group will be too variable to be recognized; and inheritance through a number of generations is necessary to show that it is a stable type.

Before dealing further with this question, a few words must be said as to the methods of study and the principles by which different races are distinguished one from another.

LONG AND BROAD HEADS

In studying race we are dealing with bodily or physical characters only, and for purposes of scientific analysis and statistical manipulation it is preferable that the characters selected should be such as can be measured accurately or described by reference to a standard scale, for example, the colour of hair, eyes and skin, which can be described as light or dark, or by matching with a graded and numbered colour scale.

It has been found as a matter of observation that there are certain parts of the body in the character or measurements of which the members of the same race or group agree with one another within a fairly well-defined and limited range, and vary significantly in these parts from the members of other racial groups.

Such a character is the size and shape of the head. The head is classified as long or broad according to the relation of the breadth to the length expressed as a percentage. This percentage as a rule falls between sixty-five and ninety. A head in which the breadth is seventy per cent of the length is long, or dolichocephalic; one of eighty per cent and over is broad, sometimes called round (the scientific term is brachycephalic), especially if the percentage is eighty-four and over.

HAIR AND STATURE

Much stress is laid on the nature as well as the colour of the hair. Whether the hair is straight, wavy or curly, or frizzy, depends on the shape of the individual hair in section. This may be round, oval or flat, and this fact is considered of such importance as to have been made by some the main criterion of racial classification. Stature, as well as the length of the limbs, is of some importance, but it is apt to vary with nutrition and other functional factors, and therefore may be deceptive. There is altogether a large number of characters considered to be racially significant, but the above are usually held to be the most important.

It is important to remember that race is a purely biological and physical term, because the word is often loosely used to cover other forms of unity, as when we talk of the French, Italian or Spanish race. In such case it designates a geographical, national or political entity, not necessarily connected with racial origins or the composition of the people. In such popular phrases as " the Latin races " or " the Celtic races," the only bond of union that should be implied is that these peoples speak languages which have a common origin. There is no Celtic, no Latin race; but a number of races speak Celtic or Latin tongues.

PURITY OF RACE

Argument on questions of race is peculiarly prone to the fallacy of " purity of race." There is no such thing. A pure type or race could persist only if the group lived and inbred in complete isolation. Fiction has often played with the fascinating idea of such a group, but science has not yet succeeded in discovering one.

Immediately one group interbreeds with another the purity of both breeds vanishes, and as man from his earliest days has proved himself capable of enduring any climatic environment, and consequently has wandered and interbred freely all over the world, it is clear that even if on " modern " man's first appearance the species exhibited only a small number of varieties conforming to our definition of race, their " purity " did not last long.

By interbreeding the characters differentiating the races are redistributed among the descendants of the original groups. If any of these new groupings of characters prove constant and transmissible by inheritance in any appreciable number of individuals, they constitute new or secondary racial types.

NEW RACIAL TYPES

Further spontaneous variations may arise which prove transmissible by inheritance and give rise to new racial types. The reasons for such spontaneous variation are obscure, but they have been attributed to the action of the ductless glands. Indeed, according to one theory which has been put forward, the more strongly marked variations in the distinctive racial characters may be attributed to quantitative or qualitative variation in the action of these glands.

Such are the only arguments by which it is possible to explain the conditions which are found to exist among modern races. There are no " pure " races. Each local group, as for example the people of England, includes a number of different racial types, not living apart from one another, but intermingled and intermarrying freely. Very frequently individuals show characters belonging to two, three or more racial types.

Take for example two contrasting types in the scientific classification of races, the Nordic, tall, fair-skinned, with fair hair, blue eyes and

MONDIALE

WOMAN OF INDIA

Many of the native rulers of India are closely akin to the Nordics, being of the Aryan type.

a long head, and the Mediterranean, short, dark-skinned, with dark hair, dark eyes, and also with a long head. If these two diverse types are crossed, the offspring may resemble one or other parent, or a mixed type may result. It is only occasionally that the characters of the two types blend in such a way that the product is an intermediate type.

In certain studies of heredity it has been shown that when " tall " is mated with " short " the offspring will be either " tall " or " short " or both, but not as a rule intermediate or " medium." An even better example is the mating of blue eyes and dark eyes, of which the offspring will normally have either blue or dark eyes, but not a blended colour.

On the other hand, skin-colour characters, especially when at opposite ends of the scale, as "black" or "white," tend to produce a blend such as mulatto, quadroon and octoroon in which the dark pigment diminishes if further white dilution is introduced; but there is always the chance of reversion to the original type. More frequently however, some at least of the significant racial characters are each the subject of a separate inheritance, and instead of one or other of the stock types a "mixed" type results, in which various individual characters inherited intact from one or other of the parents appear in combination.

PAUL HOEFLER (MONDIALE)

AFRICAN PYGMY

The Pygmies, closely related to the Negroes, live in the steaming forests of the Congo.

The colour of the hair may be inherited from the mother, and of the eyes from the father. Hence we find dark hair, which as a racial character should go with dark eyes, associated with blue eyes, or with a stature that is tall when it should be short. Or the reverse may be the case. A short fair man will have dark eyes, though normally fair colouring goes with tall stature and with light or blue eyes. Thus the offspring of such crosses are "mixed," not true intermediate types.

A confusion of racial or type characters in the individual is almost inevitable. This will be realized when it is remembered that each one of us in a period of little over two hundred years may have had as many as five hundred ancestors. Each one of these had a different and individual make-up acquired by inheritance, and each of them has contributed something physically to our own make-up. The futility of much argument about race in popular and political literature, such as has now appeared in Germany, is patent. It demands a "purity" of race which is incompatible with known historical and biological facts.

STUDY OF HUMAN HEREDITY

In these circumstances it may be urged that study of "race" is academic and of little value, scientific or other, if no more positive result can emerge. There are, however, certain facts which have to be taken into account, certain methods of study to be employed, by which order may be brought into this apparent chaos. It is the business of the study of human heredity, with the aid of the science of genetics, to investigate how and why man's physical characters are inherited as they are.

When the racial characters of any given population have been observed, recorded and studied by the appropriate statistical methods, certain facts appear. It is found that inheritance is not entirely indiscriminate. Certain characters tend to be dominant. They appear in greater numbers and with more persistence than others, with the result that these latter, the recessive characters as they are called, tend to breed out, while the dominant, which in some either amount to, or tend to become the racial type, survive.

FROM SCANDINAVIA TO ITALY

Blue eyes, fair hair, tall stature, for instance, are dominants in a population which in consequence is labelled as belonging to the Nordic type. Again, when the racial characters have been sorted out and tested by statistical methods, it is usually possible to build up a conception of the original type or types from which the population has been composed. This represents, in all probability, the main stock or stocks and the fundamental hereditary types, from which the physical characters of the existing mixed population are derived.

An example will perhaps make this clear.

Take the peoples of the continent of Europe along a line from the north of Scandinavia to the south of Italy. In the north the type is Nordic, tall, fair-haired with light or blue eyes and a long head. In Central Europe it is Alpine, medium in height, with chestnut or light brown hair, grey or light brown eyes, and broad-headed. In the south it is Mediterranean, short, dark-haired, with dark eyes and a long head.

EVIDENCE OF ADMIXTURE

In any one district along this line, the bulk of the population will tend to conform to the race-type of the region. In the north it will resemble more or less closely the Nordic type, in the south the Mediterranean; but in both cases there will be many individuals who do not conform to the dominant type. In Scandinavia there is an appreciable dark element with a tendency to broadness in the head. In some members of the population individual characters may be so modified as to form a blended or intermediate type, others will show a mixture of characters belonging to the two different types; but on the whole the fair type and fair characters will be dominant. The true racial type of the region, the Nordic, tends to persist.

The same applies to the race types in Alpine and Mediterranean regions. In the south there is correspondingly a fair element, but the dark racial type tends to persist and is the dominant, while a certain number show a mixed inheritance. In the central area in addition to the broad-headed Alpine, the characteristic type, there is evidence of admixture with the long-headed fair population to the north and the dark long-headed population which lies to the south.

VALUE OF ANTHROPOLOGY

It is owing to this admixture in the distribution of the main racial types of Europe that it is still possible to speak with precision and in accordance with the facts, of, for example, the Mediterranean element or strain in the population of Great Britain, meaning the short dark people of say Wales and the west, although the individuals to whom this description is applied have no personal connection with the Mediterranean, nor did their ancestors come from there, at any rate within some thousands of years.

It follows then that when we speak of any given population as belonging to a certain race, we mean no more than that a considerable proportion of the total population conforms more or less closely to the groupings of physical (bodily) characters, which are regarded for purposes of classification as constituting certain racial types.

When a large proportion of individuals in any one population show tall stature, fair complexion, blue eyes, fair hair and long head together that population is said to belong to the Nordic type, of which these are the characteristics; just as, if they have a black skin, woolly hair, long head, thick lips and other marks of the type we call them Negroes.

FOX

WOMAN OF CEYLON

The dominant race of Ceylon is the Sinhalese. Their ancestors came from the Ganges Valley.

When the anthropologist has worked out the distribution of such characters in the population and has determined the various types to which they belong, it becomes possible to trace the racial history of the community; that is, to decide with some probability what strains have gone in the past to make up the population. This knowledge is of great importance in social legislation and the work of social betterment.

It is only when we know the racial strains in a people that we can say with certainty to what physical standard or standards they ought to attain, and decide if they show signs of inadequate physical development, the effect of malnutrition, or of an unhealthy environment or an unsuitable or unhealthy occupation and so forth.

PRIMITIVE EUROPEAN RACES

Take, for instance, the question of stature, a physical character which seems to be very sensitive to adverse conditions. If in one area the population is of the Nordic type, the standard height will be greater than in an area in which the predominant type is Mediterranean. A comparison of the two populations with reference to physical development based on measurements of height might lead to quite erroneous conclusions, unless we know the racial standard height. The Mediterranean population, though shorter, might be better nourished than a taller Nordic population which fell short of its proper standard. Questions of health are also involved in other ways, as some races and racial types seem to be peculiarly liable to suffer from certain forms of disease, such as consumption and perhaps cancer.

We may now turn to the classification of the varieties of man into races as they exist at the present day. A scheme of classification based mainly on coloration which coincides roughly with the distribution of peoples on the great continental land masses may be taken as a starting point.

According to this scheme humanity falls into three or four divisions, each inhabiting one of the large land-tracts of the globe—the black race in Africa, the yellow race in Central and Eastern Asia (with offshoots in the Indians of America and the peoples of South-Eastern Asia and the Pacific, of which the latter are sometimes put in a separate category as the brown race) and the white race of Europe, or more correctly of the Euro-Asiatic tract, which extends up to and includes India and West Central Asia. The Australian aboriginal, sometimes regarded as a separate race, seems, notwithstanding his dark skin, to be an early offshoot from a primitive form of the " white " stock, as also is the " Hairy Ainu," the primitive hirsute indigenous inhabitant of the northernmost island of Japan and the island of Sakhalin.

One character alone is not sufficient for the purposes of scientific classification; though, broadly speaking, the classification given above stands even when other characters are added as distinctive.

If the nature of the hair and the shape of the head be added to colour, we find that in the Negro of Africa dark coloration is accompanied by woolly or frizzy hair and a long head; in the Mongol of Central and Eastern Asia the yellow pigmentation is found with coarse, lank, straight hair and a broad or round head; while Europe again stands midway. The white peoples have a tendency to wavy hair, and they also incline on the one side to the long head of the African, on the other to the broad head of the Asiatic, though in neither instance in quite such a pronounced form.

At this point, even though we are dealing with three characters only, the primary scheme of classification begins to break down and cross-classification becomes necessary. If the American Indians are included in the yellow race, as is usual, both long and broad heads are to be found in this group. Evidently another strain has been introduced, and the simple classification by colour is inadequate. The facts are more complex than is compatible with a classification which rests on colour alone.

Much the same difficulty arises in dealing with the peoples of Indonesia and the Pacific, where both long and broad heads appear in combination with both frizzy and wavy hair. This supports a suggestion put forward on other grounds that at some remote period the Pacific peoples received an influx of blood closely akin to the long-headed European type. The suggestion has no reference to recent white admixture.

It will be noted in the classification given above that the peoples of Europe stand midway between two diverse types : yellow broad-head, black long-head. This is a matter of no little interest. Some hold that the European races, in a physical sense, are the most primitive of all, representing the least modification away from the original primitive stock, while the African and the Mongol are the result of specialized development in diverse directions.

JAPAN AND CHINA

These specializations have reduced the adaptability of the black and yellow races and have interfered with their advance along lines which have been left open to the more adaptable European with his less highly specialized physique and nervous system. The argument is not vitiated by the recent cultural progress of Japan and in a less degree of China, which is due to the artificial stimulus of European impact.

DR. A. T. SCHOFIELD (MONDIALE)

BANTU BEAUTY FROM TANGANYIKA

The Bantu-speaking peoples are dominant over the greater part of Africa south of the Sahara. It is supposed that their Negro ancestors intermarried with members of a lighter-skinned people from Asia.

When only a small number of racial characters is taken into account—as, for example, in the grouping by head-form and colour—the peoples of the respective continental regions may appear comparatively uniform; but this apparent uniformity is largely illusory if a more exacting system of classification is applied. As the number of racially significant characters forming the basis of classifications is increased, e.g. as type of hair, form of nose, stature, and so on are added as classificatory characters, populations break up into smaller and smaller divisions and sub-divisions, unless an inordinate amount of cross-classification is admitted.

PYGMIES AND NEGROES

In Europe, as already mentioned, there are three main racial types—the Nordic, the Alpine and the Mediterranean. The last named is found on the northern shores of this inland sea, all along the coast of North Africa and inland as far as the Sahara. It is, in fact, a division of a race which, with local modifications, extends from Great Britain by way of the western coast of Europe, along the Mediterranean, through Palestine, Arabia, Mesopotamia and Persia to India and even beyond.

To this race as a whole, important both in antiquity and at the present day, the name of "the brown race" has been given, to be distinguished from the brown race which was mentioned above as extending from Eastern Asia into the Pacific. As the Semite it is the main stock of the Arabs. This stock, mingled with that of the broad-headed Alpine or Armenoid from Anatolia, gave rise to the Jews.

Of the peoples of Europe of today, the Scandinavians, part of the peoples of Britain, Northern France and Northern Central Europe, including some, but not all, of the population of Germany, are Nordic; the peoples of Central Europe, from Central France to Eastern Europe and including the Balkans, are Alpine. There is a large Alpine element in Germany, and the Slavs are predominantly a localized form of the Alpine race.

The peoples of South Europe are predominantly Mediterranean in type, though there is much admixture, especially in Portugal where Negro blood has been introduced, and in Greece due to the intrusion of Slav, Turkish and Anatolian peoples as well as early Nordics. Russia, partly Slav, has a very considerable infusion of Asiatic and Mongoloid (Tartar) blood.

Although the distribution of races in Africa is still a matter of considerable obscurity, up to a point the facts are fairly clear. In the north, as already stated, the population is Mediterranean with an admixture of the specialized Asiatic form of that race known as Semitic due to Arab invasion, and an infusion of blood from the negroid south.

In "Black" Africa, which begins with the Sahara and extends throughout the Continent to the southward, the distribution of peoples is perhaps most easily to be set out in terms of migrations. The earliest and most deeply rooted of existing peoples are the Bushmen, the almost extinct primitive people of South Africa, most readily distinguished by their diminutive stature, their closely coiled peppercorn-like hair and the accumulation of fat on their buttocks, a character peculiarly noticeable in the women, in whom it is considered a beauty. By some the Bushmen are thought to be descendants, or an offshoot, of the Palæolithic peoples responsible for the cave paintings found in the north of Spain.

The Bushmen are short, but not pygmy. Real Pygmy peoples are found in West and Central Africa in the forests of the Congo. Opinion is divided as to whether the Pygmies or the Bushmen represent the earliest wave of immigration to reach Africa. There is much to be said for the Pygmies; their primitive culture suggests that they belong to a very old stock.

The Pygmies are closely associated with the Negroes, who represent another early wave of migration. This dark-skinned, woolly-haired thick-lipped and broad-nosed type of West African is too familiar to need further particularization.

BANTU-SPEAKING PEOPLES

Closely related to the Bushmen are the Hottentots; but their exact racial origins are obscure. They are thought to be the result of a cross between the Bushmen and a taller and more refined Negroid stock.

The Negro was followed by a less markedly Negroid and lighter-skinned group of peoples who kept cattle. Of the earlier peoples the Bushmen and Pygmies were hunters, the Negroes agriculturists. These nomad cattle-keeping tribes were the ancestors of the Bantu-speaking peoples who are now the predominant people over the greater part of Black Africa.

The Bantu obviously have much Negro blood

FOX

SPRIGHTLY MAORIS OF NEW ZEALAND

The Maoris were formerly given to cannibalism and tribal warfare, and in the fighting the women took their stand with the men. They believed that the seat of the soul was in the left eye.

in them. Apparently they are the result of a Negro admixture with the lighter strain of cattle-keeping people, which probably came from Asia and belonged to a stock closely akin to that of the existing Hamitic peoples of North-East Africa, such as the Somali and Gallas of Abyssinia. These Hamitic peoples, if not a branch of the brown Mediterranean race, must have a strong infusion of its blood. Lastly come the Dinka, Shilluk and other tribes of the Upper Nile Valley, who represent an ancient stock of much diluted Negro blood.

The racial facts of Asia are more complex, and must be approached in a different way. Bound up with them is the racial distribution of the Pacific.

GREAT MOUNTAIN BARRIERS

In Asia the section of the great mountain chain which extends from Central France to China forms a strongly marked dividing tract, cutting off north from south, not only in the geographical, but also in the racial sense. To north and south of this tract—in the north on the plain lands of Northern Asia, which stretch from the Pacific to Lapland; in the south from Indonesia and the islands of the Pacific to Arabia—live peoples of very ancient origin, and fundamentally belonging to long-headed types. They are separated from one another by a belt of broad-headed peoples which live along the whole extent of this great series of mountain ranges.

TARTAR INVASIONS OF EUROPE

This Asiatic broad-headed group is not uniform. There are two types. If we regard the western edge of the great Central Asiatic Desert which lies between the Pamirs and China as the dividing point, to the west are peoples who resemble the European Alpine type. Their skins are fair (that is, for Asiatics), their eyes are light in colour—hazel, grey or even blue—their noses are prominent and well formed, and they can grow a full beard like that of the European.

East of the dividing point, to the south in Tibet and along the slopes of the Kuen Lun Mountains into China, and to the north in Southern Siberia, Mongolia and into China from the north, are the yellow broad-heads, familiar as the Mongolian type, with yellow skin, straight, lank and coarse black hair, dark eyes, broad cheek-bones and flat noses, and very scant facial hair.

The influence of these broad-headed peoples of the Asiatic mountain belt on the history of the world has been profound. As early as the close of the Old Stone Age they were beginning to appear sporadically in Europe. By the New Stone Age they had established themselves in the Carpathian and Alpine regions and had introduced agriculture and domesticated animals into European culture. Repeated migrations continued to pour into Europe from time to time, culminating in the great Tartar invasions of the later Middle Ages and the fall of Constantinople in A.D. 1453 before the assaults of the Turks.

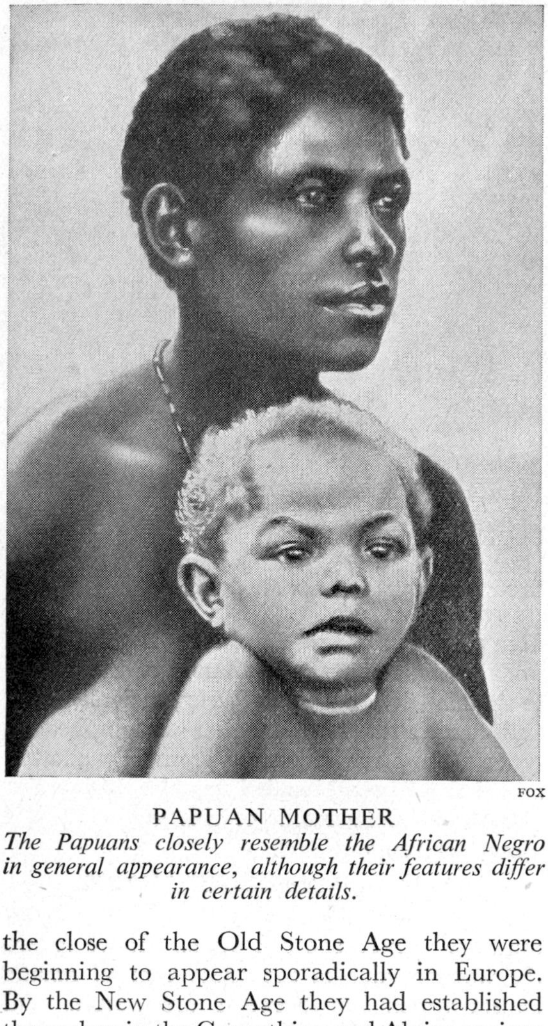

FOX

PAPUAN MOTHER

The Papuans closely resemble the African Negro in general appearance, although their features differ in certain details.

The part played by the eastern broad-heads of Asia is more readily to be appreciated than that of the western, because of the distinctive physical characters of the Mongoloid type. The ancient peoples of Northern Asia were much modified by their admixture. These northern peoples were the results of an early migration from the south-central area, possibly somewhere to the north-west of India, and dating, it may be, from the close of the middle and beginning of the late period of the Old Stone Age.

MONGOLIAN INFILTRATION

There is evidence that a people of this later period of the Old Stone Age penetrated to the Ordos Desert in Central China and to the neighbourhood of Peking (Peiping) in North China. It was also a wave of this people which first reached America, though perhaps not till the New Stone Age. In the meantime a Mongolian infiltration had taken place, as is shown in the distinctly Mongolian cast in the features of those American Indians who are thought to be the result of the later waves of migration to that Continent. Westward, Mongolian influence can be discerned, more especially in individuals, so far as Lapland. The Finns, on the other hand, represent a distinct stream of Asiatic migration which reached Finland from the south and of which traces can be seen in populations scattered along a line extending to the south so far as and including part of the population of Hungary.

In the south of Asia, Mongolian infiltration has left its traces all along the northern borders of India, in Burma and in farther India. In South-Eastern Asia its influence is especially marked, and thence it spreads into the Pacific.

South of the great mountain barrier, the broad-headed race impinged on a population which was composed predominantly of the Mediterranean brown race. To account for the local variations of this race, and the form taken in its extension into the Pacific, the racial history of Southern Asia may be reconstructed summarily and very tentatively as follows.

EARLIEST MIGRATIONS OF PEOPLES

There is reason to think that the earliest migrations of peoples—and this applies equally to Africa and Europe, as well as to Asia—must have set out from a centre somewhere to the north-west of what is now India, possibly in the southern part of the Pamir region, or just to the south of it.

If this be so, although there must have been differences between the peoples of each wave of migration when they started, differences which developed in the interval between each migration, the major variations in physical characters between the various primary races, or main racial stocks as they exist today, must have developed after they had reached, or were well on their way to the continental areas they now occupy. For example: the dark skin, thick lips, woolly hair and broad nose of the Negro are adaptations to a tropical climate which could hardly have evolved in a mountainous region in Central Asia.

EASTERN NEGROES

There is evidence in Asia, as in Africa, that a Pygmy population was an early, if not the earliest, wave of migration. There may, in fact, once have been a continuous belt of Pygmy forms extending from West Africa right across to New Guinea. In Asia they survive at present only in the Andaman Islands, the Malay Peninsula, the Philippines and Sumatra. A considerable remnant still survives in New Guinea.

There was also, again as in Africa, a wave of migration of a people, or peoples, who evolved into a Negro type. These are now to be seen in the dark-skinned frizzy-haired inhabitants of New Guinea, the Papuans, and with some modifications, in the dark-skinned natives of the islands of Melanesia.

These peoples are sometimes called the Eastern Negroes, although in shape of nose and other characters they differ from the African Negroes. This may be due to the influence of a different environment, or to a racial admixture in the course of their migrations.

JUNGLE TRIBES OF INDIA

Although there is no direct evidence that this wave of migration passed through India, the dark skins, thick lips and frizzy hair of individual natives of India suggest a trace of this blood. It may, however, be due to the contacts with Africa of which there is evidence in later times.

Another wave of migration has certainly left its traces in India and Ceylon. This is a migration which was responsible for what are now the jungle tribes of India, sometimes known as the aboriginal tribes, and the very primitive cave-dwelling Veddahs of Ceylon. This wave passed on, possibly by way of farther India, Siam, the Malay Peninsula, and almost certainly through Java to reach Australia, an even more primitive form having already reached Tasmania.

In date this wave probably coincides with the very beginning of the last phase of the Old Stone Age in Europe, when Neanderthal man was dying out and "modern" man was beginning to take his place. This would be about the same time as the wave of migration towards North-East Siberia and America was setting out on its travels.

EWING GALLOWAY, N.Y.

TRIBAL CHIEF

The chief of the Nambi tribe of head hunters in one of the islands of the New Hebrides. This island group is in the Western Pacific and has a native population of some 60,000.

As far as it is possible to draw any inferences from the relations of the physical characters of the different races of India one to another, that which has been called here the Mediterranean brown race, followed.

To this race belong the peoples of India known as the Dravidians, from the fact that they all speak languages which belong to the Dravidian group or family. As compared with the Mediterranean peoples they are by no means pure-blooded; their thicker features, darker skins and broader noses suggest that they have inherited a considerable admixture of the blood of the aboriginal tribes who preceded them.

They were at one time the main population of the Indian peninsula, and seem to have developed a high civilization, for to them are attributed the ancient cities with their elaborate culture discovered a few years ago in the Indus valley. This civilization is closely related to the early civilization of Mesopotamia as found in the cities excavated by Sir Leonard Woolley and other archæologists.

It was this race, or a variant of it, which in farther India, Burma and beyond, came into contact with the Mongoloid peoples, and

MONDIALE

INHABITANT OF PERU
Wind-dried and sun-scorched, the Titicacan of today lives very much as his ancestors lived.

according to the degree of admixture, produced the various types now found in South-Eastern Asia, extending in varying degrees of purity down into the islands of the Pacific.

The last of the more important racial incursions into India was that of the Aryan-speaking peoples. These peoples, closely akin to the Nordics of Europe, had already overrun the country which is now Persia and become its ruling class. They were pastoral and war-like nomads. After a struggle immortalized in their national epic poems, they overcame the urbanized Dravidians and became the dominant people of India, whose warrior caste were the ancestors of the ruling peoples of the native states of India today. Further, according to one school of thought it was an offshoot from this people which migrated to the Pacific and provided the ruling caste of Polynesia.

With this wave of migration the peopling of India was complete, for although it suffered invasion on many occasions in later times, except for a broadening of the head in certain areas, the effect on the racial characters of the people at large has been negligible.

With the incursion of the nomad Aryan into India the main lines of racial distributions in Asia were complete, save for the westward drive of the warrior Mongols, which overran Central and Western Asia and on more than one occasion reached Eastern Europe, from which they withdrew finally as a political power only after the World War, while descendants of Tartar tribes still live in Russia.

COMPLEXITY OF CLASSIFICATION

From what has been said, it will be seen that the problem of the classification of the varieties of mankind as " races " is one of extreme complexity. At the same time it is possible to say that on very broad lines they fall into three or four main groups with two secondary, or sub-groups arising out of admixture—a European or Caucasian group occupying (if we ignore modern emigration) Europe and extending into Northern Africa and Western and South Central Asia; a Negro group occupying Africa, with a cognate eastern negroid group in Papua and Melanesia; and a Mongolian group in Eastern Asia with secondary or sub-group, much mixed offshoots, one in America and one in South-East Asia and the Pacific; while the Australian " race " may be regarded as either a distinct and separate survival from a primitive prehistoric form, or as an early offshoot from the primitive Caucasian type.

VARIETIES ONLY

Finally, returning to the point from which we started, it cannot be emphasized too strongly that the races of man are varieties only. Although they have attained some degree of stability, and although they differ widely among themselves, they all belong to one species, *Homo sapiens*, " modern man." Some of these varieties may display inherited characters in which they resemble a primitive ancestral type more closely than others, but biological science in classifying the races of man according to physical characters regards them all equally as members of one and the same great group in the world of living things. It affords no warrant for affixing to one group rather than another the stigma of racial inferiority. The " inferiority " of backward peoples is neither racial nor innate. It is cultural and a remediable condition.

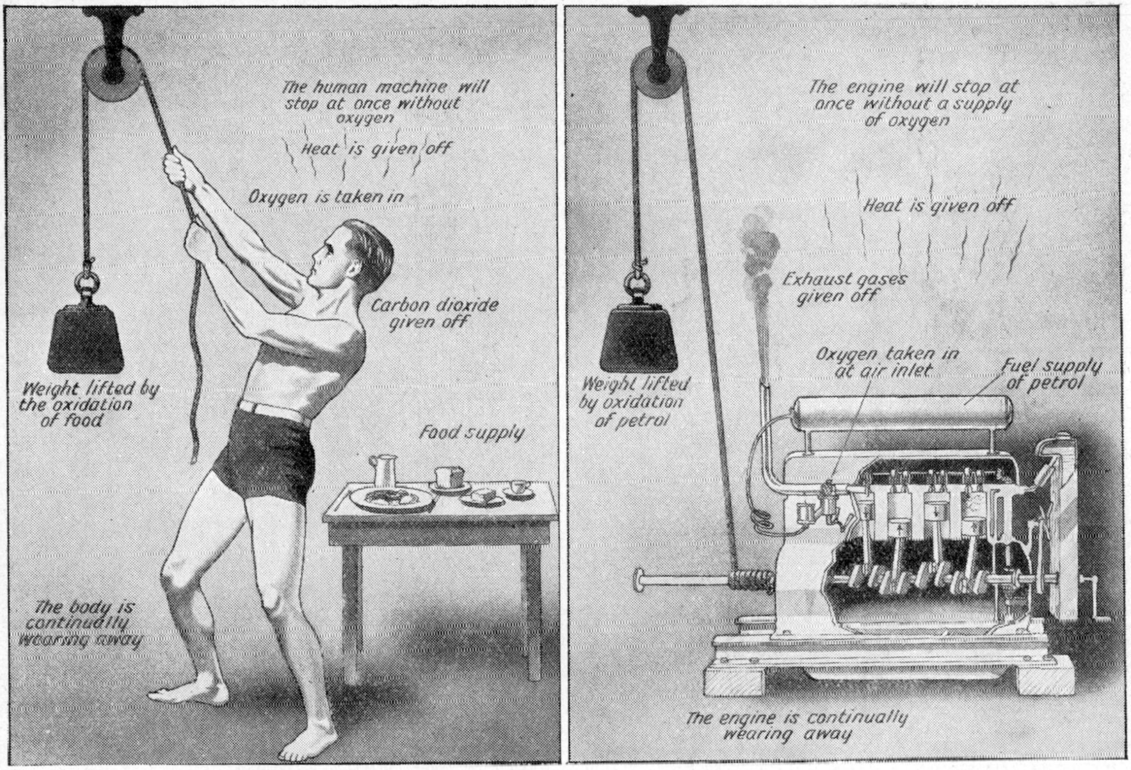

SIMILARITIES BETWEEN MAN AND THE ENGINE HE BUILDS

Both man and machine will stop without a supply of oxygen, and each gives off exhaust gases. In the one case power is produced by the oxidation of food, and in the other by the oxidation of petrol.

THE HUMAN MACHINE AT WORK

At a first glance man, with his trappings of civilization, seems a being far removed from the animal world. Yet in the development of his embryo no less than in the structure of his anatomy, *Homo sapiens*, as he is known to Science, closely resembles the higher mammals. Particularly does he resemble the gorilla.

It is believed that man, the gorilla and the gibbon have all come from a common stock. The gibbon has kept the form of his ancestors; the gorilla has progressed a little from that form, while man has evolved to his present position. If we closely examine the skeletons of the gorilla and man, it can be seen that every one of the two hundred and six bones are present in both, in exactly the same position in the body. Each bone shows the same characteristics. The differences relate to proportion, size and minor detail. For instance, man's brain-case is larger, his trunk smaller, his lower limbs longer, his upper limbs shorter. The great anthropoids are susceptible to many infectious diseases from which man suffers today.

Having accepted the fact that *Homo sapiens* is an animal, built on the same plan as other mammals and subject to the same physiological laws, scientists by experimenting untiringly on such mammals as rats, rabbits and apes have been able to deduce facts relating to the human body. In consequence, medical science is capable of curing or preventing a thousand ills for which previously there were no remedies.

In order to understand the working of the body, it must be remembered that within this complex machine are other and smaller machines which, for the smooth running of the whole, must be kept in constant good repair. These smaller machines are represented by the seven systems of the body—the osseous, the muscular, the respiratory and digestive (which may be taken together), the circulatory, the excretory, the reproductive and, last but

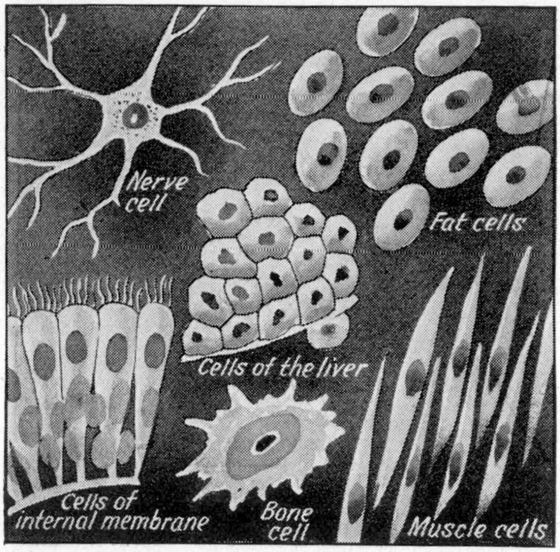

SIX KINDS OF CELL
Countless millions of cells are bound together in the human body to form the tissues.

certainly not least, the nervous system. Within each system designed for a special use are organs for special work, these organs being composed of and kept together by tissue of various kinds. The smallest units in the body are the cells, countless millions of which are bound together to form the tissues.

The special work for which the osseous or bony system has been designed is to provide a strong framework for the body; to afford support and protection to the softer structures and to give attachment to the muscles. When force is exerted by the muscles, the bones act as levers. The muscular system, then, provides the agents that bring about movement in the body.

UPKEEP OF THE MACHINE

The respiratory and digestive systems are both concerned with the upkeep of the machine. The respiratory, or breathing system, serves the double purpose of supplying fuel in the form of oxygen necessary for combustion and of ridding it of carbon dioxide, the waste product of that combustion. Other fuel is provided by the digestive system, whose work is to collect and assimilate it that it may be sent into every part of the body. This work of distribution is done by the circulatory system, which also conveys the oxygen from the lungs, the heart acting as a central pump for the blood by which the oxygen is carried. The excretory system is the scavenger of the waste products. It takes away the poisons so that the machine is left free to work smoothly.

The reproductory system is concerned with the transmission of the germ-plasm—that part of the living substance of man which is handed on from one generation to another, and by which *Homo sapiens* propagates his species. Lastly, the nervous system, with the brain as the most important control, directs and orders all other systems, ensuring co-ordination. The body as such is therefore a factory with elaborate and specialized machinery and a chemical works.

THE HUMAN TAIL

Now as to the skeleton. The vertebral column, which man has in common with fish, amphibia, reptiles and birds, is the central axis round which the body is built. Of the thirty-three vertebræ of which this column is made, twenty-four are jointed; namely, the seven cervical which make the framework for the neck, the twelve thoracic vertebræ which are the framework for the chest and the five large vertebræ in the middle of the back known as the lumbar vertebræ. The next five are jointed into one bone, the sacrum, wedged into the hip bones on either side. The last four are also fused into one bone, known as the coccyx, which is all that is now left of the human tail.

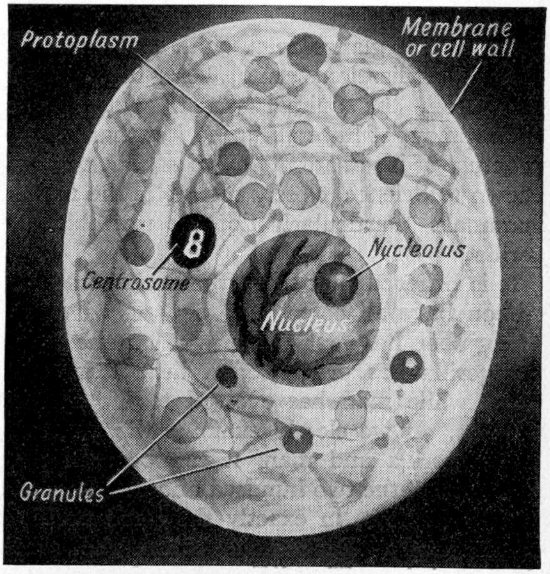

TYPICAL CELL
Showing wall enclosing nucleus and nucleolus surrounded by protoplasm. The nucleus is the ruling factor. The chemistry of the granules varies.

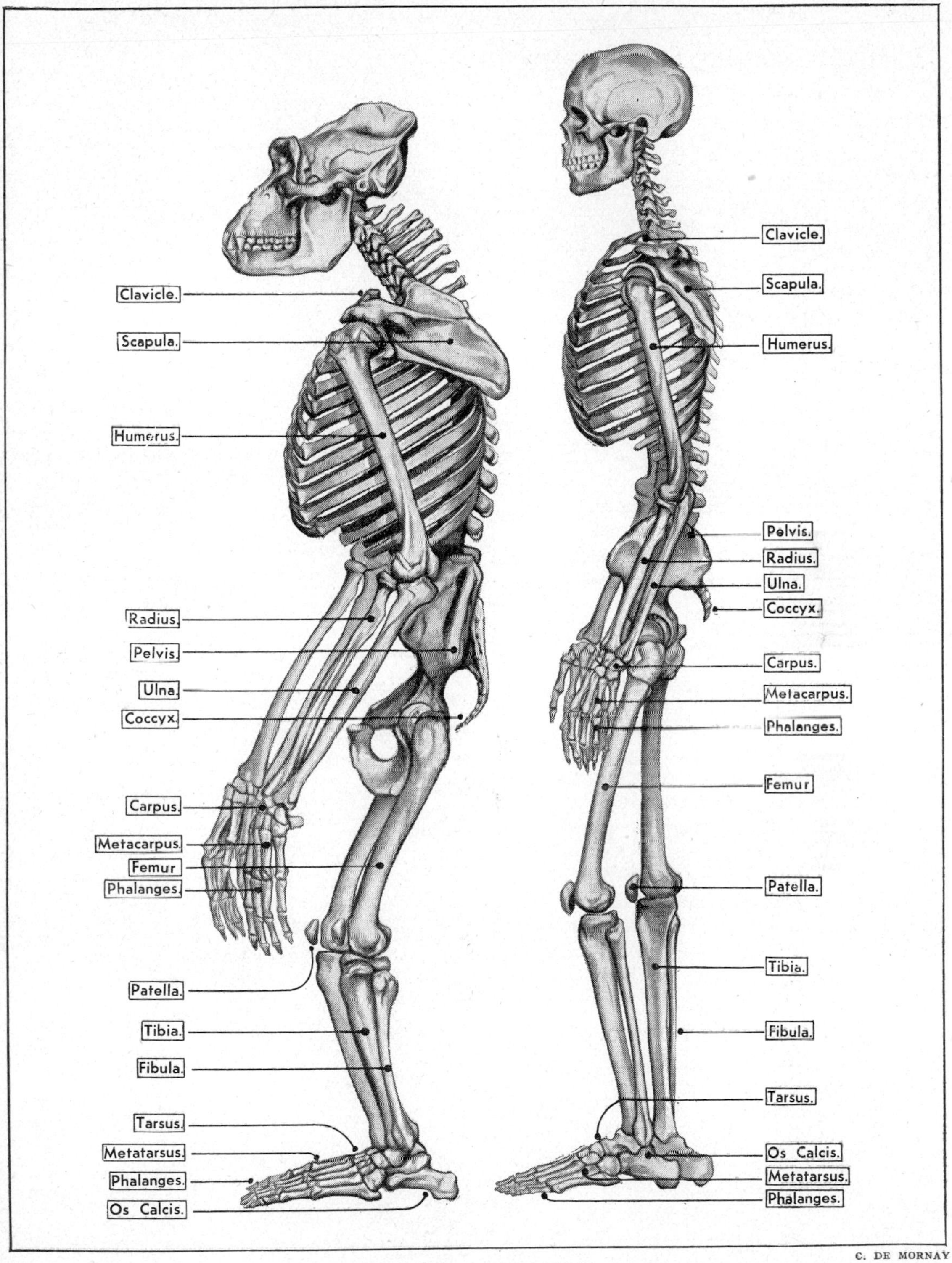

C. DE MORNAY

GORILLA AND MAN

If we closely examine the skeletons of a gorilla (left) and a man, it can be seen that every one of the two hundred and six bones are present in both, in exactly the same position in the body. Each bone shows the same characteristics but differs in shape.

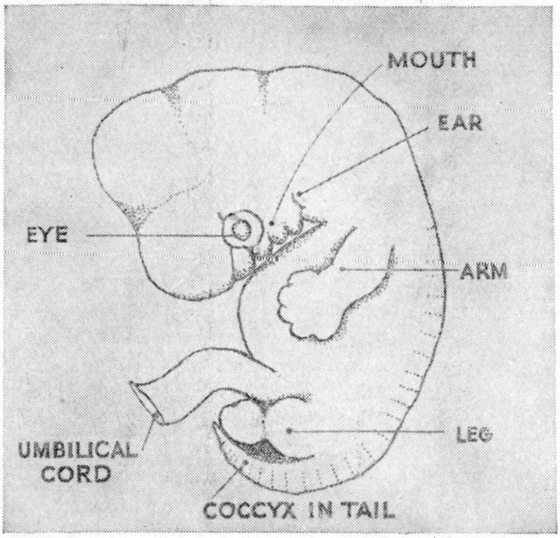

DR. A. J. E. CAVE (AFTER BROMAN)

THE HUMAN TAIL

Human embryo, showing the coccyx, which is all that now remains of the human tail.

At about the third week of the development of the human embryo the tail is clearly visible on the surface of the body, into which it later disappears. When man assumed the upright position, he no longer needed the tail for the work of balancing, although even now there are rare cases of children born with true tails.

The vertebræ, placed one above the other with soft pads of cartilage or gristle between them to act as shock absorbers, give support to the body, allowing the weight to be transferred from the head and trunk to the hips and legs. Further, the column has the advantage of being flexible until, with the coming of old age, the pads of cartilage tend to become hard. Perhaps the most important function of the backbone is to protect the spinal cord, the connecting link between the body and the brain.

HOUSING THE SPINAL CORD

Each single vertebra—except the two at the top of the column, the atlas and the axis as they are called—is made up of a bony ring, thickened in front. Jutting out from the back of the ring is a small spiky tip, and from the sides two other pointed processes project, the whole forming a kind of hook for the muscles of the back.

The bony rings of the vertebræ are joined firmly together by tough fibrous bands called ligaments which pass from the processes of one to the other, so that in the middle of the knobbly rings is a hollow tube called the spinal canal. By this the spinal cord is housed and protected.

The first cervical vertebra, the atlas, consists of a ring thickened at the sides. The two little hollows on its upper surface are designed to take the two bony knobs of the occipital bone at the back of the head. The second vertebra, the axis, has a kind of peg fitting into the atlas above. When the head is turned from side to side, both the skull and the atlas move together round this peg; but if the head is nodded, it is enabled to rock up and down because the bony knobs fit into the hollows mentioned above.

BONES OF THE FACE

The skull is made up of the brain-box, or cranium, and the face. With the exception of the lower jaw, the bones here are neatly fitted into each other by their saw-like edges. The chief of these bones are the frontal, the two parietal or side bones, the two temporal bones, and the occipital bone with its large perforation about one inch and a half across, through which the spinal cord enters the brain.

The face has fourteen separate bones, the

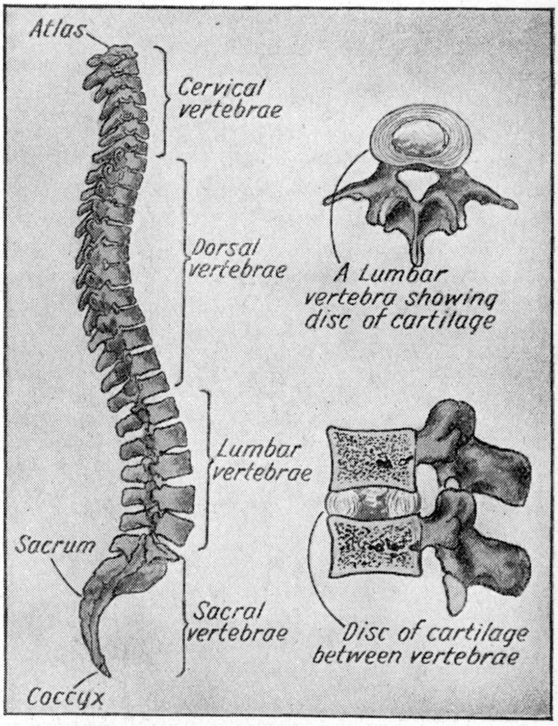

PROTECTOR OF THE SPINAL CORD

The most important function of the backbone is to protect the spinal cord, the connecting link between body and brain.

most important of which are the upper and lower jaw, the two malar bones for the cheeks, and the two nasal bones. The lower jaw, in which the lower teeth are fixed, is so jointed that it can work up and down, from side to side, and forward and back, making it possible for man to grind up his food.

PROTECTING THE CHEST

The protecting cage for the thorax, or chest, is made up thus : behind, of the twelve thoracic vertebræ; in front, of the dagger-like breast-bone, or sternum; and, at the sides, of the twelve pairs of curved ribs. Each pair of ribs is fixed to a vertebra behind and to the breast-bone in front, with the exception of the last two pairs. These are shorter than the rest and are known as floating ribs, since they end in muscle and are not connected here to any bone.

The limbs may be thought of as being in three sections : an upper part—the humerus in the arm, the femur in the leg; a middle part—the ulna and radius in the arm, the tibia and fibula in the leg; and a lower part—twenty-seven bones in the hand and twenty-six in the foot.

Both wrist and ankle are made up of small irregular bones. In the wrist there are eight carpal bones arranged in two rows of four, the second row being joined to five delicate bones, the metacarpals, in the palm of the hand. The metacarpals are jointed to the bones in the fingers—the phalanges, as they are called of which there are three in each finger and two in the thumb. In the foot the tarsal, or ankle, bones are seven, which with the metatarsal bones together go to form the arch of man's foot. Man is the only mammal to have an arch to his foot.

CHEMISTRY OF BONE

The arms and legs are connected to the trunk by the shoulder girdle and the pelvic girdle. At the neck the collar-bones, or clavicles, can be felt as they pass outwards on either side from the breast-bone to meet the scapula—the flat triangular shoulder-blade, as it is generally known. As is evident if the shoulders are shrugged, the scapula is a bone that moves very freely, being kept in place largely by the strong surrounding muscles. The outer angle of the scapula is hollowed to take the rounded head of the humerus into its cup.

In precisely the same way the femur fits into the hip-bone, which is part of the pelvic girdle. This girdle, or bony basin, is made up of the sacrum and coccyx behind, jointed to the large hip-bones curving and meeting in front. In man the whole is so tilted that with its attendant muscles it supports the intestines and the organs of reproduction.

Bone derives its rigidity from the mineral salts, largely calcium phosphate and calcium carbonate, which go to make up about two-thirds of it. Flexibility comes from the

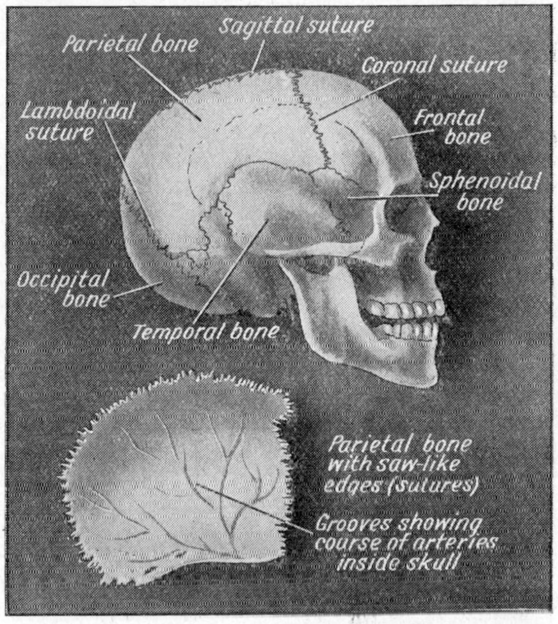

BONES OF THE HEAD

With the exception of the lower jaw the bones are neatly fitted into each other by their saw-like edges.

gelatinous one-third. Most bones, when just formed, consist of cartilage only. This explains why so often a child, if it makes a bad fall, will merely have a bone bent. It then sustains what is known as a "greenstick" fracture, whereas an adult's more brittle bone would be truly fractured. The humerus grows longer at the shoulder, the radius and the ulna at the wrist, and the femur at the knee.

Running down the middle of long bones such as the femur is the marrow, made up of blood cells and fat. Although bones are largely made up of mineral matter, yet living cells permeate every part of them, they have blood vessels to nourish them and nerve cells to stimulate them.

All bones are bound together by ligaments—strong, white, fibrous bands which, because of their elasticity, permit of a certain amount of movement without dislocation taking place. The union of two bones is called a joint.

The work of all joints, of which there are two hundred and thirty in the body, is to allow of movement between bones, and for this purpose they are admirably constructed. According to the kind of movement which takes place at any particular joint, it is known as a gliding, hinge, pivot or ball-and-socket joint.

The ends of the bones, which are lashed together by the ligaments, are provided with a glossy covering of cartilage, enabling them to move smoothly against each other. In addition, all round the joint there is a special ligament known as the capsule, which makes a kind of bag for it. The bag itself is lined with synovial membrane, a delicate tissue so named because of the lubricant it secretes, synovia.

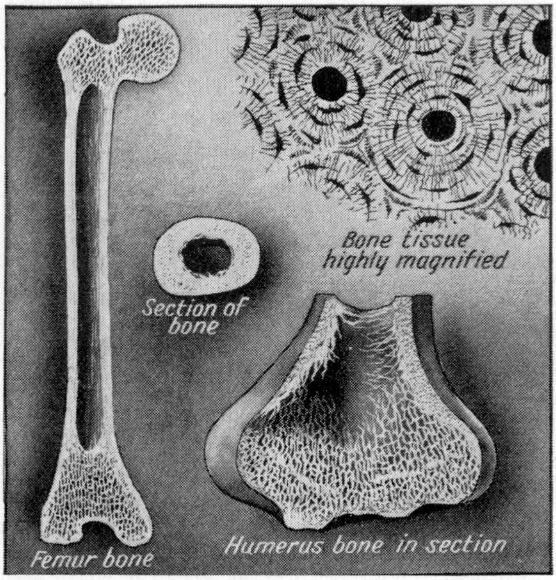

SECTIONS OF BONE

Running down the middle of long bones such as the femur is the marrow, made up of blood cells and fat. Living cells permeate every part of them.

This "joint oil" is made from the dead bodies of the cartilage-building cells at the end of the bones. In people who have rheumatism in the joints this self-lubricating device has ceased to function, for the cartilage round the bones has become dry and possibly worn away, while the joint itself creaks and grates like a piece of rusty machinery.

Gliding joints do not permit of very much movement; they are found at the wrists and between the vertebræ. Hinge joints are formed by round ends of one bone fitting into hollows of the other. By this arrangement a forward and backward movement in one plane takes place. Such joints occur at the knee, and between the phalanges of the fingers and toes.

BALL-AND-SOCKET JOINTS

An example of a pivot joint which has already been mentioned is at the meeting of the axis and the atlas, allowing the head to be turned from side to side. Ball-and-socket joints—both the hip and the shoulder joint come into this category—permit of the greatest movement of all. Here the rounded end of the one bone fits into a cup, so that the movement may take place in several planes. In the shoulder joint the head of the humerus fits into what is known as the glenoid cavity of the scapula, the whole being enclosed in the loose bag of the capsular ligament. The same kind of capsular ligament surrounds the femur and the cup—the acetabulum—of the hip bone, at the hip joint. In both the shoulder and the hip joints the bony cup is made still deeper by its rim of fibro-cartilage.

Everywhere the bones of the skeleton are covered by muscles, furnished with blood vessels and with nerves. Voluntary muscles, which are those under the influence of the will, are usually connected at one end by a tendon—a strong fibrous cord much like a ligament except that it has no elasticity—to a fixed bone, and at the other end by a tendon to the bone to be moved.

FIVE HUNDRED MUSCLES

When the striped tissue of a voluntary muscle contracts, as when the biceps muscle contracts to bend the arm, it shortens and thickens, pulls on the tendons, and the bone is put in motion. A single contraction takes about one-tenth of a second. Tendons themselves are often protected by a synovia-lined sheath, so that they are able to glide smoothly when the muscle works.

One muscle never works alone, because after a bone has been moved it is brought back to its original position by a second muscle, antagonistic in its action. Man's posture is maintained by a large number of muscles acting at the same time. For instance, the contraction of muscles at the back of the neck would pull the head backwards but for the work of those connecting the face with the clavicle and the sternum; similarly, muscles at the back of the legs would pull the body backwards but for the opposing muscles in front of the thigh,

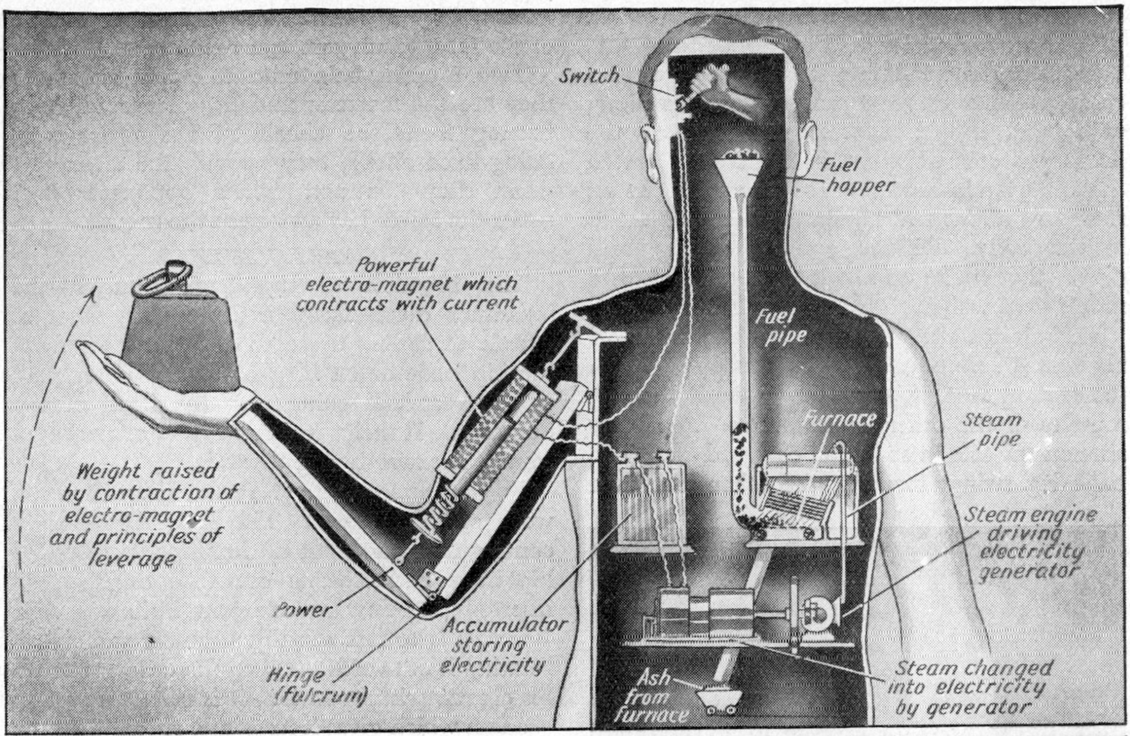

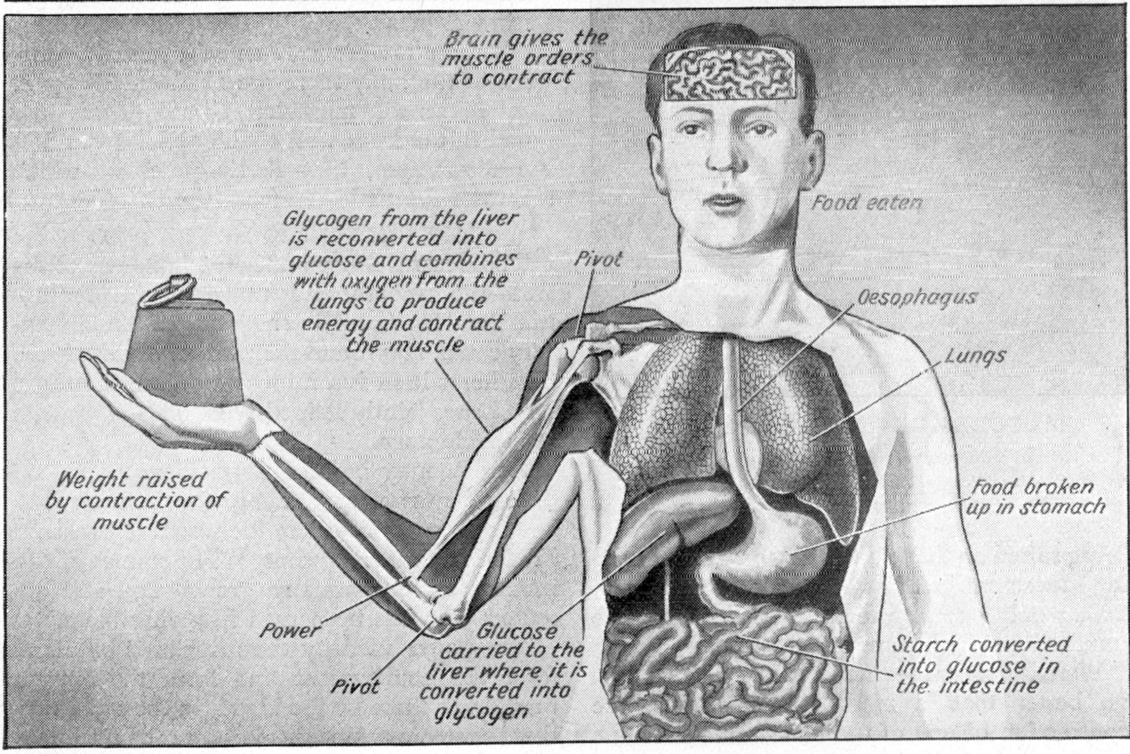

FURTHER SIMILARITIES BETWEEN MAN AND MACHINE

In the upper picture mechanical devices are performing the functions of the various living organs shown in the illustration below. There are two hundred and thirty joints and about five hundred separate muscles in the human body. The latter make up about three-sevenths of a man's total weight.

connecting the hip bone with bones of the leg.

Whether seated or standing, man uses all the muscles of the spine, and it is fatiguing to him to keep either of these positions for very long without changing. Muscles used to bend the limbs are called flexors, and those to stretch the limbs again are known as extensors. In all there are about five hundred separate muscles in the body. Differing greatly in size and shape, they make up about three-sevenths of a man's total weight.

In walking, the body's weight is transferred alternately from one leg to another. When the foot in front touches the ground, the calf muscles of the other leg contract. The body rises on the toes in order to be pushed on. The back leg swings forward, the other foot then

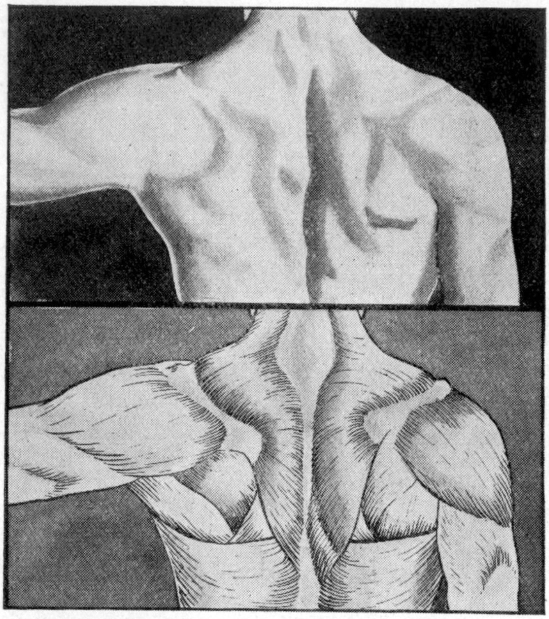

MUSCLES OF THE SHOULDERS

The rippling surface of the shoulders and the complicated masses of muscle immediately beneath the skin One muscle never works alone.

being raised on the toes to carry on the alternating movement. It has been calculated that in taking only one step forward a man uses one hundred and eight muscles.

Were it not for the muscles, the face would be no better than a mask. For example, the contraction of one of the chief muscles of the nose—pyramidalis—draws the skin down between the brows, at the same time making a groove across the nose. This gives a man a stern or even fierce expression. A dimple is formed by the contraction of another muscle of the face, the zygomaticus major.

Two muscles help man to chew his food: they are the masseter and the pterygoid, both passing from the cheek to the lower jaw. Being fixed above, they pull up the lower jaw when they contract. Their opponents pull down the lower jaw and open the mouth.

THE TAILOR MUSCLE

The broadest of the back muscles—the latissimus dorsi—forms a fan-shaped sheet of muscle spreading upwards and outwards from the hip bone and the spines of the lower part of the vertebral column to the head of the humerus. It helps to draw the arm downwards, backwards and inwards.

The swimmer's crawl stroke illustrates the work of this muscle. The long thin muscle coming from the front of the upper part of the hip bone and crossing over the thigh to be inserted just below the knee joint is the sartorius. Its work is to flex the thigh, at the same time rotating it outwards. When the tailor takes up his characteristic position, it is called into play —a fact which gives it its name, *sartor* being the Latin word for tailor.

All these are separate muscles, but in some parts of the body there are others made up of thin sheets of muscular tissue. These are found in the front wall of the abdomen and in the diaphragm, that fleshy partition which separates the abdomen from the thorax.

NOT INFLUENCED BY THE WILL

Those muscles not under the influence of the will—the smooth and unstriped involuntary muscles—are found in the walls of the alimentary canal, and round the walls of blood vessels. The heart itself is a muscular organ, the tissue here being faintly striped although the muscles are involuntary.

Here it may be of interest to note that no definite system of naming the muscles has been adopted. To quote the words of Professor Frederick Gymer Parsons, " The names of the muscles have gradually grown up, and no settled plan has been used in giving them."

The power used by the muscles is obtained from the nourishment and from the oxygen brought to them by the blood, in the same way that the steam engine gets its power by adequate stoking up and by the presence of fresh air in the furnace. How the human machine is stoked and oxygenated for its work is told in another chapter.

DIGESTION AND EXCRETION

In its use of the food supplied to it the body is a far more wonderful machine than any made by man. For not only does the food serve as fuel, which by its combustion gives the body the heat necessary to keep it working, but it is also made to repair the wear and tear inevitable in its running. In other words, food rebuilds the cells and tissues which are constantly being destroyed, in addition to making it possible for the tissues and organs to do their work.

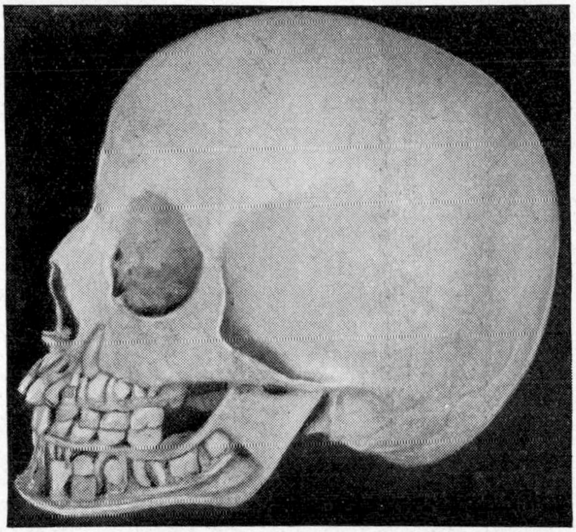

TWO SETS OF TEETH
Skull of a child showing the second set of teeth already forming beneath the first set.

The first stage of digestion is the grinding-up of the food by the teeth, which in an adult should number thirty-two—sixteen in the upper and sixteen in the lower jaw—when the saliva moistens and lubricates it so that it becomes a kind of paste that can readily be swallowed. The saliva, watery in appearance and somewhat alkaline, is brought to the mouth by three pairs of glands, the parotid, the submaxillary and the sublingual. These are found respectively below the ear, under the back part of the lower jaw and under its front portion, beneath the tongue.

From one to two pounds of saliva is secreted daily. The active principle is a valuable digestive juice called ptyalin which turns the insoluble starch of many foodstuffs into a soluble kind of sugar known as grape sugar. The sight, smell or even thought of appetizing food is enough to " make the mouth water," that is, to stimulate the salivary glands into action.

Masticated and mixed with saliva, the food begins its passage down the alimentary canal, which in an adult is about thirty feet long. On its first stage into the throat or pharynx it is pushed backwards by contractions of muscles in the cheek and tongue. Unless by an accident the food goes " down the wrong way," causing us momentarily to choke, the windpipe or trachea is skilfully avoided by the shutting down, precisely like the lid of a box, of its lid of cartilage when it receives the message that food or drink is on its way to the œsophagus, or gullet as it is more usually called.

No sooner has the food entered the funnel-like pharynx or throat than it is seized upon by muscles there and forced on into the œsophagus. This soft tube with its elastic walls is about ten inches long and runs down between the lungs through the diaphragm and on into the stomach. As the food reaches the œsophagus the muscles all along its length contract one after another in a wave. This explains how it is that jugglers and snake charmers are able to balance on their heads and yet drink large draughts of water or even eat a meal, a sight common enough anywhere in the East.

The stomach is an enlargement of the alimentary canal and resembles a pear-shaped pouch about ten inches across, with its broad end upward and pointing to the left. This muscular pouch is anchored to the abdomen by membranes known as mesenteries. The innermost of the four coats of the stomach is a mucous lining, covered with innumerable small glands secreting both mucus to moisten the surface, and during the work of digestion a juice known as the gastric fluid.

This fluid is made up of pepsin, rennin and a little hydrochloric acid. Secretion of the gastric juice begins only when food is sent into the stomach, and it has been calculated that in a healthy adult about two gallons are secreted each day. Most of this is reabsorbed into the blood later, in the small intestine.

Rennin is a ferment that coagulates milk, making a curd, casein, mixed with fat. The curd is afterwards acted on by the pepsin. This nitrogenous substance, with the help of the hydrochloric acid, is able to melt down pieces of meat, fish or white of egg and dissolve them into a jelly-like fluid. When the stomach is deficient in hydrochloric acid the melting process does not take place fast enough. This results in the pain and discomfort known as gastritis. After the insoluble compounds called proteins have been acted on by the gastric juice they are said to be peptones.

If we were to examine thc contents of the stomach some two hours after a mixed meal had reached it, we should find something like the following: some starchy foods already changed into sugar, some not yet changed; peptones from the meat, fish or eggs; fats that had melted but otherwise were unchanged; some foods still undigested, among these being hard or cellulose coverings which act as roughage, and, mixing with the whole, gastric juice. The half-digested foods would now be in the form of a thick greyish-white fluid called chyme. The average time taken to change food into chyme is about three hours: boiled tripe, for instance, takes as little as one hour, while roast chicken takes four hours.

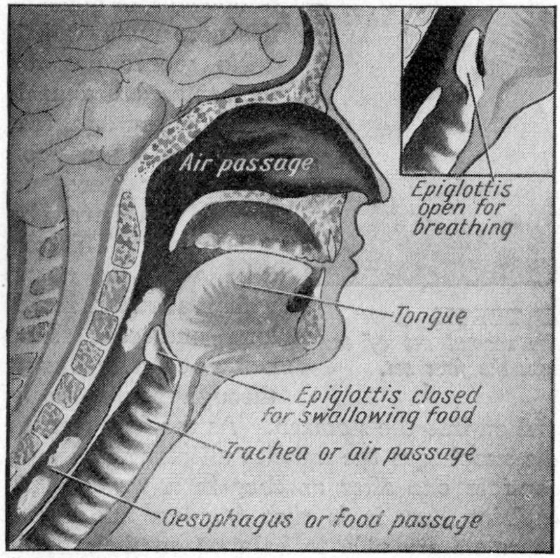

WHY WE DO NOT CHOKE
The epiglottis closed for swallowing food and (inset) open for breathing.

During chymification the muscular walls of the stomach keep the contents continually churning in a circular motion. They are always in contact with the food that the gastric juice may do its work. The stomach constantly changes its size. When empty it contracts till it will hold no more than a quart, but if very much distended it will hold as much as a gallon.

At the lower right-hand side of the stomach is an opening to the small intestine called the pylorus. It is controlled by a circular muscle, a sphincter, which at this point acts as a sentry. As the work of digestion proceeds it gradually relaxes, until finally the contents of the stomach are allowed to pass on through the opening. The peptones do not pass on but are at this stage absorbed through the capillaries into the blood stream.

CHYME BECOMES CHYLE

The duodenum, which makes up, in the form of a " C " bend, the first foot of the twenty-three feet of the coiled small intestine, is a very important organ. For in it, by the aid of two juices—the bile brought from the liver by the bile duct and the pancreatic juice, manufactured by the pancreas or " sweetbread," and taken along by the pancreatic duct—the rest of the food is digested.

Bile, which in a normal person is secreted at the rate of about two and a half pounds daily, helps the pancreatic juice to emulsify or make liquid the fats in the food. It also assists the muscles of the intestine by acting as a natural purge. The pancreatic juice, of which about three-quarters of a pint is secreted daily, has the threefold function of emulsifying fats, changing protein into peptones and starch into grape sugar. In this latter stage of digestion the chyme which came into the duodenum from the stomach becomes very much more milky in appearance, largely due to the further melting of the fats, and is now called chyle.

DISTRIBUTING THE FATS

The inner surface of the small intestine is covered with minute processes known as the villi, every one of which contains a very small blood vessel or capillary, and also another vessel, a lacteal. By the time the chyle has gone a third of the way down the small intestine most of the sugar has been absorbed by the blood vessels and most of the peptones. The fats have still to be distributed. These do not go directly into the blood vessels, but are first passed through the lymphatics. By these they are carried through the lymph glands of the abdomen into the great lymph duct, the thoracic duct. They are finally sent into one of the great veins, the superior vena cava, not far from the heart.

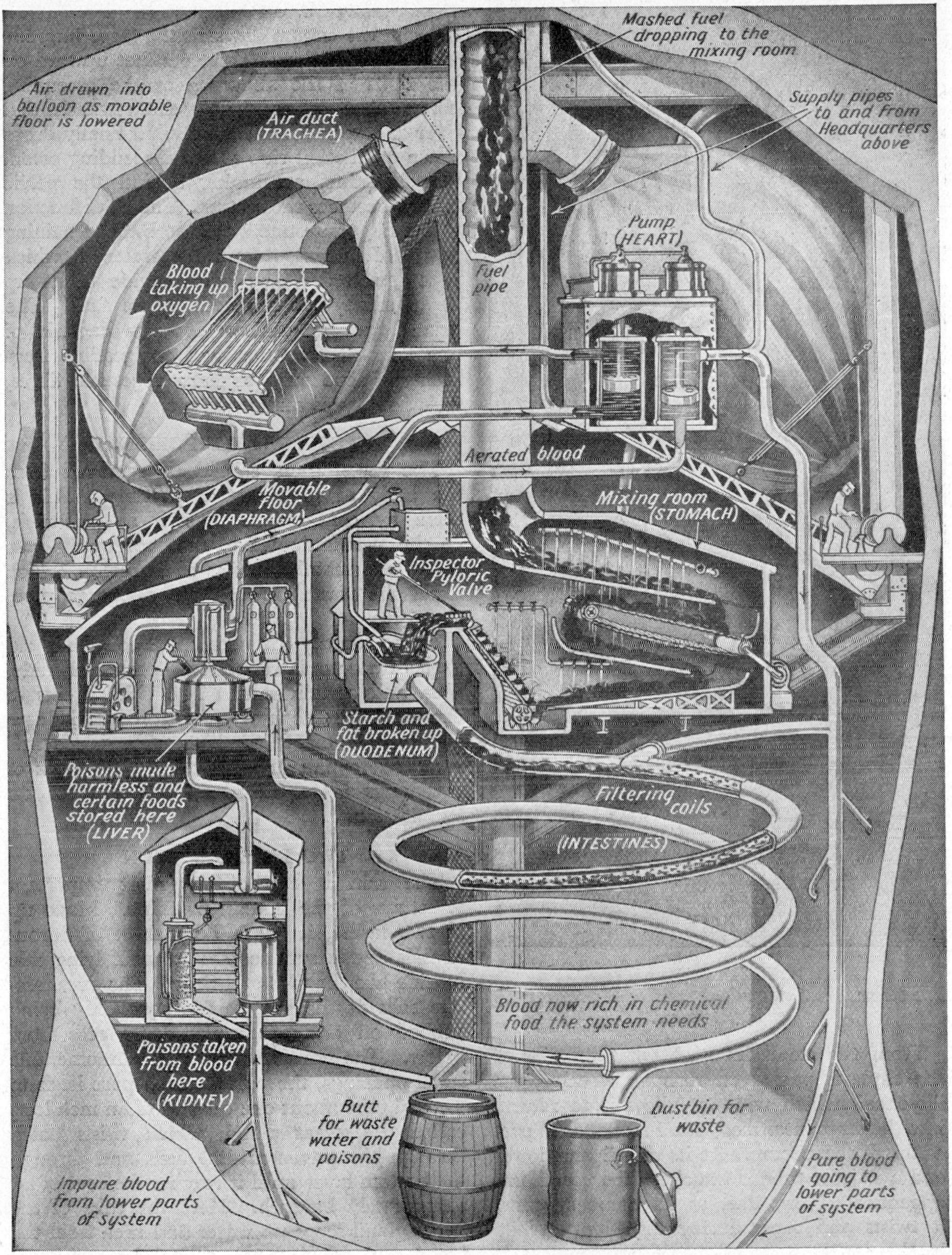

THE FACTORY WITHIN THE HUMAN BODY

The human body may be regarded as the most wonderful chemical works in the world. Some of the many varied operations that take place in the various organs are here represented in a form suited to an essentially mechanical age.

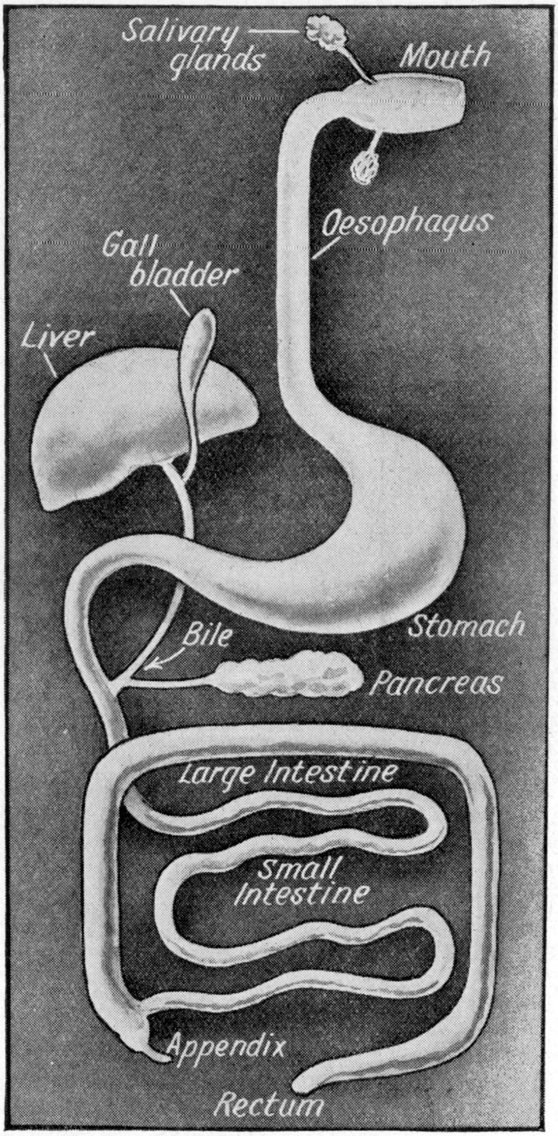

DIGESTIVE TRACT
The stomach is a muscular pear-shaped pouch about ten inches across.

From the small intestine what remains of the chyle is passed on through a valve, the ilio-cæcal, which will not allow it to return, into the large intestine. The first pouched part of this is the cæcum. At its closed and lower end a narrow tube is attached, the vermiform appendix. Worm-like, as its name suggests, it twists and turns during digestion. While in the earlier stage of man's development it may have been used as a kind of second stomach for digesting the remains of food, it has no known use today, and in many people has to be removed by an operation for appendicitis.

From the cæcum onwards the large intestine is called the colon. This goes first upward on the right of the abdomen as the ascending colon, then crosses below the stomach and liver as the transverse colon, and finally drops down on the left side as the descending colon. The intestine, continuing behind the pelvic cavity, becomes the rectum. The chief function of the large intestine is to absorb the remaining traces of nutriment and the water in which it is dissolved. The body engine burns up about ninety-five per cent. of its fuel. The dried-up waste or fæces contains bacteria of one kind and another and indigestible fragments of food such as hard vegetable fibres, fruit skins, pips and seeds, etc.

ACCUMULATED POISONS

The fæces, then, should be removed from the body as promptly as possible. This is done by contractions, known as peristalsis, or the peristaltic wave, that constantly pass along the smooth muscles of the colon, which expel the waste through the discharge pipe, the rectum.

To be healthy the body must constantly rid itself of accumulated poisons—carbon dioxide, urea and certain salts. The chief agents of excretion are the lungs, the skin, the kidneys and to some extent the liver. The blood acts as a middleman in each case. The work of the lungs is explained in the chapter on Respiration.

TWO LAYERS OF SKIN

The skin is one of the most important structures of the human machine. Made up of two layers, it has a deep sheet of fibrous strands and a surface sheet of cells lying side by side like the tiles of a floor. The dry scale-like cells at the surface are constantly being rubbed off and are replaced by cells from below. The skin is covered with innumerable small openings, the pores. Each pore leads to a spiral tube about one quarter of an inch long called the sweat gland, which twists down through the pavement-like cells and through the bottom layer until it reaches the coat of fat immediately beneath. Here the tube of the sweat gland seeps up water and urea from the blood and pours them out on the surface of the skin as perspiration or sweat.

During hot weather we sweat profusely on the palms of the hands. In this region there are about three thousand glands to every square inch, though on some parts of the body there are as few as four hundred. When the temperature of the body rises, as for instance during vigorous exercise, the heart sends an increase of blood into the skin. The sweat glands then increase their activity to purify this extra blood, and moisture is collected in droplets on the surface of the skin. This is evaporated, which cools the body in addition to carrying away some of the waste in the form of gas.

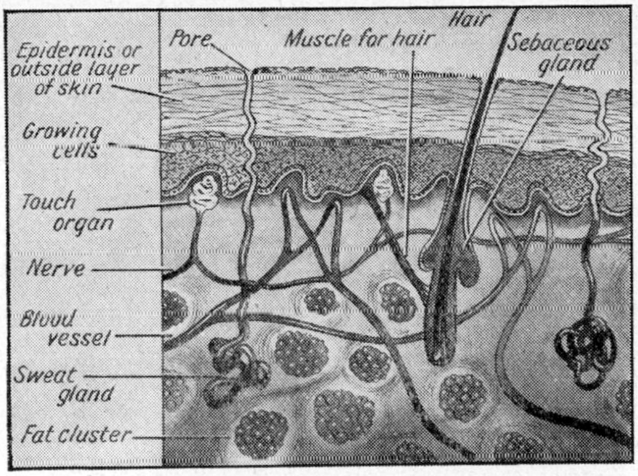

STRUCTURE OF THE SKIN
Each pore leads to a spiral tube about one quarter of an inch long called the sweat gland.

WASTE FROM THE BODY

In the course of a day about twenty ounces of water (about a pint), one ounce of carbon dioxide and about an ounce of other waste matters are given off from the body by way of the skin. " Cold sweat," induced by fear or other emotion, is brought about by an excessive secretion of the sweat glands, though in this case there has been no increase of blood to the part.

The kidneys are to be found one on either side of the upper lumbar vertebræ, at the back of the abdomen, each rather like a large bean and weighing about a quarter of a pound. Their special work is to act as a filter which deals chiefly with the waste products left in the blood from the combustion of the protein foodstuffs. The normal amount of water collected during the day is about two and a half pints, in which there is about one ounce of urea and a little uric acid.

In order that the kidneys may carry out their work properly the cells are arranged in a special way, some of them being built up into sacs or capsules, each embracing a tuft of blood vessels. The waste matter is drawn through into the capsules. Other cells in the kidney are arranged with one opening into the capsules and the other into larger ducts. By these ducts the urine is collected and then sent into the ureter, a narrow tube about fifteen inches long which leads into the oval bag of the bladder. From the bladder, which like the pylorus, has a sphincter muscle to act as a sentry, the contents are sent out at regular intervals, the sphincter relaxing for this purpose and the bladder muscles contracting.

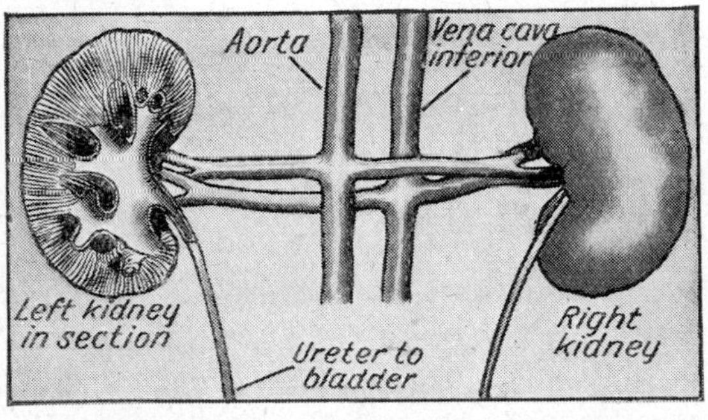

FILTER OF WASTE PRODUCTS
The kidneys deal chiefly with the waste products left in the blood from the combust ion of protein foodstuffs.

WORK OF THE LIVER

The liver, whose chief functions are to collect bile and to store glycogen from which a soluble sugar can be given to the blood, as for instance when it takes a supply to working muscles, also serves to collect urea. It is in this organ that the final breaking up of urea takes place. Nitrogenous waste is constantly produced in every tissue, but it is from the liver that this waste is passed into the blood stream, later to be removed by the kidney filters.

The liver, which may be regarded as a kind of clearing-house and has been referred to as the Ellis Island of the body, is the largest gland. It usually weighs about three pounds in an adult. In other words, about one-fortieth of the body weight, whereas in a newly born child it weighs about one-eighteenth of the total. Blood is brought to keep it in operation directly from the heart by the small hepatic artery, while the venous blood from the stomach and intestines is conveyed to it by the large portal vein and undergoes considerable changes in the gland before it passes into general circulation.

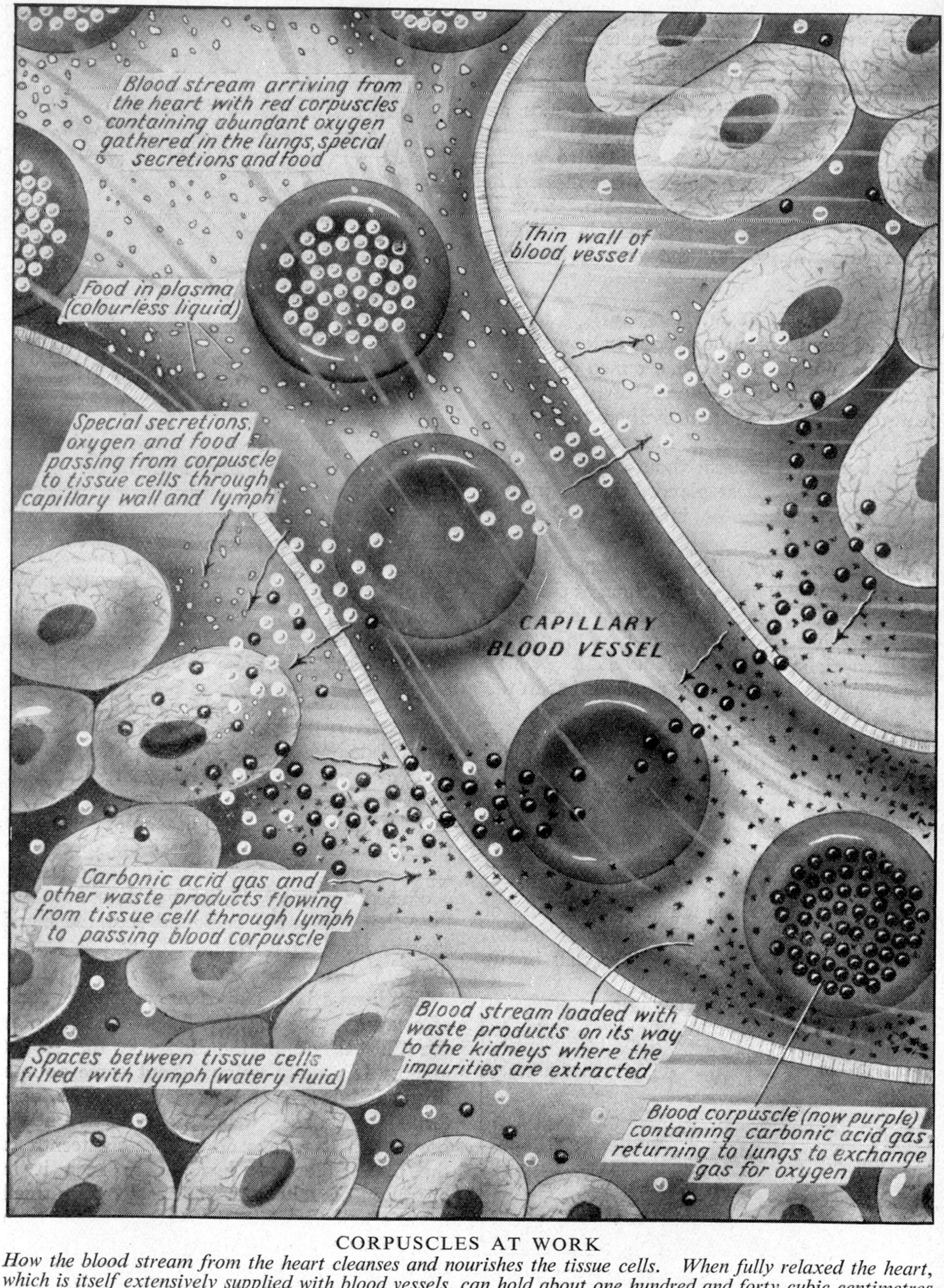

CORPUSCLES AT WORK

How the blood stream from the heart cleanses and nourishes the tissue cells. When fully relaxed the heart, which is itself extensively supplied with blood vessels, can hold about one hundred and forty cubic centimetres of blood. Through the blood vessels the heart is continuously pumping about ten pints of blood. The main delivery pipe for purified blood is called the aorta.

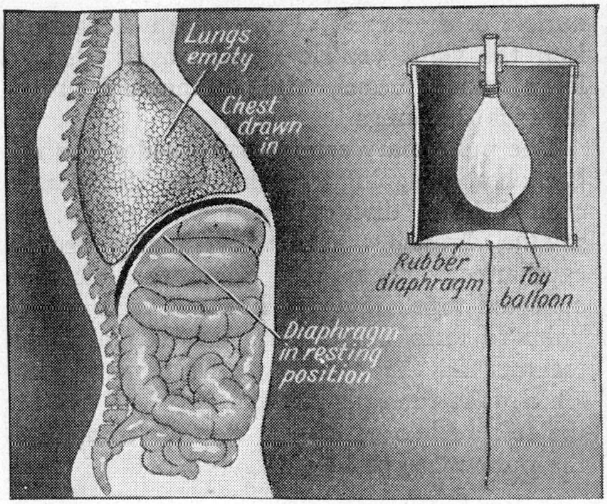

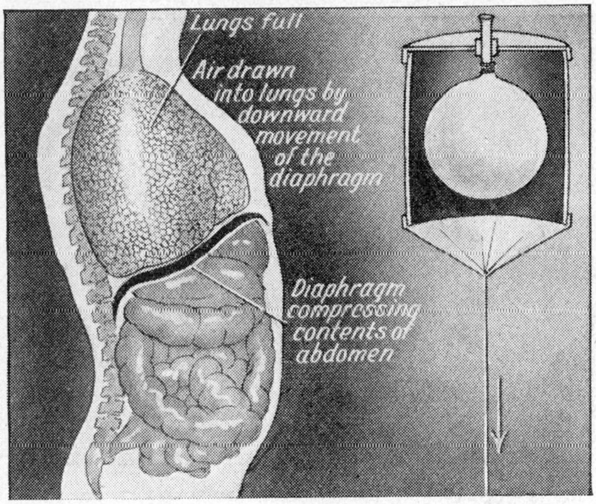

HOW THE LUNGS WORK

Once in every four seconds in normal breathing the lungs are made to expand by the diaphragm and the chest muscles when air rushes into them from the upper air passages.

CIRCULATION AND RESPIRATION

In order that adequate nutriment may be taken to the various organs of the body, and that later these organs may be able to rid themselves of waste products, the blood must be constantly renewed. For the blood is the medium by which these tasks are performed.

Every part of the body is connected with blood vessels, which are tubes of various sizes and structure; and through these tubes the heart is continuously pumping about ten pints of blood.

The heart itself, found in the thorax between the lobes of the lungs, is a muscle of a peculiar structure. Its fibres are unlike both the striped voluntary muscle of the limbs and the smooth involuntary muscle found in the intestine. While the voluntary muscle is capable of sudden contraction it is easily fatigued, and the involuntary muscle contracts slowly and continuously. In the heart the fibres contract and relax quickly but they never tire when working normally, which in the adult is at the rate of about seventy contractions a minute.

About the size of a man's fist, this peculiar muscle of the heart is protected and enclosed in a kind of double bag, the pericardium, which is connected with the neck above and the diaphragm below. When fully relaxed the heart, which is itself extensively supplied with blood vessels, can hold about one hundred and forty cubic centimetres of blood.

The central pump which keeps the blood continually on the move is built in two halves, a right and a left, completely separated from each other. Each half consists of a thin-walled antechamber, the auricle, which communicates with a thick-walled chamber, the ventricle, on the same side by means of a valve. This valve is so constructed that it will open only in one way, thus making certain the blood will travel in the one direction.

The action of the heart is marked by an alternate contraction and relaxation of its muscular walls, the whole process being termed a cardiac revolution. First there is a short contraction of the auricles, then a longer contraction of the ventricles and then a pause almost as long as the time taken by the two contractions.

Both auricles contract together and both ventricles. At each contraction of the ventricles a fresh supply of blood is forced into the great main delivery pipe for purified blood called the aorta, which within a few inches of where it leaves the heart begins to give off branches to the different parts of the body.

The aorta is the biggest artery in the body. Smaller arteries lead into every part of the human machine, acting as pipe lines to carry the blood. They are so constructed that they can withstand a great deal of pressure, for into their walls elastic-like tissue is interwoven. They may suddenly be called upon to take a large amount of blood and, after the pressure

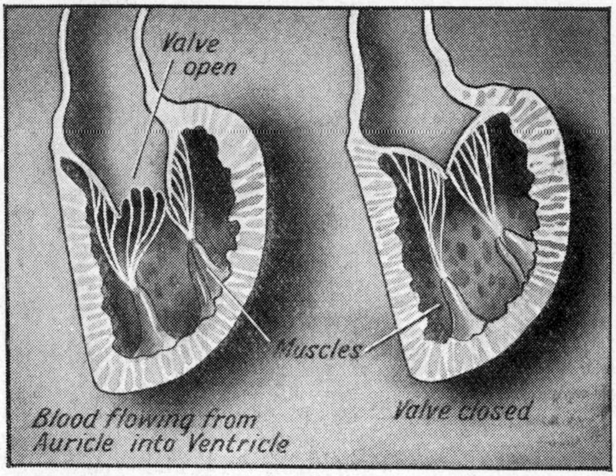

ONE-WAY TRAFFIC FOR BLOOD

The auricle communicates with the ventricle by means of a valve which opens only one way.

is diminished, to accommodate themselves to a much smaller amount. In older people, especially in older men, the elasticity of the arteries suffers and they are apt to be injured by too great a pressure, this giving rise to such diseases as arterio-sclerosis. In the limbs, and indeed over the whole surface of the body, the arteries are deeply placed. This serves to protect them from injury—an important matter, as if they are cut the blood spurts out with dangerous rapidity, sometimes resulting in death.

WORK OF THE VEINS

The pipe lines of the arteries are eventually narrowed down to form the tiniest and thinnest pipes imaginable, the capillaries. Densest and most numerous on the inner and outer surfaces of the body, they lead into every part of its substance in a fine meshwork. It is through them that the real exchange of gases and foodstuffs takes place.

After it has been taken to the various organs of the body the blood is collected into other pipe lines to take it back to the heart. These pipes are the veins, which usually run parallel with the arteries, though they are not so deeply placed. These thin-walled pipes are provided with valves to prevent any back-flow. It is when these valves lose their power of closing properly that various vein troubles arise.

The chief veins are the superior vena cava which brings blood from the upper limbs and the head, and the inferior vena cava, bringing blood from the lower limbs and the trunk. The veins empty themselves into the right auricle of the heart. From here it is pumped into the right ventricle and travels along a large blood vessel, the pulmonary artery, towards the lungs.

The pulmonary artery soon divides into two branches, one going to each lung. In the lungs each branch divides again and again into smaller branches which eventually become capillaries. From this point the blood is collected together again in small veins, which unite to form bigger ones till they all come together in the four large pulmonary veins which take the now oxygenated blood back to the left auricle of the heart, thus completing the pulmonary or lung circulation.

MILLIONS OF CORPUSCLES

In the systemic or general circulation the blood that has passed from the left auricle into the left ventricle is pumped into the aorta, and from there is sent on into every part of the body. At each contraction of the ventricles a fresh supply of blood is forced into the aorta. This makes it expand, the expansion passing quickly along every artery with each fresh heart-beat. This wave of expansion is known as the pulse. It does not mark the actual flowing of the blood. The actual flow is a much slower process. There is no wave of expansion in either the veins or the capillaries, the blood being sent on in these vessels in a slow-moving steady stream.

So much for the road on which the blood travels. Now for the blood itself. Largely water (about eighty per cent.), it is not, however, just a salt solution with various gases in it. It also contains solid bodies, called the

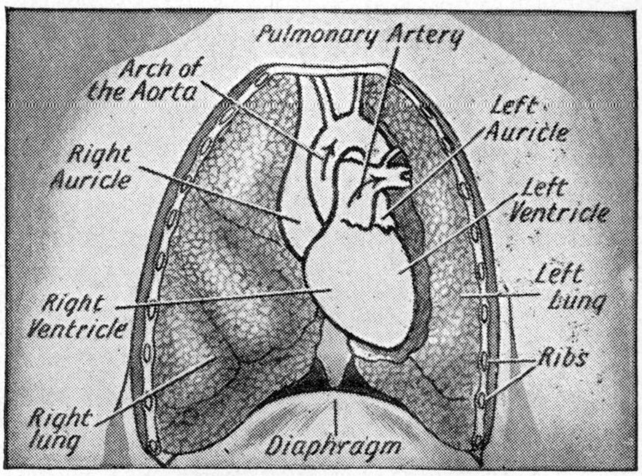

THE CENTRAL PUMP

The heart is built in two halves, a right and a left, completely separated from each other.

blood corpuscles, which float in a colourless liquid, the blood plasma.

The corpuscles are of two kinds, the white and the red. In one cubic centimetre of blood (about fifteen drops) there are something like fifty million red cells and about one hundred thousand white cells. The red corpuscles are very soft and elastic and can pass through the narrowest capillary, at the same time being able to glide over each other. They originate from the red marrow found in long bones, mentioned in the chapter on the Skeleton.

HOW CUTS ARE HEALED

The blood plasma is a complicated salt solution which is not readily altered by external agents. For instance, if a lot of salt is taken in the food it does not follow that the blood is upset. But if the body loses a great deal of salt by sweating the loss must be made good. For this reason miners in hot countries eat a great deal of salted food to correct a certain cramp which is liable to attack them if they lose too much salt from the blood.

When a blood vessel is injured and the blood flows, the normal process is for it to clot in a short time. This clotting is due to the fibrinogen in the blood plasma. Hæmophilia, "bleeders' disease" as it is popularly known, is due to the fact that in some unfortunate people the blood is unable to clot, with the result that excessive bleeding, which may end in death, takes place when even so small an operation as having a tooth extracted is performed.

POLICE FORCE OF THE BLOOD

The white corpuscles, spoken of as leucocytes, are capable of changing their shape and are able to divide like the amœbæ. Their chief characteristic is that they are able to devour bacteria and foreign bodies. When disease germs get into the blood this "police force" makes its way in great numbers through the thin walls of the blood vessels to the scene of action and makes a mass attack on the intruder. Dead and used cells are devoured in the same way.

The colour of the blood comes from hæmoglobin, a protein compound containing iron. This iron is able to combine with oxygen, and for this reason hæmoglobin is known as the oxygen carrier of the blood. How it is supplied with this oxygen will be seen in the next section.

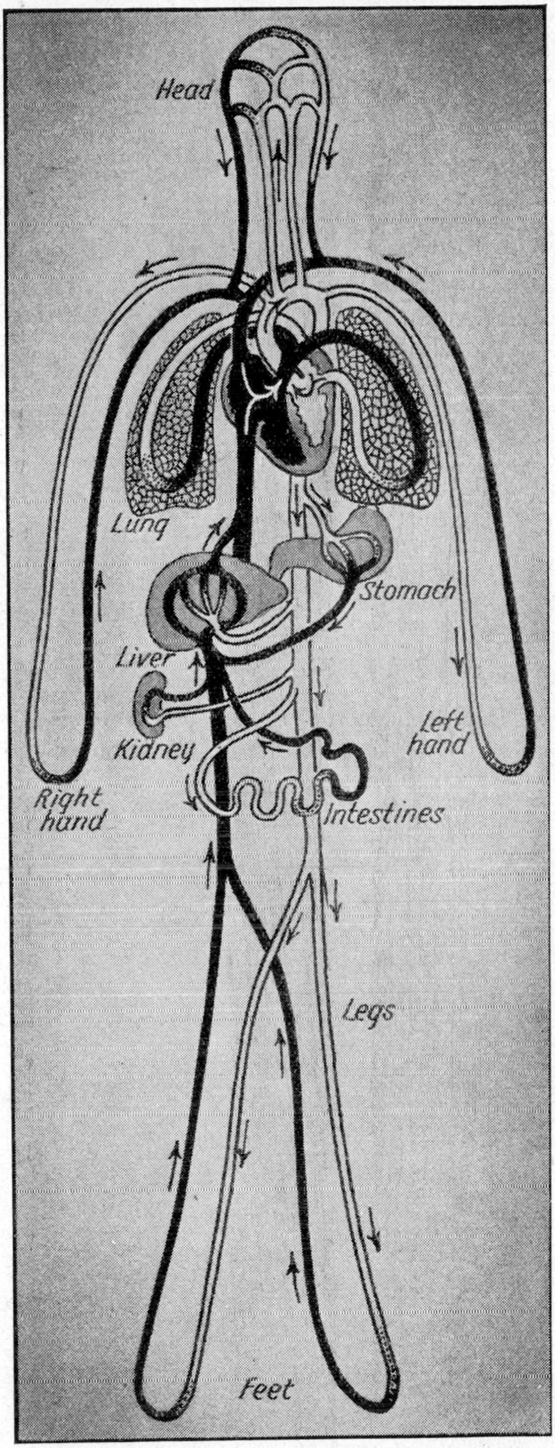

BLOOD RETURNING TO THE HEART

After it has been taken to the various organs of the body the blood is collected into other pipe lines to take it back to the heart. These pipes are the veins, which usually run parallel with the arteries.

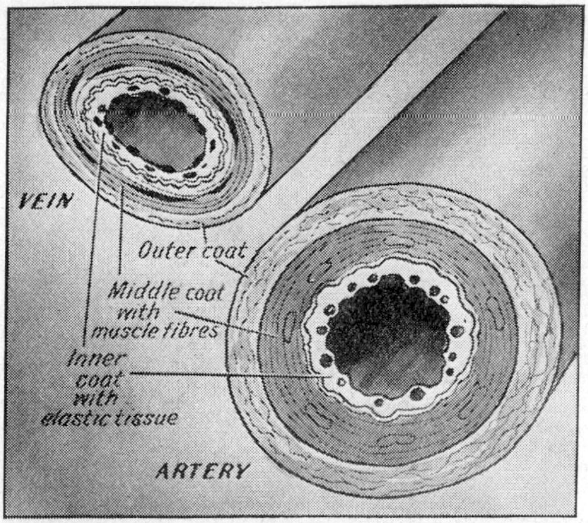

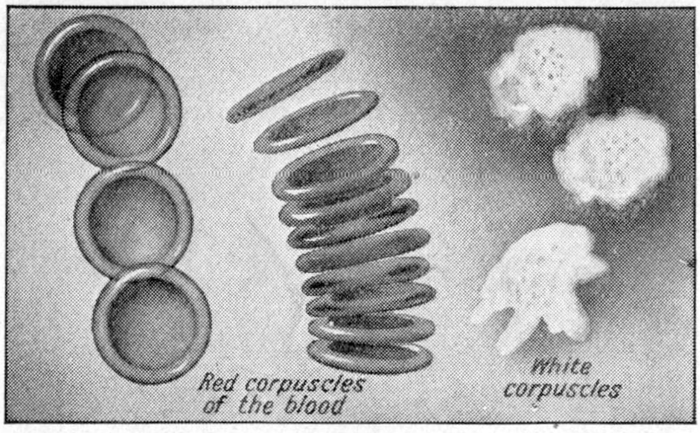

WONDERS OF THE BLOOD

Top: Structure of vein and artery. Centre: When a blood vessel is injured and the blood flows the normal process is for it to clot in a short time. This clotting is due to the fibrinogen in the blood plasma. Bottom: Red and white corpuscles. The latter are able to devour bacteria and foreign bodies.

If it were deprived of oxygen for more than a few minutes the human machine would stop working, for it is only in the presence of oxygen that the cells can obtain the necessary energy from the foodstuffs supplied to them. The oxygen brought by the red corpuscles of the blood is taken up in all parts of the body and the waste product, carbon dioxide, is given off. The process which brings the oxygen and which also removes the carbon dioxide is termed respiration or, more simply, breathing. The special organs for this work are the lungs, and it is in the capillaries of the lungs that the change from venous to bright scarlet arterial blood takes place.

CONICAL AIR-SACS

The lungs are simply conical air-sacs with as large a surface as possible concentrated into a small space. These spongy elastic organs fill most of the space left on either side of the heart with its great blood vessels. Each lung is enclosed in a double bag of membrane called the pleura, one layer of which lines the cavity of the thorax, while the other is bound to the outer surface of the lungs. There is a watery fluid between the two layers of the pleura which permits of a gliding movement up and down during respiration.

The air passages leading to the lungs are the trachea or windpipe, behind which is the œsophagus, and the bronchi or branches of the trachea leading to the lungs. The trachea is made up of a number of hoops of cartilage which, with the exception of the second, the cricoid cartilage, do not meet behind. The most prominent of these rings is the " Adam's apple " or the thyroid cartilage at the top.

WARMED BY THE NOSE

During respiration the opening to the larynx called the epiglottis, which shuts its trap-door when food is sent into the œsophagus, is wide open to allow the air, which has been warmed as it came through the nose, to pass on down the trachea into the right and left bronchi. Each bronchus enters a lung and there divides and sub-divides again and again to end in hollow air cells called alveoli. The trachea and the bronchi are lined with mucous membrane, the inner surface of which is covered with small hairs. These by their waving or lashing movement remove dust or foreign matter brought in with the air.

Once in every four seconds in normal

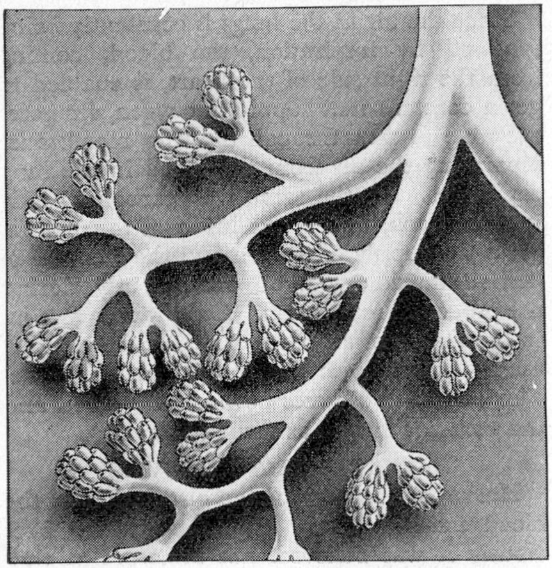

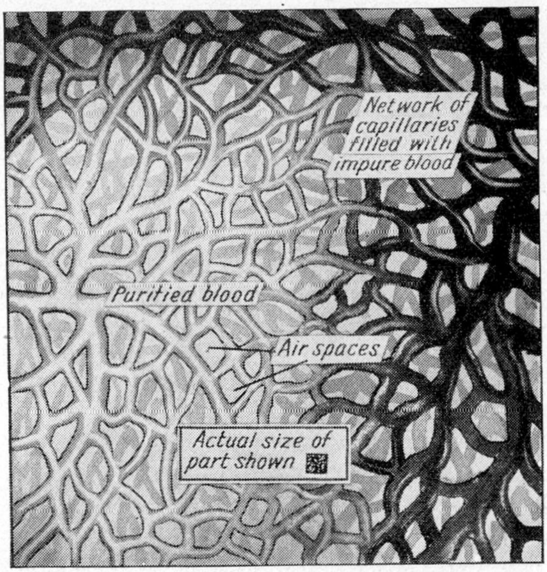

PURIFYING BLOOD IN THE LUNGS

Left: Extreme ends of the bronchioles in the lungs. They are branches of the bronchi which lead to those organs. Right: Blood going through the lungs and picking up oxygen.

breathing the lungs are made to expand by the diaphragm and the chest muscles when air rushes into them from the upper air passages. During exercise, owing to the bigger supply of oxygen which is needed, respiration takes place at a faster rate. It is a common observation that women use their thorax muscles far more than men, who compensate with the greater use of the diaphragm. If women's breathing were abdominal the diaphragm would press too heavily on the fœtus during pregnancy.

In inspiration or breathing-in the thorax is enlarged by means of the diaphragm, which moves down, and by the muscles between the ribs—the intercostals—which raise them. This

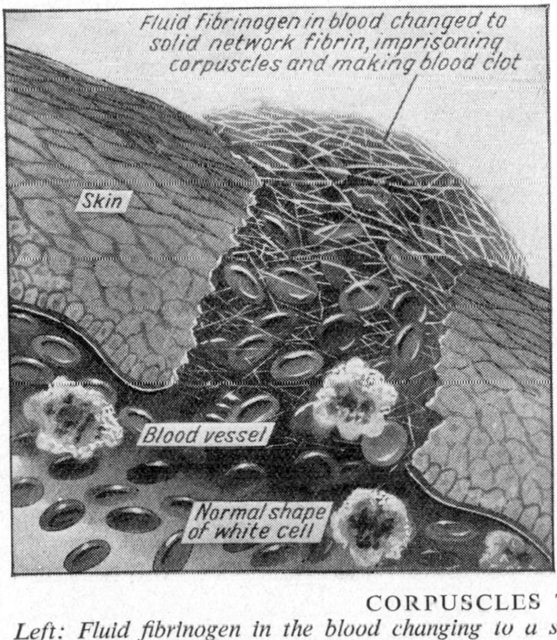

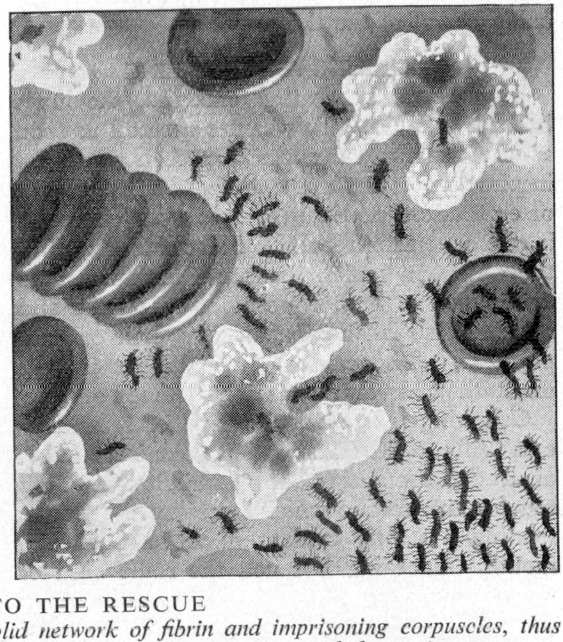

CORPUSCLES TO THE RESCUE

Left: Fluid fibrinogen in the blood changing to a solid network of fibrin and imprisoning corpuscles, thus making a blood clot. Right: White corpuscles in the blood stream absorbing and destroying germs.

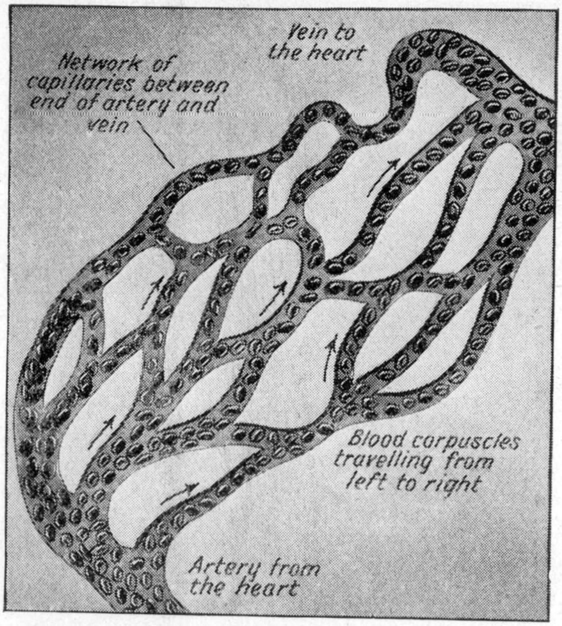

EXPLAINING A CAPILLARY
Capillaries are very small blood vessels. They are about one three-thousandth of an inch in diameter.

movement can be watched when a deep breath is taken, for the diaphragm presses on the organs in the abdomen, which is made to move outwards. When artificial respiration becomes necessary, as for instance when a person is rescued from drowning, the arms are moved up and down to bring about the necessary enlargement of the thorax.

COUGHING AND SNEEZING

The thorax being thus enlarged, the lungs become inflated. This causes a recoil as soon as the muscles have finished their work for inspiration. Ordinary quiet breathing-out, or expiration, needs no muscle work, for there is also an elastic recoil of the stretched wall of the abdomen which sends the diaphragm up again into its arched position. The ribs and sternum also fall back again into their original positions. The cavity of the thorax is thus diminished in volume and air is forced out.

Coughing is a particular kind of breathing-out. After a deep inspiration there is a sudden expiration brought about by an irritation of the mucous membrane which forces up the glottis, sending a strong current of air through the mouth. Sneezing is much the same kind of movement except that the air is forced down the nose. Laughing is brought about by short and quick expirations.

Since the air in the lungs is constantly being renewed by inspiration, the blood, coming from the right side of the heart, is enabled to get a constant new supply of oxygen, for gases are able to pass through the thin membranes separating the air from the blood in the lung capillaries. In the same way carbon dioxide is given back, freeing the blood of this poison. Thus the supply of oxygen and the removal of carbon dioxide goes on continuously during the process of respiration. Oxidization goes on in the tissues of all parts to which the blood is taken; especially is this true of muscle tissue. The exchange of gases between the blood and the tissues is known as tissue-respiration.

HARVEY'S GREAT DISCOVERY

Harvey's discovery of the circulation of the blood marked a new era in medicine. Previously it was believed, not unnaturally, that the arteries contained air, since on examination after death they were found to be empty. It was then believed that the blood moved backwards and forwards in the veins. Harvey proved that the same blood was used again and again, and that it passed through the lungs, which contained air. As he did not use a microscope, he was not able to see the capillaries, and therefore could only guess how the blood got from the arteries into the veins.

HARVEY OF CIRCULATION FAME
Through long and patient observation William Harvey (1578-1657) demonstrated the circulation of the blood.

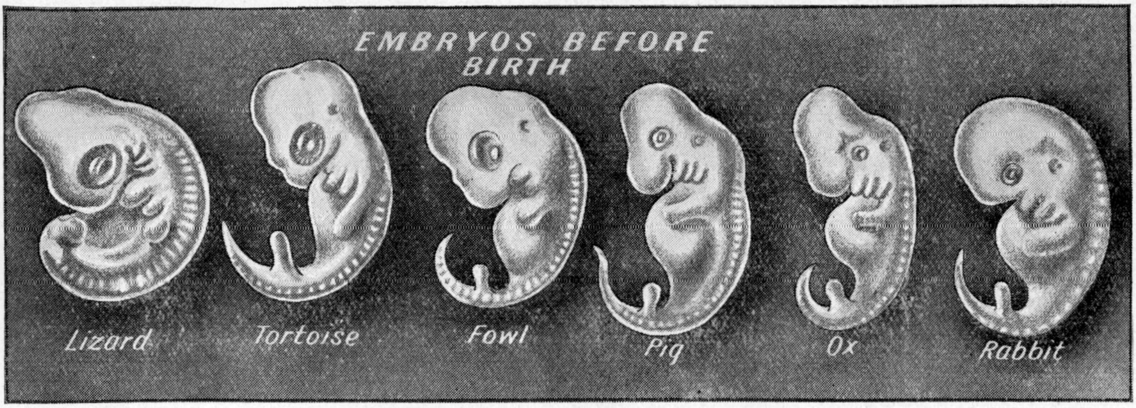

LOWER ANIMALS IN THE MAKING

So closely do the embryos of different animals resemble each other at a certain stage of development that even experienced embryologists sometimes find it difficult to identify them.

REPRODUCTION

ALTHOUGH there are in fact very many differences between the male and female body, the essential difference between the sexes is in the reproductive organs.

The male germ cell is known as the spermatozoon and the female cell as the ovum. The union of the two is called fertilization, but the process which brings this about is sexual union, or coition. Fertilization is a very simple matter—the piercing of the ovum by the head of the spermatozoon. Yet by this simple operation the complete and complex personality of two separate people is handed on and blended in a new life.

The spermatozoon is a very small cell indeed, which nevertheless has three distinct parts: a head, a body and a tail. The head is spear-pointed and hard, while the tail is long and so constructed that it waves and vibrates continually. It is by the spear-pointed head that the sperm ultimately is able to pierce the ovum and it is by the action of the vibrating tail that the sperm is conveyed along the female genital tract to the ovum.

An ovum is a much larger cell, being just visible to the naked eye. It is enclosed in a transparent capsule which, among other things, contains yolk-granules.

Spermatoza are manufactured in a pair of glands about the size of walnuts called the testes, which are enclosed in a loosely-folded bag of skin, the scrotum. Spermatozoa do not develop until after puberty is reached, after which time they are secreted continuously in great numbers in delicate compartments in the scrotum called seminal tubules. The sperm live in a jelly-like fluid called semen, which is probably the richest secretion in the body. This secretion is constantly being absorbed into the tissues, and is especially valuable as a source of nutriment to the brain and nerve cells. Sufficient semen, however, is normally left in two storage tanks called the seminal vesicles, situated behind the bladder, for an act of coition.

After the seminal fluid has been secreted in the testes it has to be taken to the seminal vesicles. This is done first by way of vessels leading from the seminal tubules to the epididymus, a very much convoluted duct, about two inches long but capable of stretching to twenty feet. The epididymus leads into the vas deferens, which joins the vessels and nerves of the testes to form the spermatic cord. The duct now runs upwards and outwards to an opening in the muscular wall of the abdomen, the inguinal canal. From this point it runs down into the pelvis and reaches the seminal vesicles at the back of the bladder.

The penis consists of muscular tissue which is highly vascular (i.e., made up of ducts conveying blood) and erectile. Throughout its length it contains the urethra, the canal which takes the urine from the bladder and which also acts as a conductor for the semen. During coition the seminal vesicles contract and the seminal fluid is squeezed first along that part of the urethra near the neck of the bladder. An important gland, the prostate, is found here. About the size of a horse-chestnut, it

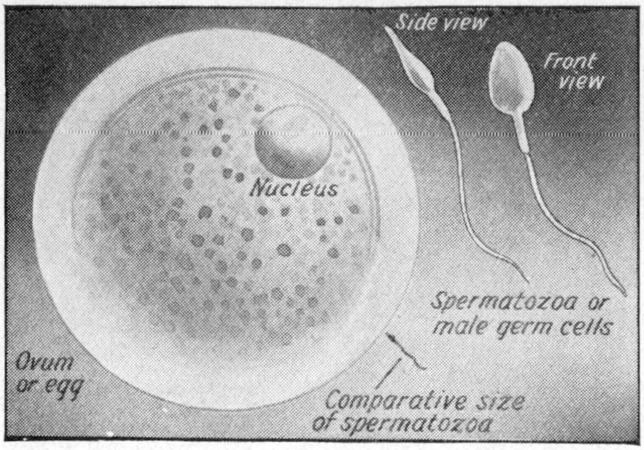

SOURCE OF NEW LIFE
Fertilization is caused by the piercing of the ovum by the head of the spermatozoon.

secretes a fluid which during coition is released into the urethra and acts as the forerunner of the semen. When the spermatozoa come in contact with the prostatic fluid they become mobile. Much more active than before, they are then able to travel the considerable distance before one of them will come in contact with an ovum.

BREAKING OF THE VOICE

In addition to the semen, the testes manufacture another internal secretion which, distributed by the blood, brings about those changes in the body that characterize the male. At puberty, for instance, the ridges across the forehead become more pronounced; the chest expands; a growth of hair appears on the face and on the genital organs. Perhaps the most distinctive of these secondary sexual characteristics, as they are known, is the breaking of the voice. Although these changes are brought about during the six years or so of adolescence, the secretion continues throughout adult life. It is thought that on it the sex instinct depends, and thus, ultimately, the procreation of life.

In women the essential organs which produce the egg-cells are the ovaries, a pair of glands, about one and a half inches long, found on either side of the pelvic cavity, lying a little behind the kidneys. They are attached by ligaments to the wall of the pelvis and also to the uterus or womb. Embedded in the fibrous tissue of each ovary are a number of rounded bodies of varying size. These are the Graafian follicles, hollow cells which surround the ova. About once in every four weeks during a woman's life, from the time of puberty until the menopause which in most women takes place at about the age of forty-five, a Graafian follicle bursts on the surface of the ovary. This bursting sets free a ripe ovum. Ova ripen at the rate of one a month, alternately in each ovary.

FERTILIZATION

When it is set free from its envelope the ovum is caught up by vibrating hairs which surround a pair of tubes or oviducts called the Fallopian tubes which run conveniently near each ovary. The Fallopian tubes are about five inches long and open at one end into the abdomen and at the other into the upper part of the uterus. Finger-like processes, fimbriæ, now grip the ovum and conduct it into the Fallopian tube, where the vibrating hairs of its lining urge it on to the uterus. It is at this stage of its journey that a ripe ovum is usually met by an ascending sperm and fertilization takes place.

The uterus is a hollow organ situated in the middle of the pelvis, with the bladder in front and the rectum behind it. Shaped rather like a pear, with its broad end uppermost, this important organ with its muscular walls is kept in position by a double fold of membrane.

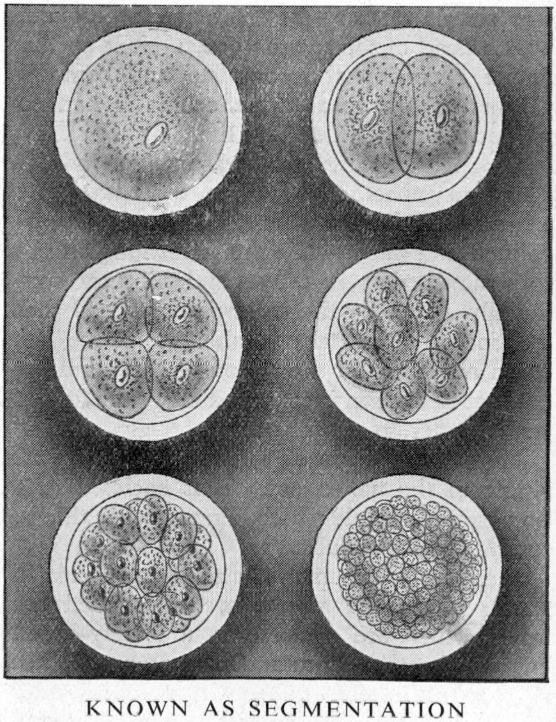

KNOWN AS SEGMENTATION
Earliest steps in the development of an egg. The cell divides into two, these into four and so on.

The latter, serving as a kind of sling for the uterus, runs outwards to the side walls of the pelvis.

It is in the walls of the uterus that a fertilized ovum first begins its development. The lining of these walls has previously been renewed and made ready by the process of menstruation. This occurs about once in every four weeks from about the fifteenth year to the fiftieth during a woman's life, except during pregnancy and in the first months of lactation or milk production.

ON A WATER CUSHION

At its narrow end the uterus terminates in the neck or cervix, whose mouth or os uteri opens into the vagina. This canal is about four inches long and leads to the exterior of the body. It receives the semen during coition and is the passage through which the uterus discharges its contents from the body. The contents of the bladder pass out by way of a separate channel, the urethra, which lies in front of the vagina.

When fertilization takes place only the head of the male cell, which is the nucleus, enters the ovum. The rest of the sperm breaks off and withers. By the time the fertilized egg reaches the uterus it has divided and redivided into a mass of spherical cells. This is gradually surrounded by a transparent sac, the amnion, in which the developing fœtus floats, as it were, on a water cushion.

BIRTH

Outside the amnion is another membrane, the chorion, whose purpose is to connect the embryo with the mother. Blood vessels in the villi—finger-like processes—of the chorion are in close contact with the blood vessels in the walls of the uterus. In the third month of pregnancy part of the chorion develops into a thickened mass of blood vessels known as the placenta, which become embedded in the tissues of the mother. By means of the placenta nutriment is supplied to the growing fœtus and its waste products removed.

After its nine months' development the baby, lying with its head below and its buttocks above, is sent through the uterus by a series of contractions into the vagina. The amnion and the chorion now burst and a swift rush of fluid from the amnion escapes. This is Nature's provision to make easier the passage of the child through the vagina. The baby is still connected with the mother by the narrow tubular part of the placenta known as the umbilical cord. This has to be cut in order to separate the child from the mother, but since it contains both arteries and veins, it needs first to be tied. That part of the cord which remains attached to the child withers away by degrees : the fold of skin known as the navel is all that persists to mark its position.

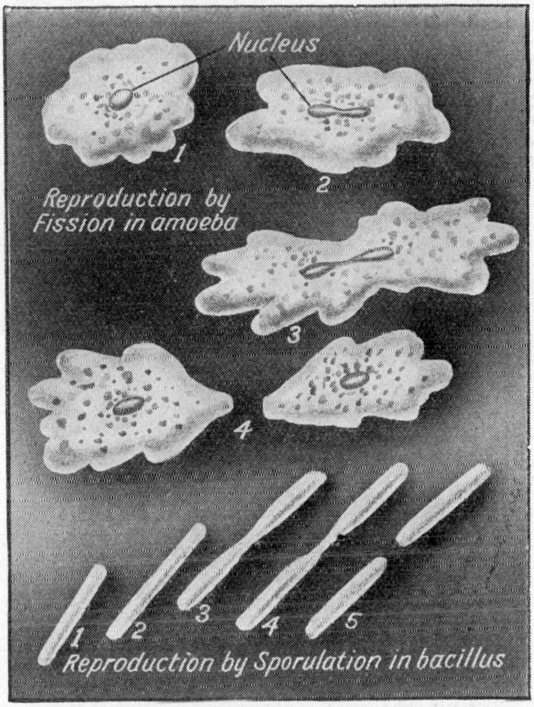

DIVISION IN AMŒBA

In amœba (1–3) *division takes place as in higher organisms. Before the nucleus divides* (4) *the chromosomes become visible, though they are very small and unrepresented in the illustration.*

After the birth the uterus again contracts in order to expel the placenta, popularly known as the after-birth. The stretched muscles of the uterus, which during pregnancy has expanded to more than ten times its normal size, gradually regain their tone.

During the nine months before the birth the mammary glands, or breasts, have been actively building up the milk granules from material brought to them by the blood vessels. This milk is manufactured by the breast tubules and conveyed by ducts which open on to the nipple. A healthy nursing mother is able to suckle her child for the first six or eight months of its life.

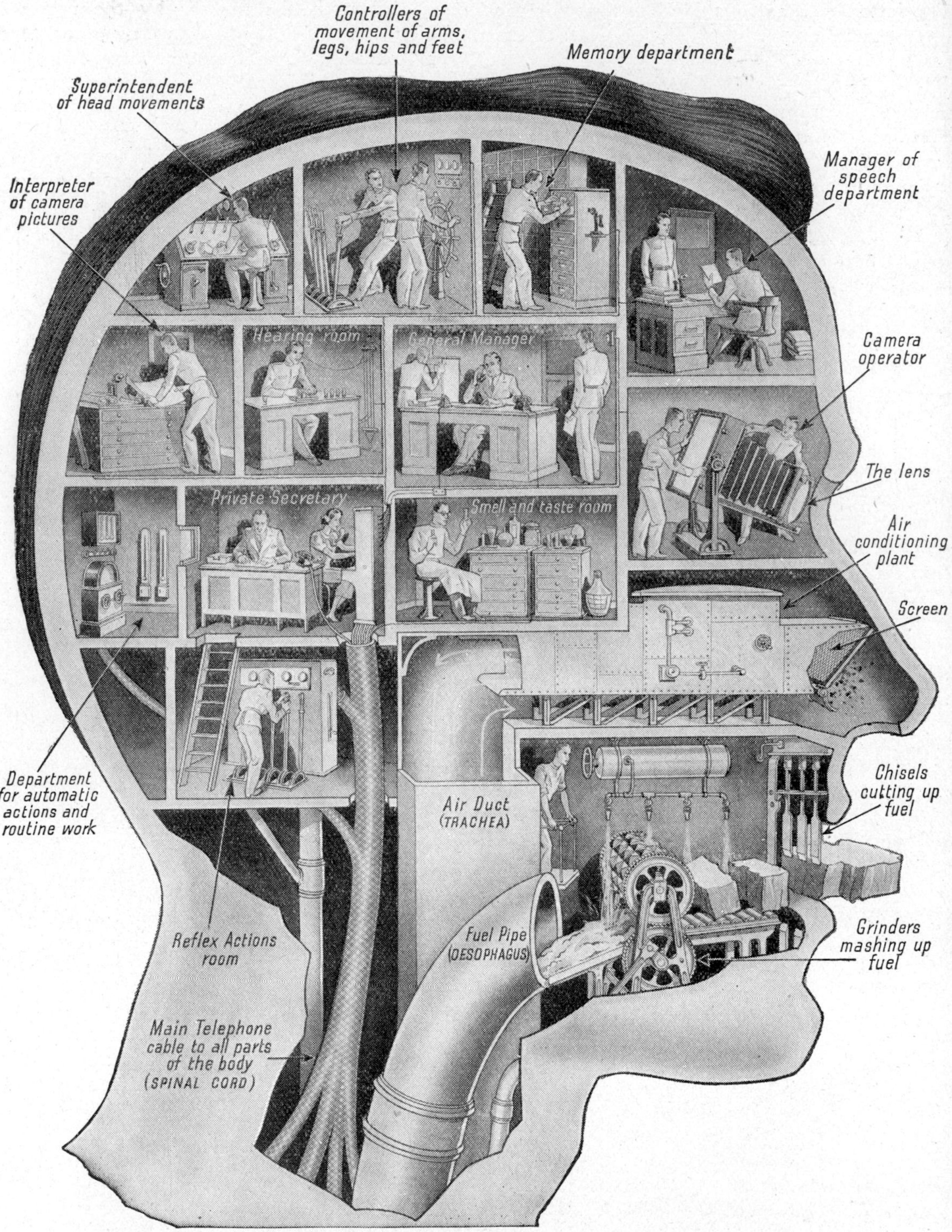

THE WORKSHOP OF THE HEAD

In this picture the various parts of the head are illustrated in a technical instead of a physiological way. It should be compared with the diagrams on pages 356 *and* 357, *where the various parts of the brain are illustrated in detail and the scientific names of the various centres are given. The brain does the work of a great central telephone exchange; while in the spinal cord are groups of nerve cells acting as local exchanges.*

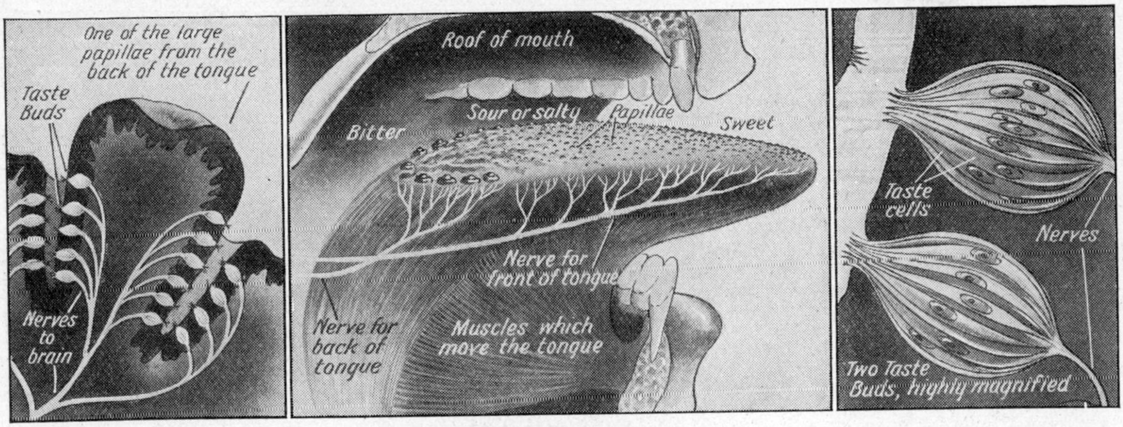

ORGAN OF TASTE

The upper surface of the tongue is supplied with taste buds, or papillæ, which are in contact with nerve-endings from the fifth and ninth pairs of cranial nerves. Note the parts where various tastes are perceived best.

THE NERVOUS SYSTEM

ALMOST every movement of the body, whether consciously directed by the will or not, is brought about and regulated by the agency of the nervous system. The various other systems of the human machine are controlled and made to work harmoniously together by the messages carried through the nerves, which may be likened to telephone wires connecting every part of the body. The brain does the work of a great central telephone exchange; while in the spinal cord are groups of nerve cells acting as local exchanges.

The nervous system is made up of two related systems : the cerebro-spinal, or central nervous system, and the sympathetic nervous system. The central nervous system consists of the brain, the spinal cord and nerves given off from both of these. The nerve fibres of this system are distributed chiefly to the skin, to the other sense organs, and to all the voluntary muscles. The sympathetic nervous system consists of a double chain of grouped nerve cells, ganglia, lying outside the spinal canal on each side of the spinal column. Nerve fibres connect the ganglia to each other and to the central nervous system.

The messages, or impulses, carried by the sympathetic nerves may originate in the central nervous system, passing through the sympathetic system to the involuntary muscles in the heart, the stomach, the intestine and to the various glands. In short, this system regulates processes which take place independently of the will.

We will deal first with the central nervous system. The brain is a large organ, consisting of a soft mass of nerve fibres and nerve cells; it weighs about three pounds in an adult. Its chief parts are the cerebrum, the cerebellum, the pons and the medulla oblongata.

The cerebrum, or greater brain, weighs about nine-tenths of the whole and takes up the upper and front part of the skull box. It is divided into a right and left hemisphere by a cleft about two inches deep. A thick layer of grey matter, consisting mainly of nerve cells, surrounds white fibrous nerve tissue. This grey matter is drawn up into a number of folds, or convolutions, a device by which the brain may be plentifully supplied with blood, for the delicate covering membrane, the pia mater, consisting of a thick meshwork of small arteries and veins, dips down into all the convolutions. Two other coverings protect the brain, a tough fibrous membrane lining the skull box and, between this and the pia mater, a thinner and transparent serous membrane which serves as a water cushion.

Partly from observation of such animals as rabbits, apes and dogs, and partly from cases of injury to man's brain, it has been found that the cerebrum is the seat of sensation, intelligence and the will. The rabbit, not highly esteemed for its intelligence, has a small cerebrum which is scarcely convoluted at all, while the ape's brain more nearly approaches man's in its size and general shape.

The various conscious movements of the body are controlled from a small strip of the brain running upwards and back from just

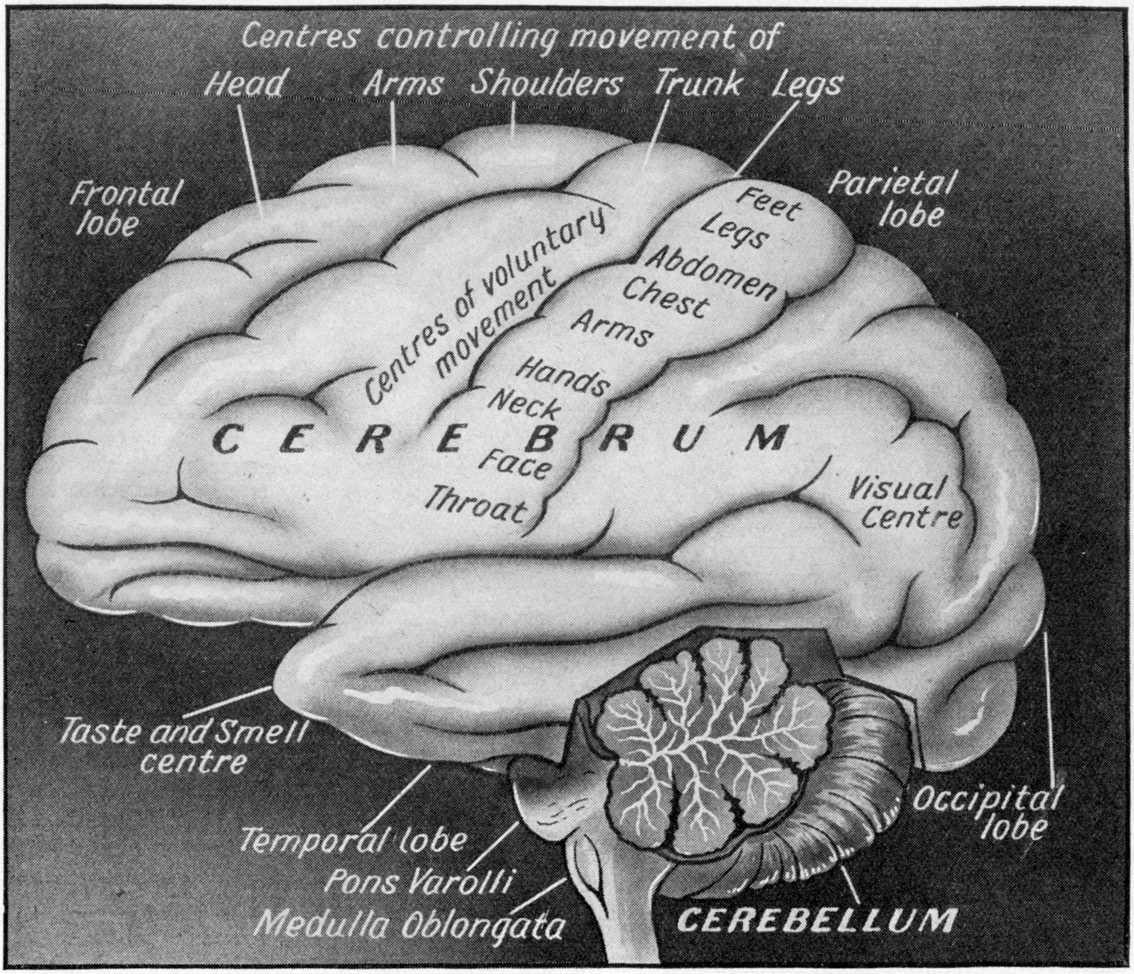

CENTRAL TELEPHONE EXCHANGE OF THE BODY

The cerebrum, or greater brain, is the seat of sensation, intelligence and the will. The chief work of the cerebellum seems to be the co-ordination of movement and the maintenance of balance.

behind the ear. Further, this small strip has been mapped out into areas controlling the hand, the arm, the foot, the thumb, and so forth. Each about two inches across, the areas for smell, hearing and sight lie along each side of the brain, and an injury to one of these areas will at once be apparent in the loss of the particular sense affected.

The only one-sided centre in the body is the speech centre which, in right-handed people, lies on the inner side of the left hemisphere of the cerebrum, a little above and a little in front of the ear-tip. A curious fact about the work of the cerebral hemispheres is that each side receives messages from, and controls the opposite half of, the body. Thus, the right cerebral hemisphere controls the left side of the body, and an injury to the left side of the cerebrum will cause paralysis to the right side of the body. All the nerve fibres in each half of the cerebrum run downwards and inwards to meet in a band connecting the cerebrum with the base of the brain and with the spinal cord.

The cerebellum, sometimes known as the lesser brain, lies beneath the back part of the cerebrum. It also is divided into two hemispheres, with grey matter surrounding the white fibrous substance. The chief work of this part of the brain seems to be the co-ordination of movement and the maintenance of balance. Experiments have proved that when the cerebellum of an animal is injured, although it can move its voluntary muscles, it can neither

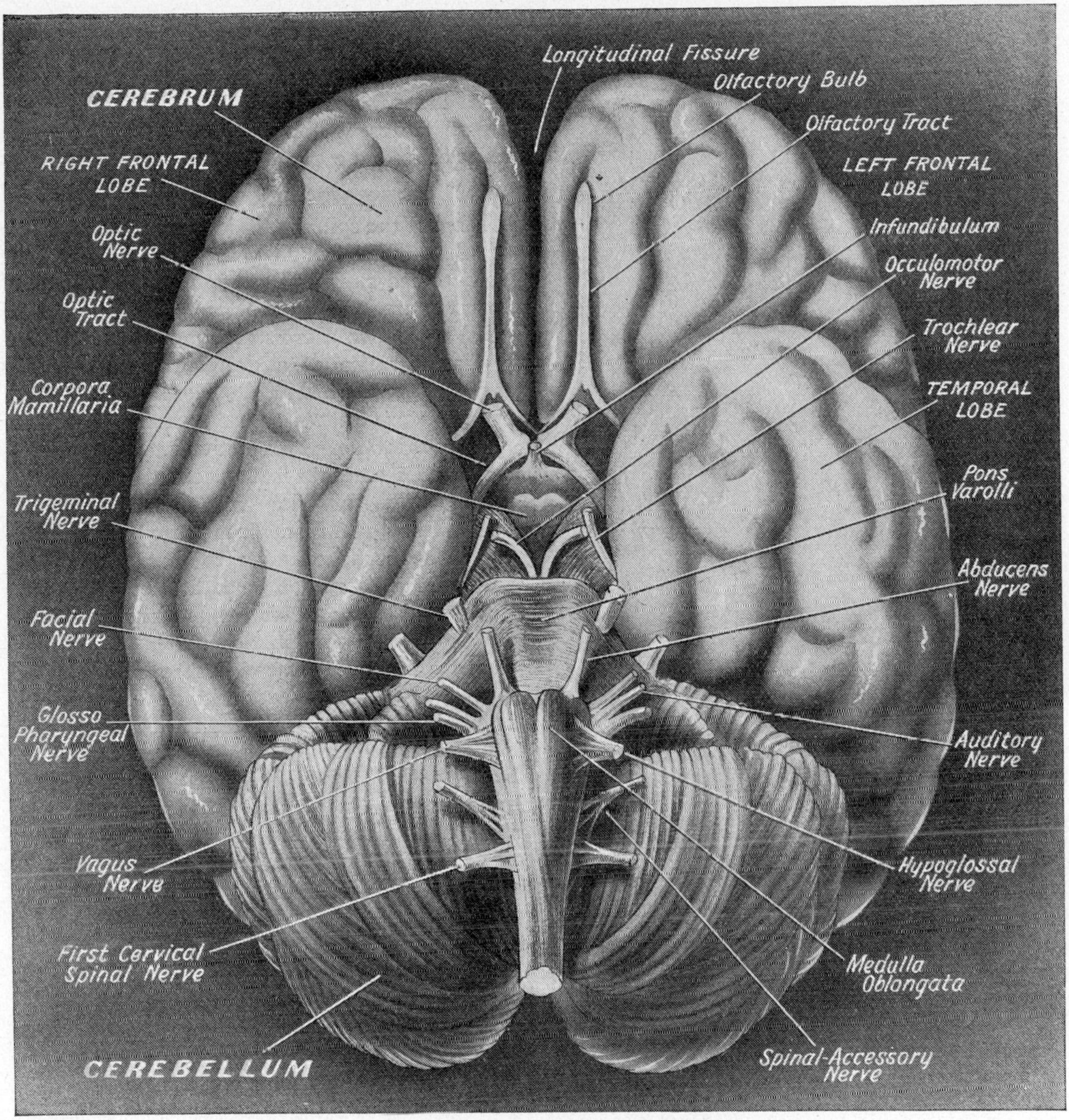

MAP OF THE HUMAN BRAIN

In the medulla oblongata (at foot on right) the nerves cross from one side to the other, which explains why the left side of the brain controls the right side of the body and vice versa.

walk nor balance properly. Below the back part of the cerebellum and connecting its two hemispheres is a broad band of fibres called the pons.

The medulla oblongata, or bulb, is the hindermost part of the brain which gives off more nerves than all the rest taken together. About an inch in length, it connects the brain with the spinal cord. If it is injured even a little, a great deal of paralysis may follow; if it is destroyed, instantaneous death results. It controls the actions of breathing and swallowing. It is in the medulla oblongata that the nerve fibres cross from one side to the other, which explains how it is that the left side of the brain controls the right side of the body and vice versa.

The spinal cord is a long tube of nervous tissue contained in the spinal canal. About eighteen inches in length and as thick as a

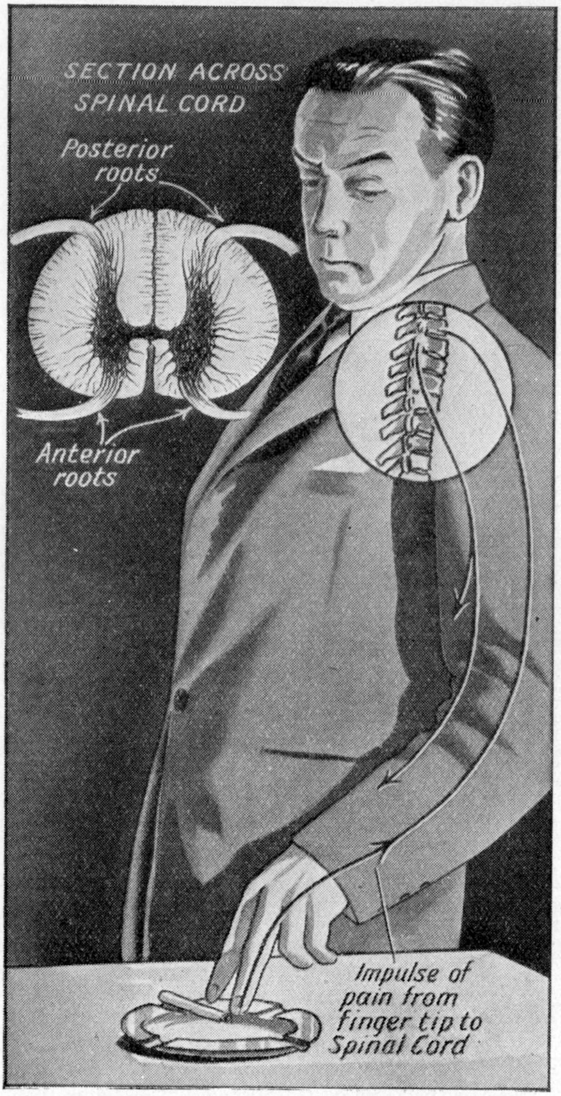

REFLEX ARC

The withdrawing of the hand when burned is an automatic action performed without the participation of the will.

man's little finger, it runs from the medulla oblongata to the first lumbar vertebra, giving off a number of branches on the way. This is the central cable of the telephone system of the body. Like the brain, the spinal cord has the delicate covering of the pia mater which gives it its blood supply, the serous covering and the fibrous covering. In addition, between the last two, there is a layer of fat which gives further protection to the spinal cord.

The central cable of the telephone system of the body gives off thirty-one pairs of branches, right and left. These are the spinal nerves. Each spinal nerve has two kinds of nerve fibres : inward or sensory fibres which bring messages from the muscles and the skin, and outward or motor fibres which take commands to the muscles and the glands.

MESSAGES FROM THE BODY

Most of the spinal cord is made up of bundles of white fibres which bear messages from the body to the brain. The central part, however, is made up of grey matter (branching nerve cells) which, in a cross section of the cord, has the appearance of a double crescent-shaped mass, joined by a bridge. The free ends of the crescents are known as the anterior horns and the posterior horns respectively. A bundle of nerve cells emerges from each of these horns, making the anterior and posterior roots. Nerve fibres run from both roots and, as they leave the cord, combine to form one mixed nerve in a common sheath. Though lying side by side, the fibres retain their respective sensory and motor functions.

In order to follow the course of a message sent to the brain from the outside world, let us suppose that a child puts his hand on a hot radiator. His next action is to withdraw the hand quickly, probably giving a cry of dismay and fear at the same time. In the skin are very small bodies, the ends of nerve fibres, which are able to feel the heat. These are irritated by the stimulus and send an impulse to the nerve cell at the other end of the nerve fibre in the spinal column. Here the message brought in at the posterior root is passed on and travels back from the anterior root to the muscles of the injured hand. This impulse causes them to contract, and so the hand is jerked away.

The path from the sense organ over the central nervous system to the motor organ is called the reflex arc. This withdrawing of the hand, then, is an example of a reflex action—in other words, of an automatic action performed without the participation of the will.

RELAYED BY THE BRAIN

The nerve fibres from the sensory path and from the motor path are connected with nerve cells whose fibres run along inside the spinal cord up to the different parts of the brain. When, on touching the hot radiator, the child feels the pain in his hand, this is because the impulse has travelled along one of those paths inside the cord and has reached that part of the brain which conveys the sensation of pain.

The brain at once sends back a message that the hand must be jerked away, though actually this message has already been sent by the centres in the spinal cord. But the brain is sending other messages in connection with the hurt hand to call various muscles into activity. The child probably cries, and this crying may bring him help. He may run away from the radiator, since he now knows it to be dangerous. He would do none of these things but for the messages relayed by the brain on receiving the initial message that the child felt pain.

SYMPATHETIC NERVOUS SYSTEM

Having had the experience of burning his hand on the hot radiator, the child in future will probably not touch the radiator at all. In this way is set up a second reflex of a higher order, called a conditioned reflex. Much of our daily life is built up of such conditioned reflexes. For instance, as already noted, the taking in of food at once induces a flow of saliva to aid digestion. Since this is so, the sight or even the smell alone of the food is enough to set the same mechanism at work. Finally, the thought of an appetizing dish of, say, grilled chop and tomatoes, will be sufficient to send a flow of saliva into the mouth.

Much investigation is still being carried out on the sympathetic nervous system, but it is believed to be outside the control of the will yet within the influence of the emotions. A characteristic is the formation of extensive bunches of nerve cells found among the viscera of the thorax and the abdomen. For instance, the nerves from the fifth to the tenth ganglia run together to form the great plexus, or network, lying behind the stomach, known as the solar plexus. A severe blow in the region of the stomach will give such a shock to the solar plexus that a man will temporarily be unable to get his breath.

IMPULSES TO THE GLANDS

In addition to supplying the involuntary muscles the nerves of the sympathetic system are believed to send impulses to the glands and to the walls of blood vessels. When the face is grey with anxiety or rosy with pleasure it is because the blood vessels are reacting to messages which have passed through the sympathetic nervous system, although they may have originated in the central nervous system.

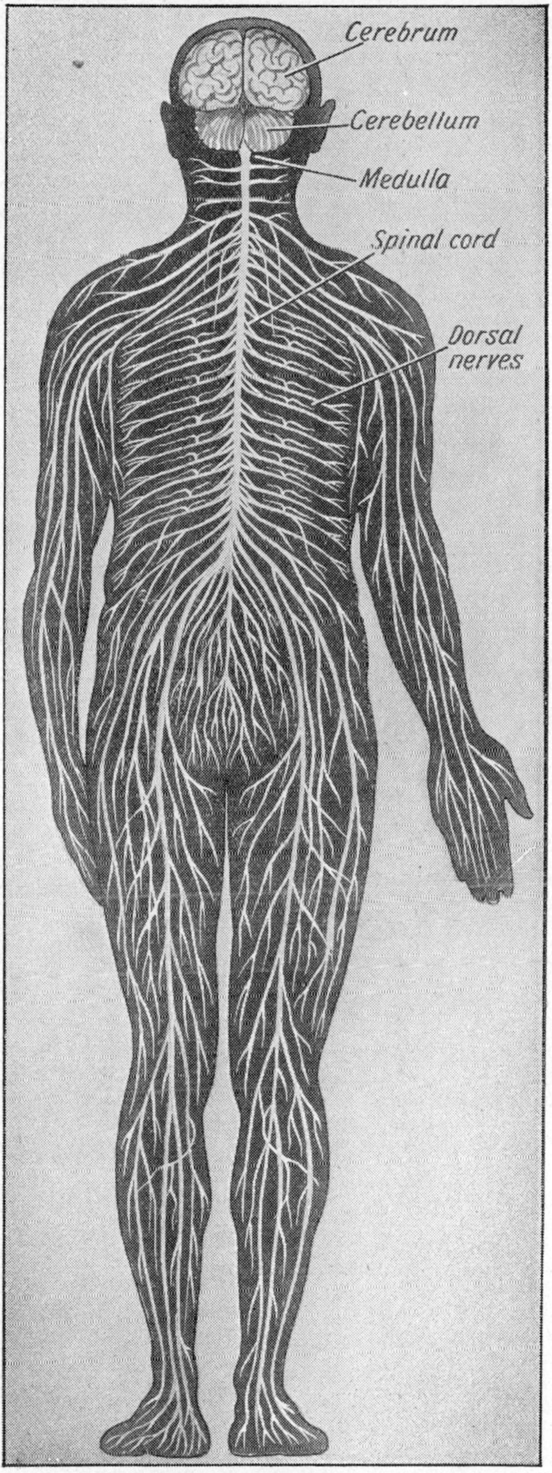

SPINAL CORD AND SPINAL NERVES

The central cable of the telephone system gives off thirty-one pairs of branches, right and left. These are the spinal nerves.

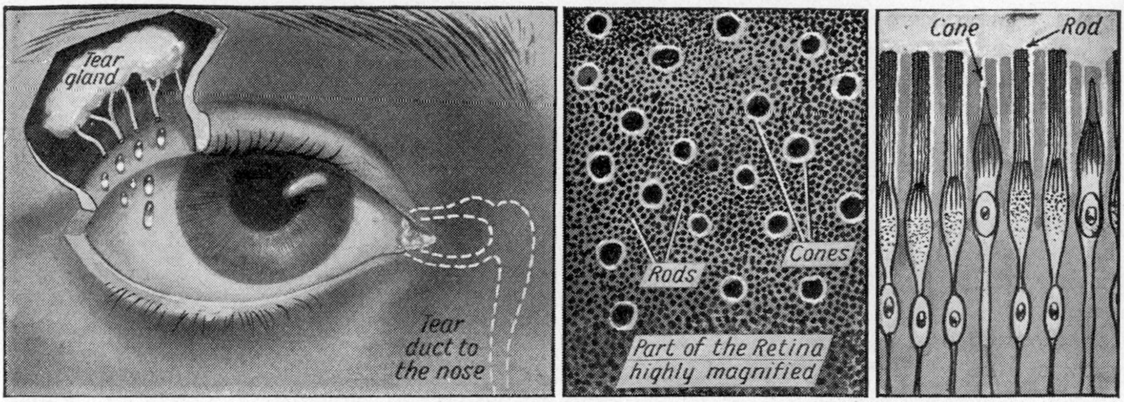

RODS AND CONES THAT AID LIGHT

The tear gland secretes a salty liquid which helps to keep the eyelid moist. The cones of the retina (right) are sensitive to the intensity of light ; the rods enable colour to be perceived.

SENSE AND SPEECH ORGANS

CLOSELY allied to the nervous system are the special organs of sense. These are the touch bodies in the skin : the eye, the ear, the nose, and the mouth. It is by means of these organs that man is connected with the outside world. Impulses are received by them and sent by nerves to the brain.

In the description of the reflex arc it was seen how the stimulus of heat was conveyed to the central nervous system and to the brain. Touch, the most widely diffused of all the senses, is not quite so simple. Scattered all over the surface of the skin are millions of tiny bulbs at the end of the nerves. Branches run from these to join larger nerves, and thus are connected with the spinal cord. The small bulbs at the nerve tips, however, have specialized work to do, owing to the fact that the end of each nerve fibre can only be excited by one kind of stimulus.

If the palm of the hand is touched with a pointed pencil that is colder than the skin itself, it is only certain spots, the cold spots, that feel this sensation of cold. Other parts of the palm respond to heat, and others to pressure. Accordingly, when any object is touched, the complicated sensation received is the result of the combined response to these stimuli. Certain parts of the skin, such as that of the tongue, the cheeks, the lips and the finger-tips, are much more sensitive to outside impressions than the rest, for it is in these regions that the small bulbs at the ends of the nerves are most numerous. They are densest of all in the tongue, which explains why a hole in a tooth explored by it seems so infinitely larger than it really is.

Every sensation we have of heat and cold, moistness and dryness, and so on, as well as many sensations of pain, is a registration by the brain of a message picked up by nerve endings in the skin and transmitted by the nerve fibre. When in certain nervous diseases the line of transmission is out of order, any or all of these sensations may be lost : the nerve endings do not respond.

The eye is, in effect, a miniature photographic camera. It is set in a bony cavity of the skull known as the orbit, and is connected with the brain at the back of it by the stalk-like optic nerve. The bony sides of the orbit protect the eyeball on all sides except the front, where its delicate surface is shielded by the lids. The lids blink automatically every few seconds, and by these regular movements clean the surface of the eyeball from dust and keep it moist.

Covered outside by ordinary skin, each eyelid is furnished on the inside with a smooth membrane called the conjunctiva. This is kept moist partly by its own mucus, and partly by the salty liquid secreted by the lachrymal, or tear, gland. This gland is at the top of the orbit, near its outer edge, and functions most actively when any foreign body gets caught between the eyeball and the lid and irritates the membrane.

Attaching the eyeball to the walls of the orbit are six small muscles. Four of these, the recti muscles, are straight bands which

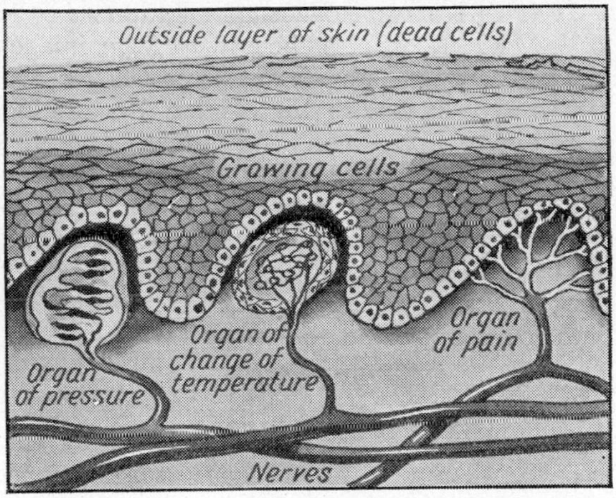

THREE ORGANS OF TOUCH

The bulbs at the nerve tips have specialized work to do because the end of each nerve fibre can only be excited by one kind of stimulus.

enable the eye to turn upward, downward, and to each side. The other two, slightly bent in their course and hence called the oblique muscles, run across the orbit and give the eyeball the power of rolling.

The eyeball is roughly spherical, but its front part projects in a slight bulge. The outermost of its three coats is the sclerotic, a tough and opaque white membrane which forms the hinder five-sixths of the sphere, and is partly visible as "the white of the eye." Let into the sclerotic in front, as a window is let into a room, is the transparent and slightly bulging cornea.

COLOUR OF THE EYE

Lining the inner surface of the sclerotic is the eye's second coat, the choroid, a pigmented membrane, plentifully supplied with blood vessels. At the border of the cornea it leaves the sclerotic and, as a circular coloured curtain, called the iris, extends across the eye at some distance behind the cornea. It is the iris which gives the eye its colour. Consisting of two layers of unstriped muscle, it regulates the amount of light entering the eye by expanding or contracting the circular hole, the pupil, which pierces its centre. No light can pass through the iris itself because of the black pigment which covers its back surface.

The innermost of the three coats of the eyeball is the retina, the most important structure in the eye. Sensitive to light, this serves as a photographic plate. Although it is only one-fiftieth of an inch thick, the retina is composed of no fewer than ten cell layers. Nearest the choroid a layer of pigment cells keeps the light from spreading. Next to these comes a layer of highly-specialized cells which take in the light, the rods and cones as they are called. The cones are sensitive to the intensity of light; the more numerous rods, which contain a substance called the visual purple, enable colour to be perceived.

WHERE VISION IS CLEAREST

In the retina a small oval pit in the middle of the back of the eye is known as the yellow spot. At the centre of this spot only cones are present, yet it is here that vision is clearest : distinctness of vision, then, is due to the cones. At the point where the optic nerve from the brain enters the retina, the characteristic red colour of the latter is varied by a small oval patch of pale pink. Here there are neither rods nor cones. Consequently, this area is insensitive to light, and is termed the blind spot.

The hollow interior of the eyeball is divided by the iris into two unequal spaces called chambers. Lying between the cornea and the iris, the small front chamber contains a clear watery fluid, the aqueous humour; the large chamber at the back of the iris is filled with a transparent jelly-like substance known as the vitreous humour. The latter is hollowed out in front to take a double convex lens, called the crystalline lens of the eye. Unlike that of a camera, this lens is not a firm body, but consists of a transparent elastic tissue set in a ring of muscular fibre, the ciliary muscle, which, on contracting, causes the lens to bulge and so become thicker in the middle.

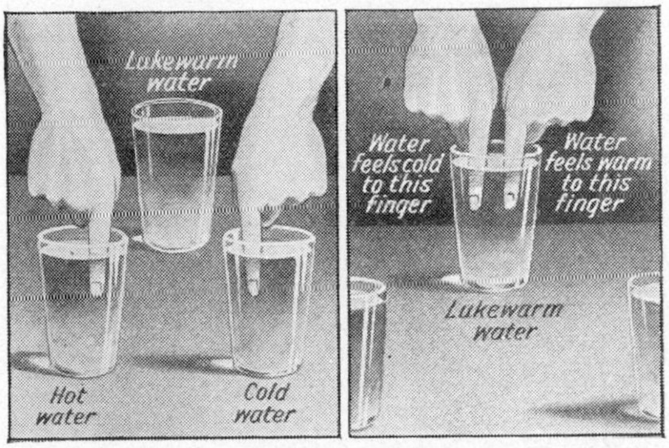

HOW THE SENSES DECEIVE US

Place a finger of one hand in hot water and a finger of the other in cold, then both in lukewarm water. The result will be as above.

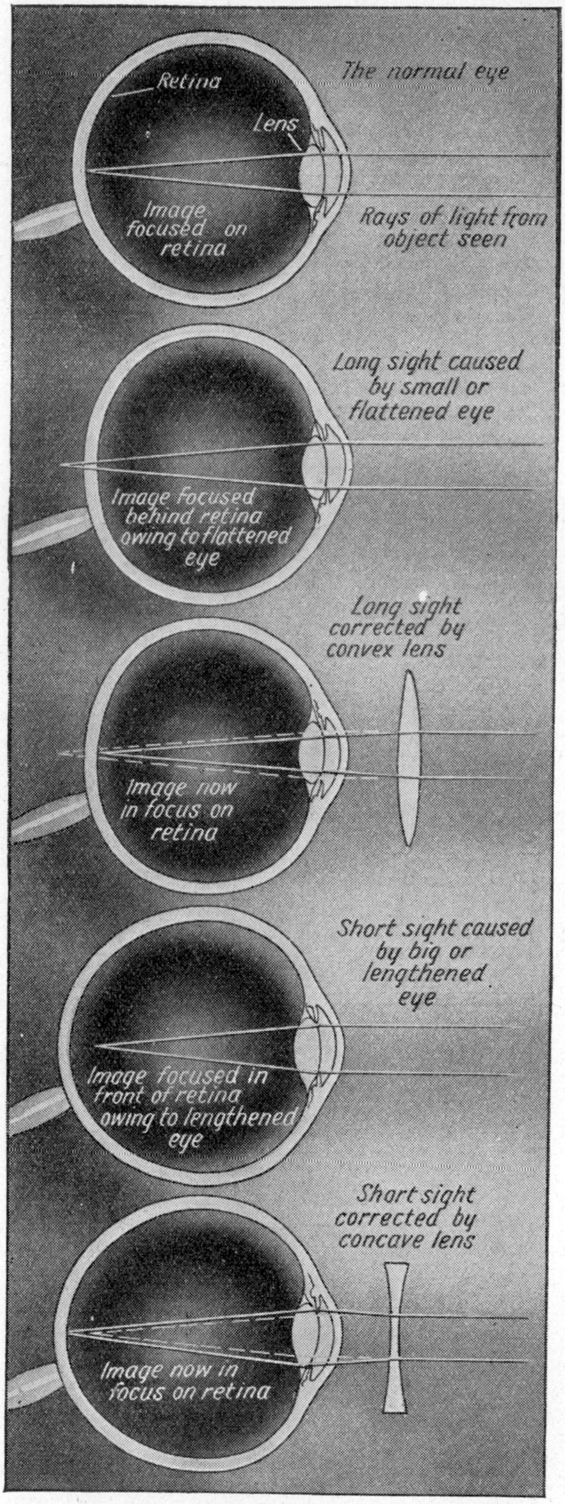

"LONG" AND "SHORT" SIGHT
Both defects can be corrected by spectacles with convex lenses and concave lenses respectively.

It is this power of accommodation as it is called, which enables the eye to form images of both near and distant objects. As the photographer focuses his camera by altering the distance between the screen and the refracting lens, so the ciliary muscle by bulging the lens of the eye makes it thicker and so capable of focusing the divergent light rays from near objects, or by flattening it brings the almost parallel rays from distant objects into focus upon the retina.

HOW WE SEE

The mechanism of sight is briefly this : light falling upon the eye is concentrated by the cornea, then by the aqueous humour and finally by the crystalline lens, where it is properly focused. Traversing the vitreous humour, which also has a minor share in the focusing, its rays strike the retina, upon which they produce a small inverted image of the object seen. Light first meets the nerve fibres in the retina. The rods and cones, which may be compared to the touch bodies in the skin, are stimulated by the light. This affects the optic nerve, and impulses are sent to the brain, producing visual sensations.

The retina has the power of retaining images made upon it for a brief time—about one-eighth of a second. This explains why a mounting rocket gives the impression of a trail of light, while a glowing rope-end, rapidly whirled, produces the effect of a circle of light.

If a bright object is gazed at for a time, that part of the retina on which the image falls is soon exhausted. This may be tested by turning the eyes from the light to a sheet of white paper, when a dark spot or after-image is seen. This is an illusion, produced because the rays of light from the seemingly dark spot are in fact falling on the exhausted part of the retina.

CAUSES OF BAD SIGHT

The comparison of the retina to a photographic plate may be carried further. In the same way as the light-sensitive layer on the plate changes chemically under the influence of light, so the visual purple is bleached. This bleached substance stimulates the rods to send impulses to the brain. The visual purple, however, has the capacity to regain its colour in a short time. Strong light falling continuously on the retina allows no time for this recovery. Consequently the retina becomes temporarily exhausted.

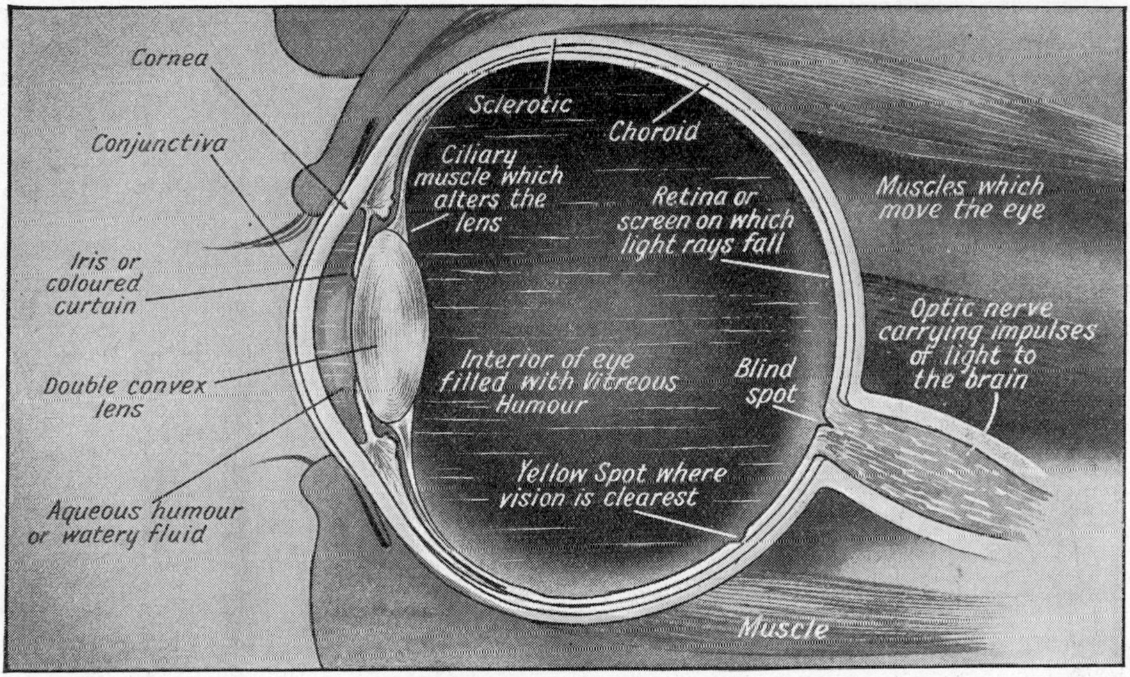

MECHANISM OF SIGHT

The retina has the power of retaining images made upon it for about one-eighth of a second. Light first meets the nerve fibres in the retina. Optic nerves carry impulses to the brain, producing visual sensations.

In the case of people whose eyes are too small and flat, or not sufficiently bulging, the rays of light are focused not on but behind the retina, and a blurred image results. This is known as " long sight." Eyes that are too big or too bulging focus the rays in front of the retina. Again the image is blurred; this type of defective vision being called " short sight." Both defects can be corrected by spectacles with convex lenses for long sight and concave lenses for short sight.

Each eye sees the object before it from a slightly different angle. But in spite of this we see only a single image. The nerve fibres of the right half of each eye unite and go to the optic centre in the right hemisphere of the brain; while the nerve fibres of the left side of each eye go similarly to the left hemisphere. In this way the stimuli from each eye become mixed and produce one image.

MECHANISM OF THE EAR

At the side of the head is the outer ear, a folded plate of cartilage covered with skin, leading into the skull by the auditory canal. Protected by the strong bones at the base of the skull lie the two chambers of the inner and the middle ear. The middle ear is separated from the auditory canal by a tightly-stretched membrane, the drum or tympanic membrane, and from the inner ear by a second and similar membrane, the fenestra ovalis. The gap between the two membranes is bridged by the chain of three small bones, known on account of their shape as the hammer, the anvil, and the stirrup. The hammer fits into the tympanic membrane, and the stirrup into the fenestra ovalis.

WHEN WE FEEL GIDDY

In order that the drum may vibrate freely and transmit the vibrations to the small bones, the hollow in which these are placed must be kept full of air. This is provided for by a pipe called the Eustachian tube which connects with the back of the throat behind the air passages of the nose. If we have a bad cold, and the mouth of the Eustachian tube becomes blocked, the drum cannot vibrate properly, and temporary deafness often results.

The inner ear consists of two parts, only one of which has to do with hearing. The auditory nerve with its three thousand minute nerve rods suspended in lymph fluid, is protected by a bony tube, wound up like the shell of a snail. This bony tube, known as the

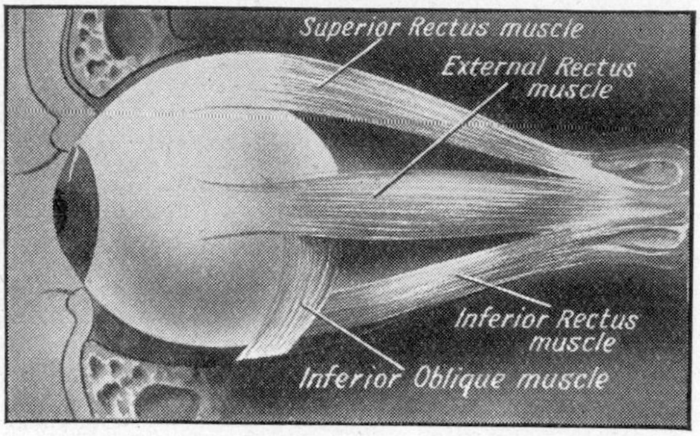

MUSCLES THAT MOVE THE EYE

The four recti muscles enable the eye to turn upward, downward, and to each side. The oblique muscles cause it to roll.

cochlea, is connected with the middle ear by the fenestra ovalis into which, as we have seen, the stirrup fits, and by the fenestra rotunda, an elastic membrane designed to give play to the vibrating lymph inside the cochlea.

Sound travels through the outer ear, which acts merely as a receiving horn, and, passing along the auditory canal, sets the whole apparatus into motion—the drum, the three small bones, the fenestra rotunda and the lymph inside the cochlea which finally excites the nerve endings. From these the impulse travels to the brain.

Inside the same chamber as the cochlea are three small curved tubes called the semicircular canals. These, arranged in three planes, are so constructed that every movement of the body, up and down, right and left, backwards and forwards, is registered.

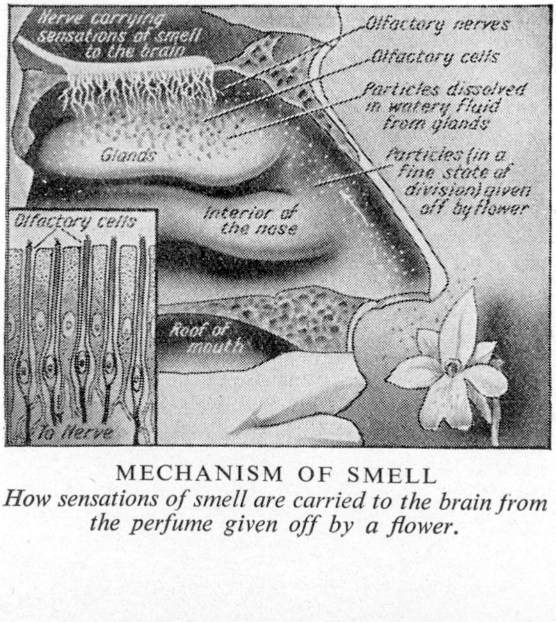

MECHANISM OF SMELL

How sensations of smell are carried to the brain from the perfume given off by a flower.

These tubes contain a fluid and are lined with sensitive hairs over which small crystals of carbonate of lime are suspended. These crystals change their place at every movement of the body, thus stimulating different hairs in different positions. The hairs, or nerve-endings, from the fluid are gathered into a large nerve running into the cerebellum. If a serious disturbance occurs in the semicircular

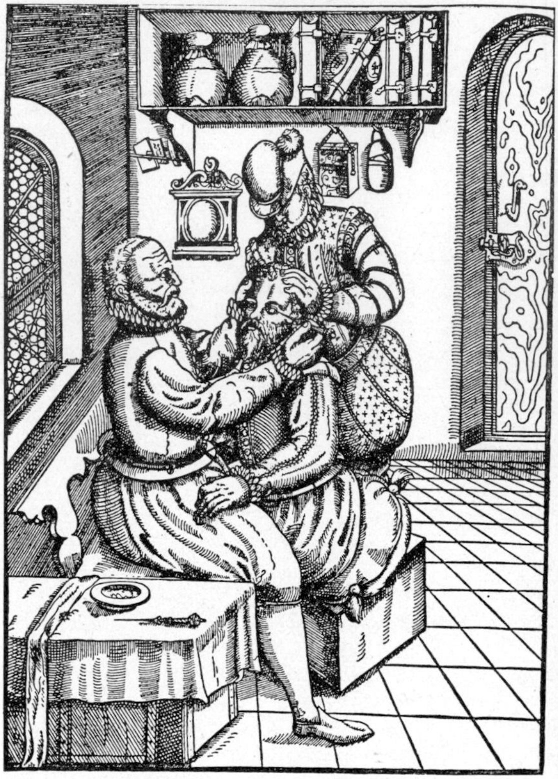

HAMILTON COLLECTION

OPERATION ON THE EYE

As pictured in the first German manual on diseases of the eye, published in Dresden in 1583.

canals, our sense of balance is upset, and we probably feel giddy. Sea-sickness, train-sickness, and swing-sickness are all explained by this fact.

The organ of smell, like the organ of taste, is not so well developed in man as in other animals. Only about ten per cent of the work of the nose is concerned with smell. Although the other ninety per cent is made for the work of breathing, it is the ten per cent which decides if the air taken in is good or bad.

The part of the nose that does the work of smelling is found at the top of the air passage, under the root of the nose. At this spot is a

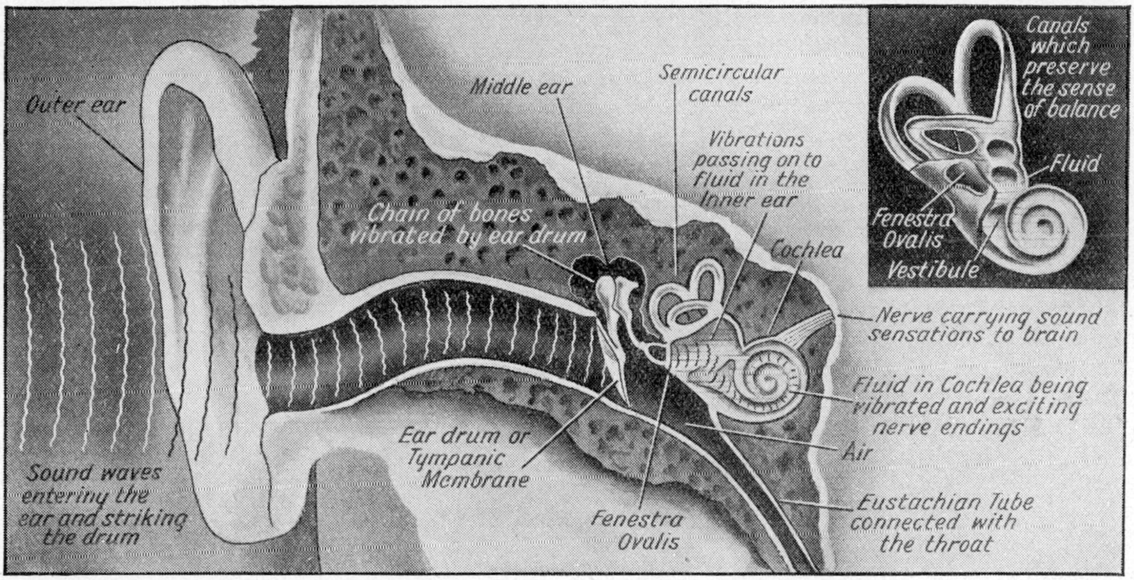

MECHANISM OF HEARING

Sound sets in motion the drum, the bones of the middle ear, the fenestra rotunda *and the fluid inside the* cochlea, *which finally excites the nerve endings. From these the impulse travels to the brain.*

patch of deep yellow mucous membrane, which is very sensitive to odours that rise to it. The appetizing flavours of coffee, grilled chop, tomatoes and so forth which set our salivary glands to work, are not really tasted at all; they are smelt by this delicate area lying at the highest and back part of the nose. Here the nerve fibres of the olfactory nerve branch out. When the nerve-ends are stimulated by odours, sensory impulses are transmitted to the brain.

The organ of taste lies in the mucous membrane of the tongue, more particularly in its upper and back part, and also in the mucous membrane of the back part of the palate. The upper surface of the tongue is supplied with so-called taste buds, or papillæ, which are in contact with nerve-endings from the fifth and ninth pairs of cranial nerves.

The only substances that can really be tasted in the mouth are those that are sweet, bitter, sour, or salty. At the back of the tongue are about ten large papillæ, arranged in two rows like an inverted V. This is the part of the tongue that is able to taste bitter substances best; while the tip and the middle, which have smaller and redder papillæ, perceive sweet and salt tastes more readily.

The sounds we make in speech are the vibrations produced by the air leaving the lungs—which act as a bellows—and setting the vocal cords in motion. These sounds are modified and enlarged by the chest, the mouth and the head, all of which serve as resonance boxes. The actual speech organ is the larynx, or voice box, i.e., the upper part of the windpipe reaching about one-third of the way down the neck.

This consists of four pieces of cartilage, to which the two vocal cords are attached. They are so arranged that the cords can be stretched and relaxed by small muscles. The more tightly these cords are stretched and the smaller the gap between them, the higher

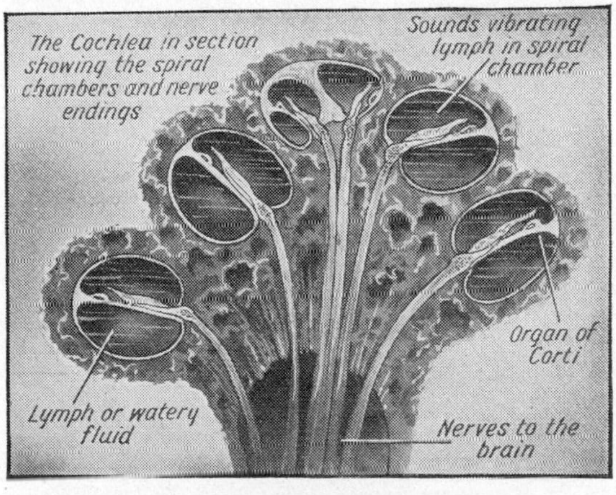

THE COCHLEA IN SECTION

The cochlea *in section, showing the spiral chambers and nerve endings vibrating in lymph.*

and shriller is the tone emitted. The more relaxed the cords and the bigger the gap between them, the softer and deeper the tones.

The tongue, the jaws and the teeth, however, modify the tones produced. The vowels can be formed by the mouth alone without other help; the consonants by blocking in various ways the stream of air sent out by the lungs, thus: "s" is shaped by closing the teeth, "m" by closing the lips, and "n" by pressing the tongue against the teeth.

In speech and song many factors are involved: regulation of breathing, movement of the muscles in the larynx, movement of the tongue and cheeks are some of the most important of these. Thus, the spinal nerves which control respiration and the cranial nerves which regulate movements of the face are in reality speech muscles. It is a pleasing thought that out of the waste air sent from the lungs man produces that wonderful thing, the human voice. When the larynx is defective in a mute the person must learn to swallow air and regulate its giving off so that by adjusting the position of the mouth speech may be produced.

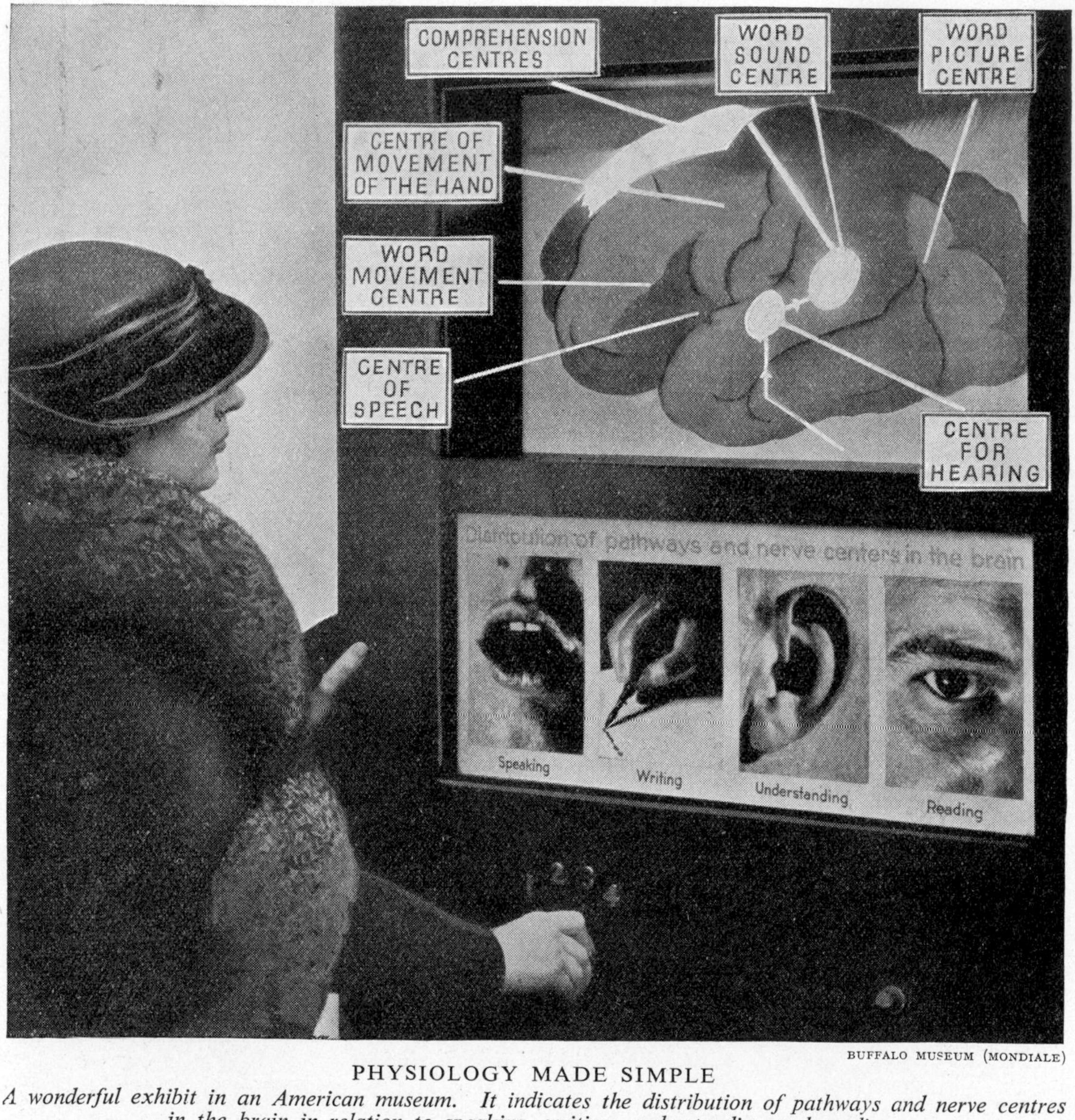

BUFFALO MUSEUM (MONDIALE)

PHYSIOLOGY MADE SIMPLE

A wonderful exhibit in an American museum. It indicates the distribution of pathways and nerve centres in the brain in relation to speaking, writing, understanding and reading.

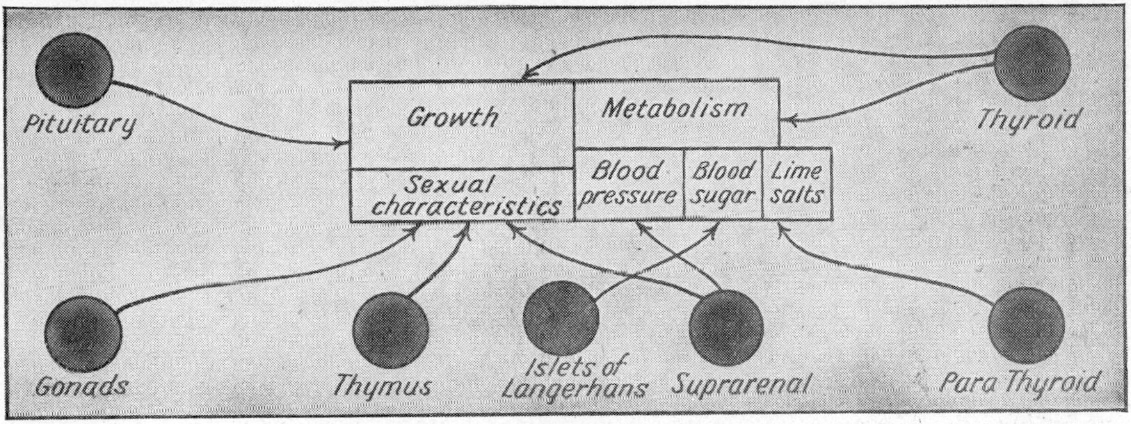

WORK OF THE DUCTLESS GLANDS

Effects on particular organs of various secretions passed out by ductless glands. They are so called because they pour their secretions straight into the blood instead of opening into a particular organ by means of a duct.

WHAT THE DUCTLESS GLANDS DO

ESSENTIAL to the well-being of both the body and the mind is the proper adjustment of the various systems one to the other. For instance, growth takes place in the human body up to about the age of fifteen, after which time there is a gradual slowing down, combined with a simultaneous development of the sex organs.

In order that these two processes may not become disproportionate, i.e., that sexual development may not take place too quickly and growth stop too early, or vice versa—the body is provided with a series of glands, known as the endocrine system. These glands have the peculiar characteristic of pouring their secretions straight into the blood, instead of opening into a particular organ by means of a duct. For this reason they are known as the ductless or endocrine glands.

The chief of these are the thyroid, the parathyroids, the adrenals, the islets of Langerhans, the pituitary, and the gonads (the testes and the ovaries which in themselves act as ductless glands).

The thyroid consists of a pair of oval-shaped bodies, weighing about one ounce and found one on each side of the "Adam's apple." The parathyroids are four pea-like organs in the vicinity of the thyroid. The adrenals, or supra-renals, are two small glands which lie just above the kidneys and are about one-seventh of the weight of the thyroid. The islets of Langerhans are areas, acting as ductless glands, which are distributed throughout the pancreas. The pituitary, a small body weighing about one-sixtieth of an ounce and shaped rather like a flattened cherry, is situated on the floor of the brain.

The secretion of any of these glands contains a substance spoken of as the hormone, whose work is to stimulate a particular organ. For example, the larynx is so stimulated in males that that phenomenon, the breaking of the voice, takes place.

The endocrine system is only just being understood. Such knowledge as has been gained has largely come about through the removal of those seemingly unimportant structures, the glands. In many cases the results have been unexpected. For instance, the thyroid has been totally removed in an attempt to cure goitre. After its removal, the patient gradually became bald, stupid, thick-skinned and pot-bellied, showing that a very vital mechanism had been interfered with. It was discovered that the giving of iodine, or alternatively of thyroid extract, in small doses could better this condition brought about by the removal of the thyroid.

This went to show that thyroxin, which is the name given to the active principle of the thyroid, is necessary to the well-being of the individual. In countries such as New Zealand and Switzerland, where the soil is deficient in iodine, the thyroid cannot produce sufficient thyroxin, and goitre develops. In Switzerland it is obligatory to mix minute quantities of iodine in the table salt as a corrective for the deficiency.

When the thyroid is over-active, the burning up of the carbohydrates in the body goes on much too fast. The person loses weight, and the heart is overtaxed. Finally, the thyroid gland becomes exhausted, when collapse or death results.

HAMILTON COLLECTION

FAMOUS IRISH DWARF

Owen Farrel, whose height was 3ft. 9in. Under-functioning of the pituitary gland leads to dwarfism.

When the parathyroids have been accidentally removed in an operation on the thyroid, it has been found that after five or six days, tetanus, or severe cramp of all the muscles, attacked the patient. Death shortly followed. The blood was discovered to be seriously deficient in its calcium content, and this was the cause of the tetanus.

The adrenals have the fourfold function of regulating the blood pressure, of regulating the supply of glucose or blood sugar, of counteracting fatigue, and of influencing normal sexual development. The blood pressure is regulated by the action of the hormone adrenalin, from the adrenal glands, upon the capillaries; this makes them contract. Incidentally, this is one means by which the body temperature is regulated.

The adrenalin acts on the glycogen in the liver, and the glycogen is turned into glucose or blood sugar. When an extract of the adrenals is injected into a normal person, he becomes much more active and less liable to fatigue. The influence of the adrenals on sexual development is as yet imperfectly understood, but their work is thought to be connected with that of the pituitary.

BOY NINE FEET TALL

The islets of Langerhans secrete a substance, insulin, which enables the tissues to take up the glucose manufactured in the liver under the stimulus of the adrenal glands. People whose blood is lacking in insulin are unable to make use of the glucose. Consequently, the blood has much too high a sugar content, a condition that is known as diabetes mellitus. Since the tissues do not get enough glucose, they become undernourished and are not able to function properly. The patient grows weaker and weaker, since he is unable to utilize the carbohydrates in his food. With the discovery of insulin it has become a comparatively simple matter to cure diabetes by injection.

The pituitary has two lobes, each with three distinct functions. The posterior lobe regulates the flow of urine, causes a contraction of the uterus in parturition, and has a certain influence on the blood pressure. The anterior lobe regulates growth, controls sexual development, and has a slightly stimulating effect on milk production. Although the secretion, comparable to the thyroxin in the thyroid, has not yet been isolated chemically, it is thought to be some kind of protein.

REGULATION OF GROWTH

The best understood function of the pituitary is its regulation of growth. Under-functioning of the pituitary leads to dwarfism and sexual under-development known as infantilism. Over-functioning during early youth leads to gigantism. There is a case on record of a boy of eleven who weighed two hundred and fifty pounds and who was about nine feet high. A recorded case of dwarfism is that of a girl of nine and a half who was only thirty-five and a half inches tall and who weighed twenty-seven and a half pounds.

When either under- or over-functioning takes place, there is also sexual under-development. If, after maturity is reached, the anterior lobe of the pituitary begins to function excessively, the condition known as acromegaly is brought about. Only those parts still capable of growth—i.e., the hands, the feet, the face, especially the chin and nose—are affected. The features become coarsened and enlarged, and the hands and feet grow excessively big.

THAT TIRED FEELING

When the hormone from the anterior lobe of the pituitary is insufficiently secreted, an obese condition is brought about. The Fat Boy of the *Pickwick Papers* who is always wanting to sleep can be explained on this basis.

In addition to the specific functions of the pituitary gland it also exerts an influence on the thyroid, the adrenals, and the gonads, though to what extent is not yet fully understood. In one sense its rôle can be compared to that of the brain in its relation to the nervous system. For it is the dominant gland of the endocrine system.

The ovaries and the testes, called the gonads in relation to this system, secrete substances which influence the development of the secondary sexual characteristics. In the female the hormone known as œstrin regulates the processes of menstruation and ovulation. When a ripe ovum is fertilized, the shed Graafian follicle (which, as we saw in the chapter on Reproduction, previously surrounded the ovum) grows out into a body called the corpus luteum. This then secretes a hormone called lutein which inhibits, or prevents, further ovulation and therefore further menstruation. It also stimulates the mammary glands to secrete milk.

In pregnant women, œstrin and another hormone similar to that from the anterior lobe of the pituitary gland are excreted in considerable amounts in the urine. This fact has been used to ascertain during the first weeks whether a woman is pregnant or not. This is the only real test, since all other indications are but conjecture.

INFLUENCE ON TEMPERAMENT

The hormones from the ductless glands, because of their influence on the body, are also partly responsible for what we conveniently term the temperament of a person. For example, a slight over-functioning of the thyroid is characterized by vivacity, while an under-functioning gives a corresponding dullness. When our knowledge of the endocrine system is much greater, it may well come about that we shall be able to explain our various moods in terms of this or that gland functioning or otherwise failing to function.

It was thought at one time that Voronoff's operation—the transplanting of testes—would overcome the symptoms of old age. This today, after much re-examination, is very much doubted. The operation has been found to produce temporary improvement only, and the same result has also been obtained in a number of other ways. The same conclusions

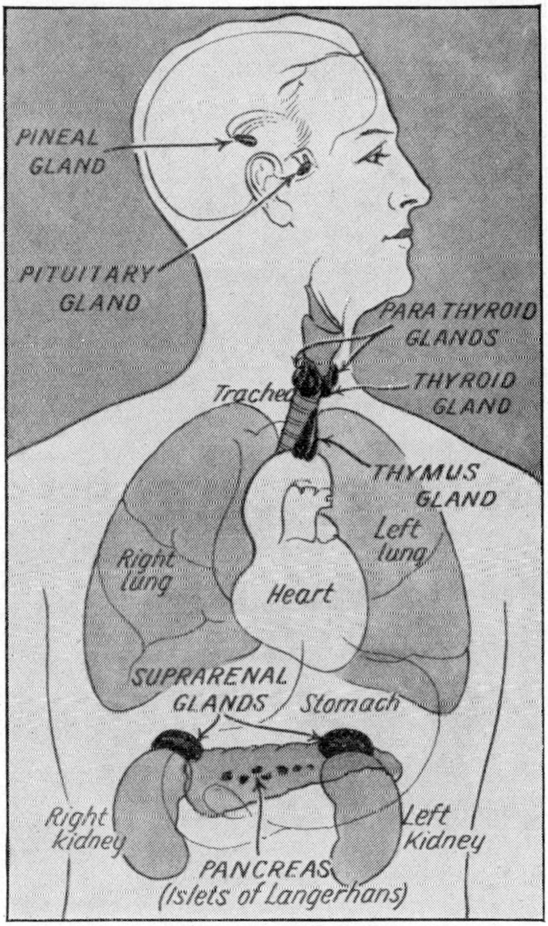

POSITION OF THE DUCTLESS GLANDS
The secretions of the ductless glands contain a substance spoken of as the hormone, whose work is to stimulate a particular organ. They are also partly responsible for temperament.

have been reached with regard to Steinach's operation, which was at first looked upon as a triumph for endocrinology, making rejuvenation possible.

Much work is still being done on these problems, and it is confidently expected that a great deal of new material will be available in the near future.

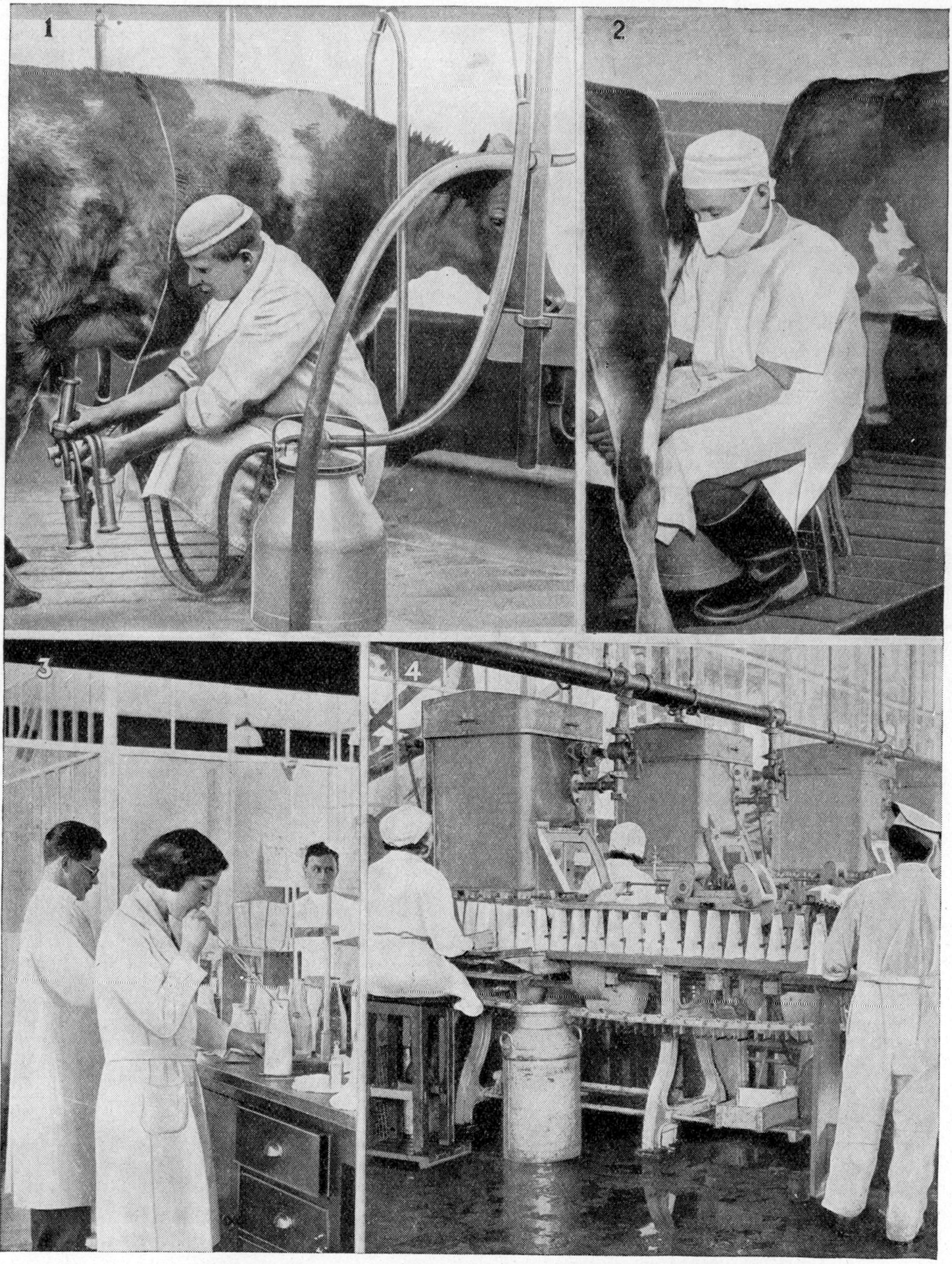

FOX

PRECAUTIONS TAKEN TO ENSURE PURE MILK

Milk, butter and cream contain vitamin A. Deficiency of it leads to diseases of the skin and of the eyes, while the lungs and intestines become susceptible to infection. 1. Milking by electricity. 2. Milking by hand, the milkman wearing a respirator. 3. Testing milk for purity. 4. Bottling in containers.

MINIMUM REQUIREMENTS AND ACTUAL CONDITIONS
Rooms regarded as necessary for a family of two and of four people. In 1931 *over* 2,500,000 *people in Great Britain had rather more than two persons to a room; over* 7,000,000 *had less than two rooms for three people.*

MAN AND HIS ENVIRONMENT

NATURE and nurture—in other words, heredity and environment—are the two great factors that make a man what he is. As to his physical and mental make-up, a man may have received a good inheritance or a bad inheritance—most people have been given something between the two—but that make-up, once given, is modified for better or worse by all the factors that enter into what is commonly termed environment. Some of the most important of these are food, housing, sunlight and air, occupation, exercise, rest and leisure.

Because of low wages and high rents few families are able to afford the number of rooms that they would like; while many families cannot afford the accommodation they require for health's sake. In every large town and city thousands of houses are to be found let off in rooms; often a whole family occupies one room or, at best, two.

The Housing Act of 1930 states the requirements of a family of two to be two rooms, and of a family of four, three rooms. This is the minimum for decency and comfort. Yet at the English census of 1931 over two and a half million people were living rather more than two to a room, while over seven million had rather less than two rooms for three people. In London, only one family in three had a house which it did not share.

Such overcrowding affects the physique of the people in a score of ways. When washing, cooking, eating and sleeping are all carried out in a very small space, sometimes in a single room, the fight with dirt and disease becomes doubly difficult. The principal source of tubercular infection, for example, is the sputum of consumptive patients, and the overcrowded dwellings of the poor are the worst breeding-places of tuberculosis.

Not merely contact with infected persons, but impure air, contaminated food, infected milk and personal uncleanliness set up a predisposition to disease. Where space is limited, the storing of food, whether cooked or uncooked, is a serious problem. For food quickly becomes contaminated in a hot, airless room which, because of poor ventilation, is charged with the waste products of the people living in it.

Sunlight and air have a most invigorating effect on the human body, and provide the best allies man has against micro-organisms. A room that is at once bedroom, sitting-room and bathroom is necessarily cluttered with too much furniture and clothing. In addition, doors and windows are often kept shut in the hope of securing a little privacy and of excluding noise and smells.

Where a house built for one family is occupied by several the water supply always presents difficulties. One or more families too often have to fetch their water from a tap a flight or two of stairs away. Consequently, the washing of the body and the washing of clothes become laborious matters. Usually the disposal of the dirty water involves the same trouble and expenditure of energy. Bathing of the body has most often to be done at the public baths, and this in many cases can be afforded only at too rare intervals. It is often impossible for every member of the family to have a regular bath each week.

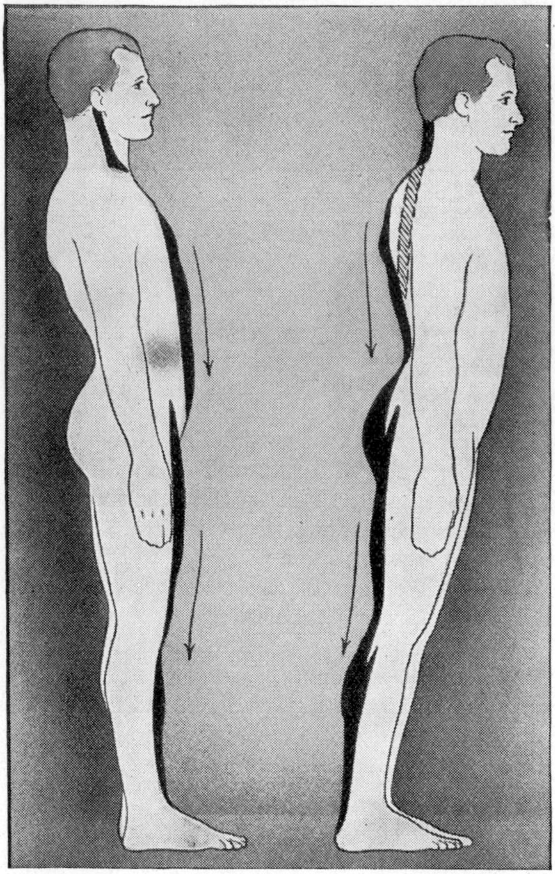

MUSCLES AT WORK
Muscles used in leaning forward or backward, and the direction in which they pull. Exercise is essential to health and should be the right of everybody.

Exercise, which may be defined as the bringing into play of those muscles which a person does not normally use at his work, should be the right of everybody. But in overcrowded areas, exercise in the park, the swimming bath, or the gymnasium is available only to a few—usually young men who have energy and initiative and a little money to spend. The Physical Fitness Campaign inaugurated by the Public Health Acts of 1936 should do much to remedy this state of affairs.

The greatest environmental factor of all is that of food. During the last fifteen years or so the study of nutrition has increasingly become the concern of scientists. The results of their research show that certain foods are necessary to health, and that a deficiency of any such foods causes a breakdown in some part of the human machine.

ENERGY NEEDS OF THE BODY

The energy needs of the body are supplied by the proteins, carbohydrates and fats in the diet, the proteins having the additional work of building up new tissue in children and of repairing worn-out tissue in the adult. While the work of the body in general is stimulated by the protein intake, other essentials are the minerals and the vitamins found in the so-called protective foods. For practical purposes only vitamins A, B, C, D, and E need be considered, although other vitamins have been discovered and much investigation in this field is now being carried out.

The chief substances which go to make up protein are called amino-acids. In order to get enough of these amino-acids for its needs, the body must take in about one hundred grams (one gram = approximately one twenty-eighth of an ounce) of protein daily. Not all protein is of the same quality. First-class protein is derived from animal products; from milk, eggs, fish and meat, with the internal organs of animals as a particularly valuable source. It is usually reckoned that an adult man needs to take about fifty grams of first-class protein every day. The rest may be obtained from such foods as peas, beans, lentils, wholemeal bread, and whole grains.

STARCHY AND SUGARY FOODS

Carbohydrates are mainly derived from the starchy and sugary foods. They may be likened to the coal of a steam-engine, since they supply the heat and energy necessary for the activity of the body. Starch is converted into sugar by the process of digestion. In the intermediate stage of this conversion it is known as glycogen, which is stored in the liver. From the latter it is distributed and absorbed into the blood. In this way the body has a supply of fuel available for its needs. The daily allowance of carbohydrate for an adult should be not less than five hundred grams. During cold weather more fuel is required to maintain body heat, and the allowance may be increased.

The chief sources of carbohydrates are cereals

FOODS IN WHICH VITAMINS ARE FOUND

The energy needs of the body are supplied by the proteins, carbohydrates and fats in the diet. While the work of the body in general is stimulated by the protein intake, other essentials are the minerals and the vitamins found in the so-called protective foods. For practical purposes only vitamins A, B, C, D, and E need be considered.

and the bread and flour made from them, potatoes, root vegetables and nuts. Green vegetables contain a certain amount of starch. With the starch is usually found some protein, vitamins and minerals. Wheat, rice and sugar, however, are today so milled and refined that they are to a large extent robbed of these valuable constituents. If possible, brown rice, wholemeal flour and bread, and brown sugar should always be bought. Wholemeal bread is a source of starch, protein, vitamin B, and the minerals lime and potash. Refined cane sugar should be replaced by honey, raisins and figs, which provide good natural sugars.

FATS SUPPLY HEAT

The minimum amount of fats needed daily by a grown man is one hundred grams. Much of the fat used by the body is built up from the starch and sugars. Weight for weight, fat provides twice as much heat as starch or sugar. It follows that in hot climates the consumption of fats is greatly reduced, while the Eskimos find it necessary to eat large quantities, which they obtain for the most part from the blubber of whales and other big sea animals. The best sources of fats are milk, butter, fresh herrings, olive oil, and some cereals such as oatmeal.

Vitamin A is found particularly in such animal fats as milk, butter and cream. Deficiency of vitamin A leads to certain diseases of the skin and of the eye, while the lungs and the intestine become particularly susceptible to infection.

THREE VALUABLE VITAMINS

Vitamin B, often called the anti-neuritic vitamin, is soluble in water. Deficiency of it leads to various forms of neuritis and to muscular weakness. Whole populations have been attacked by beriberi, a disease producing paralysis of the nerves and limbs, when there is a serious shortage of this vitamin. Its chief sources are yeast, the yolk of egg, tomatoes, potatoes, carrots, juicy fruits, leafy green vegetables, the seeds of plants and the outer coverings of grains. Grains that have had the

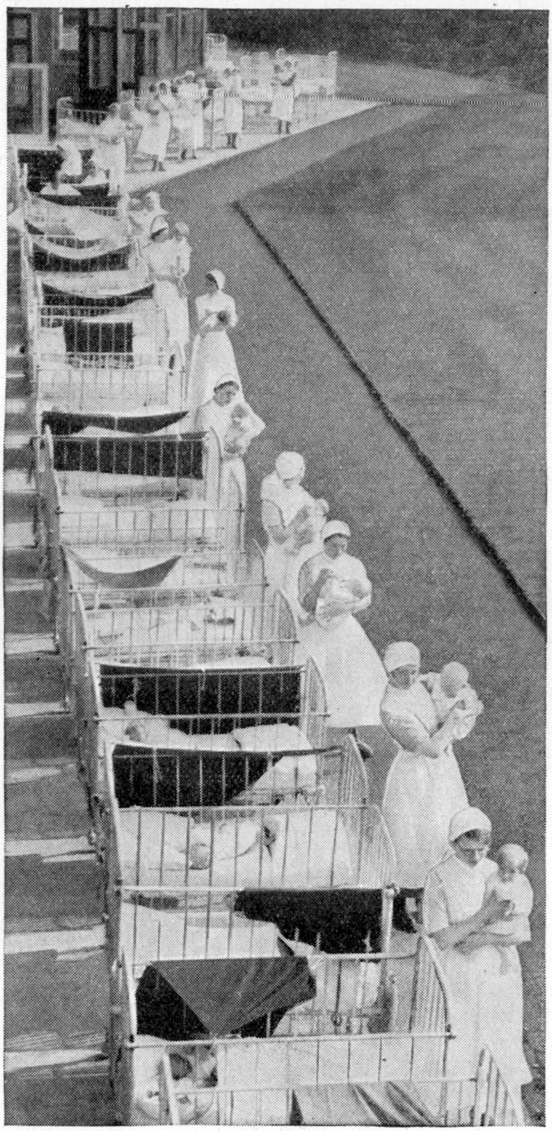

FOX

"LIFE IS A FIGHT"

Sunlight and air provide the best allies man has against micro-organisms.

germ and husks removed by milling are largely deficient in vitamin B.

Vitamin C, or the anti-scorbutic vitamin, is soluble in water and often damaged by heat when food is cooked, especially when soda is added to the water. In the absence of this vitamin there is loss of weight and muscular weakness; gums are apt to swell and teeth to become loose in their sockets. Vitamin C is found in potatoes, green vegetables, raw fruit and their juices—especially such fruits as the lemon and the orange.

Vitamin D is a fat-soluble vitamin and is essential for the utilization by the body of calcium salts and the phosphates. Deficiency quickly brings about rickets. This disease is still all too common among young children in Great Britain, although in the past twenty years the widespread use of cod-liver oil has done something to diminish its prevalence.

HERRINGS CONTAIN VITAMIN D

Apart from the deformities of the bones for which it is responsible—bow legs, knock-knees and bony changes in the chest walls are manifestations of these—rickets has as one of its most serious consequences the alteration of the shape of the pelvic bones. Narrowing of the pelvis results, and this, in later years, increases the dangers of childbirth.

Rickety children are easily attacked by infections of the throat and nose; they have poor muscular tone, and are listless and unintelligent. After six months' treatment with proper food containing vitamin D, they become vigorous and alert. It has been estimated that an ounce of this vitamin is enough to give a full daily dose to one million growing children. At the centenary exhibition of the British Medical Association an ounce crystal of vitamin D was on view. This and vitamin A are the only vitamins which have as yet been isolated.

In addition to cod-liver oil, milk and eggs are rich in vitamin D; fresh herrings and butter are other excellent sources. In the summer months the action of the sun on the skin turns ergosterol, which is present in the tissues, into vitamin D. Hence the importance of seeing that the food taken in winter includes vitamin D.

Vitamin E is found in the germ of grains and in most seeds; it is present also in the yolk of egg and in lettuce. It is supposed to be necessary for fertility and reproduction.

OTHER PROTECTIVE FOODS

Other protective foods containing calcium, phosphorus, iron and iodine all have their part to play in maintaining good health. They are to be found in fresh and dried fruits, eggs, milk, and the glandular tissues of meat. An ordinary mixed diet usually includes them.

Different classes of workers need different amounts and different kinds of foods; while children of varying ages have their special needs. The special need of a man doing heavy manual labour is for plenty of heat and energy

FOX

KEEPING HEALTHY IN THE ARCTIC

Weight for weight, fat provides twice as much heat as starch or sugar. It follows that in hot climates the consumption of fats is greatly reduced, while the Eskimos find it necessary to eat large quantities of fat. This they obtain mainly from the blubber of whales and other big sea animals which live in the inhospitable regions of the Arctic.

foods; a pregnant woman requires an abundance of foodstuffs containing minerals and vitamins.

Infants should be breast-fed if possible. If the mother has had a balanced diet during pregnancy, her milk will contain everything necessary for the child. Cod-liver oil and orange juice, however, are usually given to the breast-fed baby to make good any possible deficiency in vitamins D and C.

After six months, children need the addition of iron, since anæmia often develops at this stage. Egg yolk will provide this. The special needs of children between the ages of one and five are good protein, minerals and vitamins. Throughout this period one and a half to two pints of milk should form the basis of the daily diet.

GROWING SCHOOL CHILDREN

Growing school children need plenty of heat and energy foods, at least one pint of milk daily, about four ounces of meat or six ounces of fish. Wholemeal bread and butter should provide a large part of their dietary. For older children a safe allowance of the three main classes of foods is seventy-six grams of protein (including forty-two grams of first-class protein), three hundred and forty-nine grams of carbohydrates, and one hundred and eight grams of fat daily.

DIET OF ADULTS

The diet of adults should follow the same general principles as that of children. Luckily, if a man has sufficient income to buy a good mixed diet, he usually manages to get the essentials for health. When no particular attention is paid to the subject of diet, the well-to-do in most cases take far too much protein, while the very poor, forced to live on the cheaper starchy foods, usually have a protein deficiency. The poor, too, often suffer from a lack of protective foods—vitamins and minerals—since these are mainly derived from fresh fruit and vegetables, which are often expensive.

Apart from the deficiency diseases which have been mentioned as directly due to errors in diet, inadequate or badly balanced nutrition has much to do with the contraction of such infectious diseases as diphtheria, measles and smallpox. For the body has its resistance to disease in general lowered, and is left open to invasion by micro-organisms. These enter the blood stream from which they derive their nourishment and, unless checked, multiply at an alarming rate.

CHECKED BY WHITE CORPUSCLES

Normally, they are checked in their progress by the white corpuscles, the leucocytes, in the blood and by other wandering cells from the surrounding tissues, which are able to attack and digest them. But the waste products, or toxins, left by the invading bacteria must be neutralized. For this purpose anti-toxins, as they are called, are manufactured by the blood. This involves a very considerable expenditure of energy, and the temperature rises, a sign that the body is fighting some specific disease.

The body has its own method, apart from the work of the leucocytes, of dealing with bacteria. Either it produces substances known as the anti-genes, which straightway dissolve the germs, or it manufactures other substances, the opsonins, which aid the leucocytes to digest the micro-organisms.

If anti-genes for a specific disease have been formed, the body is in most cases immune from this particular disease. For instance, if a person has once had an attack of measles, it is unlikely that he will have a second attack : he is in a state of immunity to measles.

Immunity can also be produced by very slight infections of this disease or that, which stimulate the formation of the appropriate anti-genes or opsonins. Everybody in Great Britain has probably had a mild attack at some time of tuberculosis. The majority have overcome the attack because their blood has been able to manufacture the anti-bodies which make them immune.

For diseases which are not common but which may be fatal, immunity is established by injection of an anti-body which has been manufactured artificially. Perhaps the commonest of such anti-bodies is obtained from the lymph of a pox-infected cow. This is injected into the blood stream, and in this way the formation of the anti-body to smallpox is stimulated. Similarly, anti-bodies are manufactured for cholera and so on. For Europeans going to live in the tropics this type of inoculation is a routine preventive measure.

PROFESSOR'S DARING EXPERIMENT

The body can only build up a good resistance to invading germs, and thus demolish them, when it is in a good state of nutrition. Professor Pettenkofer of Munich drank a broth containing a plentiful supply of cholera bacteria. But he did not contract the disease. This, he contends, is evidence that bacteria can lodge in the body only if it has been weakened beforehand.

A good environment, then, is the best protection against micro-organisms. It is not any particular germ that man need fear but rather a lowered vitality which enables any and every germ to carry out its destructive work.

FOX

STANDARD FOOD OF MILLIONS

Planting rice in the East. When rice is a standard food, unpolished or brown rice has to be taken, otherwise it is apt to cause beriberi.

THE PROBLEM OF HEREDITY

WALKING through the streets, we see clearly that while men and women are built on the same general plan, no two human beings—with the possible exception of what are known as identical twins—are alike. Environmental influences account for many of the differences which we observe. Thus, both the height and the weight of people born and bred in straitened circumstances are, taking it by and large, certainly less than those of the comfortably placed.

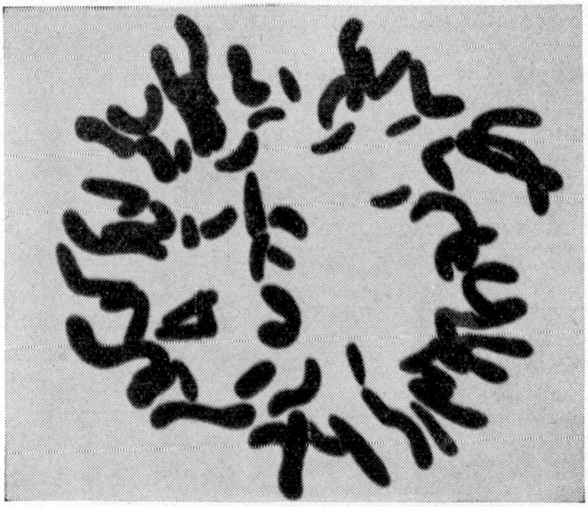

AFTER PAINTER

CHROMOSOMES OF A HORSE

Chromosomes are the carriers of the various characteristics, or genes, of the parents.

This can be demonstrated by taking at random a dozen children of a particular age from a school in a poor part of any big town, and a dozen of the same age from a typical public school. Those who come from homes where the children have had good conditions—proper nutrition, abundance of sunlight and good air, and so forth—are appreciably taller and heavier.

Yet in growth there are abnormalities which, as the saying is, run in families. There are, for example, several kinds of dwarfs. Some are miniature editions of fully-grown people. They start life abnormally small, and never reach a normal size. There are others who, although their physical development is normal at the start, have their growth interrupted between the ages of four and nine, and retain the proportions of a child of four years. In still others it is only the long bones—the bones of the arms and the legs—which stop growing. This is the commonest kind of all dwarfs.

In the chapter on the endocrine glands, it was seen that the pituitary gland has an influence upon growth generally. In all these types of dwarfism there is some disfunction of this gland. But the pituitary is not the only factor involved. There are other processes which are disturbed at the onset of these various abnormalities. To sum up: growth is not a single process, but is dependent on such environmental factors as nutrition and the after-effects of disease, and perhaps still more fundamentally on characters transmitted through the germ cells.

Environment certainly puts its stamp on the hands, the feet, and the general gait of the body. On a crowded railway platform it is fairly easy to tell the manual worker with his somewhat slow and heavy walk, and to identify those engaged in sedentary work. We do not need to be a Sherlock Holmes to put men and women roughly into categories as to their probable occupation. The physical appearance, more often than not, tells its own story.

Some characteristics, however, are independent of environment. These include hair colour (when this has not been peroxidized or otherwise altered from its natural shade), the shape of the nose and the brow, and so on.

As already noted, man is built up from a single fertilized ovum. This cell divides and re-divides again and again. The new cells, while forming one coherent whole, are nevertheless separated into groups of cells—some for this function, some for that. An ordinary cell is a very small speck of living jelly-like stuff called protoplasm, containing such chemical elements as carbon, hydrogen, oxygen and nitrogen, together with traces of phosphorus and sulphur.

The nucleus, or concentrated body in the cell apparently controls and governs it. Generally a round or oval body, it contains everything that is necessary for life, and has a definite structure of its own. Most important of all are its minute rod-like bodies—the chromosomes—which in man number forty-eight. The chromosomes are the carriers of the various characteristics, or genes, of the parents. The number of the chromosomes differs greatly in different creatures. *Drosophila melanogaster*, the fruit fly—of which more will be said later—has eight, or four pairs of chromosomes; a crayfish has two hundred, or one hundred pairs.

When an ordinary cell of the body, as distinct from a germ cell, is about to divide into two, the chromosomes of the nucleus divide throughout their length and separate. Thus, every new cell will contain the same number of chromosomes, and moreover chromosomes of the same kind. The structure and

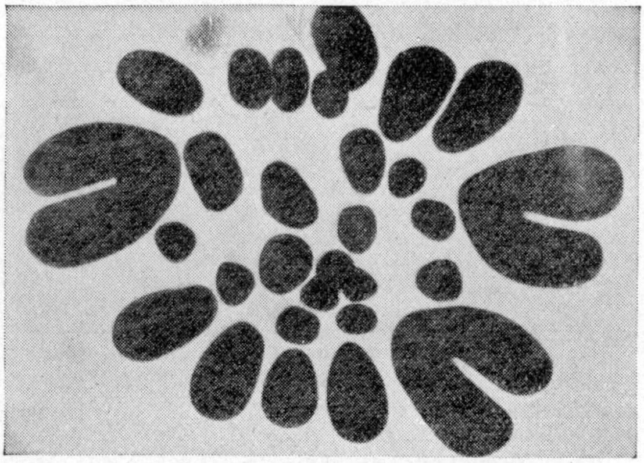

AFTER MANN

CHROMOSOMES OF GRASSHOPPER

The number of the chromosomes differs greatly in different creatures. A crayfish has two hundred.

behaviour of a germ cell is precisely the same, except that just before the germ cells—both male and female—mature, they reduce the number of their chromosomes by half. This is for the very good reason that, when union takes place between a sperm and an ovum, the fertilized ovum then contains forty-eight chromosomes — the number which remains constant for man.

In order to learn something about inheritance, experiments with plants and with animals have been carried out in which the environment has been kept constant. From the results various laws have been formulated. They apply to plants and animals alike, and have been found to hold true for man also. In 1865 Johann Gregor Mendel, the Abbot of Brun, was able to give the results of his famous experiments on the crossing of peas. When he crossed a giant variety with a dwarf variety, the plants grown were all tall. These talls were left to self-fertilize—this corresponds to inbreeding in animals—with the result that tall to dwarf were in the ratio of 3 : 1.

When the dwarfs of this generation were self-fertilized, however, the result was all dwarfs, and these were what is known as homozygous for the character. Further generations of them were also dwarfs. (Sex cells, it should be said, are known by the general term of gametes, or marrying cells. When fusion takes place, the resultant cell is spoken of as a zygote. If both gametes bear the same character, e.g., dwarfism—then the resultant cell is said to be a homozygote. If both gametes have different characters, e.g., tallness and dwarfism—then the resultant cell is said to be a heterozygote.) But when the talls of the second generation were self-fertilized, the result was that one-third of them produced talls which always bred true for talls (they were homozygous for talls), and two-thirds of them produced talls and dwarfs in the ratio of 3 : 1.

PEST BUT USEFUL

Some of the most successful results have been obtained from experiments on the fruit fly, *Drosophila melanogaster*. Pest though he is when he settles on the half-cut melon or the ripe bananas that we have on the table, *Drosophila melanogaster* (and his many near relations) has yet been of the greatest service to those scientists who are hard at work on the study of genetics or the laws of inheritance.

The success of these experiments has made it possible to predict the transmission of such diverse characteristics as flower colour, the coat colour of animals, the form of feathers and variety of comb in fowls coming of a particular cross, and the waltzing character—or lack of it—in mice. Equally, they have established the fact that man inherits in accordance with Mendel's law such characteristics as colour-blindness, albinism, and brachydactyly (i.e., a stunted condition of the hand and foot in which fingers and toes have, in effect, only two joints instead of three).

RECESSIVE AND DOMINANT CHARACTERS

To return to the fruit fly : if a grey *Drosophila* is mated to a black, all the offspring are grey. But if the offspring are mated together, twenty-five per cent of the second generation (spoken of as the second filial generation or F_2) are black, while the rest are grey. All the black, if crossed together, will breed true for black, giving black only. One-third of the rest will breed true for grey. The other two-thirds will again give twenty-five per cent of black.

In the first crossing of the grey and the black, the first generation, or F_1, was all grey.

The black character receded for the time being to reappear in the F_2 : any factor, or character, which behaves in this way is said to be recessive. The other colour dominates, and is then said to be a dominant character. The grey was the dominant.

An example of a recessive character in man is albinism. The only albinos many of us are acquainted with are the albino rabbits or albino (white) mice which we kept as pets in our youth. But most of us are familiar with the fact that the human albino has no colour in the skin, the hair, or the eye. If a homozygous albino is mated to a normal person, the children will all appear to be normal : yet they will, in fact, be heterozygous for albinism.

WHEN ALBINOS MARRY

As society is today constructed, matings (i.e., marriages) are not made between brother and sister. But cousins marry. So, if two cousins —apparently normal, but heterozygous for albinism, transmitted to them perhaps by an albino grandparent—have children, one quarter of the offspring may be albino. It follows, then, that most albinos have apparently normal parents, that is to say, normal for their colour factor. If two albinos marry, then the offspring will be all albinos, for the parents are homozygous for this factor.

Again to revert to the *Drosophila*. If the offspring from the original mating (grey with black) are not inbred but crossed with the parent carrying the recessive character, i.e., the black—then we shall have the original black crossed to F_1 grey. The results will give fifty per cent of heterozygous greys and fifty per cent of homozygous blacks. This fact is of importance if a dominant character such as polydactyly (a formation of the hand or foot which gives one or two extra fingers or toes) appears in a human family. A polydactylous person will transmit this character to about fifty per cent of his family, and they in turn will hand this factor on in the same proportion.

EXPERIMENTS WITH MICE

Up to this point we have considered only one pair of factors taken at a time : namely tall and dwarf, black and grey, polydactyly and normal, albinism and normal colour. But there may be a distribution of two or more such pairs of factors, e.g., blue eye or brown eye colour together with fair hair or dark hair.

The subject is complicated, and can best be explained by reference to actual experiments. Thus, breeding experiments have been carried out with mice which had the factors for albinism and normal colour, and had either a waltzing or a normal gait. (Waltzing is a condition in which the mouse is forced to walk and run in circles : it is probably due to some disturbance of the inner ear.) If an albino waltzing mouse is crossed with a grey mouse with normal gait, all the offspring, the F_1, are normal.

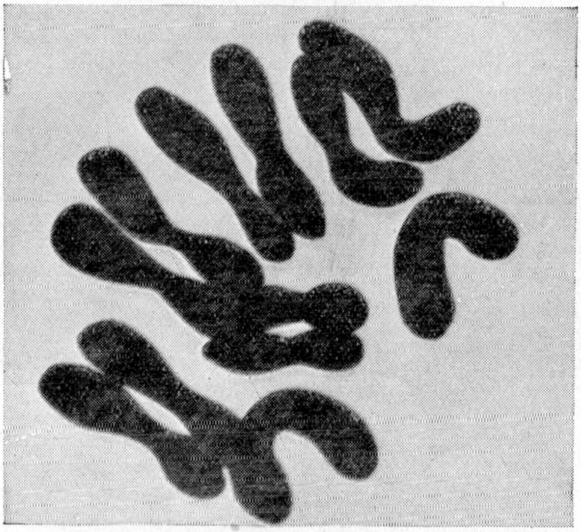

AFTER METZ

CHROMOSOMES OF HOUSE FLY

The house fly has twelve, or six pairs of these important but minute rod-like bodies.

When inbred, the F_2 give four types in the following proportions :

Nine grey mice of normal gait.
Three albino mice of normal gait.
Three grey mice of waltzing gait.
One albino mouse of waltzing gait.

This is the explanation : the albino waltzer, being homozygous for the two factors, forms only one kind of gamete, which transmits both albinism and waltzing. The grey normal parent likewise forms only one kind of gamete, which transmits the grey colour and the normal walk, and these again are independent of each other. In the F_1 the two kinds of gametes come together in the zygote, and as grey colour and normal gait are dominant over albinism and waltzing, these F_1 animals are grey and normal in their walk. They are in fact heterozygous for albinism and waltzing.

Such an animal is therefore able to form four kinds of gametes, or marrying cells.

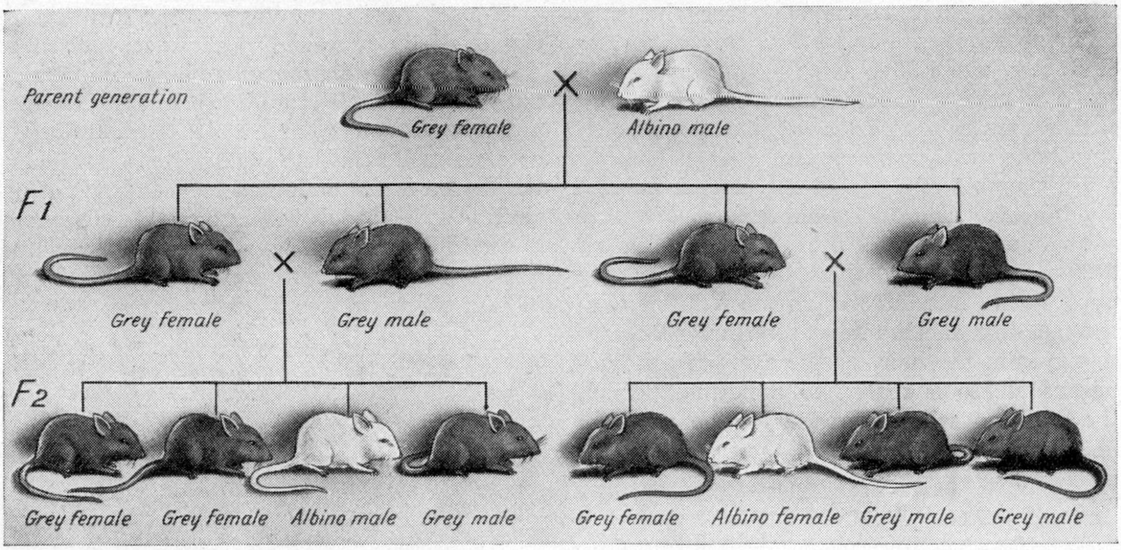

INHERITANCE OF A SINGLE FACTOR

The white fur of the father disappears in the first generation (F_1). It is not lost, but reappears in the second generation (F_2).

carrying the two pairs of factors in the following combinations :

Grey colour with normal gait.
Albinism with normal gait.
Grey colour with waltzing gait.
Albinism with waltzing gait.

If an F_1 female whose eggs may belong to any one of the four classes is mated with an F_1 male whose sperms may also belong to any one of the four classes, it is obvious that sixteen different kinds of zygotes are then possible. This is best shown by the diagram.

In all combinations where grey and normal gait are present, albinism and waltzing will recede. Thus, the waltzing albino is obvious to the eye only once in sixteen times, for this is the double recessive. The two pairs of factors may affect more than one process—as in this particular case where hair colour and sense of balance are both involved—or the two factors together may affect a single process only.

MULATTO OFFSPRING

The black colour of Negroes and the white colour of Europeans are inherited by at least three such factors. This explains why it is that in the cross between a white and a negro all shades between white and black are found in the mulatto offspring. In this case the pure white is a triple recessive and will appear only once in sixty-four times in the F_2 generation (from the original mating of black with white). Since no woman has sixty-four children, it is very rare that such a pure white will turn up. Even if a dozen offspring came of such a mating, the odds against its appearance are great; in the three or four children that are more probable, they are plainly very much greater.

DETERMINED BY MANY FACTORS

So far as experience goes to show, most of the more complicated processes of the human body are determined by many factors, or genes. This makes genetical work very difficult to follow up in man, especially since men do not marry to please those who are investigating the subject of inheritance, but rather to satisfy their own wishes.

Investigations on man have been carried out in three different ways. Pedigrees have been collected where there is a specific disease or abnormality (polydactyly, for example) in the family; cases of identical twins have been investigated; use has been made of statistics relating to the population generally.

If we look around among the twins of our acquaintance, we see that some are extremely alike, while other pairs show only the ordinary resemblances shared by members of the same family. In the first case the fertilized ovum has split during the first division and has become two separate cells, each of which has

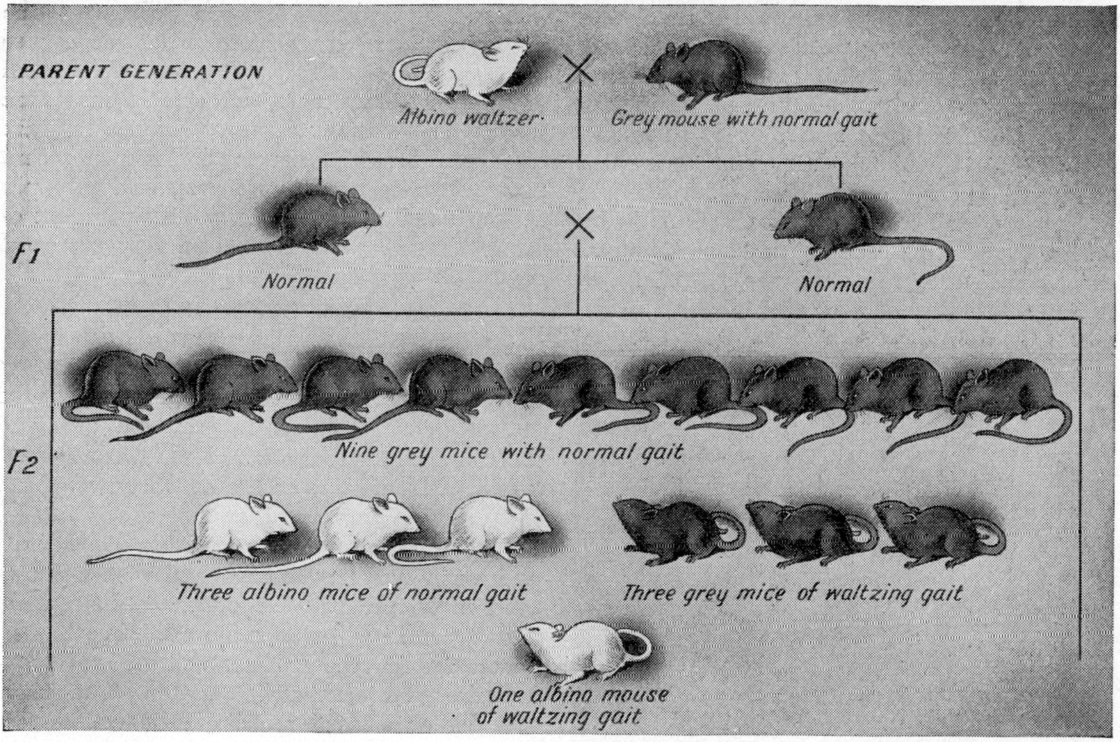

INHERITANCE OF TWO INDEPENDENT FACTORS

The combination of white fur and waltzing disappears in F_1. Although the two factors were introduced by the father they do not necessarily stay together, as borne out in F_2, where only one animal in sixteen shows the original combination.

developed into a normal embryo. These two embryos have exactly the same genetical constitution. In the second case, two separate ova were fertilized at the same time, and thus may have a very different genetical make-up. A woman who has once given birth to twins is likely to have twins again, for this propensity seems to be an inherited factor, although there is as yet no definite and conclusive proof of this.

Investigations carried out in connection with identical twins have helped to decide whether any given character is inherited or not—and not only any given character, but any given tendency or predisposition.

MICROBIC DISEASE NOT INHERITED

For instance, no microbic disease is inherited, although a child may have handed down to him by either of his parents a special susceptibility to any particular disease. Thus, while tuberculosis is not inherited, this disease does run in families. Individual members of them inherit the bodily constitution which is susceptible to the attacks of the tubercle germ.

An especially good environment may protect such subjects. But with poor nutrition, bad air, and overwork, these people become easily infected. In a great many instances they are of the same physical type—narrow-chested, fair-haired, clear skinned, with an opaque eye. Particularly with regard to the inheritance of this predisposition the investigation on twins has been valuable. Some extremely important information has been obtained.

COMPARING TWINS

The method followed was to compare twins of whom at least one was infected by tuberculosis. When identical twins were examined, it was found that in the majority of instances both were affected. Where, however, the twins had each come from a separate ovum, often only one was affected. As the environment in which twins grow up is normally the same, it was naturally concluded that there must be an hereditary basis for this particular susceptibility.

When identical twins are separated at an early age and have a different environment, it is more clearly seen what characters are most affected, and what continue in the main unaltered. In three pairs of recorded identical twins, one was given better food than the other during childhood, in the second pair one took to sports and had good muscular development, and in the third pair one man became a butcher and the other a joiner. In all three cases one of the identical twins had markedly better physique, though in their general resemblance they remained the same. As to the mental ability of separated identical twins, there is not yet sufficient evidence as to how much it is influenced by environment and how much by heredity.

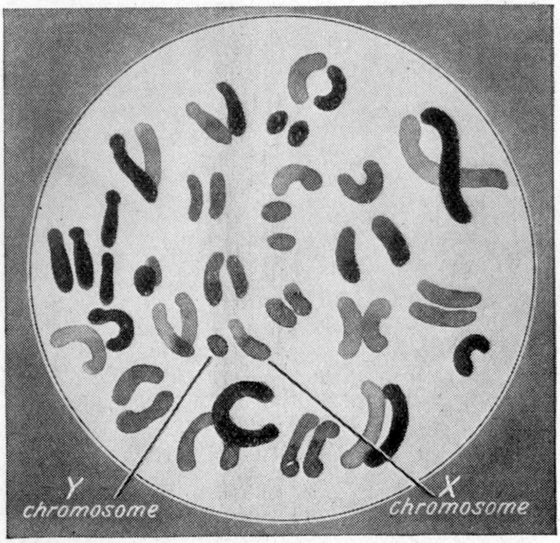

CHROMOSOMES OF MAN

Women have twenty-four equal pairs, while men have twenty-three equal and one unequal pair. This unequal pair is known as the X and Y chromosomes.

In the intellectual sphere a special talent such as musicality may be inherited, although the particular form in which this may express itself is not transmitted. For example, the Bachs —a very extensive family—inherited musicality, but Johann Sebastian Bach's capacity to play the organ was his own particular expression of it.

In the cases already discussed, it has made no difference whether the gene involved was transmitted by the father or the mother. Thus, in crossing the grey with the black *Drosophila*, the results are the same whether the male is black and the female grey, or vice versa. There is, however, another type of inheritance known as sex-linked inheritance, where the result is different according to the sex of the parent.

Drosophila normally has red eyes. But one particular gene transmitted causes the eye to be white. If a white-eyed female is crossed with a red-eyed male, all the " sons " are white-eyed, whereas all the " daughters " are red-eyed. In the F_2 generation fifty per cent of the females have white eyes, and fifty per cent are red-eyed. Similarly fifty per cent of the males are white-eyed, and fifty per cent red-eyed.

DETERMINATION OF SEX

It can be demonstrated that all the males breed true for the character they show if crossed with homozygous females—homozygous either for red or white. But the red-eyed females again give both red- and white-eyed " sons," irrespective of the constitution of the fly to which they are mated.

When the cross is made the other way round, and a red-eyed female is crossed with a white-eyed male, then all the offspring, both male and female, will be red-eyed. In the F_2 generation all the females will be red-eyed, and fifty per cent of the males. The other fifty per cent of the males will be white-eyed.

The explanation of these extraordinary results can be given only when close investigation is made of the chromosomes. Not all the four pairs of chromosomes in *Drosophila* are alike. For one pair in the male consists of a long and a short chromosome.

This is true also of mankind. Women have twenty-four equal pairs, while men have twenty-three equal and one unequal pair. This unequal pair is referred to as the sex-chromosomes, or the X and Y chromosomes. When the sperm cells are formed, two kinds of sperm are manufactured, one containing the X chromosome and the other the Y. The sperm with a Y chromosome, united with an ovum, will produce a male child, furnished with X and Y for its sex chromosomes. Thus the sex of the offspring is decided at the time of fertilization, and cannot be influenced by wishes or witchcraft.

CARRIED BY THE X CHROMOSOME

In the first cross described above, the pair of factors, red and white eye, are carried by the X chromosome. In the first cross the white-eyed female, crossed with the red-eyed male, gives only white-eyed males and red-eyed females. If the factor for white eye or red eye is carried by the X chromosome, the female of the cross will have only one kind of

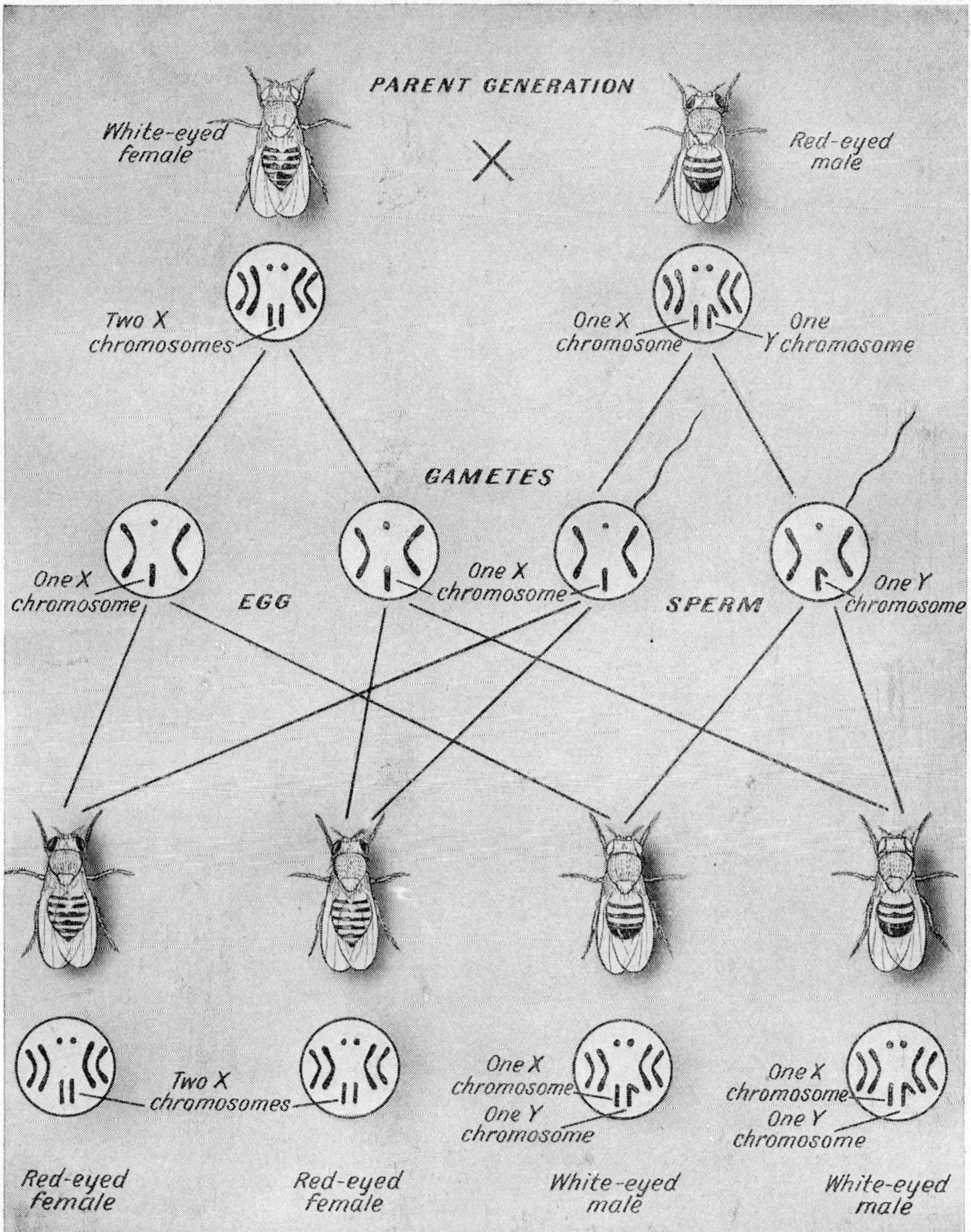

SEX-LINKED INHERITANCE

The female transmits the character white-eye to all her sons, but apparently to none of her daughters. It seems that in this case the father has no influence on the constitution of his sons. This is so because the father only contributes his Y chromosome.

gametes, namely those which transmit white eye. The male of the cross forms two kinds of gametes, one with the X chromosome carrying the factor for red eye, and the other with the Y chromosome which is devoid of any factor for colour. An egg fertilized by an X-carrying sperm will produce red-eyed females which are heterozygous for both red and white and so will bear offspring with either colour factor. An egg fertilized by a Y-carrying sperm will produce a white-eyed male.

TWO KINDS OF OFFSPRING

In the cross made with the red-eyed female and the white-eyed male, the female forms only gametes with the factor for red eye. The male forms one kind carrying the X chromosome with the factor for white eye, and a second kind carrying the Y chromosome devoid of the colour factor. An egg fertilized by an X-carrying sperm forms red-eyed heterozygous females. An egg fertilized by a Y-carrying sperm will produce red-eyed males. The females continue to produce two kinds of offspring, whereas the males will breed true.

This method of transmission is not peculiar to *Drosophila*. For in man we find certain diseases and abnormalities handed on by the same mechanism. For example, colour-blindness—the inability to distinguish between red and green—and hæmophilia—the condition in which the blood will not clot properly—are both transmitted by sex-linked inheritance.

Let us suppose that a woman with normal sight marries a man who is colour-blind. All the children will apparently be normal for this factor, i.e., they will be able to distinguish between red and green. The daughters (who are heterozygous for colour-blindness) will, no matter whom they marry, have half their sons colour-blind, whereas the sons of the original mating will not transmit this defect. It is thus handed on from a father to his daughter who will not herself show the defect but who will transmit it to fifty per cent of the male grandchildren.

Again, a woman who is heterozygous for colour-blindness may marry a man who is colour-blind. Of the children the same proportion of the sons, i.e., fifty per cent will be colour-blind. In addition fifty per cent of the daughters will be homozygous for this defect. The remaining fifty per cent of the daughters will be heterozygous, and will merely transmit the defect.

Hæmophilia behaves in just the same way as regards its transmission. The disease is so comparatively rare that there is little chance of a heterozygous woman marrying a hæmophilic man. There is as yet no known case of a homozygous hæmophilic female, although it is suspected that she would be unable to live.

Hæmophilia and colour-blindness are carried by the sex chromosomes. But it does not follow that these conditions are necessarily transmitted together. To learn more of the relations between two factors carried by the same chromosome, it is necessary to demonstrate again by *Drosophila*.

It was seen that white eye is transmitted through the sex chromosome. The same applies to another abnormality which deforms the straight bristles and hairs on the back of the fly, so that they look as if they had been singed.

If a normal—i.e., a red-eyed female with normal bristles—be mated with a white-eyed singed male, all the offspring will apparently be normal. In reality, all the females are heterozygous for the two genes.

If the F_1 flies are mated together, we expect two kinds of males : males that are normal like the grandmother and males that are white-eyed and singed bristled like the grandfather. This is not so, however. The results give, besides these two expected classes, two unexpected kinds, i.e., white-eyed, normally-bristled males, and red-eyed, singed-bristled males. The actual proportions are forty-two per cent red-eyed, normally-bristled males; forty-two per cent white-eyed, singed-bristled males; eight per cent white-eyed, normally-bristled males, and eight per cent red-eyed, singed-bristled males.

KNOWN AS CROSSING-OVER

In the original white-eyed, singed-bristled male, both factors were carried by the single X chromosome present. As in the F_2 generation white-eyed, normally-bristled males and red-eyed, singed-bristled males appeared, these two characters—i.e., white eye and singed bristle—must have become separated in some cases during the formation of the egg in the F_1 female. As we have seen, the number of chromosomes is reduced by half at the formation of the egg : only one member of each pair of chromosomes goes into the ovum. Thus, only one X chromosome is found in any one egg. It is thought that shortly before this

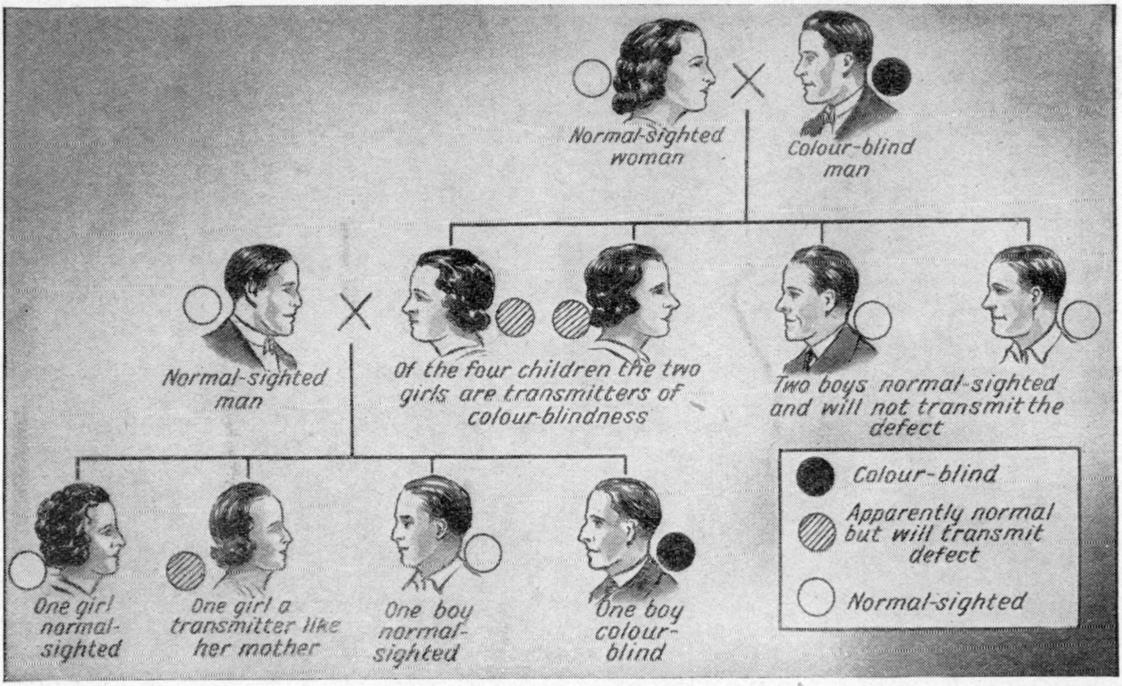

HOW COLOUR-BLINDNESS IS INHERITED

Colour-blindness—the inability to distinguish between red and green—is transmitted by sex-linked inheritance. All the children will be able to distinguish between red and green. The daughters will have half their sons colour-blind, whereas the sons of the original mating will not transmit this defect.

final reduction of the chromosomes, the X chromosomes break and exchange parts—those parts containing the two genes in question. This process is known as crossing-over.

In our cross sixteen per cent of crossing-over has taken place. The two genes are said to be sixteen units apart from each other. From the latest work done on human pedigrees it has been found that the genes for hæmophilia and colour-blindness are at least five units apart from each other on the chromosome.

Further investigation has shown that the crossing-over value between any two genes is constant. Thus in the example given—that of *Drosophila*—the value will always be sixteen per cent.

INVISIBLE TO THE MICROSCOPE

It is too technical a matter to follow the reasoning which proves the theories adopted by geneticists regarding the relations between genes and chromosomes. But the gist of it is something as follows : chromosomes are elastic-like rods in the substance of the nucleus on which the genes are threaded rather as beads on a wire. The genes are bodies so small that they cannot be seen singly even under the most powerful microscope. We do not know whether the chromosomes consist wholly or partly of genes. But we know that the genes are always present in a definite order by the amount of crossing-over they show with each other.

FOR THE GOOD OF MANKIND

It is the most fundamental discovery made in genetics that these genes are units which retain their original properties even after having been transmitted from one generation to another, quite irrespective of the company they have kept in their passage. Inheritance has become a fact which can be dealt with scientifically.

Since it has been discovered that the genes behave as physical units, geneticists have tried to apply their knowledge for the benefit of medicine and agriculture. Plant and animal breeding can now be done in a more systematic manner than by the old rule-of-thumb methods. Results obtained from experiments on animals can be applied for the good of mankind, and the comparatively new science of eugenics, with which is linked preventive medicine, is becoming of great significance. There is little doubt that its importance will increase as a result of the intensive research now being carried on.

T. WEBSTER, R.A.

AT A DAME SCHOOL

In earlier days it was held that those who belonged to the proletariat were less intelligent than those of superior social station. The mistake made was the failure to distinguish between intelligence and education: the poorly educated were assumed to be of low intelligence.

THE BETTERMENT OF HUMANITY

All through the Middle Ages, and indeed up to the middle of the eighteenth century, the population of Europe remained fairly constant, with a slight progressive increase. The birthrate was high, but this was counterbalanced by an equally high infantile mortality.

During the years of the Industrial Revolution, when industries carried on by hand in homes gave place to machines and factories, the population of England more than doubled. Towards the end of the nineteenth century the birthrate suddenly dropped, and there was much concern at what was considered to be a serious threat to the welfare of the nation.

At first this fall in the number of births was largely restricted to the well-to-do, and was far less pronounced among the workers, who were thought to be inferior from the point of view of heredity. Following the theories of Francis Galton and Charles Darwin, men agreed that the best stocks were to be found only in the upper strata of society, and that members of the latter, therefore, must be encouraged to breed more, while the working class must be urged to breed less.

The assumption was that those who belonged to the proletariat were less intelligent than those of superior social station. The mistake made was the failure to distinguish between intelligence and education : the poorly educated were assumed to be of low intelligence. In more recent years special tests have been devised to measure the intelligence. These measure the educability rather than that general culture by which intelligence was wrongly gauged in the past.

The remarkable thing is that, no matter how many times these tests are applied, the person tested gives much the same results, provided that the environment—the general conditions and surroundings—still remains approximately unaltered. If the environment is changed, however, this no longer holds true. The food shortage which came with the latter stages of the World War provided an illustration of this. The intelligence score—the I.Q., or Intelligent Quotient, as it is called—of children of the upper classes whom the shortage affected least, did not show much variation. But below a certain social level, as for instance among manual labourers, children were permanently injured by poor nutrition.

ENVIRONMENT AND INTELLIGENCE

This goes to indicate that if environment were generally favourable, there would be a fairly uniform distribution of intelligence. As today environment varies greatly with social circumstances, those with the best environment appear to have the best intelligence.

Investigations on twins show that in the matter of intelligence identical twins are very much more alike than fraternal twins or ordinary brothers and sisters. It follows from this that genetical factors—those of descent and relationship—also are involved. The various combinations of these factors show different grades of intelligence in different people, whatever their class.

We have already seen the complicated mechanism by which two independent genetical factors such as albinism and waltzing in mice are transmitted. Only one in sixteen, it will be remembered, of the offspring combine the original factors, albinism and waltzing, introduced by the one parent. Intelligence almost certainly involves more than two factors. Hence the chances of a repetition of the same combination in the one family are very small. This is why members of a family often show such a varying degree of intelligence.

NO CLASS DISTINCTION

To sum up: the degree of intelligence inherited would seem to be very much the same for all classes. Once inherited, however, it is developed or retarded to a very large extent by environment.

There seems, then, no good ground for the fear that the intelligence of the nation will sink to a low level if the upper classes have few children and the lower classes many. There is no evidence that society is so constituted that those of the lower classes have genes inferior to those of the upper.

There is, nevertheless, a type of low intelligence to be found in individuals spread fairly evenly through all ranks of society, namely, feeble-mindedness. These people are apt to become a burden on the rest of the community, since many of them are kept in special institutions maintained by the rates.

Feeble-mindedness is definitely inherited, although the exact mode of inheritance is unknown. It is certainly not due to the transmission of a single character, or gene. For example, if both parents are feeble-minded, about sixty per cent of the children inherit this condition. If one parent only has this characteristic, about twenty-nine per cent of the children are feeble-minded.

KISCHGITZ COLLECTION

IN THE NINETEENTH CENTURY

Women and boy workers in a cotton mill at the beginning of the nineteenth century. The conditions were bad and the wages between two shillings and two shillings and sixpence a week.

From these facts certain conclusions can definitely be drawn. If, like albinism, feeble-mindedness were a single recessive, in the case of both parents having the character, not sixty per cent only, but all the children would be feeble-minded. Feeble-mindedness, then, is not a single recessive. Were one parent feeble-minded and the other normal, and were this character a dominant, fifty per cent of the children would inherit the factor. But, in fact, only twenty-nine per cent do so. Equally, then, feeble-mindedness is not a single dominant. Various indications suggest that there are two recessive genes which must combine in order to produce this condition.

As those of feeble mind tend to marry their own kind and to have more children than the average normal family, it is often advocated that such persons should be sterilized, such sterilization consisting of a slight operation upon the male partner of the marriage which renders him incapable of propagating but leaves him sexually capable in all other respects.

HAMILTON COLLECTION

JOHN SEBASTIAN BACH

In the intellectual sphere a special talent such as musicality may be inherited, as was evident in the Bach family. J. S. Bach was the most famous.

Yet the prevention of such people from reproducing will not considerably reduce the number of the feeble-minded, since genes for this condition are fairly widely distributed in normal persons, and the bringing to light of this feeble-mindedness is no more than an unfortunate genetical combination in this or that particular mating.

Various forms of mental defect are inherited, and it has been proved that the mode of inheritance differs according to the form. An instance is amaurotic idiocy—a form of idiocy which appears between the ages of six and fourteen, the sufferers from which die before they reach the twenties, because the fats are not properly assimilated by their bodies. This is due to a simple recessive gene, similar to albinism and inherited in the same way.

UNFAVOURABLE GENES

It is found in communities where there is a tendency to inbreed. Thus it is rife among peasant families in the south of Sweden and among Polish Jews, both of which peoples intermarry extensively. In such communities the probabilities are that both parents, even if their relationship is not so close as that of first cousins, will be heterozygous for the gene. That is to say, these people carry the factor (inherited from one and not both of their parents) for amaurotic idiocy in their genetical make-up, but they themselves do not suffer from the disease. The trouble arises, however, when two such people of the same constitution marry. For in the combination the amaurotic idiocy is brought out in about one quarter of the offspring.

Favourable as well as unfavourable genes may be transmitted in the same way. An illustration of this comes from the mountainous districts of Cape Colony, South Africa. Settlers in one valley are notably healthy, both mentally and physically; yet there has been much interbreeding because of the difficulties of communicating with neighbours. Settlers in another valley, where the original stock was not so sound, have degenerated in a marked degree, cases of cretinism and dwarfism being frequent. Again the explanation is that unfavourable genes masked in the ancestor who had received them from one of his parents only and who therefore suffered no ill-effects himself, were passed on and, combining with their own kind time after time, produced the degeneracy.

MARRIAGE OF FIRST COUSINS

Brother-and-sister unions, which take place even today in some parts of the world, do not necessarily result in degenerate offspring. An excellent illustration of this is afforded by the Pharaohs of Egypt, who maintained a high level of physical and mental fitness through many generations. This is true, too, of the Incas—the king-priest class of Peru—who also were brother-and-sister bred. The marriage

RISCHGITZ COLLECTION

OFFSPRING OF BROTHER-AND-SISTER UNIONS

One of the Incas, the king-priest class of Peru, performing a religious ceremony. They were brother-and sister bred, yet maintained a high level of physical and mental fitness.

of first cousins is not necessarily objectionable; it depends very much whether the parents came from a sound stock or not.

THE SCIENCE OF EUGENICS

Before medicine and surgery had reached their present pitch of efficiency, weaklings tended to die, thus leaving society to be perpetuated for the most part by its more virile members. Today, medical care does everything possible to see that the weak survive. They marry and have children, to whom in some measure they hand down their own disabilities.

Galton, when he started to work out the trend of population, became alarmed at this state of affairs, and initiated a movement whose object was the betterment of the human race. This developed into a science which we now know as eugenics. Eugenics seeks to apply our knowledge of heredity and environment in order to raise the standard of human material.

Galton and his followers strongly advocated the sterilization of all who are carriers of gross abnormalities such as insanity, or gross physical defects such as lobster-claw. This is a condition in which the fingers and the toes are so united that either there are only two fingers or toes instead of five, or all five are joined together. It is obvious that such a condition is a grave handicap in industrial life.

INHERITED ABNORMALITY

In order to decide if in any particular case it will be worth while eugenically to sterilize, it must first be clear how the abnormality in question is inherited. A single dominant character which is usually transmitted to fifty per cent of the offspring will easily be eliminated in this way in the course of a generation or two. Lobster-claw is a case in point.

Again, there is a case for sterilization where a sex-linked recessive is involved. Women who do not show the character themselves may transmit the gene to fifty per cent of their sons and to fifty per cent of their daughters who, being heterozygous, will behave as carriers. Hæmophilia is an instance of this.

Yet with hæmophilia the case for sterilization is not quite so clear cut. For where there is no sterilization, the fertility of hæmophiles is only one-quarter of that of normal persons. This is chiefly because many hæmophiles die before they reach maturity, while with those who survive their disability lowers their fertility. Thus it would seem that the gene should disappear in a fairly short time.

This is not the case. From time to time in a small minority of people the gene for normal clotting of blood is changed, and a gene for non-clotting takes its place. In this way new cases are always arising; hence, while hæmophilia could be slightly reduced, it could not be stamped out by sterilization. Census figures relating to the disease show that the proportion of hæmophiles in the population has remained at roughly the same level during the past hundred years.

A new spontaneous case arising which has not been transmitted and which is then spoken of as a mutation appears in about one in one hundred thousand gametes. In this particular ovum or sperm arises the altered gene for non-clotting, and only the one person will be afflicted with the disease, his brothers and sisters escaping.

SIR FRANCIS GALTON
The eminent scientist who started a movement for the betterment of the human race. It developed into the science of eugenics.

In diseases where the mutation rate is lower, sterilization might possibly reduce the number of people afflicted with a disease transmitted by the same mechanism—namely, where the factor is a sex-linked recessive.

CAUSE OF MELANCHOLIA

The case for sterilization becomes more difficult if the disease is caused by a single recessive, as in the case of amaurotic idiocy already mentioned. There, two (as it seems) perfectly normal parents produce affected children. Although the affected children themselves die, two-thirds of the surviving brothers and sisters transmit the disease. Consequently, this condition of amaurotic idiocy will have a slow increase as time goes on.

In order to eliminate the disease, it is then necessary to sterilize all the brothers and sisters and possibly the first cousins also of an affected person. Since, however, some of these may not be carriers, and yet are indistinguishable from carriers until they themselves have offspring, it is clear that good human material and all its potentialities would be wasted.

This kind of difficulty increases if the disease is caused by two recessives or by one dominant combined with one recessive. The condition known as melancholia is brought about by such a combination. Let us suppose that one parent carries one of the factors concerned and the other parent the second. Either factor by itself has no effect on the carrier. But in the children these two genes may meet and cause this type of insanity.

STAMPING OUT DEFECTS

In this case a smaller percentage of children will be affected than in the case of one recessive (as in amaurotic idiocy), but at the same time more people are potential carriers, since they possess one of the genes. Yet this cannot be detected until several children have been born of the marriage of such a person and have, moreover, reached the age of susceptibility—which for melancholia is in the early forties.

Once it was established that heredity was responsible for a certain number of grave defects, such as deaf mutism and blindness of more than one kind, all of which are transmitted by a simple hereditary mechanism, scientists began to hold the view that in sterilization lay the hope of stamping out such defects.

This hope proved to be somewhat exaggerated, since abnormalities of this nature can be eradicated only if the mechanism is simple, i.e., if the defect is caused by a single dominant, or a single recessive, or by a sex-linked dominant, or sex-linked recessive. Even if these were stamped out in this way, there are yet the new mutations which arise.

CRIME AND HEREDITY

In some States of America the authorities have recourse to sterilization in dealing with habitual criminals. Laws making this possible were passed as the result of agitation on the part of those who were impressed by the fact that criminals often come from morally unstable families. But since children are highly impressionable to their surroundings, and since their characters are formed in the first years of life, criminality may be merely the outcome of a bad moral environment. There are, however, some indications that heredity also is involved.

Investigation of the twin of a criminal has shown that identical twins have a tendency to commit the same kind of crime more often than fraternal twins. But the way in which criminality is transmitted is very far from clear. To steal bread is an action which may arise either from necessity or from a mental instability which leads the person to steal.

To take an extreme example of such an instability, Leopold and Loeb, the Chicago boy-murderers, sons of wealthy parents, planned and executed a murder for the pleasure it gave them. Instability of this nature, while it may be cured in the person concerned, may nevertheless be handed on to appear perhaps in some other form of criminality or delinquency.

MAIN BLOOD-GROUPS

As yet, then, from the scientific standpoint, no decisive pronouncement can be made on the subject of sterilization.

The contribution which eugenists have to make to the study of racial problems is much more definite. The population of the world consists of five main races, easily distinguishable one from the other—the white, the black, the yellow, the Malayan, and the Red Indian. Though they differ in many respects, they can be mated successfully, and the children of such unions are usually intermediate for the genes of their parents—such genes as colour, height, etc. If the same kind of hybrids, (i.e., half-castes) marry, very varying combinations result—an evidence of the fact that most of the characters are determined by a number of genes.

Some single genes, nevertheless, can be isolated. Of these, one is ocanthus, which gives the slit-like formation to the Mongolian eyes. This is a single dominant; consequently, a normal white married to a Mongol will have children all heterozygous for this character, and they will all have the slit-like eye. They in turn will transmit the character to fifty per cent of their offspring, provided the other parent is a member of the white race. There was a certain amount of intermarrying between the whites and the Mongolians during the early Middle Ages. This is why we not infrequently find whites with this type of eye.

KISCHGITZ COLLECTION

IN THE BAD OLD TIMES

The employment of women and girls in mines was prohibited in 1842, and no boy under the age of ten was allowed to work underground. Here a woman is being helped by a child along a narrow shaft.

There are a number of characters which are more often found in one race than in another. Among these are the much-debated blood-groups. The discovery of these was made accidentally. While transfusion of blood from one person to another was in some cases beneficial, in other cases it brought about the sudden death of the person receiving the transfusion. Analysis indicated that there were four different main blood-groups, for convenience labelled A, B, AB, and O. If blood-cells of group A were added to the serum of group B, instead of being evenly distributed all the cells formed clots. This happened also when the process was reversed. The same clotting occurred when serum from groups A or B were added to the cells of group AB.

Yet if serum of groups A or B were added to the cells of group O, this clotting did not occur. To be successful, therefore, a transfusion can only be given when a test has been made of the donor as well as of the receiver. A list is kept by hospitals of people who belong to the blood-group O, since transfusions can be made from them to any other group. To sum up, blood from group A can be given only to group A; B only to B; and O, while it can be given to AB, can also be given to the other groups.

IMPROVEMENTS IN THE RACE

Although all the blood-groups are present in the five main races, group B is found more often than the other groups among Mongolians. In fact, the farther east one goes the more people there are in blood-group B. Group O is found to be the only group in some tribes of South Americans. In England the two most common groups are A and O. B is somewhat rarer, and AB the rarest of all.

These blood-groups are inherited in such a way that A and B are dominant over O. Where paternity is in question, one man may often be excluded by means of a blood test. If the men involved belong to the same blood-group, this method is valueless for purposes of elimination.

There has been much discussion as to the desirability of mating between members of the different races. It seems clear—at least from the physical point of view—that there is little objection except in a few particular respects. Thus, each race is specially adapted to the environment of that part of the world which it inhabits. Europeans, for example, have built up a good natural resistance to tuberculosis, a disease common in temperate climates. But they have not built up a resistance to yellow fever. The West African negroes who have acquired this resistance are very susceptible to the tubercle germ when they visit Great Britain.

It is interesting to note how such a resistance comes about. This is best illustrated by taking an example from agriculture. If a resistance against smudge, or rust, in cereals is required, a great number of plants are infected with the disease, and those which survive are selected for crossing. In the next generation the procedure is repeated and again the survivors are crossed. By this method a combination of genes is arrived at which ensures immunity to the disease in question.

In this way each community, left to itself, builds up its best resistance. Among the European nations the Jews, mainly living in ghettos, have constantly had a slum environment. Today, their resistance against tuberculosis is higher than that of the rest of the community.

These resistances are usually determined by a number of genes. Race-crossing tends to break up the favourable combination of genes, and thus the offspring are left without defences of this nature. What race-crossing involves genetically from the mental point of view is as yet quite unknown.

The differences between the main groups of mankind are very difficult to define, and though we can easily tell a negro from a white, science has yet not been able to determine exactly what the consequences of such a cross are. From this it must follow how impossible it is to judge the desirability, from a racial standpoint, of crosses say between Italians and Englishmen, of Englishmen and Jews. Whenever a judgment on the inferiority of the hybrid between two human races is passed, one has to ask each time : Has this individual had the same chances as his parents? Because if a mulatto, for instance, is regarded as an outlaw by his comrades, he has to encounter more difficulties to earn his living, and may easily develop into an undesirable character through discontent.

Whatever the race, improvement will be brought about by encouraging its good stocks, (i.e., those with no known defects) to have fairly large families. Even to maintain the present level of population, it is necessary that every family should average between three and four children.

"LORD OF CREATION"

Sound stocks of plants and animals have been built up by the application of genetics and by a favourable environment. Perhaps the day is not far distant when these principles will be more actively applied to human beings. A start at least has been made on the environment side in the field of preventive medicine. When by this means the stock has become more healthy both mentally and physically, there will then be good opportunity to better the race by careful selection of prospective parents. The time may yet arrive when the old phrase which describes man as "lord of creation" may have a new and scientific significance.

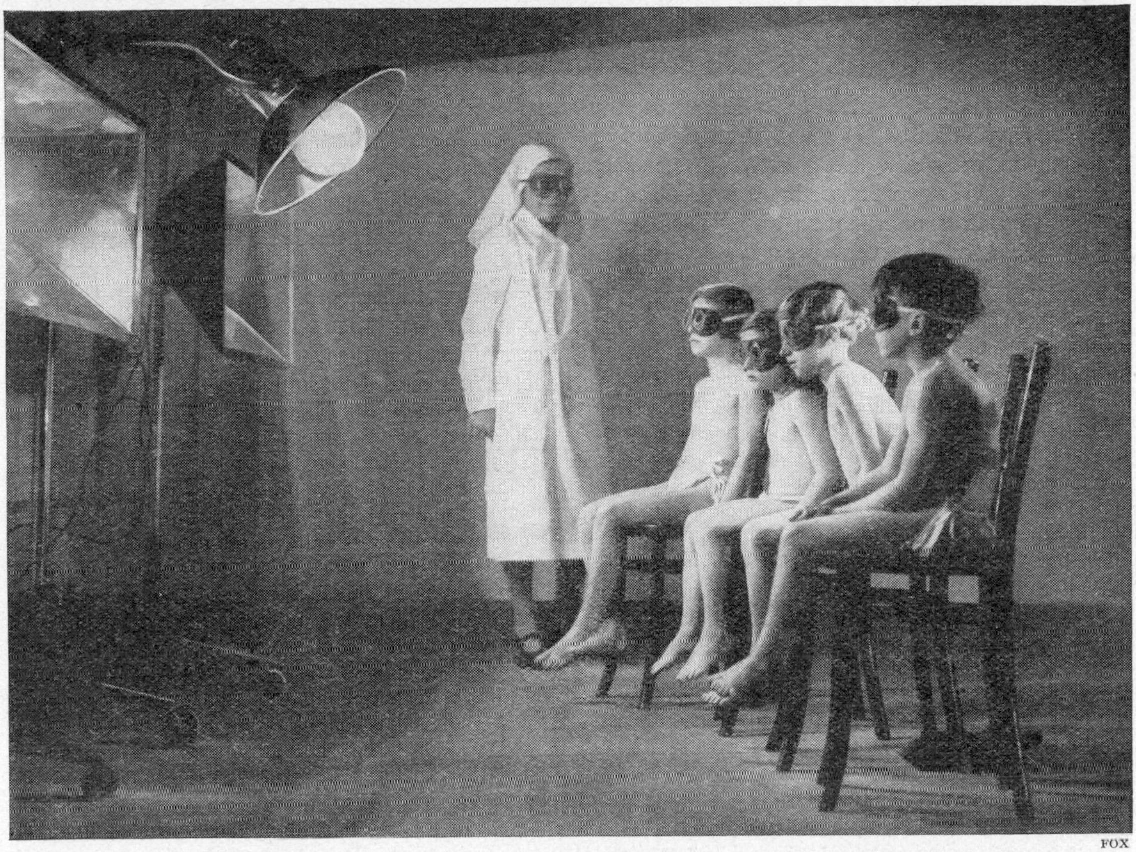

FOX

"SUNLIGHT IS THE GREATEST PREVENTIVE OF DISEASE"

So says Sir Bruce Porter, and these little people are basking in artificial sunlight. By using a combination of lamps it is possible to make use of any of the rays of sunlight in any desired proportion.

THE CONQUEST OF ILL-HEALTH

IN *Erewhon*, Samuel Butler depicted a community in which illness was treated as a crime and the sick sentenced to terms of imprisonment. The conception is satiric, but the satire has a sting of truth in it. We do not yet try a man for having a boil upon his neck, find him guilty of rheumatism, or give him twenty-eight days without the option for contracting a cold. But we do increasingly realize that Public Enemy No. 1 is ill-health; that the depredations made by sickness upon both the private and the public purse are many times greater in a single year than those of burglars and thieves in a generation; and that, whether or no the love of money is the root of all evil, health is most certainly the seed of the greatest national and individual good.

While the old fatalistic attitude that sickness is the will of God has long since been abandoned, science endorses most emphatically the belief that disease is the punishment of sin—if by sin is understood that social sin which takes the form of bad housing, bad drains, poor nutrition and lack of adequate fresh air and sunlight.

The cost of ill-health to the nation is staggeringly high. In recent years the reports of the Chief Medical Officer of the Ministry of Health show that annually among the insured workers of the United Kingdom alone some twenty-six million weeks' work (half a million years) is lost through sickness. Even this huge figure—the equivalent of the loss of a year's work of five hundred thousand people—does not include loss due to sickness for which sickness or disablement benefit is not payable. Assuming the average wages of the half-million to be as low as £2 per week, the direct loss in wages to registered workers amounts to £50,000,000 annually.

Ill-health is not restricted to any one class.

The loss in earnings to those outside the scope of National Health Insurance is probably underestimated when it is given as another £50,000,000 each year. Then there is the expense involved in the care of the sick during the period of their incapacity. Some fifty thousand doctors practise in Great Britain; many thousands of chemists and pharmacists prepare the medicines these physicians prescribe. The voluntary hospitals alone spend some £10,000,000 yearly. In short, a conservative estimate of the annual expense entailed in the care of the sick is £100,000,000. There needs to be added the huge sum spent on patent medicines. More or less worthless as many of these are, it is calculated that no less than £150,000,000 annually goes to purchasing them.

APPALLING COST OF ILLNESS

Ill-health, then, costs Great Britain some £350,000,000 each year. It is reckoned that two-thirds of this sickness is preventable.

So far, so—bad. But there is a brighter side to the medal. In a score of different fields, both nationally and locally, measures are being taken first to discover the conditions which affect the health of the individual adversely and, secondly, to remedy them, or at least to modify them so that the effect on health is less harmful.

INDUSTRIAL DISEASES

In industry preventive measures have been widely applied. They include the prevention of accidents. Beginning with that of 1897, a number of Workmen's Compensation Acts have been passed. All these are based upon the excellent principle that the cost of injury must be borne by the industry concerned, thus making it to the financial advantage of an employer to reduce accidents to a minimum. As a consequence, safety devices have been installed in works and factories, and regulations enforced to prevent workers from taking risks.

Certain occupations, owing to the nature of the goods handled or the processes used, give rise to diseases—industrial diseases, as they are called—which often end in death or disablement. Throughout this country, aided by

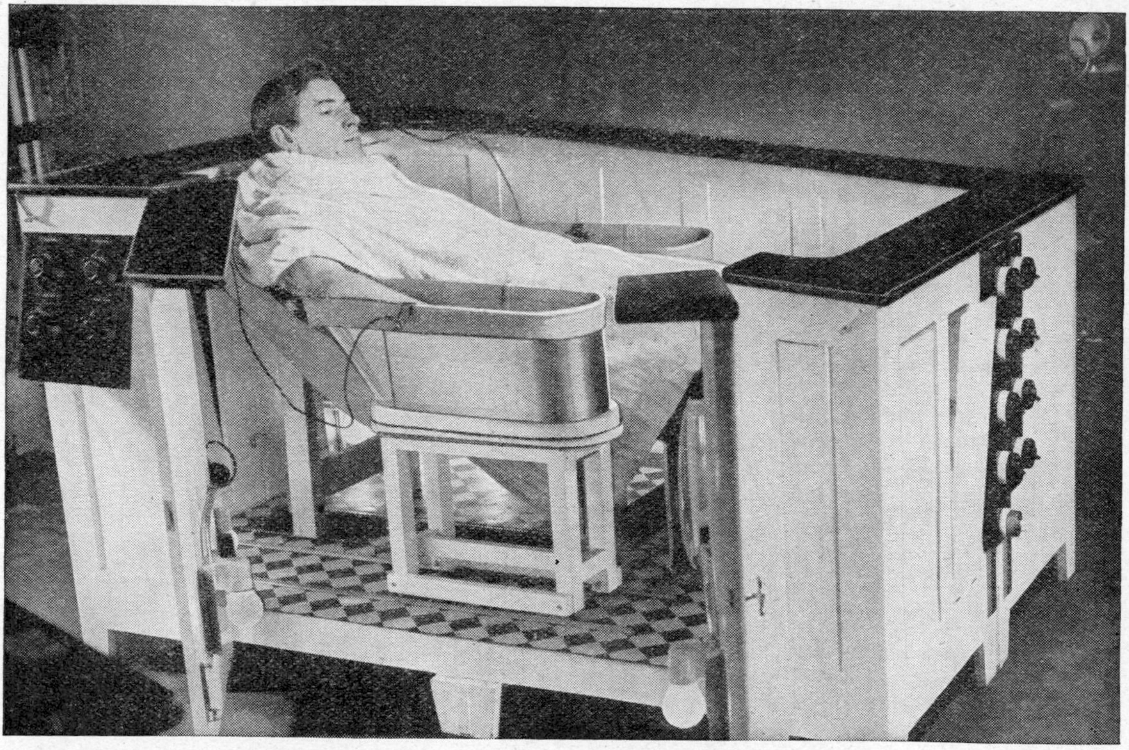

FOX

FIGHTING DISEASE BY ARTIFICIAL FEVER

One of the greatest advances of medical science is the introduction of electro-therapeutic apparatus which artificially produces in a patient fever temperatures such as are experienced in disease. The treatment is applied to rheumatic conditions and cardiac and nervous disorders.

FOX

PHOTOGRAPHING THE INTERIOR OF THE BODY

A radiologist taking an X-ray photograph with apparatus fitted with an upright screening stand. The control table contains all necessary measuring instruments and controls for making exposures. The name X-ray was given because of their mysterious nature, x *being used in mathematics to denote the unknown quantity.*

proddings from the Trade Union movement, the public has steadily developed a conscience in regard to these. As early as 1901 the Factory and Workshop Act required that the Home Office's Chief Inspector of Factories should be notified of all cases of anthrax and of industrial arsenic, lead, phosphorus and mercury poisoning, and that sufferers or their dependents should be compensated. Since then the Home Secretary has, by means of orders laid before Parliament, extended the list of compensatable diseases to include poisoning by aniline, benzene and carbon bisulphide, together with cases of toxic jaundice, chronic ulceration and other skin complaints due to occupation.

PREVENTION BETTER THAN CURE

The effect of the law has been salutary in many trades. Thus, among mule-spinners a cancer of the skin is frequently set up because the workers are in constant contact with crude oils. Today, this kind of cancer is to a very large extent being prevented by the substitution of a vegetable oil for the mineral oil previously used.

Skin diseases that originate in industry are very numerous. Even now, about forty chemicals are in use which are known to cause eruptions of the skin, unless precautions are taken against this. Since new industrial processes are constantly being introduced in which new chemical combinations are employed, modern medical science is engaged in as constant a study of the effect of these on the workers who handle them.

OCCUPATIONS THAT CAUSE ECZEMA

Roughly, one in six of all cases of eczema in this country is the result of the occupation followed by the sufferer. Metal workers and operatives in engineering works contract a particular type of eczema—an eruption which breaks out on the hands and wrists, and which, like " mule-spanners' cancer," is due to the mineral oil used. A somewhat similar kind of eczema attacks flax-workers who steep the flax in water; while a more serious variety, somewhat resembling smallpox in that it pits the face and arms, is often developed by the

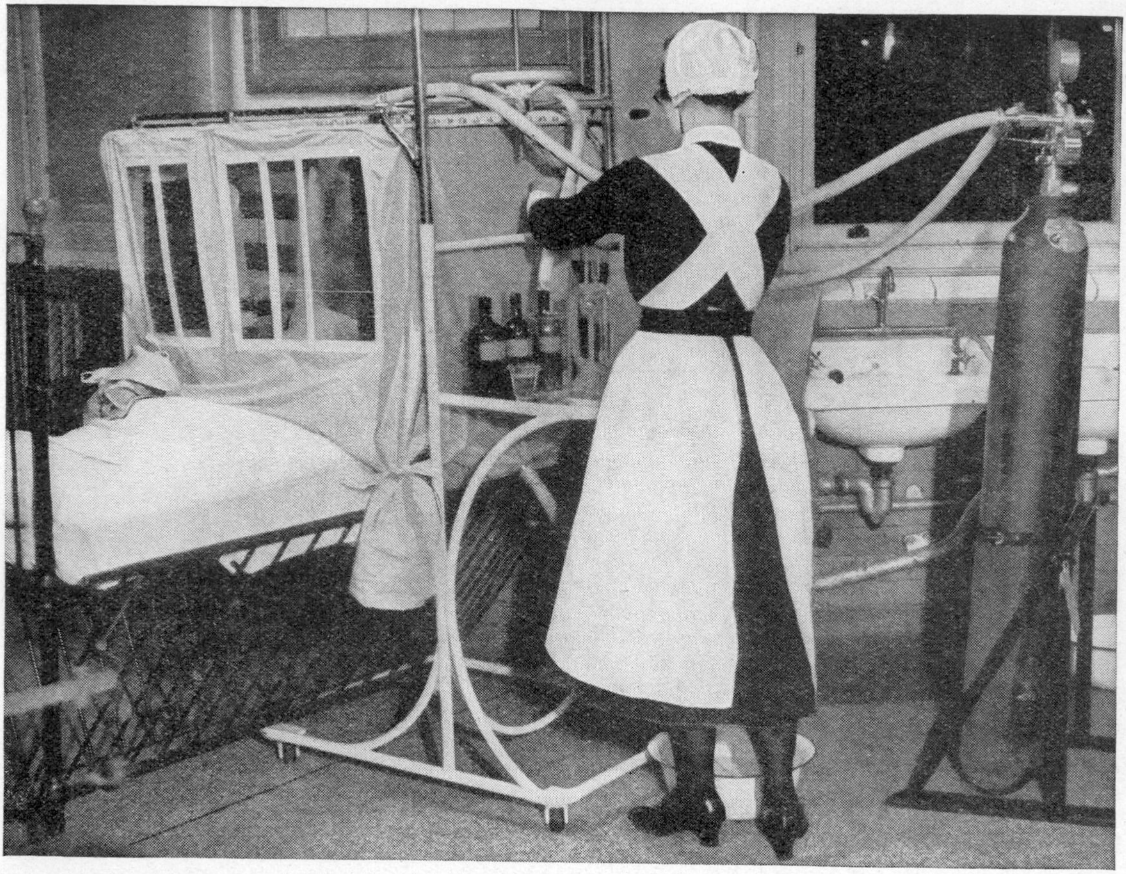

FOX

FOR THE ADMINISTRATION OF OXYGEN

An oxygen tent in which the gas is given to a patient in danger of suffocation or who for some other reason requires an aid to breathing. Before the invention of this valuable apparatus it was usual to administer the gas by means of a mask. The supply is obtained from the cylinder on the right.

" doffers " who remove the spun linen from the frames.

Baker's itch is, of all occupational eczemas, perhaps the most difficult to cure. Small blisters break out on the hands and arms of those who mix the dough; later, these blisters suppurate and spread the infection.

ONLY INJURIOUS IF WET

Men affected are often compelled to stop away from work for six months and more, while there is frequently a recurrence of the malady. Medical research has gone to show that none of the ingredients used in baking bread and in making confectionery are injurious to the skin when applied dry, but that a number of them cause skin trouble if wet.

The Bakehouses Welfare Order of 1927 was drawn up with this particularly in mind. Among other things, it compels employers to provide the necessary washing facilities so that workers may remove all dough and sugar from the skin before leaving work, and insists on immediate medical treatment on the first sign of the outbreak of skin trouble.

To turn from skin diseases to metallic poisoning. Lead, made use of in well over one hundred different trades, is of all metals employed in industry the most dangerous to the health of the worker. Lead poisoning, or plumbism, is liable to attack plumbers and painters (both house and ship), operatives in white lead factories, workers using lead glazes in the manufacture of china and earthenware, file cutters and enamellers—but not lead miners.

LESSENING THE RISKS

The principal symptoms of plumbism include anæmia—caused by a reduction of the number of red blood cells and a consequent deficiency in hæmoglobin—abdominal pain, sickness and defective vision. Dropped wrist, due to

FOX

CARAVANNING DENTIST PAYS A VISIT

A fully-equipped dental caravan which visits scores of schools controlled by the education committee of one of England's largest counties. The staff comprises a dentist and a nurse. Defective teeth are a contributing cause of ill-health, which costs Great Britain some £350,000,000 a year.

paralysis of the muscles of hand and wrist, is one of the worst features of the disease.

The Lead Paint Act of 1926 forbids the use of lead compound except as paste or paint, and prohibits the rubbing off of old paint with pumice stone, directing that, for this, one of the "wet" methods of removal shall be substituted. Paint spraying is made illegal in the interior of buildings. Employers are compelled to provide washing facilities, and to arrange for the regular medical examination of workers, who must be suspended if found suffering from poisoning. Further, the employment of women or young persons in lead painting is forbidden. In most factories where lead processes are employed, workers lessen the risks by wearing tight-fitting overalls, making use of masks when the air is dust-filled, and by taking hot baths and changing their clothes before leaving work. As the result of these various measures, plumbism has very greatly decreased in the last thirty years.

INHALING FLINT DUST

In the potteries, while there is some plumbism among lead-glaze workers, far more sickness is caused by the inhalation of fine particles of flint; this renders the soft tissues of the lungs hard and inelastic. Where this condition, known as silicosis, is present, tuberculosis can much more readily gain a footing. Now that radiographic examinations have made clear the nature of the disease, practical measures have been adopted to prevent it. Factory furniture is made, when possible, of material impervious to dust, and the walls and floors of workrooms are frequently washed.

AFFECTING TEXTILE WORKERS

Respiratory diseases brought about by dust affect textile workers also. When cotton bales arrive at a factory, they contain considerable quantities of dust. If the bales are opened by hand, the air becomes thick and the workers' breathing is affected. Irritation of the mucous membrane is set up, and the lung tissue impaired. But today this unpacking by hand has been superseded to a large extent. Mechanical bale breakers are employed which, furnished with exhausts, keep the air reasonably clear. Dust causes trouble in cotton carding rooms also, although this is not of a respiratory nature. Boxes set beneath the carding machines to collect dust shaken out during the process are emptied and cleaned by the operatives. These workers often develop asthma.

A much more serious illness following upon inhalation of dust is anthrax or wool-sorters' disease. This dust harbours a rod-shaped germ, the *Bacillus anthracis*. Within a few hours of infection a disease resembling a virulent type of pneumonia develops, and death frequently takes place in less than a day.

In the past the main source of the disease was infected wools imported from Asia and Asia Minor. The Government established a disinfecting station at Liverpool for foreign wools.

ELLIOTT AND FRY

MADE OPERATIONS SAFER

Lord Lister (1827–1912), *who introduced antiseptic conditions into the technique of surgery. Previous to his discovery most of the major operations ended in the death of the patient.*

This has proved a most successful preventive measure, for no known case of anthrax has followed the handling of wool dealt with by this station. Anthrax, usually of a milder nature, is from time to time developed by workers in the hide, skin and fur trades, and by employees in factories manufacturing hair and shaving brushes.

And so the long catalogue of industrial diseases goes on. It is impossible to describe them all. In dealing with some of them preventive measures have had notable success. Thus, that form of gangrene known as "phossy jaw" once prevalent among match-factory workers who used white phosphorus has now disappeared owing to the substitution of sesquisulphide of phosphorus following upon the law passed in 1910.

Where no such simple solution has been possible, improvement of general conditions has done much. Underground workers, for example, suffer from both fumes and dust. The better the ventilation, the less the suffering. Hence, electric suction fans have been installed in mines and respiratory diseases have decreased among miners in consequence. In 1937 the Trades Union Congress, in the interests of the workers it represents, established its own Scientific Advisory Council to obtain help and advice from leading scientists on problems of workers' welfare.

RHEUMATISM IN CHILDREN

In England there are two diseases—rheumatism and tuberculosis—which, unlike the special occupational maladies, affect practically every section of the community, and research to discover preventive measures applicable to these has accordingly been intensified.

Rheumatism is a constitutional disease, since the predisposition is strongly hereditary. For its successful prevention, therefore, the children coming of rheumatic stocks must be kept under observation, preferably from the age of two onwards.

The rheumatic child is easy to detect. He is usually highly nervous; his temperature is often abnormal. His skin, which is frequently too dry, is unable to adapt itself to changes in temperature and humidity. Among research workers on rheumatism many hold the view that the children most liable to develop rheumatism are those who have some thyroid disfunction. As yet, there is not sufficient proof, however, that the two are linked.

"GROWING PAINS"

"Growing pains," which in the days of our grandmothers were dismissed as natural in all children, are the first warning signs that rheumatism has begun to attack a child. Since about eighty per cent of children who develop rheumatism develop heart disease in addition, these warning pains cannot be disregarded. Once rheumatic heart has been contracted, the sufferer is under a severe handicap for the rest of his days. It is for this reason that in rheumatic fever patients are kept lying flat in bed for at least six weeks, and after their convalescence protective measures are advised.

Children with a tendency to rheumatism should, above all others, have a well-balanced diet with a particularly liberal supply of vitamins and minerals. In winter such a diet is especially important, for it is at this season in the year that the calcium in the blood and the iodine in the thyroid gland are at their lowest. Without exception, growing children need a good supply of calcium; with rheumatic children the need is doubled.

HARDENED TO THE CLIMATE

From early childhood the children of rheumatic parents in Great Britain should be gradually hardened to the very varying climate. After their warm baths they should become accustomed to cold spraying to tone up the skin, followed by vigorous rubbing with a rough towel. Their clothing should be warm and light, allowing the air to circulate freely.

Damp clothes—damp shoes in particular—and damp rooms must be avoided. Cold dry air is good for these children, and they should be encouraged to move about briskly whenever they are out of doors. Rheumatic children are especially liable to sore throats and colds; to a large extent, these can be warded off if windows are kept open and damp is avoided.

" Growing pains " usually occur in the muscles. The muscles, then, must be exercised in order to burn up excess fuel taken in as starchy and sugary foods. But it must be kept in mind that rheumatic children become fatigued more quickly than their more solidly built brothers and sisters. They usually have quick brains and are easily excited. Accordingly fatigue, both mental and physical, must be guarded against.

HEART DISEASE PREVENTED

St. Vitus's dance, one of the forms which rheumatism takes, is all too common among poor children who, having a lowered resistance to begin with, often do not get sufficient rest. All children with " growing pains " should be put to bed and kept there under the supervision of a doctor. If this is done, heart disease will often be prevented, or its progress checked.

When rheumatism has been contracted, it is essential that it should be kept under control. For once having developed, it recurs—or is prone to recur—not once but many times throughout life. More than half the cripples we see today owe their disability to rheumatic afflictions which would have been avoided had measures been taken against the rheumatism in its earliest stages.

It is this early control which preventive medicine seeks to secure over rheumatism today. Much has already been done. The Red Cross, for example, has established a special research department for rheumatism. A great number of treatments have been devised. They vary from the application of heat by high-frequency currents useful in relieving pain in muscular rheumatism to the vaccine treatment sometimes given in cases of osteo-arthritis.

Hot-air baths, mineral baths and Turkish baths have all been found to have value according to the form taken by the disease. Numerous drugs, plasters and poultices have been experimented with, and useful discoveries made especially in regard to iodine and its beneficial effects. Massage courses have been perfected, and the effect of artificial sunlight and regulated sun-bathing investigated.

FOX

TRACKED SOURCE OF MALARIA

Sir Ronald Ross (1857–1932), *who discovered that the malaria parasite was conveyed to man by the Anopheles mosquito.*

At Peto Place, London, is the Red Cross Clinic, where all these and many other treatments are carried out for the alleviation and cure of the various forms of rheumatism. Not only at Peto Place, but in most towns of any size, there is a clinic, usually attached to the hospital, where treatment is available for a small sum or for nothing in necessitous cases. In most of these clinics massage, infra-red rays and ultra-violet rays are given. For those who can afford it, the natural waters of such spas as Bath, Buxton and Harrogate are frequently found to be beneficial in treating rheumatic affections.

It is estimated that in England the enormous sum of £25,000,000 annually is spent on

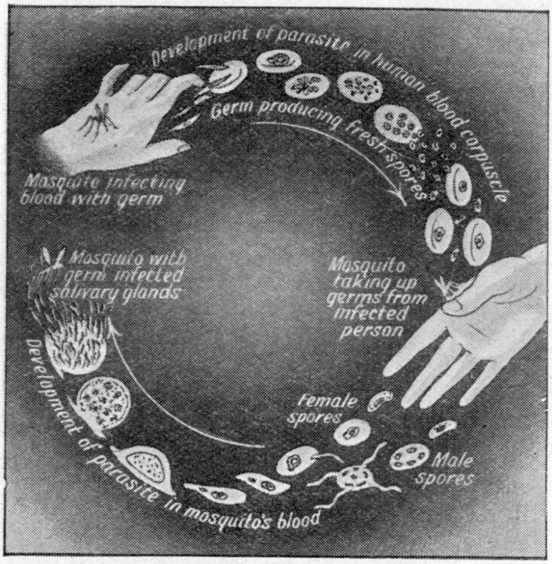

HOW THE MOSQUITO INFECTS
The tragic cycle of infection, which has now very largely been brought under control.

preventive and remedial measures designed to combat the scourge of rheumatism.

The national drive against tuberculosis has been still more vigorous and sustained. No other disease so well illustrates the value of preventive medicine. Thus, in the decade 1881–90, almost seven hundred thousand of the five million deaths in England and Wales were due to the various tubercular diseases. In the period 1921–30, with deaths still numbering roughly five millions, mortality caused by the tubercle bacillus had been reduced to four hundred thousand. Even so, tuberculosis remains the most serious of all the respiratory diseases.

The disease itself is not inherited, but a constitutional predisposition to it almost certainly is. Given a favourable environment—fresh air and sunlight, good food and freedom from overstrain, both physical and mental—even those with an inherited tendency need never contract tuberculosis. Conversely, a bad environment often leaves those with no such transmitted tendency vulnerable to attack by the germ.

The main sources of tuberculous infection are the dried sputum of consumptives and the milk of infected cows. From such milk comes the tuberculosis to which children are especially prone and which takes the form of glandular swellings and of diseased bones and joints. The pulmonary, or lung, type of tuberculosis usually originates from dried expectoration, in which the tubercle bacillus, a rod-like organism, lurks. The germ can survive for a long time in the dust, and hence dust is at all times a potential source of infection.

SYMPTOMS OF TUBERCULOSIS

Early symptoms of the disease—a cough that persists after a cold, a slight rise in temperature at night, and a general sense of weariness—should on no account be disregarded. To delay seeking medical advice is folly.

Today tuberculosis is a notifiable disease, and every county has its Tuberculosis Officer who arranges sanatorium treatment for sufferers from this disease. At the sanatorium the patient's resistance is built up. The lung tissue gradually heals. Modern treatment includes the performance of work suited to the strength of the patient. When he is capable of doing a normal day's labour with no return of unfavourable symptoms, he is discharged.

Unfortunately, at present our preventive measures do not go far enough. For too often with the patient's return to bad environment both in the home and at work, the germ reappears after a time, when a further visit to the sanatorium becomes necessary.

UNDER SHELTERED CONDITIONS

In England there is one notable exception to this. A sociological experiment in the treatment of tuberculosis has been carried out at Papworth, in Cambridgeshire. At this colony patients receive the most up-to-date treatment. When they are cured they are given employment in the village, which has its own self-supporting industries. Although they then live an ordinary life with their families, they yet have sheltered conditions. This makes further attacks of the disease unlikely. Such people, however, with their impaired lungs would break down much more easily in the hustle and bustle of normal life.

This experiment has the great advantage of protecting not only the individual himself but also the community outside the settlement. It is to be hoped that in the future such colonies as Papworth will be much more common, and that in time tuberculosis will be as rare as typhoid.

ENEMY OF BACTERIA

Today the spread of tuberculosis through infected milk is very much less than formerly. This is in part the result of more hygienic methods of dairy-farming and of the pasteurization of milk. Latterly, positive measures have been adopted to eradicate tuberculosis from cows. When scientific principles of nutrition are applied and cows are given food with a high vitamin content, especially during winter, herds can be built up which are completely free from tuberculosis.

Perhaps the greatest hope of further limiting this disease lies in the co-operation of the public in observing the rules of general hygiene and in building up the resistance of their families by securing for them as good an environment as possible. Both the State and the local authorities must do their part in improving housing conditions and providing large towns with adequate parks and other open spaces.

Bacteriology, the study of micro-organisms and their destructive work on the human body, is one of the most efficient weapons of which preventive medicine makes use in its war on disease. Bacteria thrive best at blood heat; while exposure to a high temperature kills most of them. No known bacteria can withstand the application of steam under pressure. For this reason disinfecting stations use this method in dealing with infected clothing, and so on.

MOSQUITO'S DEADLY MENACE

Bacterial disease is usually spread by the inhaling of bacilli or their spores, as in tuberculosis; by the swallowing of microbes in food or drink, when intestinal infection results as in typhoid; and by inoculation as the result of a bite from some insect, such as the female anopheles mosquito which causes malaria. With those who have a good natural resistance, any of these organisms may invade the body, but no great harm result.

There are a number of diseases—smallpox is an example—which are thought to be of microbic origin, but the specific germ has not yet been identified. In still other diseases such as hydrophobia and cancer, the actual cause is as yet undiscovered, but it is thought to be what is known as a filterable virus. The organisms cannot be seen under a microscope, but can yet be passed through a porcelain filter. Thus, the virus obtained from an infected animal can be injected into other animals of the same species which will reproduce the disease.

Since the discovery in 1897 by Sir Ronald Ross that the malaria parasite is conveyed to man by the mosquito, malaria has very largely been brought under control. Before this discovery tens of thousands of people in the mosquito-infested lands died every year. The measures taken to prevent malaria include the drainage of large areas of marshy ground where mosquitoes breed; the protection of people at night by mosquito netting about their beds, and the taking of about five grains of quinine daily by those living in a malarious district.

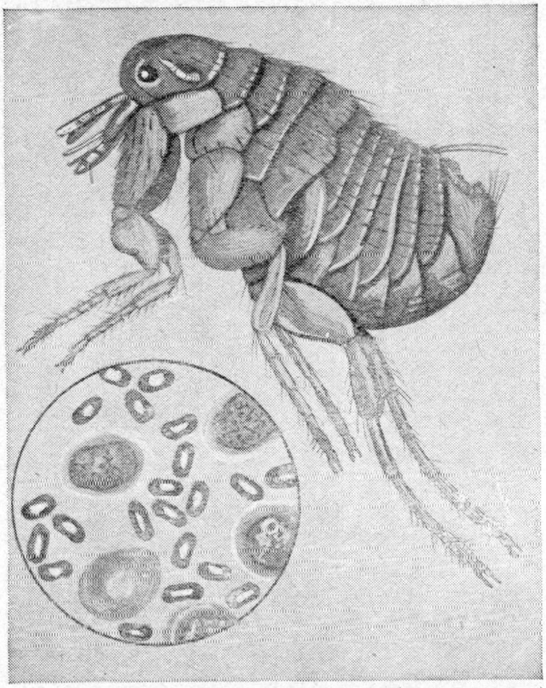

BRITISH MUSEUM (NATURAL HISTORY)

SPREADER OF PLAGUE

The rat flea, which serves as a carrier and multiplier of the germs of bubonic plague (inset). It is believed that this noisome insect was the prime cause of the Great Plague of London.

It is not only in tropical countries that the anopheles mosquito is found, although it is normally in these warm moist climates that outbreaks of malaria occur. Anopheles is by no means unknown in swampy parts of Great Britain.

In recent years there has been a great decrease in typhoid fever. This is due in part to cleaner supplies of milk, water and food; and in part to better sanitation. When the typhoid bacillus enters the body, the spleen becomes enlarged and there is ulceration of the small intestine. Strict cleanliness and disinfection of the clothing of patients prevents the fever from spreading.

The more common infectious illnesses, such as diphtheria and scarlet fever, are today very largely prevented by injection of the appropriate anti-toxin. It is no longer the practice to wait for diphtheria to attack children, and then to isolate them, as was the method in the past. Instead, they are given active protection as a matter of routine.

RISCHGITZ COLLECTION

SQUALOR AMIDST WEALTH

Slum conditions in London in the middle of the nineteenth century. A unique photograph taken about 1868.

What is known as the Schick test has been devised. This test is made by the injection of a very small quantity of the diphtheria poison into the skin. If a red patch appears round the area the child is said to be Schick-positive, and is likely to contract diphtheria, and can be rendered immune. Those who do not react to the test by developing a red patch on the skin are unlikely to contract diphtheria, should an epidemic occur.

Measles, once thought to be a very trivial illness, is now regarded much more seriously largely because of the complications, such as impaired vision and various ear troubles, which may result. In many cases an injection taken from the blood of an infected person is given, which affords immunity.

AFTER-EFFECTS OF INFLUENZA

The infectious illness which recurs most regularly in England is influenza. It was at one time thought that a certain bacillus discovered by Pfeiffer was responsible for the disease. After much research the view is now held that no germ in particular causes influenza, but that a filter-passing virus begins the trouble and that streptococci and pneumococci, which are always present in the nose and throat, carry on the disease.

Apart from the fact that it is a disagreeable illness in itself, influenza may leave heart disease, while most people have experienced the weakness and depression which are common after-effects. Preventive methods include raising the body's resistance, avoiding ill-ventilated overcrowded rooms, and the injection of small doses of vaccine prepared from a mixture of the bacteria taken from infected persons. This anti-influenza vaccine as yet has not been extensively used, but is thought to be of considerable value.

In the field of preventive medicine cancer research has a very prominent place—and very rightly so, since in England and Wales almost sixty thousand people die of this disease every year. This, it must be frankly admitted, is an appalling toll.

DISEASE OF CIVILIZATION

The real nature of cancer has not yet been discovered, although some advance towards arresting this disease of civilization—it is unknown in savage communities—has been made. It has been found that cancer cells behave differently from other cells, in that they are more independent of oxygen.

Cancer cells grow at a tremendous rate. They eat into the surrounding tissue and are able to spread into other parts of the body, destroying the normal tissues invaded by them. Radium, X-rays, and the colloidal lead

RISCHGITZ COLLECTION

PIONEER OF A NOBLE PROFESSION

Florence Nightingale (1820–1910) *revolutionized the nursing of the sick. By prompt and hygienic methods she reduced the death-rate of wounded soldiers in the Crimean War from forty per cent to two per cent. She devoted her life to raising the status of the noble profession she so ably represented, and was awarded the Order of Merit. Florence Nightingale was the first woman to receive this honour.*

treatment devised by Professor Blair Bell are used curatively, although most workers on cancer are agreed that removal of tumours by surgery at an early stage is essential if a recurrence of their growth is to be avoided.

PUBLIC HEALTH SERVICES

Although the intensive research made possible by the Cancer Research Fund and the activities of the British Empire Cancer Campaign have not yet determined the essential character of cancer, it has established that the disease attacks only damaged and poisoned organs, and that chronic irritation is frequently a contributory cause.

It follows that if men and women as individuals would keep the blood stream pure by a simple diet and a healthy mode of life, the tissues of the body would remain wholesome, and cancer—particularly cancer of the digestive tract—would greatly decrease.

The public health services are essentially concerned with preventive medicine and with the various problems involved in checking infection. Thus there are isolation hospitals for infectious disease, bacteriological and chemical laboratories for each county or large area, where examinations and tests are performed in all cases of doubt; a maternity and child welfare service; a tuberculosis service; a school medical and dental service, and a venereal disease service. The supervision of food and water supplies, housing and sanitation also come within the sphere of the public health authorities.

EXPECTATION OF LIFE

It is to these services that much of the credit for the advance in public health must be put. How real that advance is can be judged from two simple facts. In Great Britain in the decade 1871–80 the expectation of life at birth was forty-one years for a boy and forty-four years for a girl. Today, the corresponding figures are fifty-six for a boy and sixty for a girl. In brief, within two generations there has been over fifteen years' increase in the expectation of life at birth.

There is less reason for complacency over the maternal mortality rate, which remains far too high. It has been found that a large proportion

RISCHGITZ COLLECTION

NOBEL PRIZE WINNER

Robert Koch (1843–1910), *the German bacteriologist who isolated the bacillus of tuberculosis.*

of this is due to puerperal fever and a determined drive is being made by research workers on this subject. Particularly good results have been obtained during the past few years from giving mothers during the last month of pregnancy a diet with a particularly high vitamin A content. Results show that it notably improves their resistance to puerperal infection.

Working on the same lines as the German, Ehrlich, who discovered that the salvarsan compounds kill the spirochætes organism which causes syphilis, scientists have recently discovered a chemical compound known as sulphanilamide. This is injected into the blood stream and is able to destroy the bacteria present without harming the delicate tissues. Thus, it has proved effective against puerperal fever—which is a general infection—and it has also been used with great success in such localized infections as tonsillitis.

Disease involves the destruction of that living tissue which is found in the youthful body, and this tissue, once destroyed, can be replaced only by the inferior tissue typical of old age. Modern realization of this fact explains why great and increasing care is given to child welfare. For, where health is concerned, the child is indeed father to the man, and the healthy child of today is the healthy man of tomorrow. It would be well if we always bore in mind this self-evident fact.

DISCOVERED AT SCHOOL

Because pre-natal conditions have no small influence on the welfare of the child, maternity centres have been established in practically every large town. In these not only is the health of expectant mothers kept under observation, but valuable educative work is done: classes are held in which instruction is given in the feeding and rearing of infants. Once her baby is born, the mother is encouraged to attend the Infant Welfare Centre, where she is supplied with dried and pasteurized milk at half the usual price, and given all necessary advice as to the health of her child until it is two years old.

The supply of day nurseries or crèches (to which a medical officer is usually attached) is not yet equal to the demand, but in many industrial areas they are very valuable in looking after the children of nursing mothers, and so saving much good human material.

At every elementary school the children are given periodic inspections, both dental and medical. In addition, teachers consult the visiting school nurse or the medical officer for health, should any special advice become necessary. In the routine examination of school children, visual defects, diseased tonsils and adenoids, rickets, cases of curvature and flat feet are all too commonly found.

HEALTH IS WEALTH

Much is done to remedy these and other disabilities. Treatment for flat foot and spinal curvature is given by the school health visitor. Children in a state of debility are either given cod-liver oil and malt, sent to hospital, or transferred to an open-air school. When tonsils and adenoids have been removed, children are made to attend special breathing classes. Malnourished youngsters are often

FOX

ALL ABOARD ON THE HAPPINESS TRAIN.

Children at play in the Pioneer Health Centre at Peckham, London. It is the only institute of its kind in England and was founded by two biologists in 1934.

fed at school; those who are known to have had rheumatic fever, chorea (St. Vitus's dance), or scarlet fever, are watched for signs of strain. In other words, we have come to realize that health is wealth, and have given an old saying, "Save the pence and the pounds will save themselves," a new turn: "Save the children and the nation will save itself."

HEALTH CONSCIOUSNESS

Gradually a health consciousness is being evolved by the ordinary man and woman. Particularly is this true of the ordinary woman. For she begins to take a pride in the health of her family; she has an increasing desire to know which kinds of food her family should be given. In the last years of her school life she has learned valuable rules of hygiene such as were never imparted to her mother.

With each new year the attitude of the medical profession, as such, approximates more and more nearly to that fine dictum of Lord Moynihan's, "We must approach the conquest of disease through the territory occupied by normality and health." As long ago as 1921, Sir James MacKenzie founded the St. Andrews Institute for Clinical Research because he realized the enormous importance of recognizing disease in its earliest stages. All the general practitioners in the town of St. Andrews helped to supply the Institute with records of the early symptoms of disease in the families they treated. With the assistance of research workers at St. Andrews University, a health service which is preventive rather than curative is being built up.

The only institute in England on the same lines is that started by Drs. I. H. Pearse and G. Scott Williamson in 1934 at Peckham, South London. These two biologists invited a small number of families from the working-class district of Peckham to join their centre, which in the beginning was no more than a small house. Every member of each family was given a thorough medical examination, including scientific tests to ascertain in what respects they fell short of a good standard of health and efficiency. Complete records were kept, and arrangements were made for advice and treatment when necessary. While it was primarily a place for medical examination, the Pioneer Health Centre had facilities for recreation and refreshment.

BRAVER NEW WORLD

The idea of the Centre quickly seized the imagination of the more advanced of the public, including many belonging to the medical profession. Funds soon became available, and the present fine building with its recreation

FOX

CHILDREN LEARNING TO SWIM

Members of the younger generation learning to swim in the Pioneer Health Centre. All who belong to the Centre receive an education in personal hygiene, and enjoy unique opportunities for physical culture and recreation.

rooms, library, swimming pool, etc., came into being. The Centre, which is self-supporting on a small subscription basis, is of inestimable benefit to large numbers of families living in the district. All who belong to it receive an education in personal hygiene, and enjoy unique opportunities for physical culture and recreation.

Since not isolated individuals but whole families are regularly examined, the records kept at the Centre are likely to be of immense practical value in the future. Because those families come from roughly the same environment, eugenists and students of heredity will, as time goes on, have such material as has never before been available.

The Peckham Centre, it may well be, is the pioneer of a braver new world than that of Mr. Aldous Huxley.

FOX

ENGLAND'S PIONEER HEALTH CENTRE

The Pioneer Health Centre began in a small house. It now occupies the fine building pictured above, with cafés, gymnasium, dancing floor, badminton court, billiard tables, recreation rooms, library, swimming pool and other amenities, and stands in its own grounds.

HAMILTON COLLECTION JOAN WHEELER

"MASTER OF THOSE WHO KNOW"

Aristotle (384–322 B.C.) *and the Parthenon which crowns the beautiful city of Athens in which he taught. He observed and experimented, and also by sheer exercise of thought drew conclusions as to the nature of mind.*

PSYCHOLOGY THROUGH THE AGES

In the preceding chapter a description has been given of the machinery of the human body. Earlier in the book it has been shown that *Homo sapiens*, far from being unique in physical structure, is virtually identical in this respect with other species of animals. This fact naturally raises the question, why is man lord of creation? Why not the ape, the dog, the lion or the whale?

The question is not so easy to answer satisfactorily as one might think. Because man has a better brain, says someone. That sounds convincing. But turn back to page 126. There you will read that " there are solid grounds for believing that the general area of the brain offers a clue to mental capacity." Only a clue, notice. A few lines further on comes the disconcerting statement that " whales have brains rivalling that of man in complexity." No one would suggest that whales have ever shown signs of rivalling man's supremacy, so this first answer appears hardly conclusive.

But man has a superior mind, says someone else. He possesses the faculties of reason, judgment, imagination, suggests a third; while a fourth reminds us that God has endowed man alone among the animals with an immortal soul.

These answers all bear the stamp of truth. But what exactly do they mean? What are reason, judgment, imagination, mind, soul? Our answers lead us only to infinitely more difficult questions.

To attempt to answer those questions is in part the business of psychology.

What is psychology?

To ask this question to-day seems almost an insult. Everyone knows what psychology is. One can hardly open a daily paper without coming across reference to it. Countless magazine articles explain blandly the psychology of this, that, and the other; of war, peace, trade, industry, finance, crime, education, religion—in short, of almost any human activity you care to mention.

The language of the psychologist has penetrated into everyday speech and become an integral part of it. If our neighbour annoys or bores us, we get our revenge by saying he has a "complex." Any crotchety old lady of our acquaintance we describe as "neurotic." Many of us talk learnedly of "inhibitions," "phobias," and "repressions;" while among the most hackneyed clichés in our language is that unhappy (and incorrectly used) phrase "the psychological moment."

PRESS PORTRAIT BUREAU

FOUNDER OF NEW SCHOOL OF THOUGHT
Dr. Alfred Adler, who after rejecting Freud's theory of dreams founded the school of individual psychology.

Let us analyse this alleged psychological knowledge we all possess. Imagine a group of normally intelligent and reasonably well-educated people in conversation round the fireside. The subject of psychology crops up and, as is so often the case, gives rise to a long and animated discussion.

What conclusions would an impartial yet critical listener draw from that discussion? In all probability the following three.

First, that though everyone present takes it for granted that psychology has to do with the mind, beyond this point agreement as to what it is seems to cease. For one person it appears to be a method for curing nervous diseases, for another a way of dealing with naughty children, for a third a system to aid success and ensure happiness in life. And so on.

Second, that the discussion centres almost exclusively round the question of what psychology can or cannot do when applied to practical problems; and third, that opinions will vary from that of an extreme right wing which dismisses all psychology as suspect to that of an extreme left wing which regards it as a potential if not actual remedy for almost any and every human ill.

VALUABLE PRACTICAL WORK

This state of affairs is not so surprising as might at first sight appear. Disregard the lack of agreement as to the practical value of psychology, and that group reflects not inaccurately the position to-day in the world of the professional psychologist.

There, instead of a single, universally accepted doctrine of psychology will be found a number of schools of psychological thought, apparently mutually exclusive, and seemingly, to the superficial observer at least, steadily drifting farther apart, splitting as they go into still more divergent groups.

It seems obvious that little attempt is being made to construct a synthesis, or comprehensive system, of psychology which shall reconcile those various and opposing views; each school of thought is too busily occupied in developing its own particular theory.

Yet almost without exception these schools and groups are doing valuable practical work. None is content with theory alone; most are far more concerned with the applications of their findings to the solution of human problems. It almost seems as though temporarily the search for the perfect psychology had been abandoned in favour of the more narrowly utilitarian plan of putting into harness such partial truths as have already been discovered.

How has this state of affairs come about?

SERIES OF REVOLUTIONS

The answer is simple. While psychology itself is very nearly as old as the human race, during the past century or so there has been nothing less than a revolution—or to speak more accurately a series of revolutions—in the psychological world. As a result, it is almost safer to-day to talk of "the psychologies" than of psychology.

Psychology of a sort had its birth when long ages ago some unknown cave-man—or woman

—began to be troubled by the thoughts which arose in his mind or the dreams which disturbed his rest, and was moved to enquire into their nature and origin. The present-day systems of psychology are creations as modern as the motor car, the aeroplane, wireless and the cinema.

What is the nature of this revolution which has taken place? In brief, that psychology has at long last emerged from beneath the wings of metaphysics and philosophy and become a science in the full meaning of the word.

ACADEMIC AND ALOOF

While the first mutterings of that revolution were to be faintly distinguished centuries ago, it is only during the present century that it has achieved its climax. Even in the nineteenth century, as Dr. P. B. Ballard, the well-known educationist has put it, psychology was " an armchair psychology, born and bred in the study, abstract, academic and aloof." But " the twentieth century saw a new line of development. The psychologist ceased to be a pundit and became a worker. He got out of his armchair, took off his coat, so to speak, and set to work."

" Only a science which is directly related to life," said William James, one of the greatest pioneers of modern psychology, " is really a science." " It might also be said," added Alfred Adler, another of the great moderns, " that in a science which is directly related to life theory and practice become almost inseparable."

NOT AN EXACT SCIENCE

Adler's illuminating remark very exactly indicates the position of psychology to-day. In it, theory and practice have become virtually inseparable; and psychology has become not less, but more scientific on that account.

One often hears the objection that psychology is not yet an exact science. The answer is that it probably never will be; its subject matter is too elusive. But it is quite unfair to assume, as many people do, that for that reason all its hypotheses and conclusions must therefore be regarded with suspicion. If that attitude of mind were universal, all science would be suspect.

Another objection frequently urged against psychology is that it is still in the experimental stage. One might reply to this that so are all the sciences, but a far more convincing answer is briefly to review the history of psychology and to show that it is not nearly so experimental as many people imagine.

While modern psychology may rightly be called revolutionary, it has to be remembered that no revolution, however iconoclastic, can ever make a clean break with the past. It is invariably compelled to incorporate in the new system which it creates a great deal of the old system which it sets out to destroy. And modern psychology is primarily creative rather than destructive; it tends rather to remember than to forget the past.

E.N.A.

APOSTLE OF PSYCHO-ANALYSIS

Dr. Sigmund Freud, whose psycho-analysis is partly based on Greek thought of several centuries before Christ, though many of the ideas are original.

Too much prominence perhaps has been given in popular writings to what is new in present day psychology, and too little to what is centuries old. It would be quite incorrect, for example, to assume that psycho-analysis, possibly the most revolutionary and certainly the most startling of modern psychological theories, sprang full-fledged out of nothingness.

Dr. Sigmund Freud (born 1856) of Vienna, its discoverer, though fully aware of the originality of many of his ideas, goes out of his way on occasion to assert the opposite view, even when the necessity seems hardly apparent.

"As a rule," he declared in his first *Introductory Lectures on Psycho-Analysis*, "psycho-analysis only adds something new to what has been said." "Nor was I then aware," he wrote in his *Autobiography*, "that in deriving hysteria from sexuality I was going back to

HAMILTON COLLECTION

FATHER OF MODERN PSYCHOLOGY
Thomas Hobbes (1588–1679), *the English philosopher who showed how scientific principles could be applied to psychology.*

the very beginnings of medicine and following up a thought of Plato's." Later in the same book he reminds readers that "Aristotle's old definition of the dream as mental life during sleep still holds good."

Thus two of the bases of psycho-analytic theory are found to be discoverable in Greek thought of three centuries or more before Christ. And scientific psychology is older even than Plato and Aristotle.

In the sixth century B.C. Greek medical men were already distinguishing between the raw material of knowledge as acquired by the senses and thought as matured in the mind. It was becoming evident to them that there was some power or faculty in man which co-ordinated and unified the elements of knowledge, perhaps even created some of it, since it was difficult to see how abstract and universal ideas could arise out of sense-perception.

Later in the same century, Pythagoras (about 582–506 B.C.), the celebrated Greek mathematician and philospher, evolved the theory of an immortal soul prisoned in the mortal body, from which it escaped only at death; and thus opened a controversy which has raged down to the present day.

BEING AND KNOWING

Has man a soul or has he not? If he has, is the soul mortal or immortal? Or perhaps soul is the same as mind? Then how do mind and body stand in relation to each other? Are they only different aspects of the same organism, or two distinct and separate entities?

Strictly speaking, these questions belong, not to psychology, but to metaphysics, which explores the philosophy of being and knowing; yet for many centuries they dominated psychological thought. As is perhaps hardly necessary to point out, the word psychology means literally "soul-knowledge" (Greek *psyche*, soul, and *logos*, knowledge).

The reason for this preoccupation with metaphysical problems is not far to seek. Just as the boundary line between chemistry and physics, or between chemistry and biology, can never be accurately defined, neither can the boundary lines between psychology and metaphysics on the one hand, and psychology and biology on the other. In so far as psychology is a matter of biology it belongs to the natural sciences; in so far as it touches metaphysical, moral or ethical questions it falls within the province of philosophy.

THOUGHT CIRCULATED BY AIR

Now the ancient Greeks had advanced very far in philosophy, but their knowledge of biology was crude in the extreme. Consequently, though they gave attention to both aspects of psychology, their researches on the philosophical side were bound to be infinitely more fruitful than those on the scientific. When, later, the early Christian thinkers embarked on psychology, their interest was almost inevitably centred on its more spiritual aspects.

Neither Plato nor Aristotle knew anything about the nervous system; they believed that sensation, thought and energy were circulated through the body by means of air in the veins —a mistaken impression which incidentally was to persist until the eighteenth century. Aristotle imagined that thought proceeded from the heart, Plato that desire had its origin in the liver.

Both accepted unquestioningly the current medical teaching that a man's temperament depended on the ratio in which the four "humours"—blood, phlegm, black bile and yellow bile—were mingled in his body. They had, needless to say, never heard of the ductless glands, to the activity of which we now ascribe temperament.

SOUL AS DYNAMO

It is evident from the foregoing that little substantial progress could be made in psychology along scientific lines. On the other hand, two philosophers of the status of Plato and Aristotle could hardly fail materially to advance the theoretical side.

Plato (429–347 B.C.) took up the Pythagorean theory of the immortal soul, and considerably developed it. For him the soul was the dynamo which gave life to and drove the machinery of the organism. Everything living had a soul. Plants had nutritive souls which enabled them to feed, grow and reproduce their kind. Animals were further capable of sensation and voluntary movement because they had sensitive souls. Man's soul possessed all these attributes, and added the power of reasoned thought, which made it supreme.

A fantastic theory, no doubt, yet it enabled Plato to make the fundamental discovery so amply confirmed by modern psychology, that in the development of the human personality, desire, or appetite as it used to be called, is bound to come into conflict with reason, and that out of that conflict emerge judgment and will.

PLATO AMONG THE MODERNS

It should not be forgotten either that Plato was the first to apply psychology to education, nor that his educational theory was in many respects strikingly modern.

He conceived education as a process by which the soul was developed through the gradual adjustment of the individual to his environment and to the society in which he was brought up. The purpose of instruction was to train the pupil in abstract thought, for Plato held (and his opinion has been justified by that very modern invention, the intelligence test) that the highest mark of intellectual capacity lay in the ability to perceive the relations between things.

Aristotle (384–322 B.C.) evolved a very beautiful theory of the soul. Whether he regarded it as immortal or not no one has ever been able to decide, but he quite certainly rejected the idea that it was separate from the body. For him it was the form which gave shape and meaning to the matter.

HAMILTON COLLECTION

FOUNDER OF CARTESIANISM

René Descartes (1596–1650) regarded animals as machines pure and simple, working quite automatically.

Matter has no meaning without form; form cannot exist without matter. Together they produce something full of reality and meaning. A block of stone, a lump of clay, unshaped, are uncouth and meaningless. The sculptor transforms one into an angel, the potter moulds the other into an exquisite vase. Each individual is sculptor of his own individuality; and soul is the form he gives to it. Soul, in other words, is the perfected state of development when all the bodily functions are working actively and in unison.

This theory naturally led Aristotle, since he was scientist as well as philosopher, to study the functions of the body. He investigated the nature of the senses, and defined sensation as a change in the mind. Memory he regarded as a permanent impression of sensations, and human experience as a collection of memories. He traced a sequence between sensation and reason, and a similar one between desire and will. He established knowing and willing as main functions of the mind, and was careful to distinguish between mind

HAMILTON COLLECTION

OF "HUMAN UNDERSTANDING" FAME

John Locke (1632–1704) *allowed man an active mind, but regarded mental processes as a function of the body.*

and the bodily organ through which it worked.

Thus one may see that over two thousand years ago a considerable body of psychological knowledge had been built up. Aristotle's combination of methods, too, deserves notice. On the one hand he observed and experimented in true scientific fashion; on the other he philosophized, that is, by sheer exercise of thought drew conclusions as to the nature of mind.

Perhaps it will be well at this point to interpose a note on method in psychological enquiry, for it must be obvious to anyone that there are very special difficulties involved in the study of the mind.

Of course, if one denies the existence of mind as such, and regards all mental processes as physiological in origin and nature, most of those difficulties are resolved. It then becomes possible to make psychology a completely objective science, that is, one prosecuted entirely by an observer on material observed.

One investigates the anatomy of the brain, the nervous systems and the sense organs, analyses and classifies the products of mental processes as expressed in behaviour, and then correlates the two investigations.

ANALYSING MENTAL PROCESSES

This standpoint has been taken up more than once in the history of psychology, but it is one which as a general rule man has been reluctant to accept. He prefers to believe that there is some power within him that is not reducible to terms of chemical action, and that this power is the mainspring of his higher mental functions.

But how is he to investigate the nature of this power? He can only do so by looking into his own mind, observing how it works, and analysing the mental processes. This is called introspection.

The prime defect of merely using the introspective method is that the only mind any person can ever look into is his own. He has no guarantee that other minds work exactly like his, and he can never perceive any mental process in its entirety, because the act of introspection necessarily causes interference with that process.

He can of course collect from other people impressions and experiences. In doing this he is departing from purely introspective methods, which is all to the good, but he is still hampered by the fact that other people's ideas of their mental processes are of necessity as imperfect as his own.

GLOOM OF THE DARK AGES

A wise combination of introspection and objective study is the ideal method for psychology. Aristotle made this combination, and had the physical sciences been as developed in his day as was philosophy, there is little doubt that psychology would have been placed on an assured basis many centuries ago. Succeeding thinkers, lacking his breadth of vision, tended to follow either a purely physiological or purely philosophical path.

Christian philosophers, as we have said, naturally become preoccupied with the metaphysical questions of the origin, nature and destiny of the human soul. Physical science, after making a number of important discoveries, including that of the nervous system, faded out in the gloom of the Dark Ages. As a result psychology remained for centuries largely a matter of metaphysical subtleties.

Not until the wind of the Renaissance blew across Europe was there any real advance in psychological thought. We may, if we like, date the origin of the modern revolution in psychology from that time, though its results did not begin to be impressive until the second half of the nineteenth century, and can by no means be said to be fully worked out yet.

FROM IDEALS TO REALITIES

The spirit of the Renaissance was material, realistic, rational and scientific. Throughout the Middle Ages man had been largely preoccupied with the world to come. Now he became vitally interested in his life on earth; he wanted to know all about it, and about the world in which it had to be lived. One result of this revolutionary attitude towards life was that man began to look at himself from a new angle.

To put it crudely, the focus of attention was diverted from human ideals to the realities of human behaviour. Whereas formerly philosophers had assumed that the guiding principle in man was a persistent and reasoned quest for the absolute Good, now writers arose who rejected this idea utterly. Man, they declared, was not guided by reason; he was ruled primarily by his desires or appetites. This theory naturally led to a denial that man could possess an immortal soul.

Meanwhile the idea of scientific method and procedure dominated all men's minds. Everything must be proved scientifically. This led psychologists on the one hand to investigate closely the physiological aspects of mental life, and on the other to be elaborately logical in their analyses of the mental processes. It is easy to see how this attitude could lead to a mechanistic, or machine-like conception of the mind and its workings.

MIND AND MATTER

In England, Thomas Hobbes (1588–1679) drew up a scheme of psychology which defined sensation as a mode of motion excited by external stimuli in the physiological machine, and reason as an arithmetical process of adding or subtracting ideas already contained in experience.

Sensations, he said, strike inwards, exciting either pain or pleasure. The reverse process is volition, or willing, which strikes outward, away from or towards the cause of the pain or pleasure. In man volition is tempered by judgment; and the conflict between the two results, as Plato had already observed, in the will.

The value of Hobbes' work lay mainly in

HAMILTON COLLECTION

PHILOSOPHER AND HISTORIAN

David Hume (1711–1776) *put forward the famous principle of the association of ideas.*

the fact that he showed how scientific method could be applied to psychology. For this reason he has been frequently called the "father of modern psychology."

In France, René Descartes, (1596–1650), in his passion for scientific truth, threw overboard all the teachings of all previous thinkers, and began a philosophical enquiry with, so to speak, an absolutely blank page. He queried the reality or truth of everything; and then set out to discover if there were any principles which could be shown to be true beyond all shadow of doubt.

At last he found one. He expressed it in the famous dictum *Cogito, ergo sum,* "I think, therefore I am." That principle discovered, he tested all others by it. From it he "proved" the existence of God, from the nature of God the reliability of the human mind, from that the reality of the external world, and from the nature of the external world that mind and matter were completely and utterly different.

But as mind and matter obviously worked together in man it became necessary to show the relation between the two. Descartes' solution of this problem was ingenious if highly inaccurate.

HAMILTON COLLECTION

GREAT GERMAN GENIUS

Gottfried Wilhelm Leibnitz (1646–1716), *the German philosopher who introduced the idea of unconscious mental activity.*

To animals he denied mind; they were machines pure and simple, working quite automatically. Man's body was also a machine, but from it flowed feelings to the pineal gland of the brain, where the mind received them and returned to the body impulses resulting in movements. Matter was thus controlled by mind.

The bottom drops out of this theory as soon as it is discovered that animals as well as man possess a pineal gland. But that time was not yet, and as Descartes' influence on contemporary thought was very great, his views were generally accepted, and mind and body were regarded as separate and different entities.

Yet even Descartes, mistaken though he was on many points, made a substantial contribution to psychological knowledge. In effect he stated the principle of reflex action, that is, of involuntary bodily response to an external stimulus. In this he was in advance of his day; the principle was not scientifically established until the early years of the nineteenth century. He saw clearly the physiological nature of sensory and motor (movement) processes in the human body; he had much to say that was valuable about the nature of emotion and he enlarged the concept of mind by allowing it consciousness.

PRINCIPLES FROM OBSERVATION

In 1690 John Locke (1632–1704), often called "the father of English psychology," published his monumental *Essay Concerning the Human Understanding*. The fact that Locke's psychology was, so to speak, a by-product of his great philosophical enquiry into the nature of knowledge, does not detract from its value.

To demonstrate the nature of knowledge, Locke had of necessity to show how it was acquired. To do this he traced the process of knowing back to its origins; and in this enquiry lay his great contribution to psychology. Instead of assuming a supposed nature of mind, and then arguing from that, he built up principles of mental life from observation. Knowledge, he said, comes from experience. How? By sensation and reflection.

Sensation enables us to perceive the external world, which possesses quantity and qualities. It gives to the mind simple ideas. Reflection acquaints us with the internal world of the mind, where understanding and will are at work. This internal world of the mind takes the simple ideas presented by sensation, combines and compares them, and forms out of them complex ideas.

ASSOCIATION OF IDEAS

Locke's position, it will be seen, is the direct antithesis of Descartes'. The latter made body dependent on mind; the former made mind ultimately dependent on body, though in itself a source of ideas.

Locke would have nothing to do with the idea of a soul in man. He allowed man an active mind, but mental processes were a function of the body, and reasoned thought depended on sensation, that is, bodily experience.

How was experience related in the mind? Locke did not fully answer this question, but he hinted at a principle which in the hands of David Hume (1711–76) and his followers was elevated into the basis of a psychology which persisted almost down to the present day. This was the famous principle of the association of ideas.

Descartes had allowed the substantial reality of the external world : Locke that of the active mind. Hume denied the substantial reality of either mind or matter.

BASIS OF EXPERIENCE

Mind, he said, had no dynamic force. Experience was made up of impressions and ideas. The former originated both from sensation and reflection; the latter were, so to speak, mental impressions of impressions. The whole was held together by associations, of similarity, of nearness in space or time, or of cause and effect. These associations were themselves derivable from impressions. Thus mind was for Hume nothing but a vast collection of impressions united by various links.

The modern reader will at once perceive the barrenness of the "associationist" school of psychology. It robbed mind of all vitality, and reduced it to a warehouse of miscellaneous goods, neatly packed, arranged and docketed, no doubt, but still without life or power. Even will was reduced to a sequence of sensations.

The academic and arid nature of associationism had a good deal to do with the suspicious distaste with which psychology was regarded in the nineteenth century. This is not to say that the principle of the association of ideas has been discarded by the modern psychologist. On the contrary, it has been incorporated in all systems of present-day psychology, but as a factor, not as the fundamental basis.

FORERUNNER OF FREUD

Early in the long reign of associationism were heard the mutterings of the revolution which was to sweep it out of existence, and to replace it by the present psychologies which, if they agree in little else, almost all take emphatically a dynamic concept of mind.

In so brief an account as this it is impossible even to indicate many of the causes which went to bring about the present revolution. Hume's work itself was one; he finally cleared psychology of metaphysical issues, and taught that its subject matter was the phenomena of consciousness and the links between them.

The German philosopher Gottfried Wilhelm Leibnitz (1646–1716), who evolved a theory of the universe as made up of "monads," or active, independent mental substances, of which the soul is one, introduced the idea of unconscious mental activity, an idea which was later to be taken up by the German philosopher Arthur Schopenhauer (1788–1860). The latter taught that the only essential reality in the universe was will; and will he held to include both conscious desire and unconscious instinct. He was thus a forerunner of Freud.

HAMILTON COLLECTION

FAMOUS METAPHYSICIAN

Immanuel Kant (1724–1804), who influenced psychology by insisting on the importance of will and feeling.

Immanuel Kant (1724–1804) agreed with Hume that psychology has nothing to do with metaphysics or the question of the soul. It must study experience, and to do this adequately, he held, must use mathematical methods. He also profoundly influenced psychological thought by his insistence on the importance of will and feeling.

Johann Friedrich Herbart (1776–1841) actually applied mathematics to the study of mind. True, he produced a series of intricate mathematical formulæ which few understood and fewer still believed in, but the intention was sound enough. Ideas, he held, were not linked passively, as the associationists said, but dynamically by mental forces. The whole he called an "apperceptive mass."

To this apperceptive mass new ideas are

constantly being allied. Herbart, who had a keen appreciation of the practical value of psychology, applied this principle of the relating of new material to past experience to education, and earned the profound gratitude of several generations of teachers.

Herbart believed in a soul which he regarded as a quantity of energy. Every experience demanded so much energy (this was what he

RISCHGITZ COLLECTION

JOHANN FRIEDRICH HERBART

He applied mathematics to the study of mind and held that ideas were linked by mental forces.

tried to show mathematically), and the soul is perpetually concerned to maintain its unity in face of multitudinous coalescing or opposing ideas.

An idea, he maintained, enters the mind below the threshold of consciousness. If stimulated it rises until it is "apperceived." Then it may sink again into the unconscious. The significance of this theory for education will be obvious to anyone who has ever done any teaching.

Herbart's attempt to apply mathematics to psychology was not a success, but at least it pointed the way. Ernst Heinrich Weber (1795–1878), a German scientist who did much work on the senses of hearing and touch, formulated "Weber's Law," which states that "the increase of stimulus necessary to produce an increase of sensation in any sense is not an absolute quantity, but depends on the proportion which the increase bears to the immediately preceding sensation." Weber's work was carried on and developed by Gustav Theodor Fechner (1801–87), the founder of psycho-physics, which he defined as "an exact doctrine of the relation of function between body and soul."

Even before psychology was made more exact by the application to it of mathematics, a series of brilliant discoveries in physiology gave promise that at last it might become possible to build up scientifically a body of knowledge concerning mental life which should be adequate enough to resolve the mystery of mind.

NORMAL AND ABNORMAL

In the eighteenth century French scientists were undertaking the education of mentally defective persons, thus for the first time in history treating mental derangements in a natural way instead of as arising out of mystical possession by the devil. The training of deaf and dumb children was also being undertaken. In these early experiments are to be found the germs of much notable twentieth century work in education. They had a further significance also; they began to show the close relationship between the normal and the abnormal mind.

In Austria Franz Joseph Gall (1758–1828), did valuable work on the anatomy of the brain, as also did Sir Charles Bell (1774–1842), who in 1811 announced the discovery of the difference between sensory and motor nerves, and so established the principle of reflex action.

The researches of Johannes Peter Müller (1801–1858), the celebrated German physiologist and anatomist, and of the scientists who followed his lead were so important as to constitute a turning point in physiology. Müller investigated in particular the senses and the nerves, and was the first to demonstrate that the kind of sensation experienced depended on the nature of the sense organ transmitting it to the nerve terminals.

TWO GREAT INFLUENCES

By the middle of the nineteenth century two influences then were playing strongly upon psychology. On the one hand philosophers were insisting that mind was dynamic, not static; on the other, scientists were showing by exact experiments how sensory and motor impulses were passed to and from the brain. A new outlook upon psychology was maturing;

and the physiological aspects of psychology were rapidly being developed.

Then came a third and predominating influence. In 1859 Charles Darwin (1809–82) published his epoch-making work *The Origin of Species by Means of Natural Selection.* Twelve years later came *The Descent of Man and Variation in Relation to Sex*, followed in 1872 by *The Expression of the Emotions in Man and Animals.*

EVOLUTION AND PSYCHOLOGY

The influence of the Darwinian theory of evolution was as profound upon psychology as upon any of the other sciences. It can best be described in the words of Dr. Francis Aveling, Professor of Psychology in the University of London, who has said " The influence of the evolutionary hypothesis upon psychology was enormous. Like the saturated solution of a salt into which a crystal is dropped, current psychologies began to crystallize round it. The mental gulf between man and the rest of the animal kingdom was bridged."

Hitherto psychologists had studied man's mind as an isolated phenomenon; they had taken it, so to speak, out of cold storage, dissected and analysed it, built it up again out of its pieces, and regarded the matter as finished. Now, all at once, psychology was seen to be an infinitely vaster and more complicated study than had ever before been imagined. The evolutionary theory must be applied to mind as well as to body.

ENLARGING THE STUDY

That involved study of the growth of mind. Just as man's body was shown to be the result of ages of evolution from the simple one-celled organism upwards, similarly it must be assumed that mind had developed. To discover its secrets, one must go right back to the origins of mental life, and trace them upwards to the climax in man. In this study the entire animal kingdom must be surveyed. The task also involved the study of the human mind from the birth of a child onwards, and study of the life of primitive peoples, which illustrated stages of human development.

This vast field had naturally to be split into fields for specialized research; thus there came into being the sciences (or sub-sciences) of animal psychology, comparative psychology (man compared with animals as regards mental life), and child psychology.

In the *Origin of Species* Darwin discussed instincts; in the *Descent of Man* the development of mental powers in man and the animals. His destruction of the theory that animals were differently constituted mentally from man led to intensive study of animal behaviour with a view to throwing light upon human behaviour. In course of time extremely valuable results were obtained.

Similarly, since man in his pre-natal growth and early childhood demonstrates in part the

RISCHGITZ COLLECTION

GERMAN PHRENOLOGIST

Franz Joseph Gall (1758–1828) did valuable work on the anatomy of the brain.

evolution of the human species, the psychology of early childhood was attacked. Primitive peoples throughout the world became the subject of investigation, since their culture and behaviour represented stages in human development. Folk-lore, mythology, legend, primitive customs, habits, religions, ancient and medieval literature were ransacked in search of material. At the same time insane, mentally defective, neurotic and otherwise abnormal people became subjects for intensive psychological study, it being realized that much light could be thrown upon many mental processes by studying them in their more exaggerated or abnormal forms.

Herbert Spencer (1820–1903) was the first philosopher to apply Darwinism to psychology. Unfortunately he tried to confine it within the bounds of associationism, but he did good work in analysing the nature of intelligence and of mental products, and in directing attention to the part played by heredity and racial influences upon the individual mind.

Meanwhile Sir Francis Galton (1822–1911) the anthropologist began under Darwin's influence the studies which were to lead to his publication in 1869 of *Hereditary Genius*, and in 1883 of *Inquiries into Human Faculty*. Galton investigated the relation between mental qualities, and, in order to measure it, invented the "coefficient of correlation," a device that has been of enormous value on the statistical side of modern psychology.

RISCHGITZ COLLECTION

PHYSIOLOGIST AND ANATOMIST

Johannes Peter Müller (1801–58) *investigated in particular the senses and the nerves.*

In 1879 Wilhelm Wundt (1832–1920) opened at Leipzig the first laboratory entirely devoted to psychological experiment. Seven years previously he had published a *Groundwork of Physiological Psychology* in which he attempted to relate together anatomy, neurology and psychology. This book and the founding of the laboratory indicate his attitude.

Wundt believed that psychology is based upon experience and that this latter was a fit subject for exact scientific study. He approached it with an open mind, holding it impossible to predict whether any experience had a physiological or mental origin. Only investigation could show that.

Similarly he did not commit himself to any one method. The psychologist must avail himself of any and every method; introspection, observation of and experiment upon physiological conditions, study of behaviour both animal and human, research into literature, philology, religion and anthropology.

Wundt's example was quickly followed. Other laboratories were founded; other psychologists adopted his views on method. The vastness of the field to be covered invited specialization—one reason why to-day there are many schools of psychological thought.

GROWTH OF THE CHILD MIND

In 1883 the first psychological laboratory in America was opened by G. Stanley Hall (1844–1924), who devoted many years of his life to a study of adolescence. He is famous for the theory that the mental growth of every child recapitulates all the epochs of culture through which man has passed from his most primitive days to present day civilization.

The theory is not accepted in all its completeness, but it did a very great deal to throw light upon the growth of the child mind. From an early date child psychology has received much attention in the United States, Stanley Hall being only one among a large number of distinguished investigators; and a large amount of brilliant work has been, and is being done there.

Hall had been a student at Harvard University under William James (1842–1910), most revolutionary and important of nineteenth century American philosophers. A neurotic and delicate boy, James grew up a semi-invalid young man until he was twenty-eight. Widely travelled, deeply read, trained under some of the most distinguished German physiologists of the day, and fully qualified as a doctor of medicine, he remained a prey to a neurosis of a painful nature until, as he relates, he read the philosophy of Charles Bertrand Renouvier (1815–1903) and imbibed his doctrine of free will.

DETERMINISM AND FREE WILL

Liberty, declared Renouvier, is man's fundamental characteristic. We believe in it, not with our intelligence merely, but by power of will. This theory wrought a marvellous change upon James. Declaring that "my first act of free will shall be to believe in free will," he shed his youthful philosophy of determinism, or belief that human action is determined by

RISCHGITZ COLLECTION

HOME OF THE AUTHOR OF *THE ORIGIN OF SPECIES*

Down House, Kent, where Darwin wrote his epoch-making books. In the Descent of Man *the scientist discussed the development of mental powers in man and the lower animals.*

external forces, cured himself of his neurosis and embarked on a life of intense intellectual activity.

He began by teaching physiology at Harvard, where later he became professor of psychology. In 1891 he published his famous work *The Principles of Psychology*, on which he had laboured for a dozen years or more. Out of date now—so rapidly and extensively has psychology developed since—it was yet a landmark in the history of psychological thought. It incorporated and wove into a system all the various lines of development—the physiological, the psycho-physical, the analytic, the pathological, and the philosophical—which were actively contributing to produce the new outlook on psychology.

Two features were essentially modern in James's psychology: its conduct along strictly scientific lines and its concern with everyday life. James threw overboard the idea that psychology had to do with the structure of the mind, and insisted that it dealt with its functions; in simpler language he was not interested in what the mind is so much as what it does.

Evidence of the results of this new attitude were forthcoming in the work of his colleague Hugo Münsterberg (1863–1916), who in 1908 published *Psychology and Crime* and four years later *Psychology and Industrial Efficiency*.

James's influence was directly contributory to the development of two modern schools of psychological thought which had their origin in North America and are still widely accepted: Behaviourism, and Purposive or Hormic Psychology.

Insistence upon the functional rather than the structural aspect of mind involves an exact study of behaviour, which is the outward manifestation of mental activity. Any study of behaviour scientifically conducted is bound to

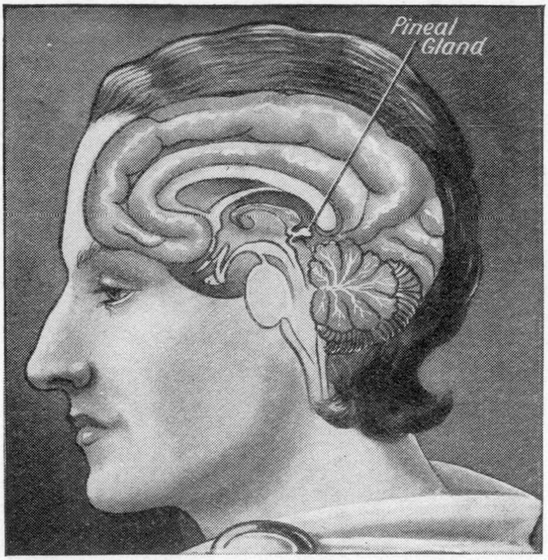

PINEAL GLAND

The pineal gland of the brain, the discovery of which in the lower animals upset Descartes' theory.

involve the question of the origins of behaviour. It is evident that both human beings and animals have to learn in some way or another how to perform every one of the innumerable acts which together constitute their daily life. What is the basis of this learning, and how is behaviour built up from its simple foundations into ever more complicated patterns?

STUDY OF BEHAVIOUR

The study of behaviour was, of course, no new thing, but until the statement of the Darwinian theory of evolution human and animal behaviour had been conceived as the result of radically different mental processes. Right up to the twentieth century psychologists were content to admit for man the principle of consciousness. Man acts as he does because he is conscious of what he is doing; in other words he directs his behaviour. But almost a century previously a series of physiological discoveries had begun which were later to suggest another train of thought.

In 1811 Sir Charles Bell established the principle of the reflex action, which is an involuntary sensory-motor response to an external stimulus. Both man and beast (right down to very lowly organisms) exhibit reflex action. We blink at a sudden bright light; an earthworm dives down its hole on hearing a bird alight on the ground. A reflex action is not learnt; it is invariable and universal to all members of the same species, and it is often performed without reference to the brain.

In 1863 there came the suggestion from Russia that psychology should be built up on the basis of the reflex action. At the same time Darwin was teaching that there was no essential difference between the behaviour of man and the animals, and that the two should be studied side by side, or comparatively.

EXPERIMENTS WITH DOGS

Following his lead, a large number of scientists embarked upon investigations into animal behaviour. At first these studies were in the main descriptive; later they tended to become more and more preoccupied with how animals learn.

Among many distinguished names that of Ivan Petrovich Pavlov (1849–1936), the Russian physiologist, stands pre-eminent. Pavlov has, indeed, been acclaimed by the behaviourist schools of psychology, on account of his discovery of the conditioned reflex, as the most revolutionary of modern scientists; and even if this extreme view be not taken, it is undeniable that his work on animal reflexes, and the conclusions he and others have deduced from it, have profoundly influenced psychological thought.

It is important to note that Pavlov was a physiologist, not a psychologist. When he began

RISCHGITZ COLLECTION

SIR CHARLES BELL

He discovered the difference between sensory and motor nerves, and so established the principle of reflex action.

HOW A CHIMPANZEE PUZZLES OUT A PROBLEM

To a human being the problem of pulling button A causing panel B to rise, giving access to orange C, as shown at the top of the page, is one that presents no difficulties. Both thought and action are almost instantaneous. To a chimpanzee the problem is exceedingly complex, as the pictures following abundantly prove.

his work he knew nothing of psychology. He was therefore untroubled by psychological theories. He was working as a physiologist on digestive processes when his attention was caught by the action of the salivary glands.

When an animal takes food into its mouth saliva is produced. The quantity and quality of the saliva varies with the nature of the food. This production of saliva, and the variation in amount and quality, is due to reflex action. But Pavlov noticed that the sight, the smell, even the sounds of preparation of food induce salivation, provided the animal has seen or smelt food before, or heard the same sounds in connection with its preparation. Upon that he began to experiment. He used dogs, as he had done for previous experiments on digestion. He isolated a dog in a quiet room, set a metronome ticking and, as soon as the animal noticed the noise, had a plate of food swung into the room.

PRESS PORTRAIT BUREAU

EMINENT BRITISH ZOOLOGIST

Professor C. Lloyd Morgan tested the theory that animals learn by a blind method of " trial and error."

The process was repeated at suitable intervals. It only required a few repetitions for the ticking of the metronome to excite in the dog all the customary signs of expectation of food—tail-wagging, licking of the chops, salivation of the mouth and so on.

UNCONDITIONED AND CONDITIONED REFLEXES

From this and similar experiments Pavlov concluded, not that the animal had " learnt " to connect metronome ticking with food but that a reflex action had been induced by an artificial stimulus, or in other words that the reflex had been " conditioned." For the dog's reaction to the ticking was in every respect exactly the same as it had been to the sight or smell of food, and precisely as involuntary.

The original and natural reaction, which had been inborn in the animal, he called an unconditioned reflex; the artificially produced one he termed a conditioned reflex. Upon the principle of the conditioned reflex a whole system of psychology has been built up.

Pavlov himself maintained that all behaviour from what we call in popular language an " instinctive " action—such as swift withdrawal of a finger from a hot poker—right up to the complicated processes necessary to solve an abstruse mathematical problem, is explicable in terms of nervous reflex to given stimuli. This theory, of course, does away with any idea of mind as the ordinary person (or the introspective psychologist) understands it.

Meanwhile a great variety of experiments had been carried out to test the intelligence of other animals, from the lowly amœba to the highest classes of vertebrates. In England C. Lloyd Morgan (born 1852), and in America Jacques Loeb (1859–1924) and E. L. Thorndike (born 1874) did pioneering work.

TESTS WITH CHIMPANZEES

Loeb investigated " tropisms," as he called them, the simple turnings of the body to or from a stimulus which are the most primitive animal reactions. Lloyd Morgan, Thorndike and others tested by experiment the theory that animals learn, not by insight which grasps a problem as a whole, but by a blind method of " trial and error " in which the solution is discovered by accident, and then impressed on the mind by repetition.

This hypothesis has not remained entirely unchallenged. Just before the World War the German scientist Wolfgang Köhler (born 1887) carried out at Teneriffe a celebrated series of

FOX

TRYING TO THREAD A NEEDLE

A chimpanzee will try to thread a needle, and is as likely to succeed as a child of two or three years of age. Young chimpanzees get tired quickly, and older ones have little ability to concentrate.

experiments upon a group of young, untrained chimpanzees, and discovered in these animals not only a high degree of manipulative skill, but evidence of mental processes which seemed indubitably to demonstrate insight. He further found that the chimpanzees exhibited emotional traits precisely similar to those of human adults.

The tests given to the chimpanzees were designed to exclude solution by trial and error. They consisted largely in placing food beyond the animals' reach, and at the same time providing means to obtain the food. Only it needed intelligence to connect the means with the food, or in other words, to grasp the relation between the aids to solution and the solution itself. It will be remembered that Plato laid it down that the capacity to see relations constituted the highest form of intelligence.

Köhler's chimpanzees readily used sticks to draw food into their cages. They fitted jointed sticks together when one stick was not long enough (this solution was originally arrived at by accident, but its possibilities were at once grasped by the animal concerned). They learned, though slowly, to tear branches from a tree to use as sticks; they piled packing cases one upon another, and they swung on ropes to get food beyond their reach.

EWING GALLOWAY, N.Y.

WEAPON OF HUMAN BONES

Following the publication of Darwin's books, primitive peoples became the subject of investigation. The spear carried by this Vantos islander is tipped and barbed with human shinbones.

WHERE APES RESEMBLE MAN

The tests revealed as clearly the limitations of ape intelligence as they did its high spots. The chimpanzees were evidently intellectually far below man; but the point was that their minds were seen to work in the same way.

On the emotional side the chimpanzees were found to resemble man much more strongly than on the intellectual. They wept, laughed and enjoyed play; kissed and fondled each other, showed marked sympathy with companions in distress, and equally marked jealousy and anger.

This wide range of experimentation discovered four types, or groups, of animal reaction to stimuli, tropisms, reflexes, instinctive reactions, and intelligent behaviour. Tropisms are not very common and are confined in the main to the lowlier forms of animal life. Reflexes are universal. Instinctive reactions are made up of a chain or series of reflexes. Intelligent action is seen only in man and the higher animals.

CONTINUOUS DEVELOPMENT

Formerly intelligence was thought to be confined to man: it was said that animals worked by instinct, man by reason. But the work of the comparative psychologist has shown a continuous development in behaviour from the amœba to man. The Behaviourist school of psychology regards this development as a purely physiological phenomenon, and consequently as a matter for entirely objective research.

While every school of psychology admits a biological basis for the subject, this extreme view is acceptable to few psychologists. What is being acknowledged more and more is the fact of an intimate but as yet very little understood relationship between physiological and psychical processes.

MONDIALE

HOW A NEEDLEWOMAN EXPENDS ENERGY

Left: An unskilled woman making an unnecessary movement at the beginning of her work. Centre: Tired after an hour's work. Right: An experienced woman with an even, sure movement who can work for hours without fatigue.

BELIEFS OF THE BEHAVIOURISTS

THE approach to Behaviourist psychology was gradual; the actual founding of the Behaviourist school dates from 1913, when John B. Watson (born 1878), then professor of experimental and comparative psychology at the Johns Hopkins University, Baltimore, Maryland, published two papers entitled *Psychology as the Behaviourist Views It*, and *Image and Affection in Behaviour*. These he followed in 1914 with a full-length statement of his doctrine in *Behaviourism, An Introduction to Comparative Psychology*.

The word Behaviourism connotes both a psychological theory and a psychological method. As a method it consists of a scientific study of the behaviour of all living things—plant, animal and human—conducted on laboratory lines in precisely the same manner as any other investigation in physical science.

Facts of behaviour are what matter to the Behaviourist. He collects them, compares them, analyses them, reduces them to statistics, and draws conclusions only from absolutely verified data. He conducts numerous objective experiments to reveal new facts, but refuses to have anything to do with introspection, for this procedure, he maintains, can produce only theories, not facts. As Dr. Watson himself has said, " Psychology, even to exist longer, not to speak of becoming a true natural science, must bury subjective subject matter, introspective methods and present (psychological) terminology."

Behaviourism is thus entirely occupied with physiological data; it deals only with phenomena which can be observed and experimented upon. In the whole long history of psychology no one has ever been able to observe the soul, mind, consciousness—call it what you please—and the Behaviourist has been no more successful in this respect than other men. He therefore denies that mind exists, or rather holds that it can be entirely explained as a series of physiological processes. These processes he holds are based on stimulus and response.

Man, like any other animal, is a physiological machine, working on the principle of the reflex action. He starts life with a few inborn reactions to a few stimuli—no one has yet determined exactly how many—and every moment of his life is engaged in weaving a more and more complicated behaviour pattern on the basis of his original reflexes.

STIMULUS AND RESPONSE

Human behaviour therefore must be studied from birth to death, nor can a single action between those events be left out of consideration. The aim of the Behaviourist is to collect such a complete dossier of information concerning the human animal that, no matter what the age of the animal, the environment or the circumstances, provided a stimulus be known he can at once and infallibly tell exactly what response must be made. Or vice versa, given the response, he can equally assert what the stimulus must have been which produced it.

At birth, says the Behaviourist, the human infant emerges into the world already responsive to a few external stimuli. For example, a loud sound or the sudden withdrawal of support causes fear in the new-born babe. No other stimulus can cause fear at this age, but these two stimuli invariably do, and the response to them is automatic; the child cries out, catches its breath or otherwise demonstrates the emotion of fear.

On this basis of a few original, innate, unlearned stimuli and responses the complicated behaviour-pattern of a mature adult is built up over the years by a continuous process of conditioning reflexes.

Just as Pavlov induced salivation in his dogs by the ticking of a metronome in close association with the production of food, so in the growing child new stimuli, by association with original stimuli, evoke the responses called out by the latter Similarly new responses to original, and later to associated stimuli, are learned. Behaviourism is thus seen to be a psychology of associationism, only in this case it is not ideas which are associated, but stimuli and responses.

A sensation, says the Behaviourist, is a response to stimulus by the nerves; emotion is a response from the glands or the internal organs. Memory is a habit acquired by the nerves. Thought is response in words.

The process of conditioning reflexes proceeds with extraordinary rapidity, particularly in the domain of the emotions, and as may well be imagined is very largely incidental, or even accidental. No parent, for example, would deliberately teach a child to be afraid of the dark, of a golliwog, or of a dog. Yet as every parent can testify, numerous young children are afraid of the dark or of such objects as golliwogs or dogs.

This means that darkness, a golliwog, or a dog have somehow become associated with one of the original stimuli exciting fear, and the response to the original stimulus has become attached to the new stimulus.

In the same way that responses can become associated with stimuli, so they can be dis-associated from them. This process is called unconditioning, and as may be imagined it has generally to be done deliberately. It is in this respect particularly that Behaviourism has been of very great practical value, particularly in the training of young children.

Suppose, for example, a child has conceived an irrational fear of dogs. The Behaviourist, who has accumulated a vast mass of information concerning infant and child behaviour, and can therefore speak with authority, will tell you that it is quite useless to pick that child up and set him by a dog and tell him not to be silly, or to conquer his fear of the " nice little friendly doggy." It is equally futile to play with the dog oneself in front of the child, or to tell the child how good and useful dogs are in protecting the house from burglars and tramps. The only method which can produce the desired result is that of deconditioning the reflex linking fear with dogs.

DO WE THINK IN WORDS?

This is done by so arranging the child's environment that a dog is brought into it, at first in a position of complete inconspicuousness, and very gradually to one of prominence. If this is done skilfully, the presence of the dog at no stage evokes fear. The child learns to tolerate dogs for the simple reason that the response of fear to that stimulus is prevented and in time fades out altogether.

The fact that the stimuli and responses known by the infant at birth are quite few, has caused

MONDIALE

BEST CARRIAGE OF THE BODY FOR CARRYING WEIGHTS

Statuettes produced from photographs of various tests. On the right is a very bad position. In carrying weights the body should be so held that the centre of gravity lies over the middle of the foot.

the Behaviourist to give up all idea of innate instincts. He says that most of what is usually called instinctive behaviour is really the result of conditioning.

That is one point in which Behaviourism differs radically from other psychologies. The second is that the Behaviourist, true to his creed that all mental processes are built up physiologically out of stimulus and response, holds that language, thought and imagination are in no way different from other mental processes, but are built up in exactly similar fashion. They are all behaviour, the result of habit-formation due to conditioned reflexes.

Just as sensation is a response by the nerves, and emotion a response from the glands or other organs, to external stimuli, so speech is a verbal response, and thought and imagination are forms of silent or repressed speech. This raises the interesting question, do we always think in words? The Behaviourist answers: No, not always; we may think in terms of objects and acts. Words are only conditioned substitutes for objects and acts, and in certain types of thought we deal only with the originals and do without the substitutes.

The Behaviourist does not confine himself entirely to individual psychology: he applies his theory to society, to nations and to races. Only here definite results are much more difficult to obtain and take much longer to arrive at. The problems are all so much more complicated.

Given a certain stimulus, say the threat of war, how will a society, a nation, a race respond? The answer must be based on verified facts, and these may take years or generations to accumulate; and in such course of time the facts themselves may alter. But the Behaviourist believes that ultimately answers can be given to all such problems.

PURPOSE IN LIFE

The Behaviourist rejects the concept of instinct; the hormic psychologist bases his theory on the reality and vitality of the instincts. Hormic is a word derived from the Greek *horme*, meaning urge, drive or impulse. The hormic psychologist sees purpose in the activity of all organic life, and finds this purpose to spring from an urge or impulse set in motion by innate instincts which are handed down to the organism from generation to generation.

The instincts to be found in man have been variously named, numbered and grouped. Some psychologists have discovered nearly forty. What may perhaps be regarded as the standard list has been compiled by Professor William McDougall (born 1871), an Englishman who for many years has been teaching in America, and who may be regarded as the founder and chief exponent of this school of thought. His list of thirteen major instincts, to which must be added a few minor ones, is as follows :—

Parental	Herd
Combative	Self-Assertion
Curious	Submission
Hunger	Mating
Repulsion	Acquisitive
Escape	Constructive
Appeal	

The instincts are not to be regarded (as the instincts so often are in popular thought) as " blind." On the contrary, they are the mainsprings of purpose; they are fundamental urges directed by intelligence towards very definite goals. Because hormic psychology thus bases its doctrine on the purposefulness of all mental life, it is often described as " Purposivism."

McDougall has defined an instinct as " an inherited or innate psycho-physical disposition which determines its possessor to perceive, and pay attention to, objects of a certain class, to experience an emotional excitement of a particular quality upon perceiving such an object, and to act in regard to it in a particular manner, or, at least, to experience an impulse to such action."

It will be seen that this definition falls into three parts. First, there is the instinct itself, an inherited or inborn natural tendency which compels attention to objects; second, this tendency sets up a particular kind of emotional excitement; and following that there is, third, action or urge to action of a character predetermined by the instinct and its accompanying emotion.

It is important not to confuse emotion with instinct. In everyday speech we often do so; we regularly talk, for example, of " the instinct of fear." Fear is not an instinct; it is an emotional excitement set up by an instinct, and not necessarily always by the same instinct, though the majority of the instincts have related to them their own special, or primary, emotions.

Fear, for example, is most regularly excited by the instinct to flight (escape), but as all parents will realize, the parental instinct often arouses this emotion. So may the instincts of repulsion, submission, or hunger. In fact, there is scarcely a single instinct which is not capable of arousing, to a greater or lesser degree, the emotion of fear.

At the same time, while emotion must be clearly distinguished from instinct, and recognized as the second part of the instinctive process, its importance must not be regarded as secondary; on the contrary, it is fundamental. The instinct itself has not sufficient force to initiate action; it is the emotion which supplies the dynamic.

PHYSICAL MECHANISM OF THE INSTINCT

If the instinctive process were absolutely fixed and invariable in its operation, man could never have risen above the animals, nor the animals to their present degrees of intelligence. But it is not invariable; it is capable of modification, and the hormic psychologist endeavours to show how all forms of human activity, no matter how complicated or sublime, are the result of modified applications of the drive initiated by instinct.

The physical mechanism of the instinct consists of four parts : (i) the sense organ and the nerves connecting it with the brain, (ii) the brain, (iii) the nerves linking the brain with the internal organs of the body and the ductless glands, and (iv) the nerves from the brain to the muscles which are involved in outward behaviour.

Parallel with these physical processes are mental processes. The activity of the sense organ and the nerves connecting it with the brain involves perception; that of the nerves between brain and internal organs (including the ductless glands) involves emotion; and that of the nerves from the brain to the muscles involves action or tendency to action.

INSTINCTIVE REACTION

Emotion is invariable; perception and action are variable. A terrified dog or a frightened child rushes madly from the dreaded object; an adult, though terrified, will in many instances stand his ground and meet the situation with courage and wisdom. He perceives the situation differently and has learnt to modify his purely instinctive reaction.

An instinct in itself is neither good nor bad; it is the way in which its urge is employed which determines the goodness or badness (i.e., usefulness or uselessness) of behaviour. Similarly, emotion is in itself neither good nor bad. As we all know, there can be righteous anger; and fear is not always ignoble.

Just as the Behaviourist holds that innumerable reflexes are built up from a few simple ones by conditioning, so the hormic psychologist holds that innumerable reactions to instinct are built up on the basis of the original ones. Both psychologies believe in the principle of association, the Behaviourist linking stimuli and responses, the hormic psychologist instincts and reactions. These, the latter says, become associated either by contiguity or similarity.

PART PLAYED BY INTELLIGENCE

In the first instance new reactions are created because an original and a different stimulus are experienced together, in the second when a different stimulus is markedly like the first. Also—and here the hormic psychologist breaks clean away from the Behaviourist—he holds that in man intelligence plays a constant and vital part in modifying reaction and consequently behaviour.

This explains in part why the behaviour of man is so different from and superior to that of the social insects. Man is born very immature, and so intelligence is able greatly to modify instinctive behaviour; a bee or an ant, on the other hand, is born practically

THE LADDER OF INTELLIGENCE
From the response to stimuli by amœba to the transmission of thought by radio.

mature, with its habit-tracks already canalized, so to speak, and its behaviour pattern already hardened into an almost invariable system.

Every now and then lurid stories showing man dominated and enslaved by a race of organized insects are published; and doubtless some readers ask themselves whether such a state of affairs can ever come to pass. The answer is No; because whereas man's behaviour is plastic and therefore adaptable to changing circumstances, the insect's is pre-ordained and is practically unable to meet an emergency.

MODIFYING INSTINCTIVE IMPULSES

It is obvious that the outlook of the hormic psychologist is absolutely antithetical to that of the Behaviourist. The latter denies the existence of instinct, the former derives all mental life from it. The Behaviourist allows man a conscious mental life, it is true, but no mind, let alone purpose; for the hormic psychologist all life, animal as well as human, is full of purpose. Even the lowliest organisms have purpose, though doubtless this is involuntary. There is no contradiction in talking of involuntary purpose; examples of it are taking place in human beings at every moment of their lives.

We have no control over our digestive processes; it is quite outside our will that the body secretes fluids in the glands, and releases those fluids at appropriate times. Yet this takes place with the very definite purpose of achieving digestion.

Yet antithetical though Behaviourism and hormic psychology may be in theory, there is strong similarity between them in other respects. To begin with, they are both eminently practical, in that they are based on study of actual behaviour. In 1912 McDougall published a book entitled *Psychology : The Study of Behaviour*, in which he defined psychology as " the positive science of the behaviour of living things." It was not until he concluded that the distinctive feature of all such behaviour was " the manifestation of purpose or the striving to achieve an end " that he parted company with the Behaviourists.

Secondly, both psychologies are genetic in character, that is, they begin with origins and trace behaviour from its simplest and lowliest elements right up to its most complex and ordered forms.

Both, too, are comparative psychologies. Each finds in the lower animals exactly the same types of processes manifested as in man.

Each sees in human behaviour the ultimate compromise between the individual and his environment, though this fact is far more stressed by the hormic psychologist than by the Behaviourist. But to admit the conditioned reflex is to admit compromise; all stimuli and responses not innate must be supplied by the individual's environment, which includes the society in which he moves.

For the Behaviourist, this compromise is arrived at as a result of physiological processes. The hormic psychologist sees it as the result of an eternal and continuous struggle between man's fundamental instincts and the demands of society. All society, every civilization, must be built by human endeavour, the urge to which is supplied by the instincts. But the moment the individual ceases to be purely individualistic and joins with his fellows in any form of society, be it only a family, he finds that his instinctive impulses must be curbed or modified. Some have to be in part suppressed, the activity of others must be diverted into other channels, a third group must be encouraged and stimulated.

If, as some writers do, we group the instincts under the three heads of Self, Sex and Social, it is clear that in order for society to exist the unbridled urge of the sex instincts must be repressed, the self or purely individualist instincts must be (to borrow a word from psycho-analysis) sublimated, that is, diverted towards less selfish forms of expression, while the social instincts need careful cultivation.

CONTRIBUTIONS TO KNOWLEDGE

This is putting very crudely what is in reality an extremely complicated proposition, but perhaps a broad generalization will best serve here. It will not, presumably, be assumed from it that the sex instincts must be entirely suppressed, or that the instinctive emotions connected with sex do not play an important part in the building of any society.

Both Behaviourism and hormic psychology can be and have been applied to problems of everyday life. Any intensive study of human behaviour scientifically conducted must result in knowledge that will prove of use in the direction of human behaviour. The contribution of Behaviourism is mainly, though not entirely, limited to problems of infancy and childhood. Hormic psychology tends rather to make clearer social problems.

DE COU (FROM EWING GALLOWAY, N.Y.)

GUARDIAN OF DEPARTED SPIRITS

Totem poles have a clannish significance, or deal with tribal history. The white races use sculpture and painting as media of artistic expression, whereas American Indians, Maoris and others use wood.

FREUD AND PSYCHO-ANALYSIS

Hormic psychology presents a picture of civilized society as a working compromise between the primitive instinctive urges of man and the rules of any social organization. Psycho-analysis reveals what it has cost man to make this compromise.

No other modern psychological theory has received a tithe of the attention devoted to psycho-analysis. None has had more enthusiastic adherents or more bitter opponents. Psycho-analysis has been welcomed in some quarters with fervour amounting to idolatry; it has been execrated in others as the foulest body of doctrine that ever proceeded from the mind of man. In one instance at least it was banned for years by the entire body of medical and scientific opinion throughout a whole country. It is still very incompletely understood by the majority of both its friends and its enemies.

In view of such a state of affairs it will be well to begin by endeavouring to find out what the word psycho-analysis actually stands for. The answer should make us very wary of pronouncing a hasty judgment on this much discussed subject, for we find at once that psycho-analysis may be defined in at least three ways.

First, it is a method of medical treatment for one group of nervous disorders—those called in medical language the *transference neuroses*, and consisting of three types of neurosis, the *anxiety-hysteria*, the *conversion-hysteria*, and the *obsessional neurosis*. This is the original and most restricted sense of the word.

Second, it is this method adapted for general enquiry into the nature of mind, and particularly of the lower, or unconscious, depths of the mind. Third, it is the scientific theory of the nature of mind evolved by Dr. Sigmund Freud in explanation of the facts observed and the conclusions arrived at by practice of the clinical methods mentioned above. In this sense it has been described by Dr. Ernest Jones, the leading British psycho-analyst, as "practically synonymous with 'the science of the unconscious,'" and Freud himself has stated that "Psycho-analysis aims at and achieves nothing more than the discovery of the unconscious in mental life."

To these three definitions there ought perhaps to be added a fourth, for of recent years the theory and technique of psycho-analysis have been applied to explain human behaviour in various fields of social activity and at various periods of history. In particular, the origin of many social practices and customs has been investigated psycho-analytically. Freud himself has written on *Totem and Tabu*, while his disciples have made exhaustive researches in the fields of folk-lore, mythology, legend, and literature.

UNDESIRABLE THOUGHTS

There is little doubt that most people think of psycho-analysis chiefly as a theory, though they are probably aware that there is a method attached to that theory. According to Freud the importance of these two aspects ought to be reversed. "As a science," he has declared, "psycho-analysis is characterized by the methods with which it works, not by the subject matter with which it deals."

This is a hard saying, because undoubtedly it is against the theory of psycho-analysis, or at least against certain parts of that theory, that opposition has chiefly been directed. Had psycho-analysis remained simply a medical treatment for nervous disorders very little would have been heard of it, at any rate outside professional circles.

What, then, is this theory, and why has it aroused such opposition? To begin with, Freud postulates three groups of mental processes, conscious, preconscious and unconscious. The conscious mental processes are those of which one is fully aware at any given moment, the preconscious those which lie latent on the fringe of consciousness and can become conscious at any time, the unconscious those of which one is not aware and which under ordinary circumstances cannot become conscious.

This postulate is often represented diagrammatically by three layers, consciousness being shown as the top one, preconsciousness the second, and unconsciousness the third and by far the deepest layer. This representation, and the name "depth psychology" which has been applied to psycho-analysis, must be understood as purely illustrative; mental processes are in no way subject to limitations of space, and the layers have nothing whatever to do with the area of the physical brain.

The mind can be acted upon either from without or within. External stimuli transmitted through the sense organs from without, or instinctive agencies from within, stir the mind to activity. All mental acts begin in the unconscious; some go on developing until they rise to consciousness, others get no further than preconsciousness, while a third group remains buried in unconsciousness. How far a thought gets depends on what amount of resistance it meets as it develops.

The mind cannot prevent the entry of thoughts into itself, but it can and does exercise a strict control over admission of thoughts to its preconscious and conscious areas. Freud calls the mental agency which thus picks and chooses thoughts the *censor*, or more fully the *endopsychic censor*, and holds that its main activity is directed to preventing undesirable thoughts from emerging out of the unconscious into the preconscious. Such thoughts are said to be *repressed*; because any attempt on their part to rise into consciousness meets with *resistance*.

There is also another form of repression. In the early years of life innate impulses in the child come into sharp conflict with the laws of organized society. The child mind accepts those laws by thrusting back its unlawful impulses into the unconscious.

The phrase "undesirable thoughts" must not be taken to be synonymous with unpleasant or immoral thoughts; the term denotes simply thoughts which, if allowed to rise into consciousness, would conflict with thoughts already there. This warning is all the more necessary because undoubtedly many of the thoughts kept repressed in the unconscious area of the mind are what society regards as unpleasant or immoral.

NATURE OF THE MIND

So far we have dealt with the structure of the mind; it is necessary also to inquire into its nature. Its basis, says Freud, is an impersonal, unconscious well of mental energy, made up largely of primitive instinctive urges. This basis he calls the *id*, or "it."

Quite early in life that part of the *id*, drawn from all three regions of the mind, which has to establish relations between the individual and the outside world of people and things, becomes pervaded with a sense of personality. It has been named the *ego* (Latin for "I"), because it represents the conscious self.

As one might expect, the *ego* part of the mind learns that in the world with which it has to deal certain things are done or not done; in other words, that society imposes rules. It accepts those rules, and consequently begins to frown upon certain of the more primitive impulses of the *id*.

CONSCIENCE

As development proceeds, and it becomes more and more apparent to the *ego* that the *id* must be kept firmly under control, the former, so to speak, details a portion of itself to act as sentry and to warn it whenever undesirable impulses from the *id* threaten to force their way into consciousness. This sentry is called the *super-ego*; and it is this which exercises, at the bidding of the *ego*, censorship over the entry of thoughts from the unconscious to the conscious.

The *super-ego* corresponds to what ordinary people call conscience, and is responsible for the feelings of guilt we all experience concerning acts or thoughts which are contrary to accepted religious, moral, ethical and social laws. Man is unique among the animals in developing a *super-ego*.

Why must this strict censorship and strong pressure be maintained against the content of the unconscious? If we are not aware of what is in that area of the mind, if the content of the unconscious cannot ordinarily rise to consciousness, why is it necessary so perpetually to guard against it?

Because the thoughts, ideas and impulses in the unconscious, though latent, are active, and are perpetually endeavouring to force their way into consciousness. In spite of all the precautions of the *ego*, they succeed in a variety of ways, notably in dreams (including day-dreams and reveries), and in the slips of the tongue and of the pen and the odd little forgettings which one experiences so regularly in everyday life.

RELIEVING THE TENSION

The active, or dynamic nature of the unconscious is due to its origin in the instincts. Here Freud's thought is closely parallel with that of the hormic psychologist, and antithetical to that of the Behaviourist. He distinguishes clearly between a physiological stimulus, a mental stimulus and a stimulus of instinctual origin.

"A stimulus of instinctual origin," he says, "does not arise in the outside world but from within the organism itself." "An external stimulus . . . acts as a single impact, so that it can be discharged by a single appropriate action," but "An instinct . . . never acts as a momentary impact, but always as a constant force," and "as it makes its attack not from without but from within the organism, it follows that no flight can avail against it."

UNDERWOOD AND UNDERWOOD

WITCH DOCTOR OF NEW GUINEA

Freud derives all religion from the superstitious practices of primitive races. A witch doctor usually exercises priestly functions.

So we have this persistent, tremendous pressure upwards from the instincts into the unconscious countered by an equally persistent resistance downwards from the *super-ego*, the most moral part of our minds. Obviously this is a situation which will give rise to acute mental tension and strain whenever the instinctual needs cannot be given adequate satisfaction within the framework of rules which society has laid down for its own protection.

The service which psycho-analysis has rendered to humanity is that it has discovered a method which gives access to the unconscious and can in some cases relieve the tension and strain found therein. It has been justly claimed for this young science that it can be distinguished "from the other branches of psychology by the fact that it takes cognizance of the causes and the effects of mental suffering."

Freud did not, strictly speaking, discover the unconscious area of the mind. The existence of this had been at least suggested a century before his day. But he is the first man systematically and scientifically to explore it.

Its material, as we have seen, is largely supplied by the instincts. It contains, not only repressed thoughts but also inherited urges and tendencies handed down to us through countless ages. Freud does not attempt to say how many instincts there are. He has proposed the classification of primary instincts into two groups, the *self-preservative* or *ego* instincts, and the *sexual* instincts, but he regards this classification more or less as a makeshift. Psycho-analysis so far has largely concentrated upon the second group because it has been found "with really surprising regularity" that mental strain and suffering, and neurotic disorders, are the result of repression of sexual impulses.

INSTITUTE OF INDUSTRIAL PSYCHOLOGY

PSYCHOLOGY IN THE FACTORY (1)

This girl was uncomfortably seated opposite neither polishing buff. Polishing "soap" on the protective curtains was occasionally blown into her face.

OPPOSITION TO PSYCHO-ANALYSIS

It is because of this finding and of the nature of the sexual life of man which Freud has disclosed that the bulk of the opposition to psycho-analysis has arisen. For Freud has developed a theory of sexuality which has been widely and bitterly resented. In particular his belief in infantile sexuality has aroused fierce opposition.

"It is not at all true," he says, "that the sexual impulse enters into the child at puberty, as the devils in the gospel entered into the swine. The child has his sexual impulses and activities from the beginning, he brings them with him into the world and from these the so-called normal sexuality of adults emerges by a significant development through manifold stages."

It is at once evident from this statement that Freud's conception of sexuality is very different from that of the man in the street, and indeed from that of many scientists. Before his time it had always been universally agreed that the young child was quite devoid of sexual impulse, which it first began to experience after the onset of puberty. Freud utterly denies this, and consequently has been accused of defiling the age-old conception of the innocence and purity of infancy. This accusation is hardly fair.

CAUSE OF NEUROTIC DISORDERS

According to Freud, the sexual instinct of a normal adult is a very complicated one which has to be gradually built up of a number of components. If, as frequently happens, these components fail to merge harmoniously in an individual, then strains and tensions and in bad cases neurotic disorders are bound to ensue.

The infant, says Freud, is born with sexual impulses. These do not, as in mature adults, centre round the genital organs and the sexual act. They are first manifested in what are called oral activities, that is, those connected with the mouth, sucking, swallowing, and somewhat later, biting, being the chief.

INSTITUTE OF INDUSTRIAL PSYCHOLOGY

PSYCHOLOGY IN THE FACTORY (2)

These new benches enabled the girl to sit comfortably at buffing, and obliged her to stand for the minor process of glossing. Seats were adjustable in height and distance from the bench, dust was extructed by fans, and finished work covered. Output was increased by twelve per cent.

Why are infants so readily and regularly pacified by a " dummy teat "? Because the action of sucking in itself, without any reference to food, gives a sense of pleasure which satisfies an innate sexual impulse. Why do so many young children suck their thumbs, and why is this habit so hard to break? For precisely the same reason. Similarly all young children pass through a stage when biting their toys is their chief occupation.

BREAKING OF HABIT

The breaking of habit raises a question of vital importance. Any thwarting of impulse, that is, arrest of instinctual desire without provision of an alternative avenue of satisfaction induces the feeling of frustration, which in its turn provokes feelings of hatred and rage.

Anyone who has observed the behaviour of infants and very young children knows that their emotional experiences are extremely violent and quite uncontrolled. There is nothing in the behaviour of a normal adult to equal an infant's rage; he howls, screams, beats his fists and kicks his legs in unrestrained passion, and the paroxysm continues—unless attention is diverted—until exhaustion reduces the child to somnolence.

FRUSTRATION AND FIXATION

Constant frustration embitters the child mind, with the result that anger—which in itself is neither good nor bad—is increasingly employed in useless, and therefore energy-wasting and harmful ways. Hence the vital importance from birth of wise training of children.

Frustration may lead also to what is called *fixation.* By fixation is meant arrest of normal development at a stage before complete development is reached. This may occur at almost any stage, but is most frequent at the later period, called *narcissism,* to which reference will be made in due course.

The first stage in sexual development is called *auto-erotism,* that is, self-love. The child finds its gratification of sexual impulse in its own body, from what are called the *erotogenic zones,* that is, those parts of the body which give particular satisfaction to the sexual impulse. Among these zones the genital organs are numbered, but at this stage they play only a relatively insignificant part.

INSTITUTE OF INDUSTRIAL PSYCHOLOGY

COMFORT AT WORK

The comfortable working position obtained by properly designed benches and adjustable chairs.

As we have seen, the first of the erotogenic zones to be affected is the mouth, or more especially the lips. This is because of the intimate relationship between sucking and the taking of food by the infant. Parents take little exception to this manifestation of sexual impulse (unless it begins to demonstrate itself in an objectionable way, as for example thumb-sucking), because they themselves have never outgrown it. With few exceptions, people find sexual satisfaction in kissing throughout their lives.

The next stage in sexual development is, to adult minds, far less pleasant. In the auto-erotic stage the infant, while finding gratification in its own body, does not realize that body as its own. The sense of individuality has not yet emerged. This is evidenced by the fact, which all parents know, that the child in learning to speak never refers to himself as "I." He always says: "Baby does this," or "Baby likes that."

CONSCIOUS SELF-LOVE

But before long comes the period of self-discovery. The child learns to distinguish its own body from external objects, and to love it with a personal love. This is the stage of *narcissism,* or conscious self-love. (The name is taken from the classical myth of Narcissus, the beautiful youth who grew so enamoured of his own loveliness that he spent his life gazing at his reflection in a pool, until he pined away, and was transformed by the gods into a flower.)

Upon discovery of his body as a lovable object the child naturally begins to explore it, and equally naturally finds his way to other of the erotogenic zones. This results in what is called the *anal-sadistic* stage.

This portmanteau word signifies a stage at which great interest is taken in those parts of the body (the anus in particular) which are concerned with the excretory functions, and much pleasure in the production of excrement. It is marked in behaviour by love of noise, of racketing about and often of cruelty (sadism means love of being cruel to others).

REPRESSED IMPULSES

It is clear that impulse and training are liable to come into very sharp conflict during the anal-sadistic period. Adults regard excrement with aversion, and the human excretory processes as ones to be performed in strictest privacy. They go so far as to dislike being seen going to or coming from the place of performance, and they utterly ban the subject in all polite conversation.

To the young child this attitude is quite foreign and at first utterly incomprehensible. He regards his excrement with a curious interest (is it not a product of the wonderful body he is just discovering?), he finds the excretory processes both satisfying and pleasurable, and consequently he prolongs them to the utmost limit, talks about them freely, considers going to the lavatory an important and highly enjoyable event—as indeed it is to him.

Society, in the persons of his parents, generally begins quickly to frown upon these—to them—

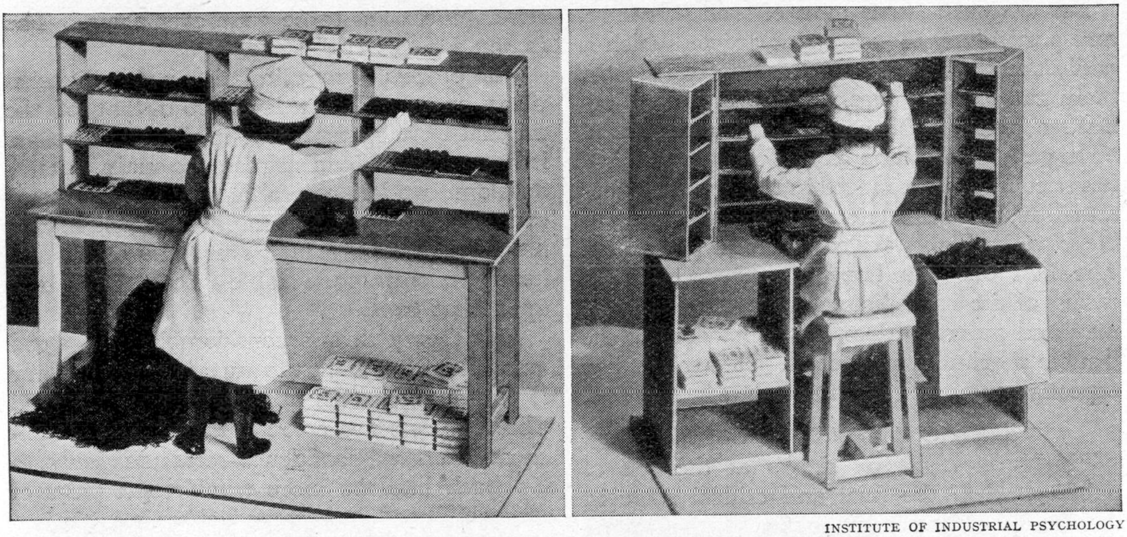

INSTITUTE OF INDUSTRIAL PSYCHOLOGY

REDUCING MENTAL AND PHYSICAL FATIGUE

With the old style of chocolate packing bench the worker had to stand and was continually stretching to reach the extreme ends of the racks. The different types of chocolates were placed haphazardly. With the improved type of bench (right) the worker can reach all the racks while seated and also use both hands.

most unpleasant and disgusting traits, and a period of conflict ensues. According to Freud, the nature and duration of this conflict largely determines character in after life.

If the adult point of view is readily accepted by the child, the conflict is slight; if it is accepted only as a result of continual threats and punishment, serious consequences may ensue, for the impulses have not been satisfied. They have been repressed; and repressed impulses always spell danger.

WHEN CHARACTER IS FORMED

It is not necessary that these consequences be immediately evident; as a general rule they are not, though the trained eye of the psycho-analyst would detect indications of their presence. The repressed impulses are buried in the unconscious; they remain dynamic, and often emerge in terrifying form at the age of puberty.

It is probably during this period of conflict that the *super-ego* comes to its full stature. Habits that give complete satisfaction to instinctual impulse have not merely to be given up but also regarded with disgust and aversion. They have therefore to be thrust deeply into the unconscious and kept firmly there.

The auto-erotic and the anal-sadistic stages are passed through during the first five years of life. This period the Freudians, in common with other schools of psychology, regard as of vital importance. It is commonly agreed that the main lines of character are laid down in these years, and that errors in treatment of children during early childhood cannot be remedied later save by special psychological technique.

This is a terrifying dictum, but its truth appears established; and one need look no further for an utterly convincing argument that all intending parents should be thoroughly trained in the science of parenthood before they are allowed to marry.

Public opinion has not yet reached the point of demanding that such training be made obligatory, but the rapidly increasing popularity of books and magazine articles dealing with children's behaviour problems is evidence of a widespread and deeply felt desire on the part of parents to inform themselves upon what is now generally realized to be a most intricate and difficult business.

LEAVING THE CAUSE UNTOUCHED

Such books and articles, when written by persons who know what they are talking about (unfortunately this is not always the case), serve a valuable purpose. They awaken people to the reality and the magnitude of a most important problem; they inspire a desire for further knowledge, and in many instances they prevent the perpetuation of gross errors in dealing with children: but they are not, and cannot be, any real substitute for systematic training in motherhood and fatherhood.

For obvious reasons most of such literature, and particularly the magazine article, which is easily the most widely read, has to deal in the main rather with cure than with prevention. But, so psychologists are almost unanimous in telling us, by the time any behaviour problem has become so pronounced as to compel anxious attention, its complete cure is virtually impossible, save by highly skilled technical procedure. The best one can hope for otherwise is an easing of the immediate situation, though this may and generally does leave the cause of the trouble absolutely untouched. It is rather like expecting a stomach sedative to cure indigestion.

EMOTIONAL DISTURBANCES

This is most clearly shown at the age of puberty, when the final and critical stage in the fusion of the components of the sexual instinct is reached.

Many thoughtful parents dread the period of pubertal development in their children. They know from their reading and observation that the profound physical and mental changes which take place between the ages of approximately twelve and sixteen are frequently accompanied by equally profound emotional disturbances which very often give rise to acute behaviour problems.

They know also that the nature of these disturbances and problems cannot be predicted beforehand, that they are not exactly alike in any two children, that they are apparently quite capricious, and that therefore no line of treatment can be thought out in advance or carried through consistently during the period. The child will pass from one mood to another for no apparent reason, and the swiftly changing moods will resemble one another in nothing save that all are equally unreasonable.

Psycho-analysis declares that the psychological problems of the pubertal stage cannot be even understood, much less dealt with, without reference to the earlier stages of sexual development. That is to say, to understand a child's perverse behaviour at fourteen one must go back ten years and analyse what happened at four. This is a feat beyond most parents.

After the auto-erotic and the narcissistic periods there follows until the onset of puberty a period of latency during which no progress in sexual development is observable. After puberty, apparently the whole of the previous development has to be gone over again. The reason for this is obscure.

The process of recapitulation naturally takes place on a different level from that of the original development, but it closely resembles it because, so Freud argues, the main lines of development laid down in the earlier phases cannot be departed from. The track having been laid, so to speak, every train, whether luxury express or humble goods, must run upon that track.

This theory throws considerable light upon many hitherto puzzling features in the behaviour of young adolescents. It explains why a child who for years has acted with initiative, intelligence and self-confidence seems suddenly to slip back into the more troublesome ways of early childhood, to become lacking in initiative, helplessly dependent, intolerably self-centred and quite uncontrolled in temper.

It explains why intelligent interests are dropped for futile ones; why so many children at about fourteen develop what is called a "lavatory mind" and delight in coarseness and vulgarity.

But puberty is not merely a matter of recapitulation of development; it marks also the final and vital advance to adult sexuality. The sexual impulse becomes centred on the genital organs and linked to the biological fact of reproduction. Until this stage the child has been satisfied with himself as the object of his sexual impulses; now he is urged to reach out beyond himself to find in the external world objects for his love and desire.

THE ŒDIPUS COMPLEX

He naturally fixes first on objects in his immediate environment, and generally on members of his own family. As a rule these are his parents. From this arises the famous Œdipus complex, as it is called, the (usually) unconscious desire of the child to do away with the parent of his (her) own sex and possess the person of the parent of the opposite sex.

The name Œdipus complex is derived from a story of classical mythology. Œdipus was the son of Laius, king of Thebes in Greece. An oracle foretold that he would kill his father and marry his mother. To avert this dual tragedy, his father had Œdipus put out to die on the hills, as was the ancient Greek custom with deformed or unwanted children. To make assurance doubly sure he drove a spike through the infant's feet, hence the name Œdipus, which means " swollen-footed."

But the child escaped death, and was brought up by the king of a neighbouring state. For years he remained in ignorance of the prophecy concerning him, until it was revealed to him by a second oracle.

PREY TO DESPAIR

Œdipus was so horrified by the thought that he would slay his father and marry his mother that he left his adoptive parents and set out to seek his fortune in foreign parts. But his destiny was not to be evaded. He met his father, and, ignorant of who he was, quarrelled with and slew him.

Later he came to Thebes, and by reading aright an obscure oracle rid the city of a terrible plague that was devastating it. The grateful citizens made him their king and gave him the widowed queen (his mother) in marriage.

The two lived together happily for years, four children being born to them. Then the awful truth was revealed, and the rest of the story is of unmitigated disaster. Jocasta, the queen, hanged herself, Œdipus thrust out his own eyes and lived a prey to misfortune and despair.

There was some mitigation of his suffering in his last days. According to Sophocles, who wrote *Œdipus Tyrannus* and *Œdipus at Colonus*, Œdipus felt towards the end that he had atoned for his crimes.

RESOLVING THE COMPLEX

Freud regards the Œdipus complex as central and fundamental to his theory. " It is," says Dr. Ernest Jones, " the most characteristic and important finding in all psycho-analysis . . . all other conclusions of psycho-analytical theory are grouped around this complex, and by the truth of this finding psycho-analysis stands or falls."

The child's character and temperament will depend very largely on how he resolves this complex. If he can come to regard his father (or a girl her mother) as a hero, an ideal, then all will be well; his feeling of hostility will be eliminated, and at the same time his affection for his mother (or father, in the case of a girl) will become a normal affection instead of a sexual desire.

Why does this Œdipus complex arise? Because the child feels that the parents share something—knowledge, experience, the secret of life—which he does not possess and from possession of which he is deliberately excluded by them. Therefore his desires urge him to part them, to rid himself of his rival and to share this secret with the parent of the opposite sex.

He imagines that the same hostility he feels towards his parents is felt by them towards him, and that as he wishes harm to them so they wish harm to him. This gives rise to terrible fears and fantasies. Of course direct expression of his wishes towards his parents is repressed, and repression (always, according to Freud, the result of fear) has to find its outlet in fantastic imaginings, which may in later life result in neurotic disorders.

RISCHGITZ COLLECTION

ŒDIPUS AND THE SPHINX

The term Œdipus complex in psycho-analysis is derived from the story of Œdipus in mythology.

What may seem to be a disproportionate amount of space has been devoted to psycho-analytic theory. This has been done quite deliberately, for several reasons.

First, because of the extraordinary interest the theory has aroused in every civilized country throughout the world. Second, because there are so many misconceptions about it, and third, because there appears to be a widespread impression that it is a theory which can be stated (or dismissed) in a brief sentence or two.

Nothing could be further from the truth. Psycho-analytic theory is both abstruse and subtle; what has been stated above is the merest sketch of its main outlines, which gives no idea of its almost endless ramifications.

Owing to the impalpable nature of its

INSTITUTE OF INDUSTRIAL PSYCHOLOGY

TEST OF MANUAL DEXTERITY

A number of pegs have to be gathered up from the table in one hand and then inserted as quickly as possible into the holes in the board. The score is obtained by combining the time taken to complete the whole operation, and the number of pegs dropped during the process.

subject-matter, psycho-analytic theory must necessarily suffer from any attempt to simplify it, and much misrepresentation of it has arisen from this cause.

The other, and more potent cause of misrepresentation is the hostility which it has aroused. As will be seen from the foregoing account, it is a theory which cannot be regarded with indifference. One must either accept it with open arms or regard it with profound revulsion.

To some people it illumines with a great and penetrating light the problem of human conduct and behaviour; in others it arouses the strongest feelings of opposition to what they regard as an utterly foul view of human nature.

The usual objection to Freudianism is that it is " all sex," that Freud attributes to man thoughts and impulses too repulsive and degrading to be even accepted as possible. This opposition aims its sharpest darts at the Œdipus complex, recently described in an authoritative analysis of the Freudian theory as " no more than a piece of purely fanciful anthropology," and frequently referred to in far less complimentary terms even than that.

MANY POINTS STILL OBSCURE

Psycho-analytic theory will continue to be a subject of dispute for many years. As Freud himself is always the first to point out, there are many points in it which are still obscure, while numerous problems which it raises still remain completely uninvestigated.

As a science, psycho-analysis is still very young, and Freud himself has more than once found occasion to modify his views on important points. This fact, the result of a strictly scientific attitude, has been somewhat inconsiderately used as a weapon of attack by critics of psycho-analysis.

Let us turn for a moment to psycho-analytic method, touching briefly on three points, the treatment of neuroses, the interpretation of dreams and the speech-slips and forgettings of everyday life.

Psycho-analysis, it will be remembered, began as a method of treating one class of nervous disorders. Dr. Sigmund Freud, who was born in what is now Czechoslovakia, but who moved at the age of four to Vienna, which has ever since been his home, began his professional life as a consultant on nervous diseases.

HYPNOTISM AND HYSTERIA

He had studied under some of the most distinguished men of his age, including the celebrated French neurologist Jean Martin Charcot (1825–1893), from whom he learnt much concerning the nature of hysteria. This disorder, then considered one found in women only, he saw treated by hypnotism.

Returning to Vienna he set up in practice and employed hypnotic suggestion as his chief instrument in dealing with the patients who soon began to flock to his consulting rooms. But though he rapidly became a popular and fashionable physician, he found himself growing more and more dissatisfied with the hypnotic method for treating nervous disorders.

He could not, he discovered, hypnotize every patient who came to him, and of those whom he could there were many who could not be put into so deep a state of hypnosis as he considered desirable.

In 1889 he travelled to Nancy in Lorraine to study the methods of Professor Bernheim, whose experiments in hypnotism were arousing widespread interest. One incident in particular impressed Freud greatly.

BERNHEIM'S EXPERIMENT

A patient, waked out of a hypnotic sleep, was asked by Bernheim to repeat what he had said during hypnosis. At first the patient declared emphatically that he could remember nothing whatever. Bernheim insisted that he could, and must. Under pressure, the patient did; at first vaguely, and then more clearly, until in the end he related exactly in every detail the conversation in which he had taken part while hypnotized.

Freud argued from this incident that the patient had had all the time in his mind knowledge of the conversation, but that this knowledge was completely unconscious, and would have remained so had not a special technique been employed to bring it back into consciousness.

This, as he has related, set him thinking that " there could be powerful mental processes which nevertheless remained hidden from the consciousness of men." It was not long before the opportunity arose to test this theory.

RECOVERING LOST MEMORY

Some years previously he had made the acquaintance in Vienna of Dr. Josef Breuer, a family physician with a taste for research. Despite the disparity in their ages—Breuer was some fourteen years older than Freud—the two became fast friends, sharing in common their mutual scientific interests.

During these years Breuer was, so to speak, the elder, wiser and more experienced brother who freely communicated his knowledge and experience to his brilliant young companion. Among other matters he told Freud of a remarkable cure of hysteria he had effected between 1880 and 1882, by an entirely new method.

He had discovered that his patient, a young woman suffering from grievous hysterical symptoms including recurrent states of mental confusion, could be relieved if she could be induced to talk about the particular fantasy which was at the time oppressing her mind.

So he began to hypnotize her, to discover during hypnosis the fantasy in question, and then after she had waked, to get her to recall the memory of the hypnotic conversations. So soon as she did this, the hysterical symptoms disappeared. Breuer thus proved to his own satisfaction that the symptoms were caused by a loss of memory, and that when that memory was recovered the symptoms were automatically removed.

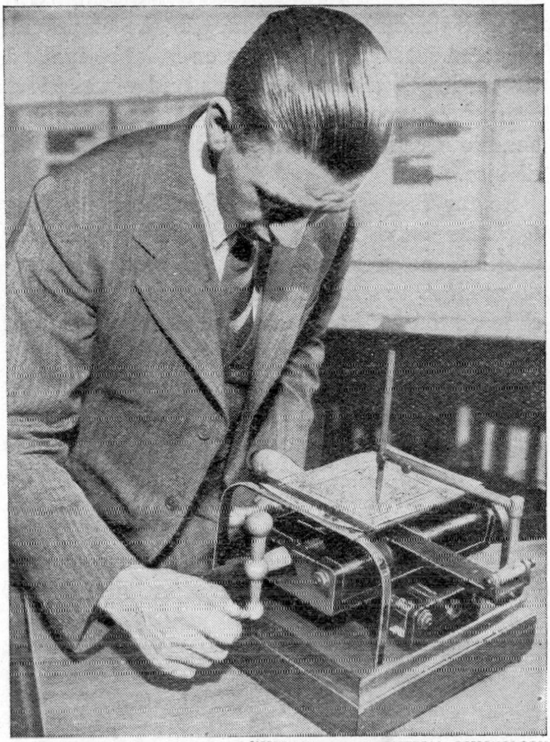

INSTITUTE OF INDUSTRIAL PSYCHOLOGY

TEST FOR MACHINE WORKERS

By combining the movements of the two handles the pencil can be made to trace round the circle. The degree of speed and accuracy with which the subject could perform this test would give a good indication of the degree of proficiency which he would probably attain with actual machines employing similar hand movements.

Freud adopted Breuer's method and found it extremely successful. In 1893 the two published a brief account of their work in this new field, entitled *On the Psychical Mechanism of Hysterical Phenomena.* Two years later they followed this paper with a full length volume called *Studies on Hysteria.* In this book is to be found the first tentative approach to the theory of psycho-analysis.

The book dealt with the origin of symptoms

in hysteria by suggesting that an hysterical symptom was caused by the damming up of an emotion. This emotion, being compelled to expend its energy in some way or another, and being denied the normal channels of satisfaction, found an abnormal one which resulted in the symptom.

FREUD'S TURNING-POINT

This led the investigators to two conclusions: first, the extreme significance of the emotional life, and second, that it was essential to make a distinction between conscious and unconscious mental acts. Clearly, no person would consciously induce in himself symptoms of disease.

So far Breuer and Freud had been working together hand in hand, with Breuer in the position of senior partner, if not, perhaps, altogether as the leading spirit. The two differed on various points of theory, but not to a degree leading to serious disagreement.

But shortly after the publication of *Studies on Hysteria* Freud made in the course of his clinical experience a momentous discovery, which was to prove the turning-point of his life, and to part him for ever as an investigator from Dr. Breuer.

It is an illuminating commentary on the criticism sometimes made that Freud has evolved the theory of psycho-analysis in defiance of facts, that nobody was more startled or taken aback by this discovery than the discoverer himself.

In his own words it was that "I now learned . . . that it was not *any* kind of emotional excitation that was in action behind the phenomena of the neurosis, but habitually one of a sexual nature, whether it was a current sexual conflict or the effect of earlier sexual experiences."

This discovery cost Freud his popularity as a physician, for he was impelled by it to question his patients concerning their sexual life, a procedure which not unnaturally large numbers of them strongly resented. Yet from others he was able to gather convincing evidence in support of his theory.

WANDERING TRAINS OF THOUGHT

Firmly persuaded that every mental phenomenon had as precise a cause as any physical one, Freud pressed on with his investigations. The greater his clinical experience grew, the more he became convinced that the causes of present mental strain and suffering were, as a rule, to be found in events which had occurred early in the patients' lives and the memory of which had long since passed from consciousness to be buried in the depths of the unconscious.

It was therefore essential to find a universally successful method of bringing back to consciousness these "forgotten" memories. So long as they remained, latent yet active, in the unconscious, they were like festering cancers in the mind, poisoning the entire mental system.

The method finally adopted was what is called *free association*. The term at once recalls the older psychological one of "association of ideas," and it is indeed this principle called into service to deal with the unconscious mind.

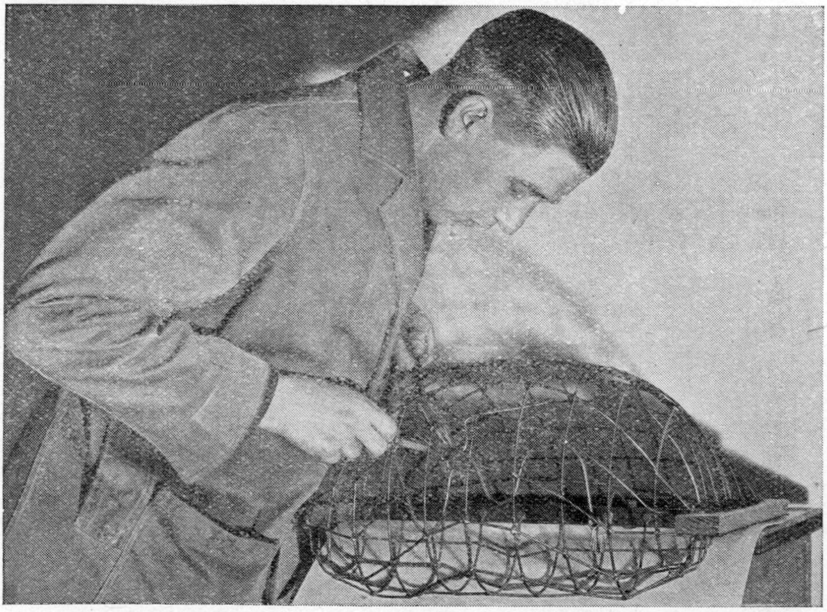

INSTITUTE OF INDUSTRIAL PSYCHOLOGY

TEST FOR MOTOR MECHANICS

Used for selecting men for occupations in which it is necessary to work with tools in a restricted space.

INSTITUTE OF INDUSTRIAL PSYCHOLOGY

TEST FOR BISCUIT PACKERS

Three of the star-shaped pieces of wood have to be collected in one hand from the tray and placed in one operation in the smaller receptacle.

Freud began his experiments leading to the use of this method by asking patients to concentrate and try to recollect events which might be conceivable causes of their symptoms. This technique was successful up to a point, but as it involved constant urging on the part of the physician to overcome the reluctance of the patient to disclose intimate or apparently irrelevant matter, or in other words to overcome the mental resistances of the patient, it proved to be intolerably fatiguing.

Moreover, it was far from perfect. The resistances of some patients could not be overcome, and even when they were, it was only a partial truth that was revealed. An endless deal of time was spent tracking the origin of a single symptom, only to find that this was closely linked up with other symptoms, and that the long and wearisome road of concentrated recollection must be travelled again to track down their causes.

Faced with this situation, Freud made a brilliant and daring generalization. He had no belief whatever in " chance "; nothing ever happened in the mind " by accident." Therefore, he argued, those wandering trains of thought which invariably pass through the mind in moments of relaxation could not be " accidental." Their course must be determined by something. That something must be the unconscious.

So he changed his methods. Instead of asking his patients to concentrate he asked them to relax, to make their minds blank, and then to relate, without omission and without in any way guiding or directing their thoughts, whatever thoughts came into their heads. In this way the whole tangled network of thoughts leading to the roots of the trouble would in time be laid bare.

This procedure is, as may be imagined, very long and often very difficult. It is not easy for anyone to make his mind a complete blank; it is infinitely harder for him to avoid guiding his thoughts. The mind plays every conceivable trick; it suppresses some thoughts as irrelevant, others as too intimate to be mentioned. It distorts thoughts, robs some of their significance, gives others an exaggerated significance.

But pursued with skill, tact and tenacity, this method gives the psycho-analyst all the material he wants for making his analysis. Note that the free association is not the analysis; it is the method which supplies the raw material for analysis.

This distinction is very important, for when the thought-material has been gathered it has still to be interpreted. This interpretation constitutes the analysis; it is also a long and intricate business which should never be undertaken save by a highly-trained analyst.

It may be advisable to interpose a warning against rushing light-heartedly into psycho-analytic treatment. The analyst is the first person to corroborate this warning. " Remember," says the Rev. Leslie D. Weatherhead, the popular minister of the City Temple, London, who is himself an analyst, " that analysis is a lengthy, expensive and often distressing treatment . . . my advice to people is to think of it as one thinks of a major abdominal operation. Avoid it if you can."

The unconscious mind does not work in the same way as the conscious. It has no idea of time; it makes no distinction between yes and no; it does not express itself in words but in non-verbal images which are frequently symbolic. It has nothing of what we call power of judgment, but is, to put it crudely, one vast mass of wishes entirely governed by what the psycho-analyst calls the *pleasure-pain principle*, that is, their one and single aim is to seek pleasure and avoid pain. The principle of reality affects the conscious mind only.

INTERPRETATION OF DREAMS

The thought-processes of the unconscious have been most fully worked out in the interpretation of dreams. Quite early in his employment of free association Freud began to find that dreams bulked largely in the material supplied; he set himself to investigate their origin and meaning, with the result that dream interpretation came to occupy a central position in psycho-analysis.

One reason for this is that while relatively few people become what the doctor calls neurotic, practically everyone dreams. If it can be shown that dreams have a meaning, and that they result from activity of the unconscious, then psycho-analysis at once has meaning for everyone, and not merely for those suffering from obvious nervous disorders.

Further if it can be shown that the thought processes which result in dreams are similar to those productive of neurotic symptoms, then it at once becomes proved that the neurotic differs from the so-called normal person only in the degree or intensity of strain he experiences and in the strength of the resistance which the conscious mind can put up against the impulses of the unconscious.

This Freud claims to have done. His claim remains unacceptable to the majority of scientists and psychologists; in fact, it is acceptable in its entirety only to psycho-analysts. But if it can be shown to be valid—and time alone can do that—then it constitutes perhaps the most significant and illuminating discovery ever made in the realm of psychology.

For it means that we have at hand an instrument which reveals the hidden springs of all human behaviour, and shows us the way to control and direct the fountain of human energy.

The first point that usually strikes any person about the dream he has just experienced is its apparently absurd mixture of the ordinary and the fantastic. The second is probably the rapidity with which the dream fades from the memory.

There are, it is true, particularly vivid dreams the memory of which will remain with us for years; but as a general rule a dream is already slipping from memory by the time we are fully awake, and unless consciously recalled at once is forgotten by breakfast time. In many cases, indeed, we can on waking recall nothing of the dream. We know we have dreamed, and that is all.

Now to Freud, with his unvarying belief that all phenomena, mental as well as physical, must have precise causes, all these and many other points to be noted about dreams must have significance.

When he began his investigations scientists believed that dreams were disturbances of sleep caused by external stimuli. Freud became convinced of the exact opposite; that the purpose of dreams was to preserve sleep.

The starting-point was certainly a stimulus of some kind, which might be either physical or mental, external or internal. This stimulus, if not dealt with, threatens to awake the sleeper. The dream therefore links on to the stimulus some wish—an unconscious and usually a repressed one—weaves the two into an experience appearing to gratify that wish and so keeps the mind happy and the sleeper still sleeping.

UNCONSCIOUS WISHES

In the dreams of very young children this process of wish-fulfilment may be observed in all its simplicity. A small boy at dinner one day is given some dish—say a favourite pudding—of which he feels he has not received a large enough portion. The thought remains with him and persists during sleep, threatening to disturb his rest; so he dreams of a gigantic pudding of which he eats the lot.

Adult dreams are much more complicated, but Freud maintains that every one is similarly a wish-fulfilment. He does not say, as he has been misrepresented to say, that all dreams are fulfilment of sexual wishes. Many of them are, but not all.

The elements which go to compose a dream,

SYMBOLICAL PICTURE OF THE CONSCIOUS AND THE UNCONSCIOUS

The difference, according to the psycho-analyst, between our minds during the day and at night. In the daytime our conscious mind reigns supreme ; the censor, represented here by a policeman, keeps our thoughts orderly and conventional. At night the censorship is relaxed, and unconscious desires well up from the deeper layers of the mind, to find satisfaction in the wish-fulfilment of dreams.

then, are a stimulus of some sort and a wish from the unconscious. This is the *latent content* of the dream. But this latent content does not penetrate into the conscious experience of the dreamer.

Unconscious wishes are of such nature that they cannot be allowed in the conscious mind even during sleep. They must be transformed into a presentable state. This process of transformation is called the *dreamwork*, and the result is the *manifest content*, or the dream as actually experienced.

"ROYAL ROAD TO THE UNCONSCIOUS"

This transformation, or *distortion*, of the latent content of a dream consists mainly of three processes: condensation, displacement, and symbolism. Condensation consists of making a single composite picture of two or more persons or places or of taking elements from a variety of persons or places and building them up into a picture. Displacement consists in making significant persons, places or events insignificant and vice versa.

Concerning symbolism a whole chapter could be written. Most symbols are sexual and many are universal. Quite a body of literature has arisen round this subject, and to that literature the curious reader is referred. Anyone who accepts the psycho-analytic theory will find it both interesting and illuminating; others will without doubt find it nauseating.

In addition to distortion, there occurs, at the moment of waking, a further transformation of the dream which is called *secondary elaboration*. This process continues after one has woken up, and is responsible for whatever of coherence or order there appears in a dream as recalled and related.

The value of dream interpretation lies in the fact that so often it reveals both what current thoughts are troubling the unconscious and also the events of infancy or early childhood which are emotionally linked with such thoughts. So highly does Freud think of dream analysis that he has described it as the "royal road to the unconscious."

It will be remembered that Freud and Breuer early found that neuroses were caused by damming up of an emotion, and that this damming up caused loss of memory. It will further be remembered that Freud sought to establish the fact that the neurotic differs from the normal person only in degree—in other words, that we are all more or less neurotic. In support of this claim he finds convincing evidence in the slight errors in mental processes that afflict all of us.

Every person knows occasions when he has the name of a person "on the tip of his tongue," but cannot for the life of him remember that name. Everyone of us has at some time or another put an important letter in his pocket, intending to post it in the first pillar-box—and forgotten all about it for hours, or it may be days. Or we keep forgetting some commission we are asked to perform, though reminded of it again and again.

Similarly, we make slight mistakes in our ordinary everyday speech, and sometimes, though less often, in our writing. Probably everyone of us has at some time or another answered "No" when he meant "Yes," or vice versa; said "I'll see you on Wednesday," when he knows perfectly well that Thursday is the day of the appointment; run two words together, or used a word opposite in meaning to the one he intended to use.

Most people put these little slips of everyday life down to "accident"; the very name "slips" suggests an unintentional, capricious origin. Yet not all such slips are excused even by ordinary folk. The husband who forgets to bring home the meat his wife asked him to call for is met with the reproach: "Of course, you would forget just that one thing." The child who forgets his homework is reminded that he never forgets to ask for his pocket money. The man who comes to an appointment only to find that the other person has forgotten it feels slighted and humiliated.

Freud maintains that every single one of these slips and forgettings has its cause in the influence of thoughts in the unconscious, that is, repressed thoughts which the conscious mind will have nothing to do with, but which keep obtruding themselves in this manner, and are a certain indication of the real trend of a person's emotions.

SLIPS AND FORGETTINGS

There must be, says Freud, a motive for our not wishing to remember whenever we forget to do something. That the motive is unconscious is obvious from the fact that we frequently forget just the very thing we are consciously most anxious to remember. Similarly, there must be a motive, again usually unconscious, behind every slip in speech.

People who borrow books or other articles

and persistently "forget" to return them will be interested (and probably indignant) to learn that the psycho-analyst holds this habit to be due to their acquisitiveness, and that in their innermost minds they have no intention of returning the borrowed article, but intend if possible to add it to their own possessions.

Those people who view with apprehension the growing toll of death on the roads will find food for thought in the Freudian theory that numerous accidents are the result of repressed murderous or suicidal tendencies. Similar tendencies are manifested in the domestic servant who, shortly after having been reproved by her mistress, "accidentally" breaks a piece of china.

This part of the Freudian doctrine is not disputed so violently by common opinion as is much of the rest of psycho-analysis. The phenomena it discusses and their causes are only too obvious, as is evidenced by the frequent misunderstandings and quarrels which daily arise between people on account of just these very slips and forgettings.

FEELING OF INFERIORITY

The more sensitive a person is, the more easily he penetrates beneath the surface to the underlying cause of one of these errors in mental functioning. He accuses the person concerned of this cause; the accusation is indignantly rebutted and a bitter quarrel follows—rendered all the more acrimonious because the one who has made the slip knows at the back of his mind that the accusation is just—and this very fact impels his conscious mind the more strenuously to deny it.

Freud's theory of psycho-analysis has not received universal acceptance even from those who were at first enthusiastic disciples. Shortly before the World War there occurred two notable secessions, headed respectively by Alfred Adler (1870–1937) of Vienna, and Carl Gustave Jung (born 1875) of Zurich. Both broke with Freud on the vital question of the importance of sexuality in mental life.

Freud accepted these secessions with equanimity: he merely requested Adler and Jung not to refer to their doctrines as psycho-analysis. As a result, Adler called his Individual Psychology, while Jung chose the name Analytical Psychology.

Adler is famous for his theory of the "inferiority complex." He believed that for every individual person the scheme on which memory is built up is different. A set of emotional motives forms the nucleus around which the memories gather. This set is different for each individual; in some persons it will be sexual in character but not by any means in all.

The principle determining the nucleus is consciousness of a need. The individual organism feels the lack of something, and because of that lack develops a feeling of inferiority. Every nerve then becomes strained towards the effort to find some way of compensation for that inferiority.

The inferiority may be real or only imagined, but in either case it tends to give rise to the inferiority complex, which Adler has defined as an "abnormal feeling of inferiority." "Complex," he continues, "is not the correct word for this feeling of inferiority which permeates the whole personality. It is more than a complex, it is almost a disease. . . ."

According to Adler, "The key to the entire social process is to be found in the fact that

PRESS PORTRAIT BUREAU

DR. ERNEST JONES

One of the earliest British followers of Dr. Freud, he has done much to popularize psycho-analysis.

persons are always striving to find a situation in which they excel." In other words, the "will to power" is the dominating force in human life. All neuroses result, not as Freud would have us believe from repressed sexual impulses, but from the failure to compensate for the feeling of inferiority.

CAUSE OF CRIME

As well as an inferiority complex there is also a superiority complex. It is quite possible for both to be found in the same person; it is only, so to speak, a case of looking at the two faces of the same medal.

Crime, Adler maintained, was a sign of a superiority complex; children start stealing because they feel they are doing something which other people are unaware of, and this feeling gives them the sense of being superior. The well-known vanity of criminals is also evidence of this feeling of superiority.

Adler, like Freud, attached the greatest importance to the early years of life. "All evidence," he said, "points to the fact that the fixing of this goal (i.e. the individual's concrete aim or ideal in life) must take place early in life, during the formative period of childhood. A kind of prototype or model of a matured personality begins to develop at this time."

Adler early rejected Freud's theory of dream interpretation. "The truth," he said, "is that there is no specific formula which will explain dreams," except their emotional character. He goes on to say that "The fact that dreams are emotionally intoxicating offers, curiously enough, a method for preventing dreams. If a person understands what he has been dreaming about and realizes that he has been intoxicating himself, he will stop dreaming." He declared that he himself had never had a dream from the moment he realized this fact.

Adler also rejected Freud's theory of the unconscious. "Consciousness and unconsciousness," he declared, "move together in the same direction and are not contradictions, as is so often believed. What is more, there is no definite line of demarcation between them."

Jung also differed from Freud on this point, but more subtly. He pictured the unconscious rather as an undeveloped form of conscious mind, and developed the theory that racial memories, the instincts and impulses which every individual inherits from his ancestry—right back to primeval days—play a predominating part in mental life, being at least as important as sexual memories, and doing more to determine character and temperament.

Jung's name is best known to the general public in connection with the terms "extravert" and "introvert." An extravert is what we should call in colloquial language a "good mixer." He is happy when among other people, miserable when alone and so thrown upon his own spiritual resources. An introvert, on the other hand, tends always to withdraw into himself; he has no great liking for society, rather dreads meeting other people, and cannot easily share or appreciate the views of others.

The typical extravert is the practical, perpetually busy man of affairs, always dealing with concrete, everyday matters, and having neither time for nor patience with "highbrow" subjects. Among the ranks of the introverts are to be found the poets, mystics, philosophers, creative artists, musicians, and all to whom the life of the spirit means more than the material round of daily existence.

Whether later some genius will arise who can weave into a single harmonious system the doctrines of Freud, Adler and Jung, or whether this result will be achieved by the modern method of team-work in scientific research, time alone can prove.

It will be seen even from this very brief outline both that there are many points at which the three doctrines, if not in complete agreement, yet march very closely together; and also that there is much in the teachings of Adler and Jung that is both attractive and incontrovertible.

IN EVERY WALK OF LIFE

Few thinking people would care to deny Adler's theory of the existence of an inferiority complex; it explains vividly much of the behaviour of human beings in every walk of life. Equally, the presence of extraverts and introverts in our midst is too obvious a fact to be overlooked. Every one of us must be conscious of a tendency in himself either to turn towards the great busy world of his fellow men or to shrink from it into the quiet recesses of his own soul.

Nor does it appear that either of these theories need of necessity be in conflict with the main tenets of the Freudian doctrine. It is rather a question of relative emphasis than of antagonism.

TEST OF MECHANICAL AND OF PRACTICAL ABILITY

Left: A number of simple mechanical objects have to be assembled. Marks are awarded for work completed within a time limit. Right: Cubes coloured on certain sides can be built up into a replica of the large cube. A score is obtained by combining the time taken to complete and the number of errors made.

THE NATURE OF INTELLIGENCE

JUNG in his work lays great stress upon the creative impulse in man, and classifies the four main functions of the mind as thinking, feeling, sensation and intuition. This theory brings us into touch with another school of psychological thought, usually referred to by the somewhat clumsy and unattractive name of " noegenetic," a school which makes its chief subject of research the nature of intelligence.

Noegenesis is a word meaning " origin of knowledge." The principles or laws governing the origin of knowledge, as formulated by Professor Charles Edward Spearman (born 1863), late Grote Professor of the Philosophy of Mind and Logic at London University, are as follows : (1) " Any lived experience tends to evoke immediately a knowing of its characters and experiencer," (2) " The mentally presenting of any two or more characters tends to evoke immediately a knowing of relation between them," and (3) " The presenting of any character together with any relation tends to evoke immediately a knowing of the correlative character." In other words :

(1) Whatever comes into our experience we tend to know as a whole made up of many components; we distinguish, for example, between sounds and sights and tastes and smells. And at the same time as we become aware of these items of our experience, we know that it is our self which becomes aware of them.

(2) As we perceive these items of our experience, we tend to notice relation between them, of likeness, unlikeness, degree, and so on. We notice, for example, whether one street is wider than another, one sound like or unlike a former one.

(3) Whenever we are presented with an item of experience and a definite relation, we tend to think of another item. For instance, the unfinished sentence " Broad is the opposite of . . ." would be immediately completed by any person of normal understanding with the word " narrow." That is a very simple illustration : on its higher planes this mental process is responsible for all invention.

These three noegenetic laws define the mental processes by which knowledge is created. Whenever these processes are put into operation knowledge results. Such knowledge must of necessity be absolutely correct.

But human knowledge, as we all know to our cost, is often far from being absolutely correct. It is ordinarily full of blemishes and errors and gaps. How are we to account for that?

It will be noted that each law uses the phrase " tends to evoke." How far the tendency goes depends upon the quantity of intelligence we possess and the conditions under which that intelligence has to work. Spearman has formulated a further five laws, called the quantitative principles (as opposed to the noegenetic laws, which deal with quality only), to cover the entire field of intellectual processes.

First, there is the principle of mental energy. Everyone possesses some mental energy. Some people possess a great deal more than others, and probably no two persons possess exactly the same amount; but the interesting point is that whatever quantity any given person may be endowed with, that quantity does not vary. It may be better in quality at one moment than at another, but the actual output is always the same.

The second principle is that of retentiveness. Stated simply, this principle says that any mental process tends to occur more easily the more often it has occurred. The third, an opposing principle, is that of fatigue, on account of which mental processes tend not to occur again.

The fourth principle is that of control of intellectual activity by the will. This is an old familiar friend. Everybody knows that when we are deeply interested in a subject we learn far more easily and acquire a far deeper knowledge than if our interest is but slight.

HOW INTELLIGENCE WORKS

In every school today there are boys who can explain fluently and accurately the workings of the most complicated and specialized motor car or aeroplane engine, but who cannot for the life of them understand quadratic equations (which are far easier), or master a column of irregular French verbs. Nor do we need telling that by sheer will power we can force ourselves to concentrate upon even a distasteful subject and make ourselves masters of it. History records innumerable instances of men and women who have achieved success in this fashion.

The fifth and final principle is that of variability in the physical and mental condition of individuals. This again needs little explanation; the well-known proverb *Mens sana in corpore sano*, " a healthy mind in a healthy body," has been current for at least two thousand years.

We all know that we tend to work less easily and more slowly, and to make more mistakes, when we are physically tired, cold, hungry, sleepy, or distressed. We know, too, that heredity and environment play important parts in determining the power of our intelligence.

The noegenetic laws do not tell us what intelligence is, but only how it works. In this connection Spearman has evolved a further theory which has received very general acceptance.

He holds that in every act of intelligent behaviour two factors are involved. The first is a general mental ability, or intellectual energy, which he calls " g," and which is present, though in varying degree, in every mental operation. This general mental ability varies from individual to individual, but in any one person tends to be constant. It grows in children, but only till about the age of fifteen or sixteen, after which it remains a fixed quantity throughout life.

The other factor, called " s," is specific, that is, it is peculiar to the type of mental operation in which it is found. In some mental acts a great deal of " g " is involved and only a little " s "; in others not much " g " but a great deal of " s."

Since " g " is involved in every mental act, it is regarded as " intelligence," and a person well endowed with " g " has what is called a good or superior intelligence. This does not necessarily mean that he will show superior intelligence in every mental act. A famous and often-quoted dictum of Spearman's is to the effect that " every normal man, woman or child is a genius at something and an idiot at something." To say that a person has superior intelligence means that in most of his mental acts he will display a high level of mental ability.

The possession of considerable " s " in any form will tend to be shown in specialized ability, sometimes unaccompanied by much " g "; thus a brilliant pianist may be a person of average or less than average intelligence, a film star, or an international footballer may be in ordinary life little better than a nit-wit. Frequent cases occur of otherwise dull or even defective individuals who possess extraordinary powers of memory or skill in craftsmanship.

INTELLIGENCE TESTS

Now intelligence itself cannot be measured, for we still do not know what it is, but we can measure its output, and since " g " tends to be constant in any one individual, that measurement will provide a reliable index at any time, provided we can find an instrument that checks only output of intelligence, as distinguished from the result of education. That instrument has been found in the intelligence test.

Many people still regard intelligence tests with suspicion, and few would claim that they are as yet anything like perfect, but they have with some justice been described as " among

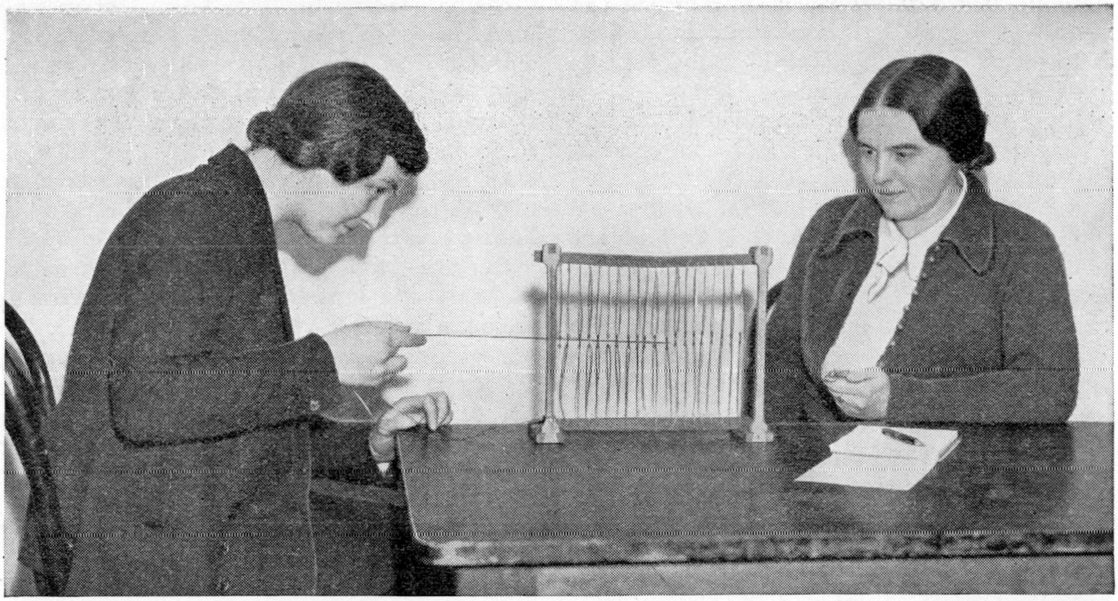

INSTITUTE OF INDUSTRIAL PSYCHOLOGY

TEST FOR WOULD-BE WEAVERS

A test of hand and eye co-ordination for weavers. The operation of threading the wire through the small eyelets closely resembles the job of "picking-up" broken threads.

the most sensitive instruments that exist for the scientific study of man."

The birth of intelligence testing is generally connected with the name of Alfred Binet (1857–1911), the French psychologist who in 1905 devised a set of tests for general intelligence that has become world famous. Mental testing, however, actually dates from long before his time; tests for sense perception had been applied for three-quarters of a century, while from about 1885 onwards tests of special abilities were being used in England, France and the United States.

Binet's work represents rather the culmination of a long period of research and experiment, but that in no way detracts from the greatness of his achievement. Asked by the Paris municipal authorities to find out why some of the children in their schools were dull and backward, he devised what might best be called a "standardized interview," composed of thirty questions and tasks designed and grouped to provide an index of a child's all-round ability.

FACULTIES OF THE MIND

Binet was not concerned to find any theoretical "g." He believed that the mind worked by "faculties"—memory, imagination, judgment, and so on—and that if he arranged in groups a variety of tests which he presumed would cover all of the faculties, he would get from them an idea of the average level of intelligence.

There was a group of tests for each year of school life; if a child passed in every test for its year its mental age was considered equal to its chronological age. So many months were deducted for failure in a test, so many added for success in a test belonging to a more advanced year.

EXAMINING TWO MILLION MEN

Binet's tests were individual, that is, they could only be given to one person at a time. Meanwhile in America group tests of intelligence, consisting of printed sets of questions and tasks which could be given to large numbers of persons at the same time, were being developed.

The group intelligence test was used on a colossal scale in 1917, when every recruit wishing to join the United States army during the World War was examined by this means. In all nearly two million men were thus tested. It is interesting to recall the shocked amazement with which America learned that the average mental age of its young manhood was only just over thirteen!

This verdict does not seem so harsh when it is realized that intelligence can only be rated in terms of mental age up to about fifteen or sixteen. There is, of course, no absolute standard by which intelligence can be judged, but today it is more usual to express it in terms of an I.Q. (Intelligence Quotient) with a norm of one hundred.

Intelligence testing is now widely used in schools, particularly in America, but increasingly in Britain, and on the Continent. It is found particularly valuable in sorting out mentally defective children, children who are dull and backward from accidental causes (i.e. illness, absence, economic or social reasons), children of superior ability, and children who for some reason or other are not working up to capacity.

DELINQUENT BOYS AND GIRLS

The importance of this work can be seen from the fact that it has been proved experimentally that without special care backward children do worse in school than their intelligence justifies, while really clever children do only about half as much better than the others as they ought.

Intelligence testing, combined with tests of personality and character, is also proving of incalculable value in vocational guidance and in selection of workers for special jobs. In England the National Institute of Industrial Psychology is the recognized centre of such work.

Here girls and boys about to leave school may undergo tests from the results of which their examiners are able to advise them in what occupations they are most likely to be successful. The after-careers of those tested are followed up, and show that a high proportion of those who follow the Institute's advice make good, while of those who reject it and go into occupations not considered suitable the majority are unsuccessful.

Intelligence testing has further had a profound effect upon the type of examination set in schools. Whereas formerly examinations concentrated exclusively upon factual knowledge, and therefore exalted memory above all other mental processes, questions are now devised to test power of creative thinking, judgment, arrangement and presentation of facts, imagination and feeling.

It is recognized also that the normal school examination tends to test attainments, that is, the result of education, rather than intelligence; consequently many education authorities now use both examinations and intelligence tests for scholarship and similar purposes.

Mental testing is also being increasingly used in criminology, and especially with delinquent children and young persons. It has long been recognized that crime may be the result of what one may call genuine criminal instincts, of environmental causes, or of some error in mental functioning. It may be news to some people, for example, that theft may be due to repressed fetish worship.

Readers who are interested in what is probably the most fascinating and certainly the most valuable type of literature on crime are advised to study *The Young Delinquent* by Dr. Cyril L. Burt (born 1883), who was for twenty years psychologist to the London County Council before he became professor of education and psychology at London University.

They will find there that of the delinquent boys and girls whom Dr. Burt examined, 52.8 per cent suffered from poverty, 57.9 from unhappy or impaired family relationships, 25.9 from immoral homes, 60.9 from defective discipline, and 45.2 from bad and degenerating influences outside the home.

Two other systems of psychological thought, so closely related as to be capable of being treated together, must briefly be considered. The first, called *Gestalt-psychologie*, was so named by the Austrian philosopher Christian Ehrenfels (born 1859), and has been developed by the German psychologists Max Wertheimer, Wolfgang Köhler, Kurt Koffka and others. The other goes by the name of Organismal Psychology.

There is unfortunately no word in English which exactly translates the German word *Gestalt*. Common renderings are " figure," " form," and " shape "; and *Gestalt-psychologie* is variously known as Configurationism, Formalism, or the Psychology of Shape.

THE PSYCHOLOGY OF SHAPE

None of these terms exactly indicates the theory of *Gestalt-psychologie*, the essence of which is that we perceive, not the mere sum of a number of elements, but in unitary wholes, and that any psychological whole is more than the sum of its parts.

This theory is based on extensive experimental work, largely in the fields of visual and auditory perception, and can easily be illustrated by examples.

When we go to the cinema, we actually have thrown upon the screen a large number of pictures representing stationary objects, yet we see a continuous picture of movement. The *Gestalt* psychologist says that at the same moment as we sense the stimuli conveyed by the successive pictures the relation between those swiftly succeeding pictures further induces a "formalizing" process which gives the impression of apparent movement.

HIGHEST MENTAL ABILITY

This formalizing process, induced by the recognition of relationship between the stationary pictures, is the result of a creative mental activity.

To take another example, a set of notes is played on a musical instrument, and we perceive a melody. That melody is something more than the sum of the notes; we can alter all the notes by transposing them into another key, but we still get the same melody. Again, a note on a musical instrument can be analysed into a fundamental tone and overtones, but if we merely add the overtones to the fundamental tone we do not get the note.

This doctrine of the perception of unitary wholes has proved of great value in both animal and child psychology, for it can be shown experimentally that the wholes perceived by various grades of intelligence are not the same.

Wolfgang Köhler's experiments with chimpanzees have been referred to previously in this section, and it was there noted that the animals found some situations much more difficult to grasp than others. This is because the "something more" which makes any psychological whole greater than its parts is a matter of insight, of the perceiving of relations, and this capacity, which as Plato discovered, is the sign of the highest mental ability, varies enormously in individuals, and is far greater in man than in animals.

THE "CLOSED" SITUATION

In other words, intellectual power (or, as the more modern *Gestalt* psychologists maintain, complicated processes in the nervous system) works upon the elementary sensations received by the sense organs.

Gestalt-psychologie postulates a physiological basis for all mental processes, holding that in the nervous system there are "configurational patterns," correlated with the mental wholes, and functioning as response mechanisms to wholes in the environment.

This sounds a little like Behaviourism, but the *Gestalt* psychologist strenuously denies the Behaviourist contention that all complexities of behaviour are built up from simple reflexes, and affirms that the child (or the animal) perceives wholes from the beginning.

These wholes are at first primitive and far from complex. They gradually become more complicated and precise in accordance with

RISCHGITZ COLLECTION

GUSTAV THEODOR FECHNER

According to Fechner (1801–87), *mental changes were accompanied by changes in the nervous system.*

the "Principle of Precision," whereby our mentally-perceived wholes "tend to become as perfect as prevailing conditions permit."

Interesting illustrations of this point can be culled from a variety of sources. It will be remembered that Köhler's chimpanzees found it very difficult to grasp the idea that a branch might be torn from a tree for the purpose of drawing food into the cage.

Numerous street accidents which happen to young children are due to inadequate grasp of a situation. A child is sent to a shop standing on the far side of a main road; he sees the shop from the opposite side of the road, and for him the situation consists only of his errand, the shop and the crossing of the road;

consideration of the traffic on the road does not enter into his mind.

Binet showed by his tests that young children, shown a drawing of a face with a prominent feature missing, will completely overlook the omission. Of four-year-old children scarcely any will be able to say when questioned what was missing from the picture, of five-year-olds only about one in three will supply the right answer, and in all age groups up to the age of ten there will be found children quite satisfied with the incomplete picture.

ELLIOTT AND FRY, LTD.

DR. CYRIL BURT
Psychologist to the London County Council (1913–32) *and originator of their intelligence tests.*

The *Gestalt* psychologist says that in all such cases there is what he calls a " closed " situation; the animal or the child has grown accustomed to perceiving a whole and finds it difficult to admit another detail which renders that whole more complex.

The " closed " situation is illustrated very clearly in an experiment frequently performed with animals. Two illuminated food-boxes are placed in an animal's cage, but the food is always placed in the more brightly-lit box. When the animal has got thoroughly accustomed to going to the brighter box, the strength of the lighting is altered, so that the formerly more brightly-lit box is now the dimmer. The animal will still go to the brighter box, though this now is not the one containing food.

We can, if we reflect a moment, recall in our own actions many examples of " closed " situations causing us to make mistakes. If a man changes his daily newspaper, he will as like as not find himself turning involuntarily to, say, page three for the sporting news (where it always figured in his previous journal), though in the paper he is reading that news will be found on page fifteen.

ELIMINATING MISTAKES

Similarly, if we go to live in a new house, we find ourselves turning to the right inside the front door instead of to the left, or vice versa. If we have gone for some time one way to the railway station, and then decide upon a change, the chances are that if we are preoccupied we find our steps carrying us in the old direction.

Of course, in the case of human beings superior powers of perception, will-power and judgment enable us quickly to eliminate such mistakes; what distinguishes man from even his nearest rivals, the man-like apes, is his capacity to adapt himself to a new situation and the speed with which he learns the requirements of that situation.

Learning, according to the *Gestalt* psychologist, is " the perfecting of response on the part of the organism to stimulation coming from the environment," and is closely connected with growth, which is looked upon as a process of increasing specialization of function. Behaviour likewise is seen as growth.

IN TERMS OF ELECTRICITY

A feature of the *Gestalt-psychologie* which many readers will doubtless find extremely interesting is the explanation in terms of electricity of its physiological basis. Perception is held to be due to differences of potential in the nervous system; this disturbance of equilibrium leads to thought, which expresses itself in behaviour that restores the equilibrium. The entire organism is regarded as a field of force existing within wider fields of force to which it reacts.

And now, the reader may well ask, after having completed this survey of the various schools of psychological thought, of what precise use is it to me as an individual? That is a perfectly fair question and demands a scrupulously fair answer.

By way of preface, however, it should be said that the foregoing account represents only the briefest of surveys of psychology throughout the ages and at the present day, and has of necessity been more concerned with exposition than with practical applications. One could hardly expect to find in a brief elementary textbook on medicine and surgery detailed instructions for the diagnosis and treatment of say, pneumonia or cancer.

VASTLY INCREASED KNOWLEDGE

All the same, it is hoped that sufficient has been said to indicate the general lines along which psychology may be of help to the ordinary man or woman who is interested enough to follow up the reading of this short account with more intensive study.

It will at least have been abundantly clear that the emphasis in psychological research during recent years has shifted from endeavours to discover the nature of mind to the infinitely more profitable field of human and animal behaviour; and that this modern emphasis has led to an enormous amount of experiment resulting in a vastly increased knowledge and understanding of individual and social behaviour.

It is true that far more attention has been devoted to the intellectual aspect of personality (cognition) than to feeling (emotion) and striving (conation), so that as yet the psychologist cannot claim to understand human personality as a whole.

INCREASE OF EFFICIENCY

But when the advances in knowledge of cognition during the past forty or fifty years are recalled, and the fact is taken into account that psychologists are as busily engaged upon problems of the will, emotion and feeling as they have been hitherto upon intellect, it seems reasonable to anticipate that within the next generation or so human personality will be understood in a way never known previously in history.

Meanwhile one may survey very briefly the advances already made. Frequent reference has been made in this summary to practical applications of psychology in education, industry, medicine and criminology.

It is safe to say that psychological research has revolutionized methods of child nurture and training during the twentieth century. Attention has been largely concentrated on the earlier years of childhood—obviously because of their extreme importance—but a vast amount of work has been done in every field of education. One may instance as outstanding results the vastly improved methods of teaching reading, writing and numbers, the present-day emphasis upon the value of art and craft work in schools and the spread of organized games.

PRESS PORTRAIT BUREAU

PROFESSOR F. A. P. AVELING

Professor of psychology at King's College, London, and author of textbooks on the subject.

Few parents nowadays doubt the value of the "Hadow" reorganization of British elementary schools into primary and secondary units, the latter with the three divergent branches of secondary, central and senior schools. This reorganization sprang entirely from a psychological basis.

In industry equally beneficent results have eventuated, though they have been perhaps less spectacular and certainly considerably less advertised. One cannot, of course, reorganize an industrial system based on individualism with the same speed or efficacy that one can reorganize a State controlled educational system.

But one may point to the large number of firms which during recent years have adopted the five-day week because they were convinced by psychological evidence that this meant increased output coupled with greater happiness and comfort for the workers.

APPLIED DARWINISM TO PSYCHOLOGY
Herbert Spencer (1820–1903) *was the first philosopher to apply Darwinism to psychology.*

One can further point to large numbers of factories, mills and workshops where the movements of workers during industrial operations have been studied and reduced in number to eliminate fatigue, where more convenient standing or sitting positions have been introduced, where better lighting and ventilating are now installed, and where the human factor receives a consideration until recently quite unknown.

The provision of canteens and rest-rooms, the organization of sports clubs and recreational facilities, and the provision of technical and general education schools in connexion with big offices and works are all indications of the work of the psychologist.

The worker's day has likewise been studied intensively, and the quality of the output from hour to hour shown in minutest detail. One result of this research is seen in the rest-periods which firms are increasingly adopting.

It is important to differentiate between the influence of the psychologist in industry and that of the " efficiency merchant " who studies industrial operations solely with a view to increasing output and so adding to the shareholders' profits.

The psychologist is certainly concerned with the increase of efficiency, but chiefly from the workers' point of view. It is one of the most firmly established psychological hypotheses that all true efficiency is based on the happiness, comfort and welfare of the worker. There is, it is perhaps needless to say, still a vast amount of work to be done in this field; everywhere one goes one still sees human work being done in clumsy, lengthy and unnecessarily fatiguing ways.

TREATMENT OF NERVOUS DISORDERS

In medical psychology an immense advance has been made in the treatment of nervous disorders, thanks very largely to the discoveries of Sigmund Freud and the psycho-analytic school. Psychological treatment of various functional diseases received an enormous impetus during the World War, when large numbers of cases of ailments due to sensory disturbances—loss of speech, memory, deafness, hysteria and so on—had to be treated.

To the study of criminology psychology has made very important contributions, which may be summed up in the statement that for the first time in history the causes which lead any person into crime are being exhaustively studied, with the result that the age-old idea of punishment for crime is being replaced by the modern idea of treatment which will eradicate the tendency to commit crime.

MENTAL EXERCISE IS NECESSARY

Finally, what has psychology done for the individual in his private capacity? It may not be inopportune, at a time when physical fitness is a practical issue in so many countries, to remind readers that no one can become physically fit merely by wishing to be so. A person must understand his own body sufficiently to know its requirements in the way of exercise, and know sufficient about ways of exercise to satisfy those needs.

In the same way, no one can become mentally fit without mental exercise and discipline. To apply that, it is necessary to know something of the mind and of the exercises that will suit it. Psychology may not yet have a complete answer to this problem, but for most of us it has a reasonably adequate one.

RISCHGITZ COLLECTION

THE APOTHECARY AT WORK

When medicine first came to England no distinction was made between the apothecaries who prepared drugs and the practitioners who administered them. The Society of Apothecaries of London has the power to grant medical diplomas. It was incorporated by royal charter of King James I in 1617.

DISCOVERERS OF LIFE'S SECRETS

To some people precedent is a stumbling-block, to others a stepping-stone. The wise regard it as neither entirely good nor wholly bad. They sift and sort their heritage of the past, discarding the dross and retaining the gold. This is the method of modern science.

It does not jeer at what it now knows were the strange fancies of devotees long since dust, realizing that guide-posts are not always strictly truthful, and that some roads which appear enticingly open sometimes lead to dead ends. Demons, the evil eye, and angry gods that were once believed to cause the ills which beset mankind have gone with the charms and incantations used to thwart or appease them, but not all ancient medicine has been relegated to limbo. The early fathers of science had to start at the beginning; the biological student of today has the accumulated knowledge of three thousand five hundred years at his disposal, for the earliest known medical treatise dates from about 1600 B.C.

The famous Hippocratic Oath, which as Dr. Charles Singer says, " has set for ever the ethical seal upon the practice of medicine," is still administered to medical graduates in some universities, though in its present form it probably dates from the beginning of the third century B.C., and some of its tenets may go back earlier still. Here are some of them :—

" According to my power and judgment, I will prescribe regimen to benefit the sick, and not to do them injury or wrong. I will neither give on demand any deadly drug nor prompt to any such course. . . . Into whatever houses I enter, my entrance shall be for the benefit of the sick, and shall be void of all intentional injustice or wrong doing. . . . And whatsoever, either in my practice, or apart from it in daily life, I see or hear which should not be spoken of outside, thereon will I keep silence, judging such silence sacred."

The Greeks were the first people to apply scientific principles to the struggle against disease and death, and the history of medicine may therefore be said to begin with them. Such medical lore as existed before their time was inspired more by superstition than by regard for facts.

The main principles of Greek medicine may be studied in the hundred-odd treatises which are popularly known as the *Hippocratic Collection.* They are so called because the best of them are supposed to have been written by a man

RISCHGITZ COLLECTION

GOD AND GODDESS OF HEALING
Æsculapius was worshipped as the God of Medicine by the Greeks. His female counterpart was Hygieia.

named Hippocrates, who was born at Cos about the year 460 B.C. Little else is known of him except that he travelled widely, was very greatly respected by his contemporaries and lived to a ripe old age.

He is called the Father of Medicine, not because of the discoveries he made, but because he was the first to practise the methods on which all medical science is based. When a patient fell ill of a disease about which Hippocrates was ignorant he was not content, like his predecessors, to ascribe the illness to the will of the gods and prescribe for its cure conventional drugs. Instead he set to work to study the symptoms, and to observe what actually happened. If the patient died he did not complacently regard it as inevitable but tried to find out where the treatment had been at fault. How acute an observer he was we know from the fact that his descriptions of certain diseases tally remarkably well with those of modern physicians.

COMPLETELY CHAOTIC

Prior to his time medical knowledge was completely chaotic, no attempt having been made to relate facts to each other; but in the *Hippocratic Collection* we have a complete system of the treatment of disease. Hippocrates originated the plan by which diseases are arranged under four main heads : acute and chronic; endemic and epidemic.

One of the most striking of his teachings was that the body contains four " humours "—blood, phlegm, yellow bile and black bile—which, if health were to be maintained, had to be present in certain proportions. If the normal relations between the humours were disturbed illness occurred.

Hippocrates lived in an age of great men : among his contemporaries were Sophocles, Euripides, Herodotus, Thucydides, Aristophanes, Socrates and Plato. The last-named had among his pupils a young man called Aristotle, who was destined to dominate scientific thought for two thousand years after his death.

The son of a Macedonian physician, he was born in 384 B.C. At the age of seventeen he joined one of Plato's classes in Athens, and sat at the feet of that great philosopher until the latter's death ten years later. In 342 B.C., after having spent five years in Asia Minor, he became tutor to Alexander the Great, upon whom he appears to have exercised a powerful influence.

HEART COOLED BY THE BRAIN

Aristotle was a biologist rather than a medical man : he may indeed be termed the first biologist. He enquired into such matters as heredity and the origin of life, and in the course of his investigations dissected about fifty different kinds of animals. He also went in for vivisection, that is, dissecting live animals.

One of his most curious ideas—curious, that is to say, in the light of later knowledge—was that the heart was the seat of the intelligence, the function of the brain being merely to cool the heart when it was in danger of getting over-heated.

About a quarter of a century after Aristotle's death in 322 B.C., a great medical school came into being in Egypt, at Alexandria, a town that had been founded by Aristotle's pupil Alexander. This school became the main centre for the dissemination of the teachings of Hippocrates.

FATHER OF ANATOMY

The two greatest men that it turned out were Herophilus of Chalcedon and Erasistratus of Alexandria, both of whom were active during the first half of the third century B.C. The former has earned the title of the Father of Anatomy. The brain and the nervous system were the main objects of his study. He rejected Aristotle's teaching about the brain, realizing that it was the most important part of the nervous system, and he was the first to grasp the real significance of the nerves themselves. He nevertheless clung to Hippocrates' teaching concerning humours.

Erasistratus, on the other hand, rejected the humoral theory, being of the opinion that most diseased states were due to an excess of blood. To reduce the supply of blood he advocated not bleeding—a very popular treatment among his contemporaries—but starvation. His sound common sense is shown by his insistence on the value of cleanliness, exercise, and properly regulated diet.

Erasistratus was a believer in the theory of Pneumatism, which taught that life depended on the existence of a vapour-like spirit, or *pneuma*, with which the body was imbued. This theory no doubt originated in attempts to explain breathing; and the *pneuma* may be said to correspond to ordinary air.

FIRST PUBLIC HOSPITALS

Although the Alexandrian School continued to exist for two centuries after the birth of Christ, it had ceased to be of any dynamic importance when in 50 B.C. Egypt became a part of the Roman Empire. At about the same time the first medical school in Rome was attaining prominence. This school had been founded by Asclepiades, a Greek, who died about 40 B.C. He vigorously propagated the Atomic theory, according to which the body was mainly composed of atoms, or solid particles, so arranged as to form pores or channels through which the fluids of the body flowed. Illnesses occurred, said Asclepiades, when the atoms got out of their proper positions and prevented the fluids from flowing freely.

This theory, elaborated by Asclepiades' follower Themison, came to be known as Methodism, and it long dominated Roman medicine.

Another follower of Asclepiades was Celsus,

HAMILTON COLLECTION

THE FATHER OF MEDICINE

Hippocrates was the author of some of the books in the Hippocratic Collection, *the first medical system.*

who, about A.D. 30, compiled *De Re Medica* (Concerning Medicine), the first Latin medical book of a scientific nature, and the first ancient medical work to be printed (A.D. 1476). The most interesting part of the book is the last, dealing with surgery. We are accustomed to think of the operation for the removal of tonsils as a late nineteenth-century innovation, but it is described in detail in *De Re Medica.* Celsus also gives accounts of operations for removing goitres, for cutting away growths in the nose and for dealing with deformed or diseased teeth.

The Romans had a well-organized army medical corps, and they were the first people to have public hospitals. Hospitals of a kind existed among the Greeks, but they were the property of private doctors. The first public hospitals of the Romans were entirely military, being designed for wounded soldiers in the outposts of the Empire, but the idea soon commended itself to the officials at home, and nursing homes were built in many Italian towns. The first hospital run on charitable lines, like our free hospitals, was built in the fourth century by a Roman Christian woman.

The last of the great classical medical men was Galen (about A.D. 130–201), a Greek who came to Rome about the middle of the second century and became physician to the Emperor Marcus Aurelius. His literary activity was prodigious: no less than one hundred and eighty medical treatises are ascribed to him, and it seems probable that about eighty of these were actually his work. They were famous in their day and continued to exercise a powerful influence on medical science until the end of the seventeenth century.

This influence was far from being entirely beneficial because many of Galen's fallacious ideas were put in so attractive a guise, and stated with so much confidence, that people tended to accept them without question. The result was that he became the ultimate authority on many medical questions.

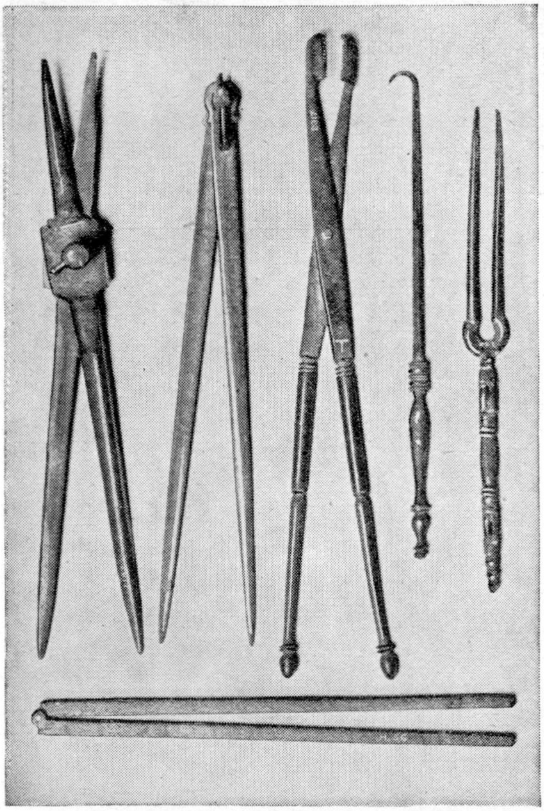

BRITISH MUSEUM

USED IN ANCIENT ROME

Top: Dividers, proportional compasses, forceps, retractor and tenaculum. Below: Folding foot-rule.

Galen rejected the Methodist theory of Themison and supported the conception of a *pneuma*, or spirit, which pervaded the whole body and was blended with the humours. The *pneuma* depended for its well-being on the correct combinations of four "influences" or "elements": heat, cold, wetness and dryness. Incorrect combinations of the influences gave rise to "distempers" which affected the humours. Galen also thought that drugs were subject to these influences, so that where, for instance, there was a case of a distemper due to a wet influence, a drug imbued with the dry influence was called for.

ARAB MEDICAL SCHOOL

His erroneous conception of the anatomy of the heart stood in the way of a proper understanding of the circulatory system until the time of Harvey. Galen was aware that this organ was divided into two main chambers, but he believed that the blood was able to pass through the partition that separated them.

Galen died in the last year of the second century, and with him ended the classical period in medicine. It was not until the ninth century that any further additions were made to medical knowledge, and then not in Europe but in Baghdad, capital of the Moslem Empire. There an Arab medical school came into being, inspired by Arabic translations of the Greek teachers.

PERFORMER OF MIRACLES

The best-known members of the Baghdad School are Rhazes (860–932) and Avicenna (980–1036). Rhazes was the first physician to give accurate descriptions of measles and smallpox, and he compiled a remarkably accurate encyclopedia of medicine. Avicenna, physician in chief to the hospital at Baghdad, was credited with miracles of healing by his contemporaries. Probably the most learned of the Arabians, he wrote a massive work which remained a standard textbook for six hundred years after his death. This and other Moslem medical books began to reach the universities of Europe in Latin translations, many of which were made by Jews, during the thirteenth century. They were received with great eagerness and led to the establishment of medical schools in many seats of learning.

One of the most famous of the medieval medical schools was that at Bologna. There

KISCHGITZ COLLECTION

MEDIEVAL OUT-PATIENTS' DEPARTMENT

The first public hospitals were built by the Romans for the use of the army ; and the first free civilian hospital of which there is any record was built in Rome in the fourth century by a Christian woman.

bodies were publicly dissected for the first time.

Among the earliest of the dissectors was Thaddeus of Florence (1223–1303). He rendered a valuable service to knowledge by insisting on the necessity of having translations of the Greek masters made into Latin direct from the original Greek versions, and not from the much-adulterated versions of the Arabs.

REVOLUTIONIZED MEDICAL THOUGHT

In 1452, about a hundred and fifty years after the death of Thaddeus, Leonardo da Vinci, one of the greatest men of all time, was born in Italy. Leonardo is chiefly remembered as an artist, but he was passionately interested in every aspect of life, and he revolutionized medical thought by daring to doubt that Galen had arrived at ultimate truth.

Leonardo began to study anatomy for the purposes of his art : he realized that a precise knowledge of the structure of the human body was necessary before it could be adequately represented on canvas. But he soon became interested in the subject for its own sake, and determined to write a textbook on anatomy. Unfortunately this project was never carried out, and his notebooks, containing about seven hundred and fifty beautiful anatomical sketches as well as records of his observations, were not accorded the attention they deserved until our own times.

FALLACIES OF GALEN

His dissections of, and experiments with, the heart conclusively proved that Galen had gone astray at more than one point. Yet curiously enough Leonardo appears to have accepted the theory that blood passed through the partition that divides the heart into two main parts.

Leonardo's inquiring spirit lived on in the

person of Andrea Vesalius (1514–1564), with whom begins the history of modern medical science. A native of Brussels, he went in search of knowledge first to Louvain and then to Paris. Being dissatisfied with the tradition-ridden spirit of both these seats of learning, he travelled on to Northern Italy, where at Padua he found an atmosphere more to his liking. The Paduans were not slow to appreciate his worth, and they made him professor of surgery at the age of twenty-three.

RISCHGITZ COLLECTION

SIXTEENTH-CENTURY SURGERY

The doctor is carrying out a delicate operation on the ear which will almost certainly kill the patient.

A year later, in 1538, Vesalius published a short treatise which did not in essentials contradict the teachings of Galen, but shortly after its publication, as the result of further researches, he found reason to doubt many of the conclusions of the famous Greek, and he immediately set to work with prodigious energy to prepare a revised and enlarged edition. This latter, called *The Fabric of the Human Body*, made its appearance in 1543. The year was also notable for the publication of another epoch-making treatise, that of Nicholas Copernicus *On the Revolutions of the Celestial Spheres.*

Vesalius's book was the work of a practical anatomical worker, endowed with an amazing faculty for observation, and as it was written in powerful and beautifully-polished language, it achieved its main object—the eradication of the fallacies of Galen—in a remarkably short space of time.

DEFEATED BY RED TAPE

So revolutionary a publication could not fail to make its author an object of suspicion in orthodox quarters. That is the common lot of pioneers. Despite that his discoveries were received with acclamation by the more forward-looking of his colleagues, those in authority contrived to annoy him to such an extent that one day Vesalius burnt his manuscripts and left Padua to become court physician to the Emperor Charles V.

He was not yet thirty years of age, but he made no further contributions to scientific thought. It is difficult to suggest why so gifted a man could have remained inactive; it may have been because he feared for his life were he further to defy accepted opinion.

In 1564, on his way back from a journey to Jerusalem—ostensibly undertaken, it is said, as a penance for having accidentally dissected a living man, but more probably indulged in to escape court life—Vesalius received an invitation to resume his professorship at Padua. By that time, apparently, after the lapse of twenty-three years, officialdom was changing its mind about the value of his work. But the fates were against him. He died the same year on the island of Zante, of a malady that was probably brought on by the rigours of the voyage.

BURNT AT THE STAKE

One of Vesalius's contemporaries, Miguel Servede (1509–1553), popularly known as Servetus, paid with his life for his zeal on behalf of truth. He had made some valuable discoveries concerning the circulation of the blood when he was condemned to death by the Inquisition. The sentence was never carried out, since he managed to escape, but he was soon afterwards burnt at the stake in Geneva by Calvin.

The anatomical discoveries of Vesalius were

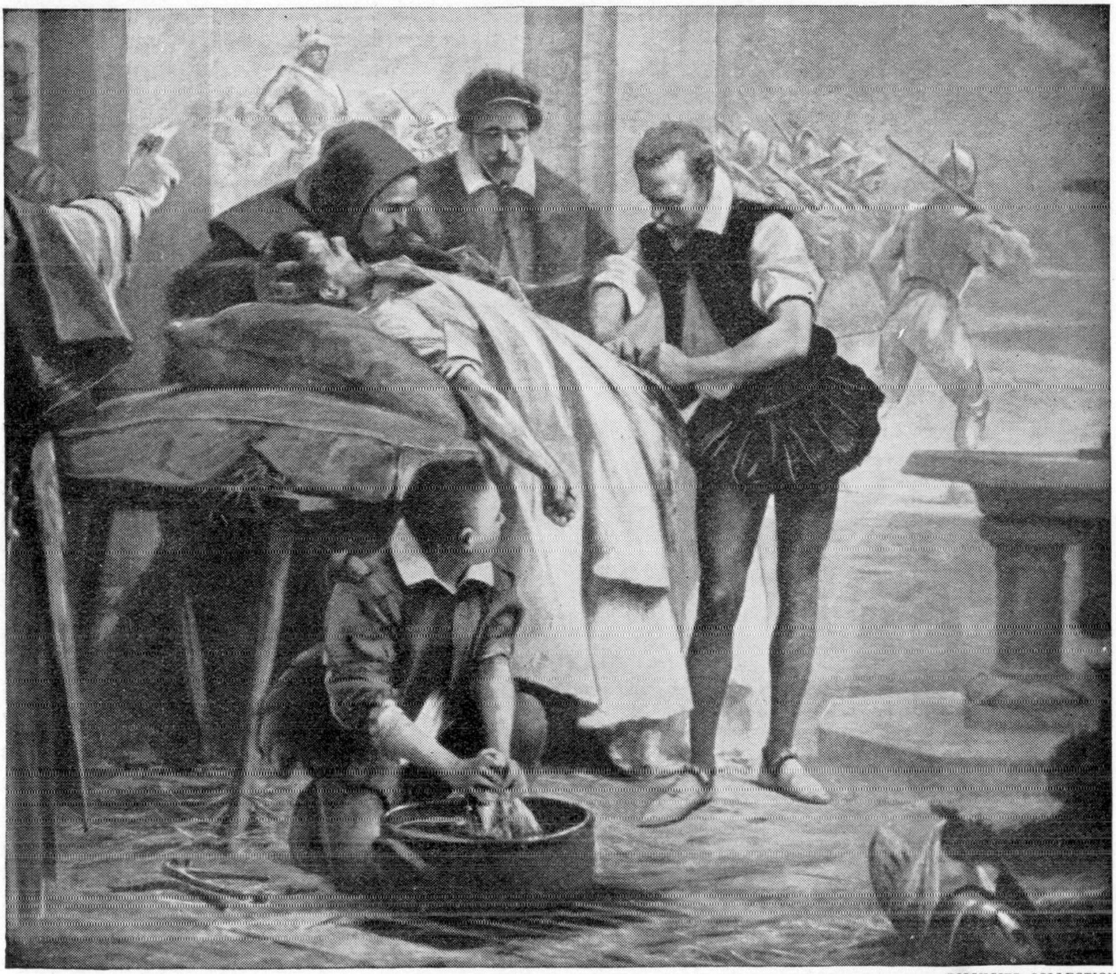

RISCHGITZ COLLECTION

GREATEST OF THE ARMY SURGEONS AT WORK

The French Huguenot Ambroise Paré (1517–1590) *eagerly devoured Vesalius's epoch-making anatomical treatise, and immediately put its findings to practical use on the battlefield, where much of his time was spent.*

eagerly seized upon by a French surgeon named Ambroise Paré (1517–1590), who put them to such practical use that he earned for himself the title of " the greatest of the army surgeons."

When Paré first took up his duties as a surgeon it was customary to give gunshot wounds a first dressing of burning oil. This treatment was painful in the extreme, but it was considered essential since such wounds were regarded in the light of poisoned burns, and the oil was supposed to draw out the poison.

One evening Paré was busily dressing wounds after a battle when, to his consternation, the supply of oil ran out. He had perforce to neglect the recognized treatment and to use an ordinary ointment. The next morning when he came to examine his patients he found that those who had gone without the oil were very much happier than the others: their wounds were healing better and they had suffered less. " Then," he tells us " I resolved within myself never so cruelly to burn poor wounded men."

Ever on the alert to lessen suffering, he gave up the old-established practice of preventing bleeding after amputations by the application of red-hot irons to the wounds, in favour of the much more effective ligature (a bandage to prevent the blood from passing to the site of the amputation). He devised numerous ingenious artificial limbs, and introduced a new technique for childbirth in certain difficult cases.

It is pleasant to be able to record that Paré's services did not, like those of many equally great men, go unrecognized. He was held in such high esteem by his countrymen that his king issued a special order that his life should be spared during the massacre of his fellow-Protestants on St. Bartholomew's Day, 1572.

Vesalius had, as has been pointed out, founded modern medical science when he published his great work on anatomy. It would be difficult to exaggerate the importance of his book. It outlined the methods of descriptive anatomy for all time, and everything that has been done in this field since his day has been merely an extension of his observations and conclusions.

IN ELIZABETH'S TIME
A foot being amputated before the days of anæsthetics and antiseptics. A drawing made in 1598.

The Fabric of the Human Body was more truly scientific in method and spirit than anything that had preceded it. It cleared away a host of superstitions and stimulated rational thought all over Europe.

We have seen, in the work of Paré, what effect it had in the surgical field. Its less immediate effect in the sphere of physiology (which is the study of the functions of the various parts of living bodies) is seen in the work of William Harvey (1578–1657), the discoverer of the circulation of the blood. Harvey did for physiology what Vesalius had done for anatomy and what Paré had done for surgery.

One of the most pregnant passages in the *Fabric* concerns the Galenic doctrine that the blood passes through the septum, or partition, dividing the heart.

STRUCTURE OF THE HEART

"In considering the structure of the heart and the use of its parts," says Vesalius, in the slightly ironical strain detectable in all his references to orthodox authorities, "I bring my words for the most part into agreement with the teachings of Galen; not because I think these on every point in harmony with the truth, but because, in referring at times to new uses and purposes for the parts, I still distrust myself. Not long ago, I would not have dared to diverge a hair's breadth from Galen's opinion. But the septum is as thick, dense and compact as the rest of the heart. I do not, therefore, see how even the smallest particle can be transferred from the right to the left ventricle through it. When these and other facts are considered, many doubtful matters arise concerning the blood vessels."

It is reasonable to suppose that had Vesalius remained in the dissecting rooms at Padua he would have made further enquiries into these "doubtful matters." Fate decreed otherwise, and the task was left to an Englishman born thirty-five years after the publication of the *Fabric*.

William Harvey was born at Folkestone in 1578, and at the age of sixteen he went to Cambridge, where he was entered on the books of Caius College, which had shortly before been refounded by John Kees (Caius), a scholar who had worked at Padua with Vesalius. Harvey himself went to Padua after four years at Cambridge to study under Fabricius, one of Vesalius's professorial successors.

CIRCULATION OF THE BLOOD

Fabricius (1537–1619) played an important part in the history of physiology, though he lacked the intellectual courage of men like Vesalius, and remained all his life in bondage to the classical teachers. He wrote the first illustrated book on embryology (the study of the development of living creatures before they leave the womb or the egg), and made valuable researches into the structures of muscles and of the eye. But, most important in the present context, he published, in 1600, a treatise *On the Valves of the Veins*, in which it was shown

RISCHGITZ COLLECTION

WILLIAM HARVEY DEMONSTRATING TO CHARLES I

The discoverer of the circulation of the blood was fortunate in having as patron and friend the king himself. Harvey accompanied Charles I to Scotland in 1633, *and was present at the Battle of Naseby.*

that all the valves are arranged with their mouths turned towards the heart. It followed, therefore, that the veins must carry blood only towards the heart, but apparently Fabricius failed to draw this obvious conclusion. To have done so would have been flatly to contradict the teachings of the masters, a thing which the timid investigator had no desire to do.

The supreme importance of this point is obvious from the following quotation from Robert Boyle, the founder of modern chemistry. "I remember," he says, "that when I asked our famous Harvey, in the only discourse I had with him (which was but a while before he died), what were the things that induced him to think of a circulation of the blood? He answered me, that when he took notice, that the valves in the veins of so many parts of the body were so placed, that they gave free passage to the blood towards the heart but opposed the passage of the venal blood the contrary way; he was invited to imagine, that so provident a cause as nature had not so placed so many valves without design; and no design seemed more probable, than that since the blood could not well, because of the interposing valves, be sent by the veins to the limbs, it should be sent through the arteries, and return through the veins, whose valves did not oppose its course that way."

These seemingly simple conclusions revolutionized physiology. In Harvey's book on the circulation of the blood, published in 1628, it was conclusively demonstrated that the blood flowed continuously in one direction. To quote the lucid words of Harvey himself: ". . . The blood under the influence of the arterial pulse enters and is impelled in a continuous, equable, and incessant stream through every part and member of the body . . . the veins in like manner return this blood incessantly to the heart from all parts and members of the body. These points proved, I conceive that it will be manifest that the blood circulates, revolves, propelled and then returning, from the heart to the extremities, and thus that it performs a kind of circular motion."

RISCHGITZ COLLECTION

FIRST TO PICTURE BACTERIA

Antonj van Leeuwenhoek (1632–1723), *a self-trained Dutch microscopist, was the first to draw bacteria.*

Once these facts were established, the way was open for subsequent physiologists to pursue detailed enquiries into the origins, nature and purposes of the blood.

Harvey was fortunate enough to win the friendship of Charles I, and received the appointment of Physician in Ordinary to the Royal Household. It was at the king's desire that he dissected the corpse of Thomas Parr, who lived to the alleged age of one hundred and fifty-two and was buried in Westminster Abbey. For some months before his death Parr had been the guest of the Earl of Arundel, by whom Harvey was sent on a picture-collecting mission to Italy. Among the treasures that Arundel wished to secure was a " booke drawne by Leonardo da Vinci."

In 1633 Harvey went with Charles to Scotland, and in the course of the journey turned aside to visit Bass Rock in order to have the opportunity of studying the flight of gannets there. This was typical of him : wherever he went, under whatever circumstances, he was always thinking of science. It is said that he sat underneath a tree reading a medical textbook within earshot of the cannons on the field of Naseby.

One very important question concerning the circulation of the blood had been left unanswered by Harvey. This was, " How is the blood conveyed from the arteries to the veins? " The man who supplied the answer was Marcello Malpighi (1628–1694), for many years lecturer on medicine at the University of Bologna, and during the last three years of his life physician to Pope Innocent XII.

PERSECUTED FOR YEARS

Malpighi was enabled to demonstrate the existence of the capillaries, the minute blood vessels that connect the arteries to the veins, by means of the microscope. This wonderful instrument, invented by Galileo, had never been used by Harvey. Its introduction into the dissecting-rooms opened up a new world for anatomists and physiologists.

Malpighi discovered the capillaries in a frog's lung. While investigating them further, this time in a hedgehog, he detected the existence of the red blood-corpuscles. Among the other great services he rendered to science were researches into the structures of plants, of the embryos of animals, and of the glands.

The greatest of the microscopists, Malpighi was gentle and unassuming, careless of rewards and recognition, but the discoveries he made excited the envy of some of his colleagues, and he was consistently persecuted for many years. His enemies even went so far as to break into his house and destroy some of his most valuable manuscripts and instruments.

FURTHER WORK ON CAPILLARIES

Malpighi was a member of the Royal Society of London, the body to which his great contemporary Antonj van Leeuwenhoek (1632–1723), sent the first drawings of bacteria ever made. The latter had received no kind of scientific education whatever when he started to study natural history, but such were his industry and enthusiasm that he contributed no less than three hundred and seventy-five papers to the Royal Society and twenty-seven to the French Academy of Sciences.

These papers contain the records of an amazing number of discoveries. Leeuwenhoek

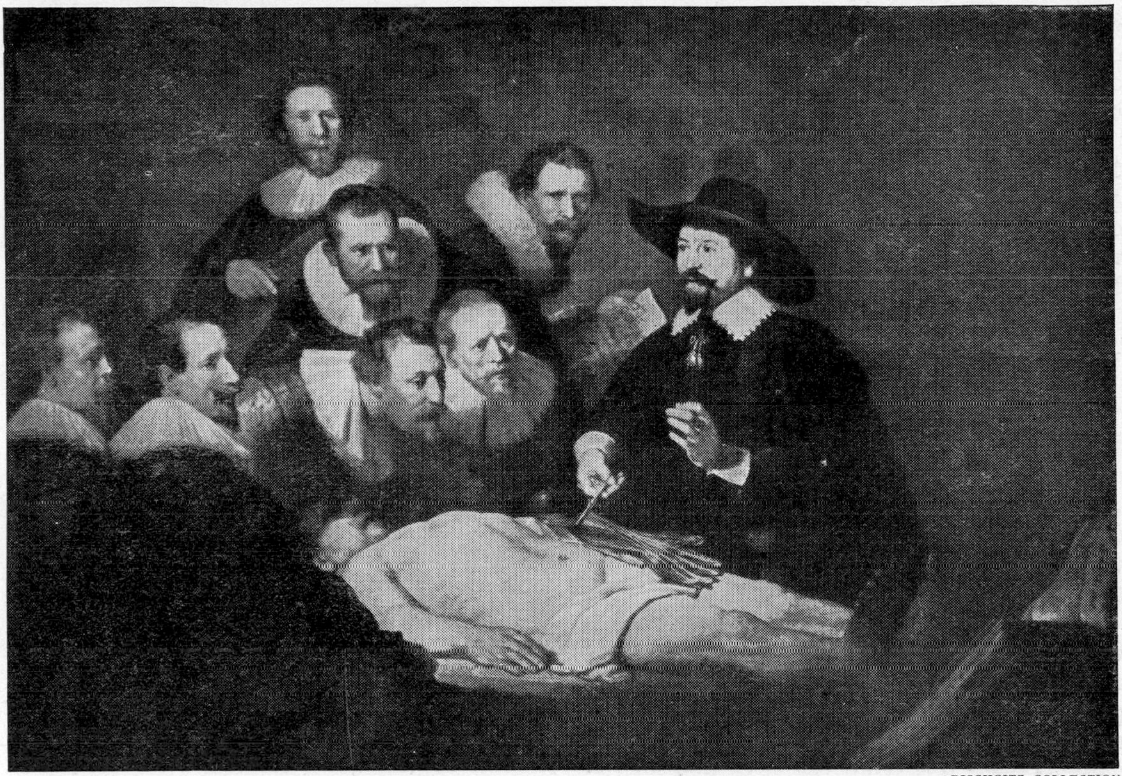

RISCHGITZ COLLECTION

THE SCHOOL OF ANATOMY

An anatomical lecturer giving a lesson on the structure of the arms, one of which has been partially dissected for the purpose. This painting, by Rembrandt (1606–1669). *is at the Hague.*

amplified Malpighi's work on capillaries and blood-corpuscles, and was the first to describe the spermatozoa, the fertilizing bodies in semen, and to give an accurate account of the fibres of the muscles. He and Malpighi between them filled in the important gaps in Harvey's account of the circulation.

THE ENGLISH HIPPOCRATES

Vesalius had finished the work by which the world remembers him at the age of twenty-eight. Thomas Sydenham (1624–1689) the physician who has been given the title of "the English Hippocrates," did not take his doctor's degree until he was over fifty. Vesalius was a man of colossal learning and unsurpassed originality. Sydenham was unscholarly and quite innocent of any desire either to discredit old theories or to propound new ones; he was just a practical physician. But the quiet services he rendered to medicine were as necessary to it as the brilliant contribution of Vesalius, for without men like Sydenham and Paré, work in the various studies, dissecting-rooms and laboratories would be useless, since it would never reach the patient.

When, about the middle of the seventeenth century, Sydenham began to practice, the average practitioner, not only in England but all over Europe, was doing very bad work. The revolutionary discoveries in theory that the preceding hundred and fifty years had brought forth had not yet been accepted by the mass of physicians, but they had had the disturbing effect of destroying confidence in techniques of treatment sanctified by many centuries of use. Then along came Sydenham, rather unimaginative, a medical Tory, but imbued with a desire to make people well, and gifted with an ample supply of common sense.

SYDENHAM'S GREAT BELIEF

Disdainful of theory, Sydenham did not waste much time writing, but one of the few works that came from his unsubtle pen, *The Method of Treating Fevers*, published in 1666, gained a great reputation among general practitioners.

He starts off by saying : "A disease, in my

opinion, how prejudicial so ever its causes may be to the body, is no more than a vigorous effort of Nature to throw off the morbific matter, and thus recover the patient."

Working from this hypothesis, he considers that the first thing the physician must do is to go to the bedside and attentively study particular diseases. He must familiarize himself with their causes, symptoms and histories; and having done this, is then in a position to aid Nature's effort " to throw off the morbific matter."

SUSPICIOUS COLLEAGUES

Sydenham did not just preach about disease. He was a triumphant success in practice, and the descriptions he has left us of gout (from which he himself suffered), smallpox, syphilis, dysentery and measles prove the assiduity with which he carried out his precepts concerning the necessity of observation.

One thing Sydenham demonstrated with very special force : to be successful as a physician a man must have a real sympathy with his patients, since it is necessary for him to treat not merely the disease itself, but the whole man. Where this sympathy is lacking all the learning of the ages will be worse than useless.

A hint at the suspicion with which some of his colleagues regarded Sydenham's untheoretical ways, as well as an indication of his quietly amused attitude to them and to the world, is to be found in a letter that he wrote to Robert Boyle in 1668. " I have the happiness of curing my patients," he says; " at least of having it said of me, that few miscarry under me; but cannot brag of my correspondency with some other of the faculty, who, not withstanding my profoundness in palmistry and chemistry, impeach me with great insufficiency, as I shall likewise do my taylor, when he makes my doublet like a hopsack, and not before, let him adhere to what hypothesis he will."

The son of a Puritan landowner, Sydenham went up to Oxford in 1642, at the age of eighteen, but he had not been there many weeks when the outbreak of hostilities between the Royalists and the Parliamentarians induced him to don military uniform in support of the latter. Four years later, after Oxford had been taken by the Puritans, he returned there to study medicine, acting on the advice of Thomas Coxe, a Paduan physician who had attended his brother.

In 1648 he secured a bachelorship of medicine as well as a Fellowship of All Souls College, rather more for political reasons than for those of scholarship ! Three years later, so little did medicine attract him that he eagerly accepted a captain's commission in the cavalry. Afterwards he stood for parliament, but being defeated, accepted a civil service post from Richard Cromwell.

It was not until after the Restoration, which made it impossible for him to hope for any advancement in a public career, that Sydenham seriously took up medicine. In spite of his bachelor's degree, he knew little of his subject, so he spent some months at the Montpellier Medical School, in France, before setting up in practice in London, at the age of thirty-seven. Even then he was not legally qualified; but although this did not greatly worry him, he took the necessary licentiate of the Royal College of Physicians in 1663. It was not until thirteen years later that he received his doctor's degree at Cambridge.

Yet despite his scholastic deficiencies Sydenham's reputation was so great that Hermann Boerhaave (1668–1738), who is often spoken of as the greatest modern physician, said of him: " I should blush to mention his name without extolling him." There is much in common between these two distinguished medical men—quite apart from the fact that they both suffered agonies from gout.

CONTEMPT FOR THEORIES

Boerhaave was more scholarly than Sydenham, but he had something of the latter's contempt for subtle theories and long-winded dissertations. He wrote very little, despite that he occupied a professorial chair at Leyden; he made no discoveries, and gave birth to no revolutionary ideas. Concerning his character we have the testimony of one of his many distinguished pupils, Haller. " Hardly anyone," he writes, " was worthy to rank with him in his truly divine character, in his goodness to all, in his benevolence even to the envious and to his rivals. No one ever heard him say a disparaging word."

He is chiefly remembered as a very great clinical teacher, who had the power to inspire his students with something of his own zeal in the struggle against disease and physical pain. The teaching methods he introduced are the basis of those practised in present-day medical schools. Moreover he was one of the

INTERIOR OF AN EIGHTEENTH-CENTURY SURGERY

Great advances were made in the technique of surgery during the eighteenth century, largely owing to the influence of John Hunter (1728–1793), *who was equally successful as a practitioner and a research worker.*

earliest users of the Fahrenheit thermometer, the first to show that smallpox is spread by contagion alone, and to establish the site of pleurisy.

WRITER ON THE NERVOUS SYSTEM

The greatest of Boerhaave's pupils was Albrecht von Haller (1708–1777), to whose eulogy of his master reference has been made. A man of immense erudition and extraordinary industry, he is chiefly remembered as a physiologist, his most famous publication being *Elements of the Physiology of the Human Body*, in which the nervous system is treated of in a masterly manner. But he also pursued investigations in many other scientific fields, particularly those of botany and anatomy, and gained a considerable reputation as a novelist and poet.

His great defect was his ultra-conservatism, his too strongly developed respect for tradition —scientific, religious and political. Had he possessed anything like the forward-looking mind of his contemporary Voltaire, he would undoubtedly rank as one of the greatest men of all time.

Haller was brought up in Berne, where even as a child he pursued knowledge with an almost fanatical intensity. His pleasures consisted in compiling dictionaries, grammars and biographies. At fifteen he entered Tübingen University, but the frivolous atmosphere of this foundation disgusted him and three years later he moved to Leyden, where he came under the stimulating influence of Boerhaave. At nineteen he took his doctor's degree and then travelled in turn to London, Paris, and Basle, ever on the search for experience and knowledge. It was in Basle that he took up the study of botany, the fruit of which was an encyclopædic work on the flora of Switzerland, published in 1742.

THREE PROFESSORS IN ONE

Six years before that date, at the age of twenty-eight, an extraordinary honour had been conferred upon him. He was invited to occupy the chairs of anatomy, botany and surgery at the newly-founded University of Göttingen, in Germany. Why he, a foreigner, who had not yet done anything very spectacular, should have been chosen for these important positions is not clear, but that the choice of the authorities was a wise one soon became obvious.

In a short time the medical faculty at

RISCHGITZ COLLECTION

THE MUSCULAR SYSTEM

A drawing by Bernard Albinus (1697–1770), *for fifty-two years professor of medicine at Leyden University.*

Göttingen was enjoying a reputation approaching that of Leyden, on which Haller modelled it. But at the age of forty-five, when the pressure of his manifold duties were threatening to ruin his health, he suddenly left Göttingen and went into semi-retirement at Berne, where he devoted himself mainly to literary activities.

The history of the healing art is full of contrasts : from the fluent, academic Haller, a doctor of medicine at nineteen, we turn to John Hunter (1728–1793), the incoherent surgical practitioner, who at twenty was contemplating enlisting in the army, since everyone seemed to be of the opinion that he was not good enough for anything else, and who never even became qualified as a physician.

As a teacher, Haller was always suave, always sure of himself, confident that he knew practically all there was to be known. The bluff, good-natured Hunter used, on the other hand, frequently to interrupt his chaotic but illuminating ramblings with the words : " You had better not write that down, for very likely I shall think differently next week ! " And when his brother William made an unsuccessful attempt to induce John Hunter to study medicine at Oxford, he said: " They wanted to make an old woman of me, or that I should stuff Latin at the University; but these schemes I cracked like so many vermin as they came before me."

IMPATIENT OF DISCIPLINE

As a boy in Lanarkshire, John Hunter showed no promise whatever, being impatient of discipline and careless of everything the word " respectability " denotes; but " he watched ants, bees, birds, tadpoles, and caddis worms," and " pestered people with questions about what nobody knew or cared anything about." He must have been a very difficult child, and we cannot blame his elders for not detecting the evidence of a scientific mind in this boyish curiosity.

His brother William, his senior by ten years, was making a name for himself as a surgeon in London, when at the age of twenty John threw up cabinet-making, to which he had been apprenticed, and started to look round for some more attractive means of livelihood. " You might do worse than join the army," said his friends, but fortunately John did nothing of the kind. He went to London and induced William to engage him as an assistant in the dissecting room.

TREATMENT OF GUNSHOT WOUNDS

At first he just secured corpses—a job calling for ingenuity and sometimes a disregard for the laws about body-snatching—and kept the dissecting-room clean and tidy. But soon he displayed a desire to dissect on his own account, and William, a most accomplished anatomist and afterwards the author of a great work on his subject, became his teacher. Delighted at the skill John showed, William made him become a surgeon-apprentice at Chelsea Hospital; and afterwards he studied at St. Bartholomew's and St. George's. His insatiable curiosity and tireless industry soon made him a master of anatomy and a brilliant surgeon.

At the age of thirty-three he became a naval surgeon, primarily in order to fortify with sea air a constitution that had been undermined by long hours spent in the unsalubrious atmosphere of eighteenth-century hospital wards and dissecting-rooms. Britain was then fighting France and Spain, and Hunter gained valuable experience of the treatment of gunshot wounds, experience which was to stand him in good stead when he came to write his greatest work, *A Treatise on the Blood, Inflammation, and Gunshot Wounds*, published posthumously in 1794.

THE DAY WAS TOO SHORT

After about two years of active service, in the course of which he visited Belle Isle, where he collected many interesting natural history specimens, he returned to London and began to practise surgery.

In 1768 he secured the valuable appointment of surgeon to St. George's Hospital. Then his practice, which hitherto had not been very lucrative, increased enormously, and within fifteen years he was making the then phenomenal sum of £5,000 a year. But he deserved every penny of it because no man could have worked harder.

PIONEER OF ANÆSTHETICS
Sir James Young Simpson (1811–1870) *was among the first to use chloroform as an anæsthetic.*

RISCHGITZ COLLECTION

DISCOVERER OF VACCINATION
Edward Jenner (1749–1823) *discovered vaccination, thereby practically stamping out smallpox.*

Out of bed at six o'clock every morning; dissecting until nine; seeing patients from nine till four; lecturing in the evening; then writing and making notes till about two o'clock the following morning. Everything he put his hand to was done with the same passionate intensity. Life was much too short for John Hunter: it annoyed him that the day only contained twenty-four hours, a few of which had to be wasted in sleeping and feeding!

GREATEST SURGEON OF HIS TIME

He began to give private lectures in 1773. These were curious affairs. Hunter, the greatest surgeon of his time, was very nervous in front of his pupils, and often he had to take laudanum before he could face a class. But he was not content just to theorize. His lectures were the fruit of his wide experience and great powers of observation: in them he gave himself, albeit stutteringly. These lectures must have had an immediate effect in the general standard of surgery.

Although he made a large income over a long period, Hunter died in debt. Not because he was extravagant in a conventional sense, but because, so to speak, he put all his money back into the business. It was spent on buying animals and human corpses for dissection and on amassing an unrivalled natural history collection. This was purchased by the State after his death for £15,000—it was cheap at the price—and is now in the museum of the Royal College of Surgeons, London.

In this museum may still be seen the skeleton of O'Bryan, the seven-foot-six Irish giant. It is said that Hunter paid away £500 in bribes to secure this specimen. O'Bryan knew before he died that the great surgeon was determined "to have his body," so when he fell ill he made his friends swear that they would see that it was buried at sea in a lead coffin. But in the end it was Hunter and not Davy Jones who had the disposal of the corpse.

CARELESS OF WEALTH

Hunter's house at Earl's Court, in the western suburbs, was one of the sights of London. Its garden was stocked with many different varieties of animals, a good many of them wild: jackals, snakes, hedgehogs, buffaloes, leopards, as well as pigs and goats, many kinds of birds and, in a pond, aquatic animals. To care for the animals and assist him at his work, a large number of human beings had also to be kept, and at one time there were nearly fifty members of his household.

This was not the way to go about making a fortune, but such was not Hunter's object. He merely wanted to learn things that would make him a better surgeon, so that when he died there would be many to say: "He reduced suffering," instead of a few to say: "He left me money."

Careless of wealth, careless of the opinion of the powerful folk who lived for its pursuit, Hunter was sublimely careless of life itself. In the course of investigations into the nature of a certain disease he accidentally contracted it by inoculation, and since there was then no cure for the malady, it must have hastened his death.

His body was placed in the crypt of St. Martin-in-the-Fields, where it remained until 1859, when it was removed to Westminster Abbey by F. T. Buckland, one of the great man's many admirers. In order to recover the body Buckland had to spend many hours searching through the decaying remains with which the vaults were crammed; and he was more than once nearly suffocated before he stumbled upon Hunter's coffin.

Hunter regarded the hedgehog as a very favourable subject for experiments, and one of his most characteristic remarks contains a reference to this animal. A pupil had written to him suggesting a theoretical explanation of some physiological difficulty. In his reply, written in August, 1775, he says: "I think your solution is just; but why think? Why not try the experiment? Repeat all the experiments upon a hedgehog as soon as you receive this, and they will give you the solution."

When the same pupil, thirteen years later, suffered a disappointment in love, Hunter wrote: "Let her go, never mind her. I shall employ you with hedgehogs, for I do not know how far I may trust mine."

This pupil proved to be worth all the trouble the great surgeon took over his education in scientific method because he lived to discover vaccination. Edward Jenner, for that was his name, came under Hunter's influence in 1770, when he was twenty-one years of age. He remained his pupil for three years, part of which was spent in Hunter's own house, and then returned to his native village, Berkeley, in Gloucestershire, to take up the practice of medicine.

It was in 1775 that he began the studies and experiments which led up to the publication, twenty-three years later, of his *Inquiry into the Causes and Effects of the Variolæ Vaccinæ*, the work which was instrumental in introducing scientific preventive inoculation against smallpox. *Variolæ Vaccinæ* is the Latin name for cowpox.

When Jenner started his investigations smallpox was one of the commonest European diseases. Hundreds of thousands died every year from its effects, and large numbers who escaped with their lives were shockingly disfigured by it.

WRAPPED IN INFECTED GARMENTS

From very early times it had been known that those who had once had the disease, even in the mildest form, were thenceforward immune from it; and in many parts of the East it was the established custom deliberately to infect children with a mild form of the disease, so that they would be immune during a virulent outbreak. The mild form, be it added, left little or no trace behind it.

In India, for instance, during mild outbreaks, children were wrapped in infected garments. In other parts of Asia, including Turkey, the virus of smallpox, after having been dried and

RISCHGITZ COLLECTION

PASTEUR AT A CONFERENCE

The first of the great bacteriologists, Louis Pasteur (1822–1897), established the fact that many diseases are caused by microscopic organisms which invade the body and multiply within it.

thus rendered less virulent, was injected underneath the skin by needles. This latter form of inoculation recommended itself to Lady Mary Wortley Montagu, the wife of the British ambassador at Constantinople, and so convinced was she of its efficacy that she had her son inoculated by a Greek doctor.

GOSPEL OF INOCULATION

Lady Montagu returned to England in 1718, and immediately began to preach the gospel of inoculation. And not without success, because her wit and beauty had won her a powerful place in society, and even the Princess of Wales at last gave in to her and had her own children inoculated. This was in 1722, after exhaustive experiments on criminals and orphan children had demonstrated to Her Royal Highness the value of the treatment.

Inoculation, or "variolation" as it was called, thus patronized by royalty, became popular not only in England but even on the Continent, where it was championed by Voltaire.

In spite of its undoubted efficacy, variolation not infrequently had very serious consequences. Sometimes the inoculated person developed smallpox in its severest form. This happened when the pus used in the inoculation was itself at the virulent stage. Sometimes, too, the germs of some other disease in addition to smallpox were in the pus. Obviously, therefore, an improved method of inoculation was called for. It was supplied by Jenner.

Jenner used to practise variolation; and one day he was struck by the fact that it had no apparent effect on those who had previously suffered from cowpox. Cowpox was a disease milkmaids and cowherds contracted from cattle. Its symptoms somewhat resembled those of smallpox, but its sores only appeared near the site of the infection and they healed up very quickly.

ROYAL SOCIETY'S REGRETS

After many years of experiment and investigation Jenner came to the conclusion that an attack of cowpox rendered a person immune to smallpox. To demonstrate the truth of his theory, he inoculated a boy with pus taken from a cowpox sore on a milkmaid's hand. That was on May 14, 1796. The boy developed cowpox, but soon recovered without ill effect. On July 1 of the same year Jenner inoculated the same boy with smallpox, but it had no effect whatever. Nor was there any effect when the last experiment was again repeated later in the year.

Jenner was overjoyed. He was convinced that he had discovered the best form of inoculation and he immediately sent an account of his experiments to the Royal Society. The Society returned it with their regrets : Jenner's ideas were interesting but no more.

DISCOVERED BY ACCIDENT

But the despised country doctor had been working on his " interesting " ideas for over twenty years. He was convinced of their soundness and in two years appeared his celebrated *Inquiry*, to which reference has already been made. This publication was very critically received, but it was followed by two others which disposed of many of the objections raised to his theories. Other doctors carried out similar experiments, and within a few years the importance of Jenner's discovery was generally acknowledged, despite the opposition of certain sections of the profession.

Napoleon was vaccinated, and he became a great admirer of Jenner. It is said that he ascribed the great increase in Europe's population at the beginning of the nineteenth century mainly to vaccination. When, during the Napoleonic Wars, Jenner wrote to Napoleon asking for the release of a certain English prisoner, the Emperor is said to have exclaimed to Josephine: " We can refuse nothing to that man."

Others were not slow to honour and reward him. Parliament granted him £30,000, and he was made an honorary member of all the greatest learned societies in Europe. Despite this, the English Royal College of Physicians refused to admit him as a Fellow unless he passed an examination in Greek and Latin. Jenner was not impressed. " I would not do it," he said, " for a diadem ! "

Like most of the great practical doctors, Jenner was extremely kind-hearted. This is shown by the way he treated James Phipps, the boy on whom he carried out his first great experiment. He built a cottage for the lad, and with his own hands planted its garden with roses. " The meek shall inherit the earth : " this phrase continually comes to mind in reading the stories of such men as Jenner, Sydenham, Malpighi and Boerhaave.

One of the most tragic pages in the history of science is that dealing with Ignaz Philipp Semmelweis (1818–1865), the Hungarian doctor to whom every woman who survives the ordeal of giving birth to a child owes a debt of gratitude. He it was who first discovered the real nature of puerperal, or childbed, fever, thereby saving countless lives.

In 1846 Semmelweis became an assistant in a Viennese lying-in hospital. Young and overflowing with energy and enthusiasm, he was determined to give himself unstintingly to the never-ending struggle against disease.

There were two wards in the hospital. In the first, where the women were attended by medical students, there was a shockingly high death-rate (averaging out at just under ten per cent) from childbed fever; but in the second, where the patients were attended by midwives, the death-rate was less by two-thirds. This puzzled Semmelweis, as it had puzzled others before him, but no explanation of it could be found.

Ward No. 1 had such a terrible reputation that when women were sent to it they fell on their knees and in tears begged to be moved to No. 2. So frightened were they of the medical treatment given there that even on the point of death they would pretend to feel quite well lest a medical student should treat them.

About a year after Semmelweis arrived in Vienna, one of his friends, Professor Kolletschka by name, died of blood poisoning as the result of a wound received while dissecting. Semmelweis attended the post-mortem, and as it was being carried out, the young doctor suddenly noticed that his friend's corpse showed pathological signs similar to those observed in the bodies of women who had died from puerperal fever.

SAVED BY CLEANLINESS

It dawned on him then that this deadly fever was nothing more or less than blood poisoning, or septicæmia; and that the very high death-rate from it in Ward No. 1 was due to the fact that the medical students were in the habit of going straight there from the dissecting-rooms, where their hands had been made septic by contact with the corpses, whereas in Ward No. 2, the midwives approached their patients with comparatively clean hands : hence the lower death-rate there.

Semmelweis immediately introduced a regulation to the effect that all students and doctors in his department must disinfect their hands with chlorinated lime-water before examining labour cases. The result was that within a year the death-rate was down to 1.27 per cent.

Semmelweis was overjoyed at his discovery, but at the same time conscience-stricken when he reflected " that God alone knew how many women he had sent to their deaths," since he himself had been in the habit of examining cases with septic hands.

TREATED LIKE A CRIMINAL

But the battle was not yet won. Incredible as it seems, many of the most distinguished medical men, in Vienna and elsewhere, refused to recognize that Semmelweis was right. Why did they so refuse? Simply because to have done so would have shown them up in a bad light. According to them Semmelweis was a charlatan and a quack. Meanwhile thousands of women were dying in agony because of the attitude of these " great " men. Could human vanity go to more terrible lengths?

The brilliant young Hungarian was hounded out of the Austrian capital like a pariah. He on whom honours should have been heaped was treated like a criminal : not, be it noted, by the ignorant layman, but by his own colleagues.

It was from his native Budapest, where he had gone ten years before, that in 1861 was published his epoch-making work on puerperal fever.

BATTLE WITH BACTERIA

By that time Semmelweis was a broken man. The injustices he had suffered had sapped his enthusiasm, his courage and his vitality. Then his brain gave way under the terrible strain and he was sent to a lunatic asylum for a time. Shortly after he had returned to work, while operating he received a wound which became infected, with fatal result. He died at forty-seven, of blood poisoning, the enemy against which he had so long and so courageously battled on behalf of others.

Semmelweis had shown that puerperal fever was due to the infection of the wounds incidental to childbirth by hands contaminated with decayed animal matter. But what was the nature of the infection?

This question, of tremendous importance in the struggle against all infectious diseases, was answered by Louis Pasteur (1822–1897), who shares with Robert Koch the honour of having founded bacteriology. Pasteur's investigations established the fact that many diseases are caused by microscopic organisms which invade the body and multiply within it. He was not a doctor but a chemist, and it was through the study of the process of fermentation in wines and beers that he became interested in disease.

The first step was the discovery that alcoholic fermentation came about through the activities of microscopic organisms. Then he found that the souring of milk was due to the same cause.

RISCHGITZ COLLECTION

INVESTIGATOR OF RADIUM

Sir William Crookes (1832–1919), *chemist and physicist, made valuable discoveries about radium.*

A very important question then arose. Where did the microbes come from? Did they, as many great chemists thought, come into being through chemical changes in (for instance) the milk itself? Or did they, as Pasteur was inclined to think, find their way into it from outside? Were they, in short, the consequences or the causes of the souring?

After years of experiment Pasteur finally proved beyond any doubt that they were the causes : they came into the milk from the atmosphere, which was thronged with countless myriads of similar destructive organisms. In the same way as they could sour milk, they could, under favourable circumstances, bring about harmful changes in the human body: in other words cause disease.

In 1865 Pasteur was invited by French silk-growers to conduct an investigation into the causes of a disease that was killing so many silkworms that complete extinction threatened the industry. He found that it was caused by a microscopic parasite, whose life history he followed. It was a simple matter to destroy all the eggs which a microscopic examination revealed as infected. Only healthy eggs were allowed to develop: the disease was stamped out and the French silk industry saved Those who had jeered at Pasteur began to think that there might be something in his ideas after all.

PIONEER OF ANTISEPTIC SURGERY

The fruits of Pasteur's further investigations into micro-organisms in relation to disease were the "vaccines" whereby animals could be inoculated against such diseases as chicken cholera and splenic fever (called anthrax in man), and human beings could be given immunity against hydrophobia, the terrible and invariably fatal disease caused by the bite of a mad dog.

Pasteur's work in the bacteriological field was carried on by Robert Koch (1813–1910), a German, who qualified at Göttingen in 1866 and after serving as a volunteer in the Franco-Prussian War, began to investigate anthrax. He worked out the complete history of the bacillus responsible for this disease.

In 1878 he published a monumental treatise on infectious diseases, wherein were described the bacteria of half a dozen varieties of surgical infection. Two years later the Government showed their gratitude by making him a member of the newly-established Imperial Board of Health. Koch then began to study tuberculosis, and in 1882 discovered its causative organism.

Koch's investigations carried him to India, Java, South Africa and German East Africa. Wherever the battle was thickest, there was he to be found. Cholera, bubonic plague, malaria: these are some of the other doughty enemies he helped to put to flight. He lived to see bacteriology grow from a tiny plant to a mighty tree.

The discoveries of Koch's forerunner Pasteur were eagerly seized upon by a young Quaker surgeon called Joseph Lister (1827–1912), who will go down to history as the chief pioneer of antiseptic surgery.

When Lister began to study medicine, major operations were still being carried out without anæsthetics. This meant not only that the patient suffered terrible agony, but that the surgeon had to rush frantically to get the operation over as quickly as possible. But in the fourth decade of the nineteenth century both ether and chloroform came into use. Ether, which was first used by an American dentist named W. T. G. Morton (1819–1868), was employed by Sir J. Y. Simpson (1811–1870) in Edinburgh in 1847. The latter also introduced the use of chloroform (first prepared by Liebig in 1832). Lister witnessed, in 1846, the first operation performed in Britain under ether.

Anæsthetics did not, however, do much to reduce the frightful death-rate in surgical wards, which was mainly due to the fact that a large number of surgical wounds went septic. How was sepsis to be overcome? This was the question that tormented the sensitive mind of Joseph Lister.

The work of Pasteur showed him that the poisoning of the wound, with the consequent putrefaction, was due to microscopic organisms. It was necessary, therefore, to find a means of destroying these. After many experiments Lister found that a certain carbolic-acid solution was effective, and after its introduction the death-rate in his wards fell from forty-three per cent to fifteen per cent. The first round in the fight against sepsis had been won. By the end of the century great advances had been made on Lister's methods, and operations had lost much of their power to terrify.

AFTER SIX HUNDRED EXPERIMENTS

In 1910, two years before Lister's death, Paul Ehrlich (1854–1915), a German Jew who had been adding to scientific knowledge on abstruse medical problems for nearly forty years, announced his discovery of a preparation called salvarsan, or "606," which has since proved to be invaluable in the treatment of syphilis. It is called "606" because it was the result of the six-hundred-and-sixth experiment he had made in the attempt to find such a chemical compound.

The above is no more than a brief summary of a few of the great ones whose names are written large in the annals of man's attempts to understand himself. There will never be a conclusive record, because while man exists the inquisitive will never cease to investigate the miracle of life.

INDEX

References to pictures are printed in *italic* type

Aboriginal, Australian, 309, *311*, 317, 324, 330
Acacia, *238*
Adder, 122, *123*
Adler, Dr. Alfred, *408*, 409, 447–448
Adrenal glands, 367, 368, 369
Adrenalin, 368
Aesculapius, *458*
Agaric, Scarlet-fly, *248*, 248
Algæ, *36*, 36, 238, 268, *269*, 269, 275, 279
Alligator, *125*, *189*
Alpine type, 323, 326, 327
Amblypod, 58, 87, 88
Ammonite, 32, *33*, 33
Amœba, 29, *30*, 92, *353*
Amorphophallus titanum, *259*, 260
Amphibians, 82, 96, 140, 170
Anemone, Sea, 30, *31*, 31, 81, 91, 109, *120*, 120, *121*, 130, *134*, 155, *155*, 166, 172, 186, 209, *211*, 211
Angler fish, 95
Animal, Definition of, 91
Animalcula, 30, 83, *92*, 92, 108, 118
Animals characteristic of chief land masses, *51*
Animals, Classification of, 91
Ant, 121, *158*, *199*, 199, *200*, 200, *201*, 201, 212, *212*
Ant-bear, *55*, 155, 160
Ant-eater, 102, 103, 114, *115*, 117, 190, 203
Ant-eater, Banded, *113*
Ant-eater, Porcupine, 76, 84, 85
Ant-eater, Scaly, *104*, 104, 107 (*see also* Pangolin)
Antelope, 50, 61, 102, *105*, 146
Antennæ, 107, 109, *111*, 117
Ant-lion, *195*
Apes, 161, 204, 205, 218, 299, 300, 302, 307, 314
Apes, Man-like, 85, 90, 148, 151, 168
Aphis, 201, 212, *212*, 232, 274
Apple, 281, *282*, 287, *291*
Apple, Breathing of, *245*, 245
Aquavivarium, 225
Archeopteryx, 46, 48, 49, 50, 76, 103, 182, 190
Aristotle, 27, *407*, 410, 411, 412, 458
Armadillo, 57, 59, 60, 85, 101, 107, *110*, 203
Arteries, 345–346, *348*
Arum, 259, 260
Aryan-speaking peoples, 330
Aryan type, *321*
Asclepiades, 459
Ash, *282*
Aspen, *282*
Aspidistra, 243, 260
Astericola, 210
Astronesthes, Black, *191*
Auk, 220
Australopithecus, 306
Aveling, Dr. Francis, 417, *455*
Avicenna, 460
Axis deer, Indian, 75

Baboon, 147, *150*, 168, 205
Bach, J. S., 382, *388*
Bacteria, 10–12, 240, 242, 243, 251, 271, 272–274, 278, 280
Bacteriology, 401
Badger, 128, *129*, 160, 214, 215
Balanoglossus, 70
Ballard, Dr. P. B., 409
Balsa tree, 266
Baluchitherium, 50, *54*, 89, 125
Bantu woman, *325*
Bantu-speaking peoples, 326–327
Barley, 244, 285
Barnacles, *96*, *121*, 185, 210
Bass, 34, 197
Basset hound, *98*
Bat, 85, *89*, 113, 117, 161, 180
Bat, Carnivorous, 182
Bat, Tropical, *115*
Bat, Vampire, *116*
Batrachians, *35*, 38
Beale, Capt. W. P., 208
Beam, White, *282*
Bear, 160, 169, *170*, 197
Bear, Brown, 85, *90*
Bear, Cat, 103
Bear, Cave, 90
Bear, Earth, 190
Bear, Honey, 103
Bear, Polar, 85
Beaver, 63, 101, *148*, *160*, 160, 194, 203
Bee, 121, 139, 154, 179, *182*, 199, 200, 202, 215, 256, 258
Bee, Bumble, 202, 234
Bee, Worker, *203*
Beetle, 175, *199*
Beetle, Blue ground, 232
Beetle, Bombardier, 121
Beetle, Death-watch, 135
Beetle, Elephant, *178*
Bell, Sir Charles, 416, *420*, 420
Bergson, Henri, *12*, 12
Bernheim, Prof., 441
Binet, Alfred, 451
Birch, 266
Birds, 84, 100, 103, 110, 114, 118, 141–146, 161–162, 182, 190, 194, 203, 204, 227
Birds, Ancestry of, 75–76
Birds, Bower, 142, 144, 155, 157, 194, 207
Birds, Coloration of, 128
Birds, Courting displays of, *145*
Birds, Crocodile, 208
Birds, Early, 48
Birds, Extinct, *49*
Birds, Humming, *89*, 114, 145, *156*, 159, 228, 259
Birds, King, 158
Birds, Man-o'-War, 145
Birds, Migration of, 63
Birds, Oven, 157
Birds, Protection of, 228
Birds, Royal Society for the Protection of, 227
Birds, Tailor, 157, *158*
Birds, Umbrella, *145*
Birds, Weaver, 159
Birds of Paradise, 142, *143*
Bison, American, 224
Bison, Indian, *215*
Blackbird, *117*, 157
Black race, 321
Blackthorn, *283*
Bladderwort, *246*, 247
Bladderwrack, 253, *254*, 268
Blenny, 86, 165, 186
Blind spot of the eye, 361, *363*
Blood, 346, *347*, 347, *348*, *349*
Blood-groups, 391–392
Blowfly, 178
Bluebirds, 24
Boa-constrictor, *166*
Boar, Wild, *221*, 221
Body, Human, as a factory, *341*
Body-positions, *425*, *427*
Boerhaave, Hermann, 468–469
Bone Implements from Piltdown, *307*
Bones, Composition of, 335, *336*, 336
Bony system, 332
Bowfins, 155
Brain, 124–126, *125*, 355, *357*, 358–359, *366*
Bream, 171, 197
Breast bone, Keeled, *89*, 89
Breeding experiments, 379, *380*, 380, *381*, *383*
Breuer, Dr. Joseph, 441, 442
British Museum, Natural History Department, 230
Brontosaurus, *125*
Broom, *290*
Brown race, 324
Buffalo, 175, *176*
Buffalo, Water, 106, *109*
Buffon, Comte de, *14*, 14
Bug, Boatman, *103*
Bug, Pill, 113
Bug, Plant, 131–132
Burbank, Luther, 288 289, *290*, 291
Burrowers, 50, *98*
Burt, C. L., 452, *454*
Bushmen, 326
Bustard, Great, 224
Butler, Samuel, 393
Butterfly, 115, 259, 264
Butterfly, Blue, 212, *257*
Butterfly, Leaf, 130
Butterfly, Monarch, 131
Butterfly, Painted-lady, *257*
Butterfly, Peacock, *182*
Butterfly, Swallowtail, 128
Butterfly, Viceroy, 131
Butterwort, 246
Buzzard, 87

Cactus, 289, *293*
Cactus, Prickly-pear, 232
Camel, 50, 61, *77*, 77, 85, 168, 169, 192
Camouflage, Natural, 127–135
Cancer, 218, 402, 403
Capillaries, 346, 348, *350*, 350
Carbohydrates, 372
Carcharodon, 186
Cariama, Great, *49*
Caribou, 206, 207
Cassowary, *146*, 146, 163
Cat, Domestic, 124
Cat, Evolution and the, 68
Caterpillars, 128, 132, 175, 232
Cat-fish, *76*, 105, 121, 197
Cat-fish, Electric, 123
Cats, 85, 106, 114, *125*, 162, 169, 222
Cats, Fishing, 218
Cat's-ear parachute, *261*
Cattle, Evolution in, 67
Cave drawings, 219
Cells of the human body, *332*, 332
Celtic race, 321
Centrosaurus apertus, *43*
Century Plant, 252, *253*
Cephalopods, *33*
Cerebellum, *356*, 356, *357*
Cerebrum, 355, *356*, 356, *357*
Chaillu, Paul du, 18
Challenger, Expedition, 71
Chameleon, 103, *115*, 116, 129, 140
Chameleon, Horned, *132*
Charcot, Jean Martin, 440
Cheetah, 176, *179*, 218
Cherry, *282*, 286
Chestnuts, Sweet and Horse, *283*
Child-welfare, 404
Chimpanzee, 124, *125*, 148, 150, *168*, 168, 205, *214*, 299, 300, *303*, 310, *421* *423*, 424
Chlamydomonas, 279
Chlorophyll, 131, 237, *240*, 242, 243, 246, 268
Chloroplasts, 266
Cholera germ, 272
Chromosomes, 377, *377*, 378, *378*, *379*, 382, *382*, *383*, 384, 385
Cichlids, 197
Cinaba moth, 128
Cinchona, 296
Circulatory system, 332, 345–350, *347*
Clam, *88*, 88, 154, 185
Clam, Giant, 153, 173
Climbing perch, 95
Clover, 234, 240, 242
Coal-forests, Life in, 37–38, *39*
Coatis, 128
Cobego, 133, 180, *184*, 184
Cobras, 122
Coccyx, 332, *331*
Cochineal dye, 218, 228
Cochlea, *365*
Cockchafer, *98*, *111*
Cock of the Rock, *145*
Cockroach, 121, 124, 175, 234
Cocoa, 271, *298*
Coconut, 261
Cod-liver oil, 242–243, 374
Coelenterata, 93
Coloration, Animal, 127–135
Colour-blindness, 384, *385*
Columbus, 210, 292, 298
Commensalism, 207
Condor, 46, 89, 180, 182
Conger eel, 101
Copepods, 179
Coral, *83*, 83
Coral animals, 30, *31*, 153–154, 172
Coreopsis, 243
Cormorants, *101*, *103*, *225*
Cormorants, Fishing, 218
Corn-bluebottle plant, *263*
Corpuscles, 29, *344*, *348*, *349*, 376
Cosmos daisy, 243
Courtship, Animal, 137–150
Coypu, *222*
Crabs, 34, 78, *103*, 118, *154*, 165, 187, 188, 211
Crabs, Fiddler, *82*, 82, *137*, 137
Crabs, Hermit, 121, *155*, 155
Crabs, Land, 33, 205
Crabs, Pea, *155*, 210
Crabs, Spider, 130, *134*
Crabs, Varieties of, *73*
Crane, 146, *181*, 182
Crane, Crested, *224*
Craw-fish, 137
Crayfish, *173*
Crayfish, Burger's, *98*
Crickets, 117, 137
Crickets, Mole, 154, *154*
Crocodiles, 49, *50*, 101, *103*, 110, 112, *125*, 140, 173, 188

Crocodiles, Estuarine, 45
Crô-Magnon Man, 312, *313*, 313
Crookes, Sir Wm., *475*
Crows, 157
Cruelty, Human monoply of, 126
Crustaceans, 34, 35, 86, 88, 94, 118, 187
Cuckoo, 162
Cucumber, 239, *292*
Curie, Mme. Marie, 26
Cuttlefish, 33, 45, *96*, 115, 173, 179, 187-188

DAISY, Shasta, 288
Dandelions, 261, *263*, 263
Darwin, Charles, 13, 15–18, *21*, 30, 82, 262, 299, 306, 386, 417, 418, *419*
Dawn Age, 50, 57
Dawn of Life, 9–12
Deer, 61, 102, 111, 112, 119, 146, *174*, 175, 204
Deer, Water, 190, 192
Delphinium nudicaule, 285
Dentist, Travelling, *397*
Descartes, René, *411*, 413, 414, 415
Descent of Man (Darwin), 16, 18
Devil's coach-horse, 232
Diatoms, *17*, 268
Diatryma ,*49*, 58
Digestion and excretion, 339–344
Digestive system, 332, *342*
Dik-dik, *174*
Dimetrodon gigas, *41*
Dinichthys, 35
Dinoceroses, 50
Dinornis struthioides, 60
Dinosaur, 40, 41–42, *43*, *44*, 44, 46, 48, 49, *50*, 89, 90, 108, 119, 180
Diphtheria, 402
Diplodocus, *29*
Dipnoi, *33*
Diver, Wingless, *49*
Dodder, 247, *248*
Dodo, *49*, 60, *89*, 220
Dogfish, 197, 226, *227*
Dogs, 106, 111, 116, *125*, 126, 162, 174–175, *175*
Dogs, Draught, 218, *219*
Dogs, Evolution in, 66–67
Dogs, Varieties of, *73*, 74
Dolphin, *103*, 180
Donkeys, 169, *220*
Dormouse, 197
Dragon-fly, *172*, 172
Dragons, Flying, 46
Dravidians, 329, 330
Dromedary, *77*
Dryopithecus, 306, 307
Dubois, Dr. E., 308
Duck, 110, 177
Duck, Sheld, 157, 207–208
Duckbill, 77, *125*, 190
Duckmole, *65*, 76, 84–85, 160
Duckweed, 278
Duodenum, 340
Dyes, Vegetable, 296

EAGLE, *89*, 118, 150, 177
Eagle, Golden, 161
Ear, *117*, 363–364
Earthworm, Common, *80*
Ebony, 266
Echidna, 77, *78*, 85, *117*, 118, *125*, 168 (*see also* Ant-eater, Porcupine)
Echinoderm, 93
Eel, 37, *198*, 198
Eel, Electric, 123, *124*
Egrets, 217, 233
Egrets, Cattle, 48, 208, *209*
Ehrlich, Paul, 404, 476
Electricity, Animal, 123–124
Elephantiasis, 214
Elephants, 57, 58, 61, 62, *85*, 85, 87, 88, *90*, 106, 112, 124, *125*, 146, 168, 176, 190, 192, 193, 202
Elk, Irish, 20, 90
Elodea, 252, 266
Embryo, Human, *334*, 334
Empids, 139
Emu, 60, 146, 163
Environment, Man's, 371–376
Eoanthropus, 308
Epochs, Geological, 26
Erasistratus, 459
Erinus Alpinus, 262, *264*
Esparto Grass, *296*
Ethylene gas, 246
Eucalyptus, 278
Eugenics, 389
Euplectella, *93*
Eustachian tube, 363
Evolution, 65–90
Evolution, Meaning of, 13–28
Evolutionary Tree of Life, *19*
Evolution on Land, *35*
Eye, *360*, 360, 361, *362*, 362, 363, *364*

FABRE, Henri, 199
Fabricius, 464
Falcon, 177
Fallopian tubes, 352
Fallow deer, *75*, 75
Fat, 373, *375*
Feathers and hair, 104–108
Fechner, Theodor, 416, *453*
Feeble-mindedness, 387, 388
Feeding, Means of, 185–196
Fermentation, 270
Ferments, Plant, 244
Fern, Hen-and-Chickens, *252*, 252
Fern, Royal, 266–267
Fern, Spores of, *268*
Ferns, 266–267
Ferret, 162, 218
Fertilization, Artificial, 81
Fever, Artificial, *394*
Fever, Biliary, 235
Fever, Rocky Mountain, 235
Fig, Smyrna, 258
Filaria, 214
Filter-passing organisms, 275, 278
Fish, 76, 82, 83, 101, *103*, 104, 109, 114, 117, 139, 155, 170, 171, 195, 196, 197, 203, 210, 225–226
Fish, Angler, 130, *133*, 186, *195*, 196
Fish, Archer, 121, *195*
Fish, Blue, 187
Fish, Climbing, *40*
Fish, Colour-changes in, 129
Fish, Coral, 209, *211*
Fish, Dragon, 180
Fish, Ear-bones of, *119*
Fish, Flat, 197
Fish, Flying, 180, *183*
Fish, Leaf, 130
Fish, Lung, 197
Fish, Pile, *134*
Fish, Pilot, 209
Fish, Pipe, *161*, 165, 166
Fish, Puffer, *198*
Fish, Siamese fighting, 139
Fish, Speed of, 177
Fish, Sucker, 210
Fish, Trigger, 185, *197*, 197
Fish, Varieties of, 73
Fish crows, 24
Fish-lizards, 44
Flagellates, *173*
Flamingo, *114*, 114, *115*
Fleas, 234, 235
Fleas, Water, 199, *200*
Fleming, Sir Ambrose, 314
Flint implements, *306*
Floscularia, 152
Flowering Plants, Age of, 39
Flowers, Organs of, 254, *255*
Flukes, 32, 210
Fly, Caddis, *152*, *153*, 154
Fly, Green, 212, 230, *231*
Fly, Hover, 131, *231*, 232, *257*
Fly, Lace-wing, *231*, 232
Fly-trap, Venus, *251*
Fœtus, 353
Food, Storage of, *193*
Foraminifera, 25
Forest, Petrified, *277*
Forests, Destruction of, *241*
Fossils, 20, 24, 25–27, 50
Fowls, Domestic, *145*
Fowl, Varieties of, *67*, 67–68
Fox, 160, 169, 175, *206*, 214
Fox, Arctic, 111, 128
Fox, Silver, *235*
Foxglove, 258
Fox-hunting, 222
Freud, Dr. Sigmund, *409*, 409, 431–448
Frog, *39*, 82, *103*, 104, *115*, 116, *117*, *118*, *125*, 140, 156, *158*, 180, *184*
Frog, Darwin's, 164
Frog, Tree, 99, 128
Frogmouth, *196*, 197
Fruit, Wind-carried, *256*
Fruit trees, Fertilization of, 256
Fungus, 238, 268, 269–270, 275, 280
Fungus, Empusa, *271*
Fungus, Stinkhorn, *272*

GALEN, 460, 464
Gall, Franz J., 416, *417*
Galley-Hill Man, *315*
Galton, Sir Francis, 386, 389, *390*, 418
Game Reserv 6atins, 23o
Gametes, 378, 379
Gannet, *49*, *115*, *205*
Garden of Plants, Paris, 224 (*see also Jardin des Plantes*)
Gazelle, Thompson's, 176
Gerarde's *Herbal*, 292
Gestation-periods, 85
Gibbon, 103, 299, 300, 331
Gigantactis macronema, *133*
Gila Monster, 123
Gipsy moth, 230
Giraffe, *58*, 59, 114, *125*, 168, 176
Glacier National Park, Montana, *233*
Glands, Ductless, 367–369, *367*, *369*
Goat, 161, *233*
Goby, 139, 165
Golden orfe, 234
Goldfish, 104, 270
Goldfish, Evolution in, *68*, 68, *69*
Gonads, 369
Gopher-rat, *193*, 194
Gorgonias, *83*
Gorilla, 18, 90, 151, *168*, 168, 299, 300, 331, *333*
Grapple plant, *262*
Graptolites, 31
Grasshoppers, 36, *37*, 37, 117, 134, 193
Great Barrier Reef, 33
Grebe, Great Crested, *144*, 145
Gregory, Prof. W. K., 95, 307
Greyhound, 82, 176
Guano, 195, 218
Gulf weed, *270*
Gull, *157*, 157, *270*
Gum trees, 278, *280*
Gurnard, 95, *100*, 180

HÆMOGLOBIN, 347
Hairy Ainu, 324
Haldane, Prof. J. B. S., 11, 172
Halibut-liver oil, 242–243
Hall, G. Stanley, 418
Haller, Albrecht von, 469, 470
Hamadryad, *123*, *190*
Hands, Varieties of, *97*
Hare, Mountain, 128
Harvey, William, *350*, 350, 464, *465*, 465–466
Haussas, 206, 208
Hawk, 118, *181*
Hawk, Duck, 177
Hawk, Fish, 159
Hawtho.n, *283*, 288
Head, The workshop of the, *354*
Hearing, 116, 363–364, *365*
Heart, 338, 345, *346*
Hedgehog, 106, 197
Heidelberg Man, *303*, 310, 311
Herbart, Johann Friedrich, 415, 416, *416*
Heredity, Problem of, 377–385
Hermaphroditism, 137
Heron, 177, *180*, 208
Herophilus, 459
Herring, 86, 203
Herrings, King of the, 33
Hippocrates, 458, *459*
Hippopotamus, 62, 147, *148*, 168, 192, *209*
Hippopotamus, Pygmy, 106, *108*
Hoatzin, 75, 159, 182
Homes, Animal, 151–160
Homo sapiens, 65, 299, 312, 313, 314, 318
Honey-bear, 168
Honey-eater, 159
Honey-guides (birds), 215
Honey-guides (on flowers), *203*
Honey-locust, *274*
Hormones, 369
Hornbill, 157, *158*
Horse, *10*, 50, 61, *90*, *125*, 126, 168, 175, 192, 204
Horses, Evolution in, 68
Hottentots, 326
House-leek, *244*
Housing conditions, *371*, 371, 372
Hume, David, *413*, 414, 415
Hunter, John, 470–472
Huxley, Aldous, 80, 406
Huxley, Dr. Julian, 11, 37, 199, 212, 227
Huxley, T. H., 17, *21*, 225
Hydra, 81
Hyena, *170*

ICHNEUMON fly, *213*, 213, *231*, 232
Ichthyosaurus, *23*, 44, *45*
Iguanodon, 42
Ill-health, Cost of, 393–394
Inbreeding, 388
India, Woman of, *321*
Indians, American, 206, *317*, 324, 328
Indicator birds, 215
Industrial conditions, *387*, *391*
Industrial diseases, 394–398
Industrial Psychology, *434*, *435*, *436*, *437*

Influenza, 218, 402
Inoculation, 376
Inquilism, 207
Insects, 36, 88, 109, 117, 118, 172, 175, 178, 179, 199–203, 208
Insects, Brains of, 124, *125*
Insects, Leaf, 131
Insects, Organs of Smell in, *111*
Insects, Silver Fish, *199*, 212, *213*
Insects, Stick, 131
Intelligence, 386, 387, 449–456
Intelligence, Ladder of, *429*
Intelligence tests, *440*, *441*, *442*, *443*, *449*, *451*

JAMES, William, 409, 418, 419
Jardin des Plantes, Paris, 14 (*see also* Garden of Plants)
Java ape-man, 64, 69, 307
Jaw, Lower, Evolution of Man's, *305*
Jay Shrike, *145*
Jelly-fish, 30, 31, 83, *93*, 93, 120, 128, 173, 208–209
Jenner, Edward, *471*, 472–474
Joints of the body, 336
Jones, Dr. Ernest, 431, 439, *447*
Jung, C. G., 447–449

KANGAROO, 42, 59, *78*, 78, *84*, 84, 85, *90*, 98, 100, 101, *125*, 192, 220
Kant, Immanuel, *415*, 415
Kelvin, Lord, 11, *12*
Kidneys, *343*, 343
King crab, 32, 71, *72*
Kingsley, Charles, 18, *22*
Kiwi, 110, *112*, *117*, 163
Koala, 78, *79*, 102, 220–221
Koch, Robert, *404*, 476
Kruger National Park, *232*, 236

LADYBIRD, *178*, 230, *231*, 232
Lady of Lloyd's (skull), 312
Lamarck, Chevalier de, 14, 15
Laminaria, 268
Lamprey, 33, 70, 76, 155, 186, 210
Lampshells, 70, *72*, 94
Lancelet, 33, 70
Langerhans, Islets of (glands), 367, 368
Latin race, 321
Leaf, Section of, *242*
Leeches, 175, 210
Leeuwenhoek, Antonj van, *466*, 466
Leibnitz, Gottfried W., *414*, 415
Lemmings, 206
Lemur, 64, 114, *115*, *125*, 160, *184*
Leonardo da Vinci, 13, *14*, 27, 461
Leopard, 74, 185, *186*
Leucocytes, 347
Lice, *210*, 235
Lichens, 275–276
Life, Duration of, 167–172
Limbs, Parts of, 335
Limpet, 130, 154, 178
Limpet, Slipper, 226
Ling, 86, 161, 171
Linnæus, Carl von, *275*, 296
Lion, *74*, 74, *90*, 124, *136*, 146, 147, 161, 162, 169, 196, 202, 204, 206
Lister, Lord, 273, *398*, 476
Lizards, 41, 42, 47, 81–82, 96, 101, 103, 104, 110, *115*, *117*, 118, 122, 123, *125*, 129, 157, *184*, 217
Lizards, Flying, 180
Lizards, Frilled, 134
Lizards, Monitor, 44, 62, 140, 164
Llama, 85, *87*
Locke, John, *412*, 414, 415
Locomotion, Aquatic, *103*
Locusts, 193, 217, *229*, 230, *282*
Lobster, 100, 109, 117, 120, 171–172, 173, *185*, 186, 187, 188, 203, 227
Lungfish, 37, *38*, 197
Lungs, 96, *345*, 346, 348, 349, *349*

McDOUGALL, Wm., 428, 430
Macrocystis pyrifera, 278
Magpies, 157, *194*
Malaria, 235, 296, *399*, 401
Malpighi, Marcello, 466
Malthus, Rev. T. R., *15*, 15–16
Mammals, 84–86, 88, 89, 90, 182
Mammals, characteristic of Africa, *56*
Mammals, characteristic of Asia, *54*
Mammals, characteristic of Europe, *55*
Mammals, characteristic of North America, *52*
Mammals, characteristic of South America, *53*
Mammoths, 25, *26*, *27*, 28, 62
Man, Brain of, 124, *125*
Man, Family-tree of, 299–315
Man, Viability of, 167
Man and an Engine, Similarities between, *331*, *337*
Mangroves, *245*, 245
Mankind, Races of, 317–330
Mantids, 131, 135
Mantis, Praying, 135, 138
Marmoset, *125*, 126, 148, 162, 168
Marmots, Prairie, 160, 207
Marsupials, *57*, 77, *84*, 84
Mastodon lizard, 38
Mastodon pit in Central Asia, 23
Mastodons, *13*, 62
Mastodons, Shovel-tusked, 59
Maternal mortality rate, 404
Mayimba, 215
Mediterranean type, *318*, 318, 321, 323, 324, 326, 327, 329
Medulla oblongata, *357*, 357–358
Megatherium, 59
Mendel, Abbé Johann Gregor, 14, *15*, 283, 284, 285, 378
Menstruation, 353, 369
Micro-organisms, *374*, 376
Microscopes, 350
Milk, Precautions taken to ensure purity of, *370*
Millipedes, 35
Mistletoe, 247, *249*
Mitchell, Sir Peter Chalmers, 167
Mites, *199*, 214
Moa, 60, *60*, 220
Mole, *98*, 113, 155, 159–160
Mole, Star-nosed, *117*
Mole cricket, *98*
Molluscs, 32, 33, 88, 89, 94, *95*, 118, 121, 137, 172
Mongolian type, 318, *319*, 324, 326, 328, 330
Mongolian wild horse, 68, *71* (*see also* Horse)
Mongoose, 233
Monkeys, 64, 85, 103, 112, 120, *125*, 148, 151, 159, 161, *193*, 193, 194, 204, 205, 206, 217, 218, 299, 300, 306, 314
Monkey, Guenon, 112
Monkey, Howler, 146, *149*
Monkey, Night, of Guiana, *162*
Monkey, Proboscis, 112
Monkey, Rhesus, 168
Monkey, Snub-nosed, 112
Monkey, Squirrel, 126
Monkey, Woolly, 102, 103, 106
Monkey-nut, 262
Moose, 112
Morgan, C. Lloyd, *422*, 422
Morphology, 302
Mosasaurs, 44
Mosquito, 117, *119*, 121, 234, 235, *400*, 401
Moss, Iceland, 276, *278*
Moss, Irish, 268, *270*
Moss animals, 93
Mosses, 267–268
Moth, Coco-nut, 232
Moth, Drinker, *111*
Moth, Humming-bird hawk, *257*, 259
Moth, Hawk, *138*
Moth, Oleander Hawk, *111*
Moth, Owl, 179
Moth, Promethea, *165*
Moths, 115, 132, 139, 259
Moths, Wing, 131
Mousterian Man, 310, 311
Mud-skipper, 95, 101
Mullet, Grey, 197
Muntjac, 192
Muscular system, 332, 336, 338, *338*, *372*
Muskrat, 220, 223
Mussel, 186, 213
Mussel, Edible, 210
Mussel, Zebra, 227

NANDI bear, 28
Narwhal, 192
Nautiluses, 32, *32*
Neanderthal Man, 65, *66*, *303*, *309*, *310*, 310, 311, 312, 313, 314, 318, 329
Negroes, 323, 324, 326, 327, 329, 330
Nervous system, 332, 355–359, *359*
Newt, 38–39, *39*, 96, 122, 140, 171
Nightjars, 133
Nordic type, *320*, *321*, 321, 322, 323, 324, 326, 330
Noses, *117*, 364–365
Nutria fur, *222*
Nutrition, 372–376

OAK, Section of an, *266*
Octopus, *95*, 115, 129, *173*, 173, 187–188, *188*
Œdipus complex, 438, 439 *439*
Okapi, 28, 59, *115*
Opium poppy, 298
Opossum, *35*, 78, 103, 106
Orang-utan, *97*, 99, 103, 146, *149*, *150*, 151, 168, 204, 299, 310
Orchid, 158, 261
Orchid, Epiphytic, *249*
Origin of Species (Darwin), 16, 18, 299
Orioles, 157, 158
Os coccyx, 101
Ostrich, 49, *60*, 60, 84, *89*, 89, 146, 157, 163, 169, 176
Otters, 101, *103*, 173
Owen, Sir Richard, 20, *22*, 60
Owl, Arctic, 206, *207*
Owls, 118, 170
Ox, 111, *125*, *167*, 168
Ox-pecker, 48, 208
Oxygen tent, *396*
Oyster, 81, 82, 86, *173*, 173, 185, 190, 210, 226

PANDA, Giant, *128*
Pandas, 128
Pangolin, *55*, 102, *104* (*see also* Ant-eater, Scaly)
Papuans, *328*, 329
Parachuting animals, *184*
Parasitism, 207
Parathyroid glands, 367, 368
Paré, Ambroise, *463*, 463, 464
Pariasaurus baini, *41*
Parmentier, Antoine, 292, *294*
Parrot, 110, 115, 170
Partridge, 182, 194
Pasteur, Louis, 272, 273, 274, *275*, *473*, 475–476
Pavlov, Ivan P., 196, 420, 422, 426
Peach, Hairy, *285*
Peacock, 128, *130*, 145, 150
Pearly Nautilus, *32*
Peat, Stacks of, *295*
Peckham Health Centre, *405*, *406*, 405–406
Peking Man, 307, 308, 309, 310, 311, 312, 314
Pelican, *145*, 145, *147*, *193*
Penguin, *88*, *89*, 89, *103*, 104, 114, 141, 162
Perches, 197
Petrel, *9*, 156
Phalarope, *142*, 145
Pheasant, 128, *151*, 222
Pheasant, Argus, *143*, 144, 145
Photocorynus spiniceps, *139*
Phyla, 92
Pig, 85, 111, 112
Pigeon, *125*, 223
Pigeons, Varieties of, 67
Piltdown Man, *301*, *303*, *305*, 308, 309, 310, 312, 314
Pitcher plant, 247, *249*
Pithecanthropus, *308*, 308, 309, 311, 312, 314
Pituitary gland, 367, *368*, 368, 369, 377
Placenta, 84, 353
Plane tree, *261*, *283*
Plane tree, Flowers and fruit of, *254*
Plankton, 128, 199
Plant-breeding, 281–298
Plant Kingdom, 237–298
Plants, 39, 91
Plants, Anatomy of, 265–280
Plants, Breathing of, *244*
Plants, Man and, 295–298
Plants, Reproduction of flowering, 251–264
Plato, 410, 411, 424
Plum, 286, *289*
Pollack, 109
Polyps, 30, 31
Polytoma, 279
Pond-life, *10*
Poplar, White, *283*
Population problems, 15
Porcupine, 86, 103, 106–107, *110*, 146
Porpoise, *90*, 111, *125*, 126, 220
Potato, 240, 244, 246, 266, *281*, 290, *291*, 292, 294
Prairie Hen, 142, 145, *145*
Prawn, 129, 209
Prawn, Burrowing, *98*, 154
Pronuba, *258*, 258
Prostate gland, 351–352
Protozoa, 92, 203
Psycho-analysis, 409–410, 431–448
Psychology, 407–456
Ptarmigan, 128
Pteranodon Occidentalis, *48*
Pterodactyls, 46, 48, *89*, 180
Puerperal fever, 404
Puffin, 145, *145*, *147*, 157, 208
Pygmies, *322*, 326, 329
Pythagoras 410, 411
Python, 112, 119, 129, *218*

QUAGGA, 220
Quinine, 296

RABBIT, 77, *90*, 102, *105*, 112, *125*, 162, 207–208, 222
Radiolarians, *24*, 25
Radium, 26
Rat, 86, *90*, 169, 217, 222, 233
Rays, 83, 123, 186
Rays, Sting, 121
Rays, Torpedo, 123
Red-river hog, 85
Reflex action, *358*, 358
Regeneration, 81–82
Reindeer, 204, *217*
Reinora, 209, 218
Renouvier, C. B., 418
Reproduction, 332, 351–353
Reproduction, Sexless, 80–81
Reptiles, 81–82, 84, 140, 156, 164, 170, 178, 180, 188, 195
Reptiles, Age of, 24, 32, 40, 41, 45, 48, 50, 104
Respiratory system, 332, 348–350
Retina, *360*, 361, 362
Rhazes, 460
Rheumatism, 398–400
Rhinoceros, 28, 57, 62–63, *63*, 85, 106, 107, 112, 168, *169*, 176, 192, 208
Rhipiphorus paradoxus, 213
Rhodesian Man, *303*, 304, *312*, 312, 314
Rice, 295, *376*
Rickets, 374
Rodents, 57, 85–86, 160, 184, 190, 193, 206
Root-hairs, 239–240, *240*
Ross, Sir Ronald, *399*, 401
Rotifer, *92*, 152, *152*, 185
Rust-fungus on barley, *288*

SALAMANDER, 37, 38–39, *39*
Salamander, Japanese, 164, 171
Salmon, *125*, 139, 155, 177, 225, *226*, 227
Salt bush, Australian, 264
Sand-hoppers, 78, 80, *80*
Scallop, 118, 185
Scent, Courtship and, 146
Schizostega, 268
Schopenhauer, Arthur, 12, 415
Scorpion, *137*, 138
Scorpion, Great Water, *126*
Sea-cow, 62, 100
Sea-cucumber, 93, 120, 209, *211*
Sea elephant, *113*, 113
Sea-fan, *83*, 83
Sea-horse, 101, 130, *134*, 165, 166
Seal, *91*, *103*, 148
Sea lion, 85, *86*, *103*, 161, 169
Sea scorpions, 32–33, 34, 35, 88
Sea squirts, 31, 69–70, *70*, 130, 185
Sea urchin, 31, 70, 93, 94, *94*, 186
Semen, 351, 352, 353
Semmelweis, Ignaz Philipp, 474–475
Sense-organs, 360–365
Senses, The, 108–119
Sensitive plant, *239*
Sequoia, 251, 276, 278
Servetus, 462
Sex, the driving force, 80
Sex-ratios, 82
Sex-reversal, 82
Sexual union, 351
Shark, 35, 44, 83, 121, 180, 186, *187*, 209, 210
Shark, Goblin, 36
Shark, Port Jackson, 36
Shark, Thresher, 101
Sheep, 106, 146, 168, 204, 234
Shrew, 113, *114*, 180
Shrew, Teurce, 106, 107
Shrikes, Butcher, 194
Sight, Mechanism of, 118, *362*, 362, 363
Simpson, Sir J. Y., *471*, 476
Sinhalese Race, *323*
Skate, 123, 197, 210
Skeleton, Human, 332, *333*
Skin, 342–343, *343*
Skull, 334, *335*
Skulls, Ancient and Modern, *301*
Skunk, 128, 146
Sleep, Kinds of, 196–197
Sleeping sickness, 235
Sloes, 286, *289*
Sloth, 59, 61, *97*, 99, 101, *102*, 102, 106, 112, 114, 128, 130, 177–178, 205
Slums, *402*
Smell, Mechanism of, *364*, 364–365
Snail, 33, 115, 154, 176, 178, 197, 199, 264
Snake, 103, 110, *112*, *115*, 116, 122, 140, 170, 176, 189, *190*, 217
Snake, Coral, 132
Snake, Hog-nosed, 134–135
Snake, Rattle, 207
Snake, Tree, 129, 159
Snipe, 110, 145, 222
Society, Animal, 199–216
Society for the Prevention of Cruelty to Animals, 224
Solitaire, *49*, 60, 220
Sparrow, 84, 158, 222, *223*, 223
Spartina, 264, 285
Spearman, C. E., 449–450
Speech, Mechanism of, 365–366
Speed-chart, *177*
Speeds of animals, 176
Sperm, *173*
Spermatozoa, 351, *352*, 352
Sphagnum, 268
Spider, 121, 138, 154, 180, 203, 214
Spider, Golden, *122*
Spider, House, *122*
Spider, Orchid, 131
Spider, Red, 232
Spider, Trapdoor, 160
Spinal cord, 357–358, *359*
Sponge, 30, *81*, 81, 83, 92, 185
Springbok, 206
Squa Gull, 123
Squid, 89, 115, *188*, 188, *193*
Squirrel, 102, 160, *184*, 194, 220, 262
Squirrel, Flying, 184, *184*
Squirrel, Grey, 106, 223–224
Squirrel, Tent-peg, 133
Starfisher, 31–32, *32*, 33, 81, 93, *94*, 94, 118, 209, 210
Stegosaurians, 42, 101
Stegosaurus stenops, *44*
Sterilization, 388, 389, 390, 391
Stickleback, 139, 164, 234
Stomach, 339, 340, *342*
Stork, 146, *159*, 228, 230
Stork, Adjutant, *146*, 146, *193*
Stork's bill (plant), 262
Sugar beet, 281, *284*
Sugar-cane, Hawaii, 230
Sundew, 246, *247*
Sunlight, Artificial, *393*
Swallow, 157, 177, 182, 228
Swallower, Black, *193*
Swift, *89*
Swim bladder, 96
Swordfish, 177
Swordtail fish, 82
Sycamore, 261, *283*
Sydenham, Thomas, 467–468
Symbiosis, 207
Syphilis, 404
Systems of the human body, 331–332

TAILS, 100–104
Tarsier, 99, *125*
Tarsius, 64, 300
Taste, Mechanism of, 365
Taungs, 306
Tear gland, *360*
Technid flies, 232
Teeth, *339*, 339
Teeth used as tools, *99*
Telescope-eyed fish, *69*
Termites, 120, 154, 199, 202–203, *204*, 236
Terrapin, Mata-mata, *195*, 195
Testes, 369
Thrush, 218
Thyroid gland, 367, 368, 369
Tiger *90*, *127*, 129
Tiger, Sabre-tooth, 78, 90
Tinamous, 163
Tit, 157
Titanotheres, *59*, 59
Titicacan, *330*
Toad, 39, 96, 122, 140, 171
Toad, Midwife, *164*, 164
Tobacco, 240, 271, *274*, 274
Tomato, 243
Tongue, 113, *115*, *355*, 360, 365
Tortoise, 41, 46, 60, 190, 210, 220
Tortoise, Giant, 167, 170
Tortoise, Greek, 170, *189*
Totem and Tabu (Freud), 432
Totem poles, *431*
Touch, Sense of, 108, 360, *361*
Trachodon mirabilis, *43*
Trade Union movement, 395
Trades Union Congress, 398
Travel, Modes of, 173–184
Trawling, Steam, *228*
Tree, *250*, 265, 296
Tree, Californian Big, *280*
Tree, Japanese Dwarf, 278
Tuatera, 156
Trilobites, 32
Trout, 155
Tsetse-fly, 235
Tuberculosis, 376, 381, 392, 400–401
Turkey, Australian Brush, *163*, 164
Turtles, 41, *46*, 140, *141*, 161, 190, 195, 210
Twins, 381, 382
Typhoid fever, 401–402

ULTRA-VIOLET radiation, 11
Unicorn, Sea, 130
Univalves, 154
Urchins, Sea, 210
Uterus, 352, 353

VAGINA, 353
Vampire bat, 61
Vantos Islander, *424*
Veddahs, 329
Vegetarians, 168, 169
Veins, 346, *348*
Venus's Flower-basket, *93*
Vermiform appendix, 342
Vertebral column, 332, *334*, 334
Vertebrates, 95, 104
Vesalius, Andrea, 462, 464, 467
Victoria regia, 278, *279*
Vilmorin, M., 281
Vine, Grape, Experiments with, 289
Violets, 243
Viper, Russell's, 218
Viscacha, 107, 194
Vitamins, 372, *373*, 373, 374, 375
Volvox, 268, *269*
Voronoff's operation, 369
Vulture, 169

WALLACE, Alfred Russel, 15–16, *20*
Wallunnkukk, 156
Walnut, *282*
Walton, Isaac, 110
Walrus, 190
Warblers, 141
Wart-hog, 193
Wasp, 101, 121, 124, *126*, 128, 154, 155, 199, 200, 202, 213
Wasp, Sting of, *131*
Water-lily, Giant Amazon, 278, *279*
Watson, John B., 425
Weapons, Animal, 119
Weapons, Reptilian, *123*
Weber, Ernst H., 416
Weever fish, 121–122
Weevil, Apple-blossom, 232
Weevil, Beech-leaf Roller, *234*
Whale, 42, *55*, 57, *61*, 62, *90*, 100, 101, 111, 116, 126, 130, 167, 169, 190, 220
Whale, Sperm, *90*, 115
Whale, Sulphur-bottom, 89, *90*
Whale-shark, 89
Wheat, 285, *286*, 290, 295
Whelk, 87, *121*, 153, 155, 165, 186, 209
Whipsnade Zoo, 106
Willow, Dwarf, 278
Willow-herb, *260*, 261
Wistman's Wood, Dartmoor, 278
Witch-doctor of New Guinea, *433*
Witherby, H. F., 227
Wolffia arrhiza, 278
Wolverine, 63, 160, 194
Wombats, 59, 78, 204
Woodpeckers, 104, *107*, 114, *115*, 215
Woolley, Sir Leonard, 330
Worms, 93, 113, 118, 166, 176, 185, 218
Worms, Bristle, 137, 166
Worms, Cat, 166
Worms, Flat, 80
Worms, Glow, 138, *138*, 232
Worms, Home-making, 152–153, *152*
Worm-tubes, *121*
Wrasses, 155, 186, 197
Wrens, Desert, 159
Wundt, Wilhelm, 418
Wych elm, *282*

X-RAY photograph, *395*

YEAST, 270, *272*
Yellow fever, 392
Yellow Jack, 235
Yellow race, 324
Yellow Rattle, 247
Yellow spot of eye, 361, *363*
Yucca, *258*, 258

ZANONIA, *263*
Zebra, *74*, 85, 129, *132*, 204
Zebra mussel, 86
Zoological Society of London, 224
Zuckermann, Dr., 205
Zululand, Natives of, *299*

BIRDS
REPTILES
AM
LAMP SHELLS
SPINY-SKINNED ANIMALS
SEA
BALANC
WO
HOL
A
SPON
THE TR
CILIATES
FORAMINIFERA
AMOEBAS
COLOURLESS FLAGELLATES